PROGRESS SERIES

STEREOCHEMISTRY

PROGRESS IN
STEREOCHEMISTRY
1

Editor

W. KLYNE, M.A., B.Sc., Ph.D.

Reader in Biochemistry
University of London
(Postgraduate Medical School)

LONDON
BUTTERWORTHS SCIENTIFIC PUBLICATIONS
1954

BUTTERWORTHS PUBLICATIONS LTD.
88 KINGSWAY, LONDON, W.C.2

AFRICA :   BUTTERWORTH & CO. (AFRICA) LTD.
DURBAN : Goodricke's Buildings, Masonic Grove

AUSTRALIA :   BUTTERWORTH & CO. (AUSTRALIA) LTD.
SYDNEY : 8 O'Connell Street
MELBOURNE : 430 Bourke Street
BRISBANE : 240 Queen Street

CANADA :   BUTTERWORTH & CO. (CANADA) LTD.
TORONTO : 1367 Danforth Avenue

NEW ZEALAND : BUTTERWORTH & CO. (AUSTRALIA) LTD.
WELLINGTON : 49/51 Balance Street
AUCKLAND : 35 High Street

U.S.A. Edition published by
ACADEMIC PRESS INC., PUBLISHERS
125 EAST 23RD STREET
NEW YORK 10, NEW YORK

Set in Monotype Baskerville type
Printed in Great Britain by R. J. Acford Ltd., Industrial Estate, Chichester

CONTENTS

		PAGE
PREFACE		ix
ACKNOWLEDGEMENTS		x

1 THE SHAPES OF SIMPLE MOLECULES 1

A. D. WALSH, M.A., Ph.D., Professor of Chemistry, Queen's College, Dundee, University of St. Andrews (formerly of the University of Leeds)

Main Methods of Determining the Structures of Molecules ...	1
Results for the Ground States of Molecules	2
Empirical Generalizations	24
Theoretical Explanations of the Empirical Generalizations ...	29

2 THE CONFORMATIONS OF SIX-MEMBERED RING SYSTEMS... ... 36

W. KLYNE, M.A., B.Sc., Ph.D., Reader in Biochemistry, Postgraduate Medical School, University of London

Definitions and Possible Structures...	37
Fundamental Methods of Investigation	42
Applications of the Concept of Non-Bonded Interaction Energy to More Complex Compounds...	47
The Consequences of Different Conformations	56
Boat Forms	78
Unsaturated Six-Membered Rings...	81

3 STEREOCHEMICAL FACTORS IN REACTION MECHANISMS AND KINETICS 90

P. B. D. de la MARE, M.Sc., Ph.D., Lecturer in Chemistry, University College, London

Stereochemistry of Nucleophilic Substitution	90
Ester Hydrolysis and Esterification...	111
Stereochemistry of Nucleophilic Elimination	112
Stereochemistry of Addition Reactions	114
Steric Effects in Racemization of Derivatives of Diphenyl ...	120

4 THE RELATIONSHIPS BETWEEN THE STEREOCHEMISTRY AND SPECTROSCOPIC PROPERTIES OF ORGANIC COMPOUNDS ... 126

E. A. BRAUDE, Ph.D., D.Sc., F.R.I.C., Reader in Chemistry and E. S. WAIGHT, Ph.D., A.R.C.S., Assistant Lecturer in Chemistry, Imperial College of Science and Technology, University of London

Visible and Ultra-violet Light Absorption in Relation to Geometrical Isomerism about Double Bonds...	128
Ultra-violet Light Absorption in Relation to Steric Conformation about Single Bonds in Conjugated Systems	136

CONTENTS

PAGE

4 THE RELATIONSHIPS BETWEEN THE STEREOCHEMISTRY AND
SPECTROSCOPIC PROPERTIES OF ORGANIC COMPOUNDS—contd.

Infra-red Light Absorption in Relation to Geometrical Isomerism
about Double Bonds 156

Infra-red Light Absorption in Relation to the Conformation of
Alicyclic Rings 164

5 THE CORRELATION OF CONFIGURATIONS 177

J. A. MILLS, Ph.D., M.Sc., Division of Biochemistry and General
Nutrition, Commonwealth Scientific and Industrial Research
Organization, Adelaide, Australia, and
W. KLYNE, M.A., B.Sc., Ph.D., Postgraduate Medical School,
University of London

Methods Available for the Establishment of Configuration ... 182

Chemical Correlations without Disturbance of the Asymmetric
Centre 182

Displacement Reactions Involving Asymmetric Centres... ... 194

Asymmetric Synthesis 198

Correlations from the Study of Quasi-racemic Compounds ... 201

Correlations from the Study of Optical Rotations... 204

Enzymic Evidence 213

X-ray Evidence 214

6 THE STEREOCHEMISTRY OF THE HYDROGEN BOND 223

L. HUNTER, Ph.D., D.Sc., F.R.I.C., Professor of Chemistry,
University College of Leicester

Is the Hydrogen Bond Linear ? 224

The Hydrogen Bond as a Directed Link 228

'Hindered' Alcohols and Phenols 233

The Hydrogen Bond and Geometrical Isomerism... 236

Hydrogen Bonding deduced from the Strength of Acids 241

The Hydrogen Bond as a Factor in Crystal Structure 242

7 THE STEREOCHEMISTRY OF COMPOUNDS OF HIGH MOLECULAR
WEIGHT... 250

E. J. AMBROSE, M.A., The Chester Beatty Research Institute,
The Royal Cancer Hospital, London

General Principles 250

Experimental Methods of Investigating High Polymer Structure 253

Long Chain Hydrocarbons... 257

The Structure of Proteins 263

Polymers containing Ring Structures in the Main Chain... ... 278

8 STEREOSPECIFICITY OF ENZYME REACTIONS... 285

V. P. WHITTAKER, M.A., D.Phil., Assistant Professor of
Physiology, University of Cincinnati, College of Medicine,
Ohio, U.S.A.

Examples of Stereospecificity 286

Stereospecificity and the Mechanism of Enzyme Action... ... 316

vi

CONTENTS

PAGE

9 THE STEREOCHEMISTRY OF COMPLEX COMPOUNDS...   322

    R. S. NYHOLM, M.Sc., Ph.D., D.Sc. (Professor of Chemistry Elect at University College, London), Associate Professor of Inorganic Chemistry, New South Wales University of Technology, Sydney, Australia

Theoretical Basis of Stereochemistry   323
Physical Methods of Investigation   328
Stereochemistry in the Periodic Table   341
Steric Changes during Chemical Reactions   348

APPENDIX: BOND LENGTH AND VALENCY ANGLES   361

    ALLAN MACCOLL, M.Sc., Ph.D., Reader in Chemistry, University College, London

Bond Lengths...   361
Bond Angles   364
van der Waals' Radii   365

ADDITIONAL REFERENCES   366

SUBJECT INDEX   371

PREFACE

INTEREST in stereochemical problems has been growing during the last few years. This interest was strikingly demonstrated by the attendance at the Symposium on Dynamic Stereochemistry held in Manchester in March 1954. No major work on stereochemistry has appeared since Freudenberg's great textbook of 1933. To write a complete textbook today would be almost an impossibility, even with a large team of contributors. We have therefore tried in this volume to discuss a few of the recent advances in the field. These are chiefly stereochemical problems or concepts which were unknown at the time of Freudenberg's book, or which have developed very largely since 1933.

In an endeavour to correlate the different chapters of the book, which cover widely scattered fields in physical, inorganic, organic and biological chemistry, a draft of each chapter was circulated to all the other contributors, and much valuable criticism resulted. We hope that by this means we have linked the chapters together, where possible, and avoided serious overlaps. The literature has been covered up to late 1953, and in some cases to early 1954. A few important additional references which have appeared while the book has been passing through the press are listed on pages 366-9.

We should like to thank the many colleagues—including our fellow-authors—who have read typescripts and proofs of the various chapters, or who have supplied unpublished information; we are grateful also to the authors and publishers of diagrams which have been reproduced from other books and journals. (A list of these is given overleaf.)

The editor is particularly indebted to Professor D. H. R. Barton, F.R.S., for many helpful discussions during the preparation of this book, to Dr P. B. D. de la Mare and Mr A. A. Wright for their kind help in reading the proofs, to Miss June Felton for much secretarial work and for assistance with the Index, and to the staff of Messrs Butterworths the publishers for their constant and willing help at all stages of the production.

W. KLYNE

ACKNOWLEDGEMENTS

The editor and publishers wish to thank the following authorities, and the authors concerned, for permission to reproduce diagrams : Chapter 1, *Figure 2* : Chemical Society. Chapter 4, *Figure 10* : Dr D. M. Simpson and the Chemical Society ; *Figure 11* : The American Petroleum Institute. Chapter 6, formula XI : Dr W. Cochran and Einar Munksgaard, Copenhagen ; formulae LXI–LXV, Dr A. F. Wells and Oxford University Press (from *Structural Inorganic Chemistry*, 2nd edn.). Chapter 7, *Figure 3* : Dr C. W. Bunn, F.R.S., and the Faraday Society ; *Figure 4* : *Journal of Chemical Physics* ; *Figures 6* and *8* : Dr C. W. Bunn and the Royal Society ; *Figures 7, 13,* and *15* : Professor L. Pauling and the National Academy of Sciences, Washington D.C., U.S.A. ; *Figure 9* : Dr C. S. Fuller and the American Chemical Society ; *Figure 11* : The Royal Society ; *Figure 16* : Schweizerische Chemische Gesellschaft ; *Figure 17* : Dr K. M. Rudall and the Faraday Society.

1

THE SHAPES OF SIMPLE MOLECULES

A. D. Walsh

IN this chapter it is proposed to deal with the shapes of the simplest
polyatomic molecules. The stress will be primarily upon the experimental results that are now available, upon the empirical generalizations that can be made from these results, and upon what can be
said from a theoretical point of view to explain those generalizations.
It is desirable, however, to begin with a brief indication of the main
methods that have been used to determine molecular shapes.

MAIN METHODS OF DETERMINING THE STRUCTURES OF MOLECULES

These methods are three in number: (*a*) the diffraction of x-rays,
(*b*) the diffraction of electrons, (*c*) spectroscopic methods.

X-Ray Diffraction

This method is usually only of practical importance when the substance to be examined can be obtained as a crystal at temperatures
fairly close to room temperature (perhaps down to $-15°C$), though
a few studies have been made at lower temperatures. For this reason
it has been applied more to fairly large molecules than to the simplest
polyatomic molecules. Since, however, many simple ions exist in
crystals at room temperature, x-ray diffraction has often been the main
source of information about the shapes of these (*e.g.*, the nitrite,
nitrate and carbonate ions). The method does not usually fix the
relative positions of hydrogen atoms; but, particularly in fixing the
positions of heavier atoms, it is capable of high accuracy. Usually,
the bond length values obtained have been considered reliable to
about $0·02$ Å but only the more recent analyses have been carried
out with sufficient precision to justify this figure. During recent
years, realization of errors introduced by the techniques used to interpret the diffraction photographs and careful estimation of those
errors have improved the reliability of results and the precision with
which they can be stated (see Jeffrey and Cruickshank, 1953). It
should be emphasized, however, that the structure of a substance in the
solid form is not necessarily the same as that of gaseous molecules of the
substance. For example, nitrogen pentoxide in the solid state is an

assembly of equal numbers of NO_2^+ and NO_3^- ions (Grison, Eriks and de Vries, 1950); but in the gas phase consists of covalently bound molecules of probable structure

$$O_2N—O—NO_2$$

(Maxwell, Mosley and Deming, 1934). Further, the bond lengths of a molecule may not be exactly the same in a crystal as in the gas phase; though unless the crystal forces are strong (*i.e.* the crystal has a high melting point), the difference is not expected to be considerable. Iodine is one of the few substances which has been studied both in the solid state by x-ray methods and in the gas phase by spectroscopic methods. From the x-ray studies the bond length is reported as 2·70 Å, but from analysis of the electronic spectrum as 2·666(6) Å. The discrepancy is probably partly real because it appears that in the solid something approaching chemical bonds exists between one molecule and another (Townes and Dailey, 1952).

For details of the x-ray diffraction method, the reader should consult *e.g.* Bunn (1945) or Lonsdale (1948), and, for results, the successive volumes of *Structure Reports*, issued by the International Union of Crystallography.

Diffraction of Electrons

This method has the great advantage that it can be applied to determine the structures of simple substances that are gaseous at room temperature. It has been so applied to a very large number of substances [see the extensive tables compiled by Allen and Sutton (1950) for results obtained up to that date]. On the other hand, the accuracy obtainable is often much less than in methods (*a*) and (*c*). Like the x-ray method, method (*b*) does not locate hydrogen atoms accurately in the presence of much heavier atoms. Furthermore, once the experimental work is completed, a model has to be set up which, calculation shows, would lead to the same scattering pattern as observed. By trial and error, the model is adjusted until agreement of calculated and observed patterns is obtained. It is then not always certain that the *only* model which would yield good agreement with the observed pattern has been obtained. Partly because of this and partly because of over-optimistic guesses at probable errors, many of the earlier results obtained by electron diffraction have had to be revised. To take but one example out of the many possible, the ClF_3 molecule was reported as a regular pyramid (see Allen and Sutton, 1950), but is now found by x-ray diffraction and microwave methods to be planar and of a slightly distorted T-shape. Values obtained for interbond angles are usually subject to greater uncertainty than values for bond lengths. For example, in the SO_2 or ClO_2 molecules the S or Cl

2

atom has a much greater scattering power than the O atoms. As a result, the two S—O or Cl—O terms in the scattering equation have much more effect on the diffraction pattern than has the single O—O term. Hence, any alteration in the bond angle assumed makes little difference to the theoretical intensity curve; and the S—O or Cl—O distances can be obtained much more accurately than the OSO or OClO angles. It is therefore not particularly surprising that the OClO angle in chlorine dioxide was first reported as 137° (Pauling and Brockway, 1935), but has later (Dunitz and Hedberg, 1950) been revised to $116 \cdot 5 \pm 2 \cdot 5°$. Even in ozone, where the atoms do not differ in weight, the apex angle has been reported (Shand and Spurr, 1943) as $127 \pm 3°$, but has since been determined by more accurate, microwave, methods as 117°.

In recent years, considerable improvement in experimental techniques [especially the introduction of the so-called sector method (Finbak, 1941; Finbak and Hassel, 1941; and Debye, 1939), used particularly by the Norwegian School (Viervoll and Hassel, 1947)], in methods of interpreting the experimental data (*e.g.* Viervoll, 1947; and Karle and Karle, 1949), and attention to freeing the results of systematic errors and estimating the random errors (Cruickshank and Viervoll, 1949), have led to great advances in the reliability of results. In a particularly favourable case (the C—Br length in CBr_4) studied by the sector method the standard deviation has been estimated as only $\pm 0 \cdot 004$ Å (Cruickshank and Viervoll, 1949); but in general the bond length values obtained are not to be trusted to more than about $0 \cdot 02$ Å, and are usually reliable only if determined in the last few years. At best the accuracy of the bond angle values reported is only plus or minus a few degrees. The uncertainty attaching to all the earlier results should be borne in mind when considering data from electron diffraction studies presented later in this chapter.

For details of the electron diffraction method, the reader should consult the above references and also Pirenne (1946) and Beach (1950).

Spectroscopic Methods

These methods fall into three main divisions: (*i*) the study of rotation spectra, (*ii*) the study of vibration-rotation spectra, and (*iii*) the study of electronic spectra.

Rotation Spectra
The rotation spectra of molecules lie in the so-called microwave region *i.e.* at wavelengths from about 5 to $0 \cdot 5$ cm. The elaboration of radar during the war led to a rapid development of this field in the post-1945

3

period. For a general account of the methods used, the reader should consult Gordy, Smith and Trambarulo (1953). The method yields the moments of inertia of molecules. These in general are not sufficient to determine all the bond lengths and angles in a molecule; but since the lengths and angles are expected to be the same for isotopic molecules, combination of the moments of inertia determined for isotopic molecules may lead to a complete structure determination. The moments of inertia are yielded with very high accuracy because the resolving power in the microwave region is very great. Spectral lines as close as 4×10^{-6} cm^{-1} can be separated. In other words, micro-wave frequencies can be measured to an accuracy of about 1 in 10^6.

The accuracy with which moments of inertia can be deduced from these frequencies is limited by uncertainty in the value of Planck's constant, the latter only being known to about 1 part in 10^4. The accuracy with which bond lengths can be deduced from the moments of inertia may be further limited when, as is usually the case, data for isotopic molecules have to be combined. Strictly, the moments of inertia referring to the equilibrium point of a potential curve or surface should be used, for the equilibrium internuclear distances (r_e) depend only on the force field which is justifiably assumed to be unchanged by isotopic substitution. The moments of inertia referring to the lowest vibrational level are less appropriate because the mean internuclear distances (r_o) change with zero-point amplitude and so with isotopic substitution. r_o differs from r_e because the vibrations are not harmonic, so that a potential curve is not symmetrical about r_e.

In addition, one has to remember that, even though for a simple harmonic vibration the mean internuclear distances are not altered by the zero-point motion, the mean of the squares of the distances from the centre of gravity is altered; and it is on this latter quantity that the moment of inertia depends. The r_o values obtained from spectra are thus effective values of a special kind and not simply average values of r in the lowest vibrational level. It is the moments of inertia referring to the lowest vibrational level that are obtained directly from micro-wave spectra and are commonly used, reducing the accuracy of the derived bond length values. The correction may be important, since the computed bond lengths are very sensitive to any change of inter-nuclear distance on isotopic substitution. It is true that even for r_o the equality of bond lengths for isotopic molecules holds to within 0·002 Å; but a change of mean internuclear distance of 0·001 Å on substitu-tion of mass 33 for mass 32 may lead to an error of 0·03 Å in the value of the derived bond length (Whiffen, 1950). Errors of 0·005 Å may also be introduced by uncertainty of the exact isotopic masses.

4

Unless allowance has been made for the zero-point effects, bond lengths derived from isotopic moments of inertia should not be trusted to better than 0·01 Å.

In order to correct the mean moments of the lowest vibrational level to the equilibrium moments, it is necessary to know the moments in the higher vibrational levels and to extrapolate to zero vibrational energy. This is not generally possible in the microwave region. However, where bond lengths and angles have been determined by microwave studies, they are usually more accurate and reliable than data from other sources except those obtained from the study of vibration-rotation spectra (see below). Further advantages are that the method can be used to obtain other important data such as the magnitudes of dipole moments (by use of the Stark effect) and nuclear spins. On the other hand, except in special cases (*e.g.* O_2), the method can only be applied to molecules with a permanent dipole moment. However, this in itself may provide a way of deducing molecular shape. Thus, since the H_2O molecule has a pure rotation spectrum, it must have a dipole and cannot therefore be linear.

Vibration-rotation spectra are not restricted to polyatomic molecules with a permanent dipole moment. Vibration spectra are studied, under low resolution, by the use of either Raman or infra-red techniques. The selection rules that determine the number of 'lines' obtained in the Raman and infra-red spectra depend very much upon symmetry. Thus a linear triatomic molecule BAB has two strong lines in its infra-red spectrum and only one strong line (of a different frequency) in its Raman spectrum. The two spectra are complementary. It is in fact always true that if a molecule has a centre of symmetry then a strong line obtained in the Raman spectrum will not be obtained in the infra-red spectrum and vice versa; though of course care has to be taken not to be misled by chance coincidences. This mutual exclusion rule affords a simple method of determining whether a molecule has a centre of symmetry. Furthermore, the polarization of the scattered light in the Raman effect also depends upon the molecular symmetry. By studying the number and polarization of strong lines in the Raman and infra-red spectra it is thus often possible to say at once whether a given molecule is linear or nonlinear. As an example, sulphur dioxide has three strong infra-red absorption frequencies; and these frequencies also occur in the Raman spectrum (though two happen here to be rather weak). It is concluded therefore that the SO_2 molecule is not linear. (It is always desirable that such deductions be checked by alternative arguments, for sometimes absorption frequencies may not be observed in the infra-red or Raman spectra simply because they are not strong enough and not because they are forbidden on account of a symmetry property of the molecule.)

5

Vibration-rotation Spectra

These are studied by the use of high resolution infra-red techniques. Until the recent development of photoconductive infra-red detectors (lead sulphide, selenide and telluride), much higher resolution was obtainable if the spectrum was detected by photographic means than by *e.g.* thermocouples. For the study of the rotational fine structure of a vibration band it has therefore been desirable to use bands in the so-called photographic region of the infra-red. The difficulty was that the strong infra-red bands usually occur at longer wavelengths than those of the photographic region, the bands occurring in the latter region being the comparatively weak higher overtone and combination bands. During recent years Herzberg and his co-workers, and others, have overcome this difficulty by the use of very long absorbing paths obtained by repeated reflections of the light. The rotational fine structure of a vibration band depends upon the symmetry of the molecule and upon the particular vibration change responsible for the band. Particular vibration changes, for a linear molecule for example, are labelled $\Sigma-\Sigma$, $\Pi-\Sigma$, $\Pi-\Pi$, *etc.* $\Sigma-\Sigma$ bands have simple P and R branches [corresponding to changes of the rotational quantum number (J) by -1 and $+1$] with one rotation line missing between the two, while $\Pi-\Sigma$ and $\Pi-\Pi$ bands have in addition a Q branch (corresponding to $\Delta J = 0$). For molecules with a centre of symmetry, alternate rotation levels are symmetric and anti-symmetric with respect to an exchange of the identical nuclei. In consequence there is an alternation in the intensities of successive rotation lines (or alternate lines are missing if the nuclear spins are zero). Conversely, when a simple band with P and R branches only is observed, one knows at once that the molecule is linear; and when an intensity alternation (or alternate missing lines as with CO_2) is observed with that molecule, one knows that the molecule has a centre of symmetry. These conclusions can be drawn immediately from the appearance of the bands under high resolution without detailed measurements. From the observation of $\Sigma-\Sigma$ bands in this way it has been shown, for example, that the electronic ground states of N_2O, CO_2, C_2H_2 and diacetylene are all linear, and that the last three have a centre of symmetry. The absence of an intensity alternation shows that N_2O has the configuration NNO and not NON.

Detailed measurement yields the moments of inertia of the molecules. For CO_2, the moment of inertia yields directly the $C{=}O$ bond length. For other molecules, the bond lengths and angles can be obtained by using also the moments of inertia of isotopic molecules. For example, two isotopic species are obviously required for the C_2H_2 molecule; two for the C_2H_4 molecule; and three for the diacetylene molecule. As regards C_2H_2, both C_2HD and C_2D_2 have been studied, thus over-determining the structure. For diacetylene, however, no isotopic molecules have yet been studied and so, although the moment of inertia is known accurately, it is not yet possible to deduce from it the bond lengths except on the basis of such assumptions as that the C—H and C≡C lengths are identical in diacetylene and acetylene. The remarks made above about the importance of distinguishing between r_0 and r_e values apply just as much to bond lengths derived from vibration-rotation spectra as to those derived from microwave spectra. However, the study of vibration-rotation spectra has the advantage of allowing one to investigate the effect of vibration on the rotational constants and so to eliminate the influence of zero-point vibration*. The r_e values may then be accurate to about 0·001 Å. CO_2, C_2H_2, C_2H_4, CH_4 and C_2H_6 form examples of molecules wherein very accurate values of bond lengths have been determined from vibration-rotation spectra; see TABLES 1–4 (pp. 10–23). These molecules are all ones where the microwave method could not be applied because of the absence of a permanent dipole moment. It is most satisfactory that where a molecule with a permanent dipole has been studied—*e.g.* HCN and HCNO—the very accurate moments of inertia obtained from the vibration-rotation bands agree excellently with the also very accurate values from microwave spectra. For details of the infra-red work, the reader should consult Herzberg (1945).

Electronic Spectra

The study of electronic spectra is not confined to any particular class of molecule, except that it is usually only with gases that a structure determination can be made. It has the advantage that it is capable of yielding not only the shape of the ground state but also that of the upper electronic state. Our knowledge of the shapes and sizes of molecules has usually been confined to the ground electronic states. Knowledge of the shapes and sizes of excited states has only recently begun to accumulate and is still in its infancy. Yet from the point of view of a theoretical understanding of the factors that influence molecular shape and size it is most desirable that more knowledge of excited states should be obtained. The possible electronic-vibration bands that may appear are governed by selection rules that depend upon the symmetries of the equilibrium forms of both lower and upper states. It is often possible therefore to say something about the symmetries of the lower and upper states from a vibrational analysis of an electronic band system. For example, vibrational analysis of the 2600 Å system of benzene indicates that the molecule has a symmetry at least close to that of a regular hexagon in both combining states.

*For the ground state of the H_2 molecule r_0 is about 2 per cent greater than r_e. Rather similar differences apply to the r_0 and r_e values in the ground states of the CO_2 and C_2H_2 molecules.

Application of the Franck-Condon principle and observation of the intensities observed in vibrational progressions may also lead to conclusions about the shape and size of the excited state relative to the ground state. For example, in the 2600 Å absorption of benzene the intensities observed in vibrational progressions involving the breathing frequency of the carbon hexagon have led to the conclusion (Craig, 1950) that in the equilibrium form of the upper state each side of the hexagon has expanded by 0·037 Å. If an electronic transition covers an extensive range of the spectrum one may deduce that the size, and perhaps the shape, of the excited state differ markedly from the ground state. In the near ultra-violet absorption of carbon disulphide long progressions in what is probably the bending frequency of the upper state have been observed; strongly suggesting that the initially linear molecule has become bent in the equilibrium form of the upper state (Mulliken, 1935). A vibrational analysis of an electronic band system may lead to the determination of force constants controlling the vibrations in the upper state; and so, by empirical relations between force constants and bond lengths, to dimensions of the upper state. This method has been applied by Garforth, Ingold and Poole (1948) to the 2600 Å system of benzene, yielding upper state C—C lengths in good agreement with the work of Craig quoted above.

It is always desirable that a vibrational analysis should be supplemented if possible by rotational fine structure analysis of the various bands; partly because the ' origins ', and so the accurate vibrational frequency separations, can be fixed only by rotational analysis, and partly because the fine structure analysis yields the polarization of the bands and so checks the vibrational analysis. Further, if the rotational fine structure can be resolved, it may lead to a determination of the moments of inertia of both the upper and lower states; in principle, therefore, especially if isotopic molecules are also studied, it can lead to a determination of the bond lengths and angles in both combining states. Such a fine structure analysis for an electronic-vibration band has, for example, been carried out for certain bands in the near ultraviolet absorption spectrum of formaldehyde (Dieke and Kistiakowsky, 1934); and partially for the 2491 Å band of nitrogen dioxide (Harris and King, 1940). Nitrogen dioxide is a sufficiently simple molecule for the moments of inertia to yield the bond lengths and angles without study of isotopic molecules. Even without detailed measurement of the fine-structure lines or even if the fine structure is not completely resolved, it is often possible to deduce something about the change of equilibrium dimensions in the upper state relative to the lower. Thus from the observed degradation of the so-called J and K fine structure of the 3900–3400 Å absorption bands of sulphur dioxide, one can conclude (Metropolis, 1941) that the upper state has a

8

slightly increased apex angle and S—O length. Similarly, one can conclude from certain emission bands of CF_2 (Venkateswarlu, 1950) that the molecule is not linear in either electronic state and has a larger apex angle in the upper than in the lower (ground) state.

It is important to bear in mind that polyatomic molecules differ from diatomic molecules in that, on electronic excitation, the shape in the equilibrium position may change. There are as yet few cases where the shape of a molecule in an electronically excited state is definitely known. However, in addition to the example of the carbon disulphide 3980–2767 Å absorption mentioned above, the following may be mentioned. The upper electronic state of the 2400–2100 Å acetylene absorption bands, unlike the ground state of acetylene, is non-linear; it has a planar, centrosymmetric, zigzag, form (King and Ingold, 1953). The first excited state, unlike the ground state, of the HCN molecule is probably bent; while the first excited state, unlike the ground state, of the HCO radical is probably linear (Ramsay, 1953). An emission band system believed to be due to carbon dioxide molecules (which are linear in their ground state), and occurring in flames of carbon monoxide, almost certainly involves molecules with a bent configuration (see Mulliken, 1942a; Walsh, 1953b). The upper state of the formaldehyde fluorescence bands, unlike the ground state, is probably slightly non-planar (Walsh, 1953f). The lowest-energy absorption transition of ethylene probably leads to a shape of the C_2H_4 molecule wherein the arrangement of bonds around each carbon atom is slightly non-planar and one CH_2 group has been twisted through 90° relative to the other (Mulliken, 1942b; Walsh, 1953i).

There is unfortunately no good modern book which deals with the electronic spectra of polyatomic molecules; the reader who desires more information on the theoretical side should consult Sponer and Teller (1941).

The above methods of determining the shapes of molecules do not exhaust the ways of obtaining information. Other methods, notably the study of dipole moments also have their importance. For a recent tabulation of the dipole moments of molecules, see Wesson (1948). The list should especially be supplemented by values obtained from microwave spectra and listed in the references given in the discussion above of these spectra. The above methods, however, represent the main sources of our knowledge.

RESULTS FOR THE GROUND STATES OF MOLECULES

Where limits of error are quoted in TABLES 1–4, they are as given by the original authors and do not necessarily imply that the present author believes them to be justified.

9

TABLE 1. TRIATOMIC MOLECULES

No. of valency electrons	Molecule	Shape	Inter-bond angle	Bond lengths Å	Method	Ref.
			(A) AH_2 molecules			
	H_2O		θ_e, 104°27′	r_e, 0·958		1
			θ_o, 105°3′	r_o, 0·957	Vibration-rotation	
8	H_2S	Isosceles triangle	θ_o, 92°16′	r_o, 1·334	spectra	2*
	H_2Se		∼90°	1·49	Vibration-rotation spectra	98
	H_2Te		∼90°	1·69	+Badger's Rule	
			(B) HAB molecules			
10	HCN	Linear		r_o(CH),1·059, r_o(CN),1·157	Vibration-rotation spectra	3
				r (CH),1·061, r (CN), 1·157	Microwave spectra	22
14	HOBr HOCl	Expected to be triangular				
			(C) BAB and BAC, non-hydride, molecules			
15	CO_2^+			r_o, 1·177	Electronic emission spectrum	5
	CO_2			r_e, 1·159	Vibration-rotation spectra	1
	CS_2			r_o, 1·554	Electronic spectra	4
	OCS			(CO), 1·164 (CS), 1·559		27, 29
	OCSe			(CO), 1·159 (CSe), 1·709		28
	TeCS			(TeC), 1·904 (CS), 1·557		112
	ClCN			(ClC), 1·629 (CN), 1·163	Microwave spectra	26, 25
	BrCN			(BrC), 1·790 (CN), 1·158		25
16	ICN	Linear		(IC), 1·995 (CN), (1·158)		25
	N_2O			(NN), 1·126 (NO), 1·191		90
	NCS^-			(NC), 1·25 (CS), 1·59	x-Ray diffraction	71
	NCO^-					1
	BO_2^-				Vibration spectra	1
	N_3^-					1
	NO_2^+				General expectations and vibration spectra	6
	$ZnCl_2$, $ZnBr_2$				Vibration spectra	1
	ZnI_2			2·42±0·02		104
	$CdCl_2$			2·23±0·03	Electron diffraction	105
	$CdBr_2$			2·39±0·03		105

* Only one band so far analysed; hence θ_e and r_e cannot be given.

TABLE 1. TRIATOMIC MOLECULES (continued)

No. of valency electrons	Molecule	Shape	Inter-bond angle	Bond lengths Å	Method	Ref.
16	CdI_2	Linear		$2·60\pm0·02$	Electron diffraction	104
				$2·56\pm0·03$		105
	$HgCl_2$			$2·34\pm0·01$		106
				$2·27\pm0·03$		107
	$HgBr_2$			$2·44\pm0·01$		106
	HgI_2			$2·61\pm0·01$		106
	$ClHgBr$, $ClHgI$, $BrHgI$				Vibration spectra	1
	$AgCl_2{}^-$, $AuCl_2{}^-$				x-Ray diffraction	113
	$UO_2{}^{2+}$				x-Ray diffraction + vibration spectra	7a 7b
17	NO_2		$154\pm4°$	$1·28$	Electronic spectrum	8
			$132\pm3°*$	$1·20\pm0·02$	Electron diffraction	9
18	SO_2	Isosceles triangle	$119°\ 2·1'$	$1·432$	Microwave spectra	10
			$119°\ 53'$	$1·432$		80
	O_3		$117°$	$1·277$		11
			$116°\ 49'\pm30'$	$1·278\pm0·003$		103
	$NO_2{}^-$		$114\pm4°$	$1·25\pm0·04$	x-Ray diffraction	12
			$115°$	$1·23\pm0·02$		13
	FNO		$110°$	(NF), $1·52$ (NO), $1·13$	Microwave spectra	114
	ClNO	Triangular	$116\pm2°$	(NO), $1·14\pm0·02$ (NCl), $1·95\pm0·01$		19
	BrNO		$117\pm3°$	(NO), $1·15\pm0·04$ (NBr), $2·14\pm0·02$	Electron diffraction	19
	$SnCl_2$, $SnBr_2$, SnI_2; $PbCl_2$, $PbBr_2$, PbI_2					105
19	ClO_2	Isosceles triangle	$116°\ 30'$	$1·49$	Electron diffraction	14
20	F_2O		$101°\ 30'\pm90'$	$1·38\pm0·03$	Vibration-rotation spectra + electron diffraction	95, 96
	Cl_2O		$110°\ 48'$	$1·70$	Electron diffraction	14
	Cl_2S		$101\pm4°$	$1·99\pm0·03$		16
			$103\pm3°$	$2·00\pm0·02$		17
	Br_2Te		$98\pm3°$	$2·51\pm0·02$		18
	$(BrF_2)^+$ $(ICl_2)^+$	Expected isosceles triangle				

* R. A. Spurr, using the electron diffraction data of (44) found θ, 141°; r, 1·21Å [quoted by (99)].

TABLE 1. TRIATOMIC MOLECULES (continued)

No. of valency electrons	Molecule	Shape	Inter-bond angle	Bond lengths Å	Method	Ref.
22	(BrIBr)⁻	Linear				77
	(ClICl)⁻	Possibly linear			x-Ray diffraction	73
	I₃⁻	Linear				72, 20
	(ClIBr)⁻	Linear				74, 75, 76

TABLE 2. TETRATOMIC MOLECULES

(A) AH₃ molecules

6	BH₃ CH₃⁺	Probably planar	Probably 120°			
8	OH₃⁺	Probably pyramidal				
	NH₃		106° 47′	1·014	Vibration-rotation spectra cf micro-wave spectra	1, 79
	PH₃	Pyramidal	93° 30′	1·42	Combination of microwave and vibration-rotation spectra	78 cf 109, 110
	AsH₃		92° 0′	1·53		78 cf 109
	SbH₃		91° 30′	1·73		78 cf 109

(B) AB₃ and B₂AC*, non-hydride, molecules

24	CO₃²⁻		120°	1·31±0·01	x-Ray diffraction	
	NO₃⁻		120°			
	NO₂F			(NO), 1·23	Microwave spectra	115
	SO₃		120°	1·43±0·02	Electron diffraction	16
	BO₃³⁻		120°		x-Ray diffraction	119
				1·29	Vibration-rotation spectra	1
	BF₃	Planar	120°	1·30±0·02		31
	BCl₃		120°	1·72±0·02		81
	BBr₃		120°	1·87±0·02		31
	InCl₃		120°	2·46		117
	InBr₃		120°	2·58	Electron diffraction	117
	InI₃		120°	2·76		117
	GaCl₃		120°	2·22		117
	GaBr₃		120°	2·34		117
	GaI₃		120°	2·50		117
	Cl₂CO		∠ ClCCl, 112° 30′±90′	(CCl), 1·74 ±0·02 (CO), 1·18± 0·03		45

* This category includes only molecules in which all the B and C atoms are linked directly to A. It excludes, e.g., B—A—B—C molecules.

TABLE 2. TETRATOMIC MOLECULES (continued)

No. of valency electrons	Molecule	Shape	Inter-bond angle	Bond lengths Å	Method	Ref.
24	Br_2CO	Planar	∠ ClCCl, 116°	(CBr), 2·05± 0·04 (CO), 1·13 (CCl), 1·70 (CS), 1·63	Electron diffraction	15
	Cl_2CS					15
25	ClO_3	Probably pyramidal				
26	IO_3^-	Pyramidal	98±3°	1·80	x-Ray diffraction	119
	ClO_3^-					119
	BrO_3^-		108°			24
	NF_3		102° 9′	1·371	Microwave spectra	21
	PF_3		104±3°	1·55		30
	PCl_3		100° 6′±20′	2·043±0·003		23
	PBr_3		101° 30′±90′	2·18±0·03	Electron diffraction	66
	PI_3		102°±2°	2·43±0·04		66
	AsF_3		102°±2°		Microwave spectra	111
	$AsCl_3$		98° 25′±30′	2·161±0·004		23
	$AsBr_3$		100° 30′±90′	2·33±0·02	Electron diffraction	66
	AsI_3		101°±90′	2·55±0·03		66
	$SbCl_3$		99° 30′±90′	2·325±0·005	Microwave spectra	23
	$SbBr_3$		97°±2°	2·51±0·02		66
	SbI_3		99°±1°	2·67±0·03		66
	$BiCl_3$		100°±6°	2·48±0·02		67
	$BiBr_3$		100°±4°	2·63±0·02		67
	Cl_2SO		∠ ClSCl, 114° ±2° ∠ ClSO, 106° ±1°	(SCl), 2·07± 0·03 (SO), 1·45± 0·02	Electron diffraction	16
	Br_2SO		∠ BrSBr, 96° ±2°	(SBr), 2·27± 0·02		68
28	ClF_3	Planar, slightly distorted, T-shaped molecule	∠F′ClF, 87° 29′	Two ClF bonds, 1·698 ClF′, 1·598	Microwave spectra	100
			∠F′ClF, 86° 59′	Two ClF bonds, 1·716 ClF′, 1·621	x-Ray diffraction	101

(C) H₂AB molecules (both H atoms directly bound to A)

12	H_2CO	Planar	∠ HCH, 118 ±2°	(CH), 1·12± 0·01 (CO), 1·21± 0·01	Microwave spectra	116
14	H_2NF	Probably pyramidal				

TABLE 2. TETRATOMIC MOLECULES (*continued*)

No. of valency electrons	Molecule	Shape	Inter-bond angle	Bond lengths Å	Method	Ref.
		(D) H—A—A—A, H—A—A—B *and* H—A—B—C *molecules*				
	HN₃	N₃ group linear	∠HNN, 112° 39′ ±30′	(HN), 1·021 ±0·01 (N₁N₂), 1·240 ±0·003 (N₂N₃) 1·134 ±0·003		34
	HCCCl	Linear		(CH) 1·052 (CC) 1·211 (CCl) 1·632	Microwave spectra	89
16	HNCO	NCO group linear	∠HNC, 128° 5′ ±30′	(HN) 0·99± 0·01 (NC) 1·21± 0·01 (CO) 1·17± 0·01		33
	HNCS	NCS group linear	∠HNC, 130° 15′	(HN) 1·013 (NC) 1·2158 (CS) 1·5609		102, 32
18	HONO	ONO non-linear	cis and trans forms, trans being more stable ∠ONO {114° cis 118° trans}	(HO) 0·98 (NO) 1·20 (ON) 1·46	Vibration-rotation spectra	83
		(E) H—A—A—H *molecules*				
10	C₂H₂	Linear		r_e (CH) 1·060 r_e (CC) 1·203	Vibration-rotation spectra	40
14	H₂O₂	Non-linear and non-planar	∠HOO, ~97° Azimuthal angle between planes containing OH and OO bonds, 94°	(OO) 1·49	x-Ray diffraction	49
	H₂S₂			(SS) 2·05± 0·02	Electron diffraction	17
		(F) B—A—A—B, *non-hydride, molecules*				
18	Hg₂Cl₂	Linear		(HgCl) 2·23 ±0·03	Electron diffraction	107
	C₂N₂			(CC) 1·37± 0·02 (CN) 1·16± 0·02		118

TABLE 2. TETRATOMIC MOLECULES (continued)

No. of valency electrons	Molecule	Shape	Inter-bond angle	Bond lengths Å	Method	Ref.
24	N_2F_2	Non-linear but planar	cis and trans isomers $\angle$ NNF, 115 $\pm5°$	(NN) 1·25$\pm$ 0·04 (NF) 1·44$\pm$ 0·04	Electron diffraction	108
26	S_2Cl_2	Non-linear and non-planar	$\angle$ ClSS, 103 $\pm2°$	(SS) 2·05$\pm$ 0·03 (SCl) 1·99$\pm$ 0·03	Electron diffraction	16

(G) A_4 molecules

20	P_4	Tetrahedron		(PP) 2·21$\pm$ 0·02	Electron diffraction	15
	As_4			(AsAs) 2·44 $\pm$0·03		15

TABLE 3. PENTATOMIC MOLECULES

(A) AH_4 and AB_4 molecules

CH_4	↑			r_o, 1·094	Vibration-rotation spectra	1
SiH_4		Regular tetrahedron				
CCl_4						
GeF_4	↓			1·67$\pm$0·03		52
VCl_4					Electron diffraction	93
$TeCl_4$		Irregular tetrahedron				94

(B) BAC_3 and B_2AC_2 molecules* (hydride and non-hydride)

CH_3F	↑		$\angle$ HCH, 110°0′	(CH) 1·109$\pm$ 0·01 (CF) 1·385	↑	30
CH_3Cl			$\angle$ HCH, 110°20′$\pm$1°	(CH) 1·103$\pm$ 0·01 (CCl) 1·782 $\pm$0·003		60, 26, 130
CH_3Br		Symmetric top	$\angle$ HCH, 110°48′$\pm$1°	(CH) 1·101$\pm$ 0·01 (CBr) 1·938$\pm$ 0·003	Microwave spectra	60, 58
CH_3I			$\angle$ HCH, 110°58′$\pm$1°	(CH) 1·100$\pm$ 0·01 (CI) 2·140$\pm$ 0·005		60, 26
CHF_3			$\angle$ FCF, 108°48′	(CH) 1·098 (CF) 1·332		30, 121
$CHCl_3$	↓		$\angle$ ClCCl, 110°24′	(CH) 1·073 (CCl) 1·767	↓	37, 121

*In this category, the B and C atoms are all joined directly to atom A.

TABLE 3. PENTATOMIC MOLECULES (*continued*)

Molecule	Shape	Interbond angle	Bond lengths Å	Method	Ref.
CHBr$_3$	↑	∠BrCBr, 110°48′±16′	(CH) 1·068± 0·01 (CBr) 1·930± 0·003	↑	48, 129
CF$_3$Cl			(CF) 1·328 (CCl) 1·740		126, 127
CF$_3$Br			(CF) 1·33 (CBr) 1·908		127, 128
CF$_3$I			(CF) 1·33 (CI) 2·134		127
SiH$_3$F			(SiH) 1·503± 0·036 (SiF) 1·593± 0·003		36
SiH$_3$Cl		∠HSiH, 110°57′	(SiH) 1·50 (SiCl) 2·048		92, 122
SiH$_3$Br		∠HSiH, 111°20′	(SiH) 1·57± 0·03 (SiBr) 2·209 ±0·001		124
SiHF$_3$		∠FSiF, 108°6′±30′	(SiF) 1·561± 0·005		59
SiHCl$_3$		∠ClSiCl, 109°26′	(SiCl) 2·02		125
SiF$_3$Cl	Symmetric top		(SiF) 1·560± 0·005	Microwave spectra	59
SiF$_3$Br			(SiF) 1·560± 0·005		59
GeH$_3$Cl		∠HGeH, 111°4′	(GeH) 1·52 (GeCl) 2·147		122
GeH$_3$Br		∠HGeH, 112°0′±1′	(GeH) 1·55± 0·05 (GeBr) 2·297 ±0·001		38
GeF$_3$Cl		∠FGeF, 107°42′±90′	(GeF) 1·688 ±0·017 (GeCl) 2·067 ±0·005		82
POF$_3$		∠FPF, 102°30′±2°	(PF) 1·52± 0·02 (PO) 1·45± 0·03		64
POCl$_3$		∠ClPCl, 103°36′±2°	(PCl) 1·99± 0·02 (PO) 1·45± 0·03		64
PSF$_3$	↓	∠FPF, 100°18′±2°	(PF) 1·53± 0·02 (PS) 1·87± 0·03	↓	64

TABLE 3. PENTATOMIC MOLECULES (continued)

Molecule	Shape	Interbond angle	Bond lengths Å	Method	Ref.
PSCl₃		∠ClPCl, 100°30′±1°	(PCl) 2·02± 0·01 (PS) 1·85± 0·02		64
ReO₃Cl	Symmetric Top	∠OReO, 108°20′±1°	(ReO) 1·761 ±0·003 (ReCl) 2·230 ±0·004	Microwave spectra	30, 63
SO₂F₂		∠OSO, 129°38′±30′ ∠FSF, 92°47′±30′	(SO) 1·370± 0·01 (SF) 1·570± 0·01		65
SO₂Cl₂		∠OSO, 119°30′±5° ∠ClSCl, 111°±2° ∠ClSO, 106°±2°	(SO) 1·43± 0·02 (SCl) 1·99± 0·02	Electron diffraction	16
CH₂F₂		∠HCH, 112° ∠FCF, 108°	(CH) 1·09 (CF) 1·36		134
CH₂Cl₂	Asymmetric Top	∠HCH, 112°0′±20′ ∠ClCCl, 111°47′±1′	(CH) 1·068± 0·005 (CCl) 1·7724 ±0·0005	Microwave spectra	125
CrO₂Cl₂		∠OCrO, 105°±4° ∠ClCrCl, 113°±3° ClCrO, 109°30′±3°	(CrO) 1·57± 0·03 (CrCl) 2·12± 0·02		16
MoO₂Cl₂		∠OMoO, 109° 30′ assumed ∠ClMoCl, 113°±7° ∠ClMoO, 108°±7°	(MoO) 1·75 (MoCl) 2·28	Electron diffraction	66

(C) Miscellaneous molecules

Molecule	Shape	Interbond angle	Bond lengths Å	Method	Ref.
HCCCN	Linear		(CH) 1·057 (C—C) 1·382 (C≡C) 1·203 (CN) 1·157	Microwave spectra	91
C₃O₂	Linear		(CC) 1·28± 0·03 (CO) 1·19± 0·03	Electron diffraction	39
CH₂CO	Planar; CCO linear	∠HCH, 122°0′± 2°30′	(CH) 1·075± 0·010 (CO) 1·16± 0·10 (CC) 1·32± 0·10	Microwave spectra	131 cf 62

TABLE 3. PENTATOMIC MOLECULES (*continued*)

Molecule	Shape	Interbond angle	Bond lengths Å	Method	Ref.
$HONO_2$	Planar	∠ONO, 130°±5° ∠ON—OH, 115°±2°30′	(NO) 1·22± 0·02 (N—OH)1·41 ±0·02	Electron diffraction	44
			(NO) 1·24 (N—OH)1·30	x-Ray diffraction	84
HCO_2H	Planar	∠OCO, 123°30′	(C=O) 1·213 ±0·03 (C—O) 1·368 ±0·03	Electron diffraction	123
		∠OCO, 125°±1°	(C=O) 1·225 ±0·02 (C—O) 1·41 ±0·02	Vibration spectra	88

TABLE 4. SELECTED HEXATOMIC AND LARGER MOLECULES

Molecule	Shape	Interbond angle	Bond lengths	Method	Ref.
C_2H_4	↑	∠HCH, 119°55′	(CC) 1·353 (CH) 1·071	Vibration-rotation spectra	41
C_2F_4		∠FCF, 114°±2°	(CF) 1·313 ±0·01 (CC) 1·313 ±0·035	Electron diffraction	46 / 47
C_2Cl_4	Planar	∠ClCCl, 113°30′	(CCl) 1·72± 0·01 (CC) 1·30± 0·03		
CH_2F_2	↓	∠HCH, 110° ∠FCF, 110°	(CH) 1·07 (CF) 1·32 (CC) 1·31	Microwave spectra *cf* electron diffraction	133 / 46
N_2H_4	Non-planar and probably staggered		(NN) 1·46	x-Ray diffraction *cf* vibration spectra	50 / 85–87
N_2O_4	Planar	∠ONO, 126°±1°	(NO) 1·17± 0·03 (NN) 1·64± 0·03	x-Ray diffraction	53
BH_3CO	Symmetric top	∠HBH, 113°52′	(BH) 1·194 (CO) 1·131 (BC) 1·540	Microwave spectra	97
CHO·CHO	Planar	*trans* form ∠CCO, 123°±2°	(CO) 1·20± 0·01 (CC) 1·47± 0·02	Electron diffraction	66

18

TABLE 4. SELECTED HEXATOMIC AND LARGER MOLECULES (*continued*)

Mole-cule	Shape	Inter-bond angle	Bond lengths Å	Method	Ref.
CH₃CN	↑	∠HCH, 109°8′	(CH) 1·092 ⎫ (CN) 1·158 (CC) 1·460		132
CH₃NC	│ Symmetric top	∠HCH, 109°46′	(CH) 1·094 (NC) 1·167 (CN) 1·158 assumed	Microwave spectra	132
CF₃CN	│ ↓	∠FCF, 108° assumed	(CF) 1·335 (CC) 1·464 (CN) 1·158 assumed ⎭		127
CH₃COF		∠CCF, (110°) ∠OCF, (125°)	(CF) 1·37± 0·02 (CO) 1·16± 0·02 (CC) 1·50± 0·03 ⎫		42
CH₃COCl		∠CCCl, 105°±5° ∠OCCl, 122°30′±2° 30′	(CCl) 1·82± 0·02 (CO) 1·17± 0·04		43
CH₃COBr		∠CCBr, 105°±5° ∠OCBr, 125°±5°	(CBr) 2·00± 0·04 (CO) 1·17± 0·04	Electron diffraction	43
CH₃COI		∠CCI, 110°±5° ∠OCI, 125°±5°	(CI) 2·21± 0·04		43
(CH₃)₂CO		∠CCO, 119°36′±3°	(CO) 1·22± 0·03 (CC) 1·55± 0·02 ⎭		54
C₂H₆		r_o r_o	(CH) 1·102 (CC) 1·543	Vibration-rotation spectra	61
C₆H₆	Planar		(CH) 1·08± 0·02 (CC) 1·39	Electron diffraction	51
B₂H₆	Non-planar bridge structure	∠HBH, 121°30′± 7°30′	(BB) 1·770± 0·013 (BH) 1·187± 0·03 (BH) bridge 1·334±0·027	Electron diffraction	69
B₂H₄Br₂	Bridge structure. Bridge H atoms above and below plane containing the other atoms			Microwave spectra	70

REFERENCES FOR TABLES 1–4

1. See Herzberg, G. (1945) *Infra-red and Raman Spectra* New York, Van Nostrand
2. Cross, P. C. (1935) *Phys. Rev.* **47**, 7; (1937) *J. chem. Phys.* **5**, 370; Crawford, B. L. and Cross, P. C. (1937) *ibid* **5**, 621
3. Herzberg, G., Patat, F. and Verleger, H. (1936) *Z. Phys.* **102**, 1
4. Liebermann, L. N. (1941) *Phys. Rev.* **60**, 496
5. Mrozowski, S. (1942) *ibid* **62**, 270
6. See Gillespie, R. J. and Millen, D. J. (1948) *Quart. Rev. chem. Soc., Lond.* **2**, 277
7. (a) Zachariasen, W. H. (1948) *Acta cryst., Camb.* **1**, 277, 281; (b) Sutton, J. (1952) *Nature, Lond.* **169**, 235
8. Harris, L. and King, G. W. (1940) *J. chem. Phys.* **8**, 775
9. Claesson, S., Donohue, J. and Schomaker, V. (1948) *ibid* **14**, 207
10. Crable, G. F. and Smith, W. V. (1951) *ibid* **19**, 502
11. Hughes, R. H. (1953) *ibid* **21**, 960
12. Truter, M. R. (1951) Private communication revising an earlier statement (*Nature, Lond.* **168**, 344), which gave $\theta=132°\ 48'$, $r=1.14$ Å
13. Carpenter, G. B. (1952) *Acta cryst., Camb.* **5**, 132
14. Dunitz, J. D. and Hedberg, K. (1950) *J. Amer. chem. Soc.* **72**, 3108
15. See Brockway, L. O. (1936) *Rev. mod. Phys.* **8**, 231
16. Palmer, K. J. (1938) *J. Amer. chem. Soc.* **60**, 2360
17. Stevenson, D. P. and Beach, J. Y. (1938) *ibid* **60**, 2872
18. Rogers, M. T. and Spurr, R. A. (1947) *ibid* **69**, 2102
19. Ketelaar, J. A. and Palmer, K. J. (1937) *ibid* **59**, 2629
20. See Pimentel, G. C. (1951) *J. chem. Phys.* **19**, 446
21. Sheridan, J. and Gordy, W. (1950) *Phys. Rev.* **79**, 513
22. Simmons, J. W., Anderson, W. E. and Gordy, W. (1950) *ibid* **77**, 77
23. Kisliuk, P. and Townes, C. H. (1950) *J. chem. Phys.* **18**, 1109
24. Zachariasen, W. H. (1929) *Z. Kristallogr.* **71**, 501
25. Townes, C. H., Merritt, F. R. and Holden, A. N. (1948) *Phys. Rev.* **74**, 1113
26. Simmons, J. W. (1949) *ibid* **76**, 686
27. Strandberg, M. W. P., Wentink, T. and Hill, A. G. (1949) *ibid* **75**, 827
28. Shulman, R. G. and Townes, C. H. (1950) *ibid* **77**, 500
29. Strandberg, M. W. P., Wentink, T. and Kyhl, R. L. (1949) *ibid* **75**, 270
30. Gilliam, O. R., Edwards, H. D. and Gordy, W. (1949) *ibid* **75**, 1014
31. Lévy, H. A. and Brockway, L. O. (1937) *J. Amer. chem. Soc.* **59**, 2085
32. Beard, C. I. and Dailey, B. P. (1950) *J. chem. Phys.* **18**, 1437
33. Jones, L. H., Schoolery, J. N., Shulman, R. G. and Yost, D. M. (1950) *ibid* **18**, 990
34. Amble, E. and Dailey, B. P. (1950) *ibid* **18**, 1422
35. Sheridan, J. and Gordy, W. (1950) *Phys. Rev.* **77**, 719

36. Sharbaugh, A. H., Thomas, V. G. and Pritchard, B. S. (1950) *ibid*
    78, 64
37. Unterberger, R. R., Trambarulo, R. and Smith, W. V. (1950) *J.
    chem. Phys.* **18,** 565
38. Sharbaugh, A. H., Pritchard, B. S., Thomas, V. G., Mays, J. M.
    and Dailey, B. P. (1950) *Phys. Rev.* **79,** 189
39. Mackle, H. and Sutton, L. E. (1951) *Trans. Faraday Soc.* **47,** 937
40. Herzberg, G., Patat, F. and Spinks, J. W. T. (1934) *Z. Phys.*
    92, 87
41. Gallaway, W. S. and Barker, E. F. (1942) *J. chem. Phys.* **10,** 88
42. Mackle, H. and Sutton, L. E. (1951) *Trans. Faraday Soc.* **47,** 691
43. Allen, P. W. and Sutton, L. E. (1951) *ibid* **47,** 236
44. Maxwell, C. R. and Mosley, V. M. (1940) *J. chem. Phys.* **8,** 738;
    (1940) *Phys. Rev.* **57,** 1079
45. Schomaker, V. (1950) quoted by Allen, P. W. and Sutton, L. E.
    Acta cryst., Camb. **3,** 46
46. Karle, I. L. and Karle, J. (1950) *J. chem. Phys.* **18,** 957, 963
47. — — (1952) *ibid* **20,** 63
48. Williams, J. Q., Cox, J. T. and Gordy, W. (1952) *ibid* **20,** 1524
49. Abrahams, S. C., Collin, R. L. and Lipscomb, W. N. (1951) *Acta
    cryst., Camb.* **4,** 15
50. Collin, R. L. and Lipscomb, W. N. (1951) *ibid* **4,** 10
51. Karle, I. (1952) *J. chem. Phys.* **20,** 65
52. Caunt, A. D., Mackle, H. and Sutton, L. E. (1951) *Trans. Faraday
    Soc.* **47,** 943
53. Broadley, J. S. and Robertson, J. M. (1949) *Nature, Lond.*
    164, 915
54. Allen, P. W., Bowen, H. J. M., Sutton, L. E. and Bastiansen, O.
    (1952) *Trans. Faraday Soc.* **48,** 991
55. — and Sutton, L. E., unpublished work
56. Amble, E. and Schawlow, A. L. (1951) *Phys. Rev.* **82,** 328
57. Simmons, J. W. (1950) *ibid* **76,** 686; see also ref. 60
58. — and Swan, W. O. (1950) *ibid* **80,** 289; see also ref. 60
59. Sheridan, J. and Gordy, W. (1951) *J. chem. Phys.* **19,** 965
60. Gordy, W., Simmons, J. W. and Smith, A. G. (1948) *Phys. Rev.*
    74, 243
61. Hansen, G. E. and Dennison, D. M. (1952) *J. chem. Phys.*
    20, 313
62. Bak, B., Knudsen, E. S., Madsen, E. and Rastrup-Anderson, J. (1950)
    Phys. Rev. **79,** 190
63. Amble, E., Miller, S. L., Schawlow, A. L. and Townes, C. H. (1952)
    J. chem. Phys. **20,** 192
64. Williams, Q., Sheridan, J. and Gordy, W. (1952) *ibid* **20,** 164
65. Fristrom, R. M. (1952) *ibid* **20,** 1
66. Quoted by Allen, P. W. and Sutton, L. E. (1950) *Acta cryst., Camb.*
    3, 46
67. Skinner, H. A. and Sutton, L. E. (1940) *Trans. Faraday Soc.* **36,** 681
68. Stevenson, D. P. and Cooley, R. A. (1940) *J. Amer. chem. Soc.* **62,**
    2477

69. Hedberg, K. and Schomaker, V. (1951) *ibid* **73,** 1482
70. Cornwell, C. D. (1950) *J. chem. Phys.* **18,** 1118
71. Zvankova, Z. V. and Zdanov, G. S. (1949) *Zhur. fiz. Khim.* **23,** 1495
72. Mooney, R. C. L. (1935) *Z. Kristallogr.* **90,** 143
73. Wyckoff, R. W. G. (1920) *J. Amer. chem. Soc.* **42,** 1100
74. Mooney, R. C. L. (1935) *Phys. Rev.* **47,** 807
75. — (1938) *Z. Kristallogr.* **98,** 324
76. — (1939) *ibid* **100,** 519
77. Bozorth, R. M. and Pauling, L. (1925) *J. Amer. chem. Soc.* **47,** 1561
78. Loomis, C. C. and Strandberg, M. W. P. (1951) *Phys. Rev.* **81,** 798
79. Weiss, M. T. and Strandberg, M. W. P. (1951) *ibid* **83,** 567
80. Sirvetz, M. H. (1951) *J. chem. Phys.* **19,** 938
81. Hedberg, K., Schomaker, V. and Jones, M. E., *Abstr. 2nd Gen. Ass. int. Un. Cryst.* Stockholm, June, 1951
82. Anderson, W. E., Sheridan, J. and Gordy, W. (1951) *Phys. Rev.* **81,** 819
83. Jones, L. H., Badger, R. M. and Moore, G. E. (1951) *J. chem. Phys.* **19,** 1599
84. Luzzati, V. (1951) *Acta. cryst., Camb.* **4,** 120, A239
85. Wagner, E. L. and Bulgozdy, E. L. (1951) *J. chem. Phys.* **19,** 1210
86. Scott, D. W., Oliver, G. D., Gross, M. E., Hubbard, W. N. and Huffman, H. M. (1949) *J. Amer. chem. Soc.* **71,** 2293
87. Giguère, P. A. and Liu, I. D. (1952) *J. chem. Phys.* **20,** 136
88. Williams, V. Z. (1947) *ibid* **15,** 232
89. Westenberg, A. A., Goldstein, J. H. and Wilson, E. B. (1949) *ibid* **17,** 1319
90. Coles, D. K., Elyash, E. S. and Gorman, J. G. (1947) *Phys. Rev.* **72,** 973
91. Westenberg, A. A. and Wilson, E. B. (1950) *J. Amer. chem. Soc.* **72,** 199
92. Sharbaugh, A. H. (1948) *Phys. Rev.* **74,** 1870
93. Lipscomb, W. N. and Whittaker, A. G. (1945) *J. Amer. chem. Soc.* **67,** 2019
94. Stevenson, D. P. and Schomaker, V. (1940) *ibid* **62,** 1267
95. Bernstein, H. J. and Powling, J. (1950) *J. chem. Phys.* **18,** 685
96. Maxwell, L. R. (1940) *J. opt. Soc. Amer.* **30,** 374
97. Gordy, W., Ring, H. and Burg, A. B. (1950) *Phys. Rev.* **78,** 512
98. Stevenson, D. P. (1940) *J. chem. Phys.* **8,** 285
99. Yost, D. M. and Russell, H. (1944) *Systematic Inorganic Chemistry* New York, Prentice Hall
100. Smith, D. F. (1953) *J. chem. Phys.* **21,** 609
101. Burbank, R. D. and Bensey, F. N. (1953) *ibid* **21,** 602
102. Dousmanis, C. C., Sanders, T. M., Townes, C. H. and Zeiger, H. J. (1953) *ibid* **21,** 1416
103. Trambarulo, R., Ghosh, S. N., Burrus, C. A. and Gordy, W. (1953) *ibid* **21,** 851

104. Hassel, O. and Strømme, L. C. (1938) *Z. phys. Chem. B.* **38,** 466
105. Lister, M. and Sutton, L. E. (1941) *Trans. Faraday Soc.* **37,** 406
106. Gregg, A. H., Hampson, G. C., Jenkins, G. I., Jones, P. L. F. and Sutton, L. E. (1937) *ibid* **33,** 852
107. Maxwell, L. R. and Mosley, V. M. (1940) *Phys. Rev.* **57,** 21
108. Bauer, S. H. (1947) *J. Amer. chem. Soc.* **69,** 3104
109. Nielsen, H. H. (1952) *J. chem. Phys.* **20,** 759
110. Sirvetz, M. H. and Weston, R. E. (1953) *ibid* **21,** 898
111. Kisliuk, P. and Geschwind, S. (1953) *ibid* **21,** 828
112. Silvey, G., Hardy, W. A. and Townes, C. H. (1952) *Phys. Rev.* **87,** 236A
113. See Sidgwick, N. V. and Powell, H. M. (1940) *Proc. roy. Soc. A* **176,** 153
114. Magnuson, D. W. (1951) *Phys. Rev.* **83,** 485A ; (1951) *J. chem. Phys.* **19,** 1071
115. Smith, D. F. and Magnuson, D. W. (1952) *Phys. Rev.* **87,** 226A
116. Lawrance, R. B. and Strandberg, M. W. P. (1951) *ibid* **83,** 363
117. See Stevenson, D. P. and Schomaker, V. (1942) *J. Amer. chem. Soc.* **64,** 2514
118. Pauling, L., Springall, H. D. and Palmer, K. J. (1939) *ibid* **61,** 927
119. See Wells, A. F. (1945) *Structural Inorganic Chemistry* Oxford University Press
120. Elliott, N. (1937) *J. Amer. chem. Soc.* **59,** 1380
121. Ghosh, S. N., Trambarulo, R. and Gordy, W. (1952) *J. chem. Phys.* **20,** 605
122. Dailey, B. P., Mays, J. M. and Townes, C. H. (1949) *Phys. Rev.* **76,** 136
123. Schomaker, V. and O'Gorman, J. M. (1947) *J. Amer. chem. Soc.* **69,** 2638
124. Sharbaugh, A. H., Bragg, J. K., Madison, T. C. and Thomas, V. G. (1949) *Phys. Rev.* **76,** 1419
125. See Gordy, W., Smith, W. V. and Trambarulo, R. F. (1953) *Microwave Spectroscopy* London, Chapman and Hall
126. Coles, D. K. and Hughes, R. H. (1949) *Phys. Rev.* **76,** 178
127. Sheridan, J. and Gordy, W. (1952) *J. chem. Phys.* **20,** 591
128. Sharbaugh, A. H., Pritchard, B. S. and Madison, T. C. (1950) *Phys. Rev.* **77,** 302
129. Williams, J. Q. and Gordy, W. (1950) *ibid* **79,** 225
130. Miller, S. L., Kraitchman, J., Dailey, B. P. and Townes, C. H. (1951) *ibid* **82,** 327
131. Johnson, H. R. and Strandberg, M. W. P. (1952) *J. chem. Phys.* **20,** 687
132. Kessler, M., Ring, H., Trambarulo, R. and Gordy, W. (1950) *Phys. Rev.* **79,** 54
133. Roberts, A. and Edgell, W. F. (1949) *J. chem. Phys.* **17,** 742; (1949) *Phys. Rev.* **76,** 178
134. Lide, D. R. (1952) *Phys. Rev.* **87,** 227

EMPIRICAL GENERALIZATIONS FROM THE RESULTS
IN TABLES 1–4

(*i*) *In simple molecules the inter-bond angle does not in general fall below 90°*
As regards triatomic molecules, the O_3 molecule has several times been suggested as an exception to this; but it may now be taken as established that the angle is obtuse. All triatomic molecules have their apex angles in the range 90°–180°. As regards tetratomic molecules, the P_4 and As_4 molecules form exceptions. The ClF_3 molecule forms a possible exception, since it has been reported as having two FClF angles of $\sim 87°$. With this possible exception and excluding P_4 and As_4, the inter-bond angles of AB_3 or B_2AC tetratomic molecules (in which the B or C atoms are directly joined to A) all lie in the range 90°–120°. As regards larger molecules, *cyclo*propane and ethylene oxide form obvious exceptions.

(*ii*) *In simple molecules, substitution of halogen atoms for hydrogen atoms does not usually make a large change in the inter-bond angles compared with the range of values covered by the angles in general*
As examples of this generalization, compare
   (*a*) H_2O and F_2O. $\angle HOH = 104°$. $\angle FOF = 101°$. The change is only 3°, which is very small compared with the total range (180° to 90°) of the apex angles of triatomic molecules.
   (*b*) HCN and ClCN, BrCN, ICN. The apex angle remains at 180° in all these molecules.
   (*c*) H_2CO and Cl_2CO. Both these molecules are planar. $\angle HCH = 118 \pm 2°$. $\angle ClCCl = 112°30' \pm 90'$.
   (*d*) The methyl halide molecules. In all these molecules the HCH angle remains close to the tetrahedral angle found in CH_4.
   (*e*) NH_3 and NF_3. $\angle HNH = 106°47'$. $\angle FNF = 102°9'$. The difference ($\sim 5°$) is small compared with the total range (120° to 90°) of the inter-bond angles of AB_3 molecules. (The change in angle from PH_3 to PF_3 or AsH_3 to AsF_3 is somewhat larger, but still only $\sim 10°$.)
   (*f*) C_2H_4 and C_2Cl_4. Both are planar molecules. $\angle HCH = 119°55'$. $\angle ClCCl = 113°30'$.
   Linked with this generalization, except in such obvious cases as $CH_4 \longrightarrow CH_3Cl$, substitution of halogen atoms for H atoms leaves the symmetry class unchanged. As examples, H_2O and F_2O both belong to the so-called C_{2V} symmetry class of isosceles triangle molecules; HCN, ClCN, BrCN and ICN all belong to the linear $C_{\infty V}$ class of molecules; H_2CO and Cl_2CO both belong to the C_{2V} symmetry class; NH_3 and NF_3 belong to the so-called C_{3V} symmetry class. As a consequence of these facts, we may confidently predict that the hypothetical molecule HgH_2 would be linear, since the molecules $HgHal_2$ are linear. Similarly, ZnH_2 and CdH_2 should be linear because

the molecules ZnI_2 and CdI_2 are linear; and the hypothetical molecule N_2F_4 may be predicted to have the same shape as N_2H_4. In larger molecules the corollary is not always true. For example, butadiene is probably planar, but hexachlorobutadiene is reported as non-planar (Kohlrausch and Wittek, 1942; Szasz and Sheppard, 1953).

A further corollary to this generalization is that change from F to Cl to Br to I makes no or comparatively little change in inter-bond angles. Examples may be seen in (b) and (d) above; in the acetyl halide molecules; in the pairs of molecules POF_3–$POCl_3$ and PSF_3–$PSCl_3$; and in the XF_3, XCl_3, XBr_3 and XI_3 molecules, where X is P or As.

(*iii*) *If a change of* BAB *angle does occur on change of* B *from hydrogen to halogen, it is usually a decrease rather than an increase*

As examples, the angle decreases from H_2O to F_2O; from NH_3 to NF_3; from $\angle HCH$ in H_2CO to $\angle ClCCl$ in Cl_2CO; from $\angle HCH$ in C_2H_4 to $\angle FCF$ or $\angle ClCCl$ in C_2F_4 or C_2Cl_4 respectively; from $\angle HCH$ in CH_4 to $\angle FCF$ in CHF_3; and from $\angle HSiH$ in SiH_4 to $\angle FSiF$ in $SiHF_3$. The increases of angle from PH_3 to PF_3 and from AsH_3 to AsF_3, and the very small increases from $\angle HCH$ in CH_4 to $\angle ClCCl$ in $CHCl_3$ or $\angle BrCBr$ in $CHBr_3$, form exceptions.

It seems of some importance to state this generalization because one might have thought that the main consequence of substituting halogen atoms for hydrogen atoms would have been an increase of BAB angle, because of repulsion between the lone pair electrons of the halogen atoms. Such repulsion no doubt exists, but the facts show that it is neither the only nor (usually) the predominant effect.

(*iv*) *In triatomic molecules* B—A—B *or tetratomic molecules* AB_3 (*all* B *atoms joined directly to* A), *change of* A *for an atom in the same sub-group of the periodic table but of higher atomic weight either leaves angle* BAB *unchanged or causes a change (usually a decrease) that is generally small compared with the total range of apex angle found in such molecules*

As examples, (a) the apex angle does not change on passage from ZnI_2 to CdI_2 to HgI_2; (b) the apex angle decreases from H_2O to H_2S to H_2Se to H_2Te, but the total range of the decrease ($14°$ at most) is small compared with the range ($180°$ to $90°$) possible for the apex angles of B—A—B molecules; (c) the HAH angle decreases from NH_3 to PH_3 to AsH_3 to SbH_3, but the total range of the decrease ($15°$ at most) is still only moderate compared with the total range covered by the inter-bond angles in AB_3 molecules ($120°$ to $90°$).

We may deduce from this generalization that the hypothetical molecule BeH_2 would be linear, since we have already deduced that the molecules ZnH_2, CdH_2 and HgH_2 should be linear.

O_3 and SO_2 form an example where change of O to S causes a small increase ($\sim 2°$) of apex angle.

(v) The presence of lone pair electrons is of great importance in determining molecular shapes

This can be seen from the fact that the molecule BH_3 is planar whereas NH_3 is pyramidal; or from the expectation that BeH_2 is linear, but OH_2 bent. As soon as lone pair electrons appear on the central atom, a sharp change of configuration is apparent; the molecule bends as though the bond electrons had become subject to a repulsion.

(vi) The importance of pure number in determining molecular shape

This is the outstanding generalization. *All* non-hydride, triatomic, molecules containing 16 or less valency electrons are linear. We may confidently predict that the molecules C_3 (the possible emitter of a certain group of bands at 4050 Å, first known in cometary spectra) and N_3 (a species suggested as responsible for some of the properties of active nitrogen) are linear in their ground states. Moreover, the generalization is not confined to molecules built from the lighter atoms. It appears to hold for molecules containing atoms drawn from anywhere in the periodic table; witness the ions $AgCl_2^-$, $AuCl_2^-$ and UO_2^{2+*}.

All non-hydride, triatomic, molecules containing 17, 18, 19 or 20 valency electrons are non-linear. Moreover, as the number of valency electrons increases, the apex angle (θ) steadily drops from 180° towards 90°. 16-electron molecules have $\theta = 180°$. For NO_2 (the only example of a 17-electron molecule that has been studied) there are two values reported for θ which unfortunately are discrepant. However, the mean value is $143 \pm 11°$, which represents a drop of $37 \pm 11°$ from the value for 16-electron molecules. For 18-electron molecules, the values of θ all lie between 110° and 120°. The mean value represents a drop of $\sim 26°$ from the mean value for NO_2. It is most remarkable that, although of course the values of θ for 18-electron molecules differ among themselves, the range they cover (10°)† is very small compared with the total range (180–90°) covered by the apex angles of triatomic molecules as a whole. There is unfortunately only one example of a 19-electron molecule whose apex angle has been studied, *viz* ClO_2. The value reported lies at the lower end of the range covered by the values for 18-electron molecules. However, as explained in TABLE 1, there must be a considerable uncertainty attaching to an OClO angle reported from electron diffraction studies. One may predict that the true value will turn out to be a few degrees lower than 116·5°. The values of θ for 20-electron molecules all lie between 98 and 111°; again the spread is small compared to the total range covered by

---

* The uranium atom has six valency electrons, the configuration in the ground state being —— $(5f)^4 (7s)^2$, where the $(5f)$ and $(7s)$ orbitals have closely similar binding energies. The ion UO_2^{2+} may thus be said to have 16 valency electrons.

† If we omit the value for FNO, the range covered is only 5°.

the apex angles of triatomic molecules as a whole. The mean value represents a drop of about 14° from the mean value for 18-electron molecules. It is urgently important that a re-investigation of the apex angles of the NO_2 and ClO_2 molecules should be undertaken.

To sum up, all 17-, 18-, 19-, and 20-electron molecules have non-linear ground states; the apex angle drops considerably from 16- to 17-electron molecules; and also from 17-, to 18-electron molecules; the apex angle also drops, but less markedly, from 18- to 19-electron molecules and from 19- to 20-electron molecules. Intuitively, one may connect the decreasing inter-bond angle, as the number of valency electrons increases from 16 to 20, with the accumulation of lone pair electrons (or of electrons partially localized on A) on the central atom A [see generalization (v)]. From the point of view of orbital theory, the 17th, 18th, 19th and 20th electrons fill two additional orbitals and it is not surprising to find that these orbitals are expected theoretically to be predominantly localized on atom A (Walsh, 1953b). When we proceed to 22-electron molecules, the trend to smaller apex angles is strikingly reversed. All 22-electron molecules are either linear or nearly so. One would predict that 21-electron molecules, if they existed, would be bent with an apex angle roughly midway between 100° and 180°.

In view of our prediction of linearity for BeH_2, HgH_2, etc, it appears that triatomic AH_2 molecules are linear if they contain 4 valency electrons, but probably non-linear if they contain 5, 6, 7 or 8 valency electrons. 4, 5, 6, 7, 8-electron AH_2 molecules are the analogues of 16, 17, 18, 19, 20-electron, non-hydride, triatomic molecules. The values of θ for AH_2 molecules containing 8 electrons vary somewhat, but all lie within a range (14° at most) that is small compared with the total range covered by the apex angles of triatomic molecules as a whole. The mean value is close to that for 20-electron, non-hydride, triatomic molecules. As regards HAB molecules, it appears that those containing 10 valency electrons are linear in their ground states and those containing 11, 12, 13 or 14 electrons are bent. We may predict the hypothetical molecules HBO and HBeF to be linear, but the 12-electron molecule HNO (which has been postulated as an intermediate in the photochemical decomposition of nitrites and the catalytic oxidation of ammonia) to be bent.

As regards AH_3 molecules, those containing 6 valency electrons are planar; those containing 8 are pyramidal. For non-hydride molecules (containing three atoms all linked directly to a central atom), all those containing 24 valency electrons or less are planar; all those containing 26 electrons are pyramidal. There are no known exceptions to these statements. We may predict the CO_3 molecule (postulated by Garner, Stone and Tiley, 1952), as an intermediate in the reaction between CO and O_2 on Cu_2O at room temperature

27

the NO_3 molecule (formed in the decomposition of N_2O_5, see

Sidgwick, 1950), and the $S-S\begin{smallmatrix}\diagup O\\ \diagdown O\end{smallmatrix}$ molecule (Vallance Jones, 1950),

to be planar. The 6-electron BH_3 molecule is planar, but when the coordination complex

$$OC \longrightarrow BH_3$$

is formed, electrons are donated to the BH_3 group which may then be said to contain more than 6 electrons; in the complex therefore the BH_3 group is pyramidal. Similar statements apply to the BF_3 group in the complex

$$(CH_3)_2O \longrightarrow BF_3 \text{ (Dunderman and Bauer, 1946).}$$

The inter-bond angle (θ) is expected to decrease as the number of valency electrons increases from 24 to 26. There has unfortunately been no study of the structure of a 25- electron molecule. A study of e.g. the ClO_3 molecule is urgently desirable. 24-Electron AB_3 molecules have $\theta = 120°$. Except for the one rather doubtful value for BrO_3^-*, 26-electron AB_3 molecules all have θ lying between 99° and 104°; the spread is small compared to the total range (120–90°) covered by the inter-bond angles in AB_3 molecules as a whole. 28-Electron molecules are expected to be planar. Of such molecules, only ClF_3 has been studied; it is reported to be planar, but (unexpectedly) to have a distorted T-shape.

As regards H_2AB molecules, the probability is that 12-electron molecules are planar, but 13-, 14-, 15-, and 16-electron molecules non-planar.

This dependence of inter-bond angles on pure number is quite remarkable. Pure number determines the order of magnitude of the angles surprisingly closely. Whatever its explanation, all other effects are of subsidiary importance.

(vii) *The shape of the first excited state of an n-electron molecule resembles that of the ground state of the similar molecule containing $n+1$ or $n+2$ electrons*
All the above generalizations refer only to the ground states of molecules. We turn now to a generalization about the shapes of electronically excited molecules. It is based upon results quoted above. Examples of its truth are as follows.

The first excited states of the 16-electron molecules CO_2 and CS_2 are probably bent, like the ground states of the 17-electron molecule NO_2 and the 18-electron molecules SO_2, O_3, etc. The first excited state of the 12-electron HCHO molecule is probably pyramidal, as expected for the ground state of the 14-electron molecule NH_2F.

---

* The structure of HIO_3 (Wells, 1949; pyramidal IO_3 groups held together by hydrogen bonds, with the O—I—O angles all between 95°40' and 101°25') suggests a smaller angle than 108° for the IO_3^- ion and hence for the BrO_3^- ion.

The first excited state of the 12-electron C_2H_4 molecule probably resembles the ground state of the 14-electron molecule N_2H_4. From the known shape of the first excited state of the 10-electron C_2H_2 molecule we may predict the ground state of the hypothetical radical HCOH to be planar with the shape

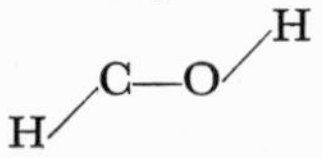

$$
\begin{array}{c}
\text{H} \diagdown \\
\text{C}\!-\!\text{O} \diagup^{\text{H}} \\
\text{H} \diagup
\end{array}
$$

THEORETICAL EXPLANATIONS OF THE EMPIRICAL
GENERALIZATIONS

It is possible to explain many of the empirical generalizations given in the previous section by the following procedure(Walsh, 1953a). We first decide the possible molecular orbitals for some particular class of molecule of fixed symmetry (*a*) when its nuclei are arranged in one symmetry pattern, and (*b*) when they are arranged in a second pattern. Each of the sets of possible orbitals is then arranged in an energy order. The orbitals of the one set are then correlated with those of the other; and finally it is decided whether each particular orbital becomes more or less tightly bound as some parameter is varied to make the arrangement of the nuclei change from the one symmetry pattern to the other. Such a procedure results in a correlation diagram which is of great value in interpreting the shapes of molecules containing various numbers of electrons and in both ground and excited states. It is also of great value in predicting the characteristics of particular electronic transitions. The procedure is most simply illustrated with reference to AH_2 molecules. Limitations of space prevent the detailed discussion here of other classes of molecules; but similar correlation diagrams may be plotted for HAB, AH_3, AB_3 *etc* molecules (Walsh, 1953a–j).

AH₂ Molecules

Let us choose for our two symmetry patterns (*i*) the linear arrangement H—A—H (*ii*) the bent arrangement $\text{H} \diagup^{\text{A}} \diagdown_{\text{H}}$ where angle HAH is 90°. The first thing to do is to write down a list of the possible molecular orbitals when the nuclei occupy the linear arrangement and to put these in an energy order. Confining ourselves to the lowest-lying, intra-valency shell, orbitals of a linear AH_2 molecule and assuming these to be built solely from *s* and *p* atomic orbitals, we have:

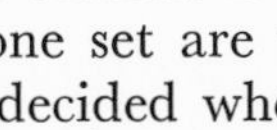

(*i*) Two orbitals binding the H atoms to the central atom. These may be thought of, for the purpose of discussing molecular shape, as each formed by the overlap of an *sp* hybrid atomic orbital on A with the $1s$ orbital of H (see Chapter 9, TABLE 1). They will be orbitals of σ type. For the purpose of discussing spectroscopic transitions

29

involving these orbitals, one must take into account the fact that there is no way of distinguishing the one bond from the other. In other words, one has to take combinations of the localized bond orbitals. These combinations may be of two types, in-phase or out-of-phase. They may be referred to as non-localized orbitals; and, being non-localized, may be described as σ_g and σ_u respectively.

(ii) A π_u orbital. This is simply a p orbital localized on the A atom and pointing in a direction at $90°$ to the HAH line. It is non-bonding. Since there are two such directions that are independent but equivalent (except for a rotation by $90°$), the orbital is two-fold degenerate. If the apex angle were changed from $180°$, the degeneracy must become split. The order of decreasing binding energy of the orbitals is σ_g, σ_u, π_u.

The next thing to do is to write down a list of the possible molecular orbitals when the nuclei occupy the bent, $90°$, arrangement and to put these in an energy order. A bent AH_2 molecule belongs to the so-called C_{2V} symmetry class. The definitions of the symbols appropriate to the non-localized orbitals of such a molecule are given below. The z axis is taken as bisecting the HAH angle and lying in the molecular plane. The y axis is taken as lying in the molecular plane and parallel with the H------H line (see the formula adjacent to TABLE 5). $C_2(z)$ means a rotation by $180°$ about the z axis, $\sigma_v(y)$ means a reflection in the xz plane, and $+$ and $-$ mean respectively that the wave function does not or does change sign when one of the symmetry operations $C_2(z)$ or $\sigma_v(y)$ is carried out.

TABLE 5. MOLECULAR ORBITALS OF BENT AH_2 MOLECULE

Symbol	$C_2(z)$	$\sigma_v(y)$	
a_1	$+$	$+$	
a_2	$+$	$-$	A
b_1	$-$	$+$	
b_2	$-$	$-$	H H

The lowest-energy, intra-valency shell orbitals of an AH_2 molecule whose apex angle is $90°$ are then as follows:

(i) Two orbitals binding the H atoms to the central atom. These may be thought of, for purposes of discussing molecular shape, as each formed by the overlap of a pure p atomic orbital on A with the $1s$ orbital of H. For the purpose of discussing spectroscopic transitions involving them, one must take non-localized combinations of the two localized orbitals, just as described for the linear molecule. The combinations (see FIGURE 1) may be either in-phase, in which case the appropriate molecular symbol (see TABLE 5) is a_1; or out-of-phase, in which case the appropriate molecular symbol is b_2.

(ii) A p orbital on atom A pointing in the x-direction. TABLE 5 shows that the molecular symbol to be applied to this orbital is b_1. It is non-bonding.

(*iii*) An *s* orbital on atom A. It is non-bonding. TABLE 5 shows that the molecular symbol to be applied is a_1. To distinguish it from the a_1 bonding orbital, we shall label it a_1 (lone pair).

The order of decreasing binding energy is expected to be a_1, b_2, b_1. The a_1 (lone pair) orbital is more tightly bound than the b_1, but where it lies in relation to the b_2 orbital is not obvious; there are certain spectroscopic reasons, however, for placing it between the a_1 and b_2 bonding orbitals.

The next task is to correlate the orbitals of the bent molecule with those of the linear molecule and to decide whether a particular orbital

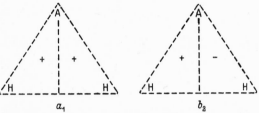

$$a_1 \qquad\qquad b_2$$

FIGURE 1. Combination of orbitals for non-linear
AH_2 molecule

becomes more or less tightly bound as the apex angle is changed from 90° to 180°. Clearly, if the HAH angle is gradually increased, the a_1 and b_2 bonding orbitals must eventually become the σ_g and σ_u bonding orbitals respectively of the linear molecule. At the same time, the orbitals must become more tightly bound because (*1*) the bonding orbitals of the 90° molecule, in their localized form, are built from *p* atomic orbitals of A, while those of the linear molecule are partly built from an *s* atomic orbital of A, and (*2*) an *sp* hybrid valency gives rise to a stronger bond than does a pure *p* valency (see Walsh, 1947). As the HAH angle is increased, the b_1 non-bonding orbital must become one of the two π_u non-bonding orbitals of the linear molecule. Since to a first approximation, the orbital is the same when the apex angle is 90° as when it is 180°, its binding energy is expected to be approximately constant as the angle changes. It is easily seen that the remaining orbital in the 90° molecule [a_1 (lone pair)] must correlate with the remaining π_u orbital of the linear molecule. While the HAH angle is held at 90°, the a_1 (lone pair) orbital does not mix ('hybridize') with the bonding orbitals. Increase of the angle from 90° implies such mixing. The bonding orbitals, instead of being built from pure *p* valencies of A, are built more and more from the *s* orbital of A; while at the same time the a_1 (lone pair) orbital, instead of being built solely from the pure *s* orbital on A, becomes built more and more from a p_z orbital on A. In the linear molecule, the bonding orbitals are built from the *s* and p_y orbitals of A, with no contribution from the p_z orbital; while the non-bonding orbital has no contribution from the p_y atomic orbital. In other words, as the HAH angle increases from 90° to 180°, the bonding orbitals increase in binding energy; while the non-bonding orbital labelled a_1 (lone pair) decreases in binding energy until at 180° it becomes one of the degenerate π_u orbitals.

FIGURE 2 is a correlation diagram between the lowest-energy orbitals possible for bent and linear AH_2 molecules. It incorporates the conclusions reached above. Each of the curves must be a maximum or minimum on the 180° line, since from 180° to 270° the curves must repeat their behaviour from 180° to 90°. The two most tightly bound orbitals are ones with a minimum on the 180° line.

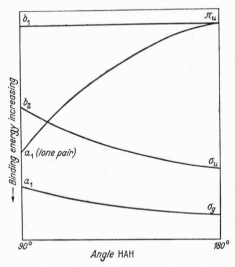

FIGURE 2. Correlation diagram between lowest-energy orbitals for AH_2 molecule

One therefore expects that all AH_2 molecules containing only four valency electrons will be linear in their ground states. This is in accord with the conclusions we reached on pp. 24–7. On the other hand, the ground states of AH_2 molecules containing 5, 6, 7 or 8 valency electrons are expected to be bent because at least one electron has to be placed in the a_1 (lone pair)–π_u non-bonding orbital. Similarly, the first excited state of HgH_2 or BeH_2 is expected to be bent. The a_1 (lone pair)–π_u orbital curve rises steeply from left to right in FIGURE 2 because, as already explained, it changes from a pure s orbital to a pure p orbital. The ground state of the H_2O molecule, with eight valency electrons, has therefore a bent configuration. The CH_2 molecule, with six valency electrons, is similarly expected to be bent ; since the binding energy of the b_1 orbital is not expected to vary greatly with change of apex angle, the angle in the CH_2 (or NH_2) ground state should not be very far from that in the H_2O molecule.

32

FIGURE 2 thus shows how generalizations (*vi*) and (*vii*) (pp. 26 and 28) can be explained. Moreover, the essential reason for the bent nature of the 5-, 6-, 7- and 8-electron molecules is the steep rise of the a_1 (lone pair)–π_u curve for one of the lone pair orbitals on A. One can therefore understand generalization (*v*). Instead of speaking of hybridization, an alternative way to explain the bent nature of the 5- to 8-electron molecules would be to say that when electrons are placed in the a_1 (lone pair)–π_u orbital on A repulsion between them and the electrons in the bond orbitals occurs, resulting in the bond electrons tending to move to one side of A (carrying the H atoms with them) and the lone pair electrons tending to move to the other side of A. The last statement, for example, is the analogue of saying that the hybrid $s-p_z$ lone pair orbital projects on the side of A away from the H atoms. It is this repulsion or hybridization effect that dominates the forces at work determining the apex angle. Generalization (*ii*) shows that this statement is still true even when the hydrogen atoms are replaced by halogen atoms. Bond–bond or bond–lone pair repulsions around central atoms carrying several bonds or lone pairs are much more important than *e.g.* repulsions between the nuclei or lone pair electrons of atoms not directly bound to each other. When the central atom has no lone pairs, an AH_2 molecule is linear because of the bond–bond electronic repulsion. If halogen atoms are substituted for the hydrogen atoms in such a molecule, the bond electrons move a little further away from atom A, but the bond–bond repulsion still causes the molecule to be linear (*cf* $HgHal_2$ and the expected form of HgH_2). When, however, the central atom possesses a lone pair, the outward movement of the bond electrons on substituting *e.g.* F for H causes their repulsion to be a little less, so that the inter-bond angle, under the influence of the lone pair–bond repulsions (the lone pair electrons now lying a little closer to A), decreases a little. In hybridization terms, the valencies of A towards the F atom acquire a little more p character and the lone pair orbital acquires a little more s character (Walsh, 1947); having more p character in the valencies used, the inter-bond angle is slightly less. This is the explanation of generalization (*iii*). The essential reason is the greater electronegativity of halogen atoms relative to hydrogen atoms.

16-Electron AB_2 molecules are linear like 4-electron AH_2 molecules. 17-, 18-, 19- and 20-electron AB_2 molecules are bent, like 5-, 6-, 7- and 8-electron AH_2 molecules. 22-Electron AB_2 molecules become linear again. The essential reason for the latter fact may be traced (Walsh, 1953b) to the possibility of constructing *two* molecular orbitals by hybridizing the s and p_z atomic orbitals of atom A, one projecting in the $+z$ direction and one in the $-z$ direction. When both these molecular orbitals are filled, a triatomic molecule will be linear because the bond electrons are subject to as much repulsion in the $+z$ as in the $-z$ direction.

Substitution of an atom of higher atomic weight but in the same sub-group of the periodic table for A in AH_2 is in one respect like substitution of halogen atoms for hydrogen atoms when A is fixed. Change of O in H_2O to S, for example, means that the bond electrons move slightly away from the central atom. This implies that the bond–bond repulsion is lessened and (if the bond–lone pair repulsion remained the same) the inter-bond angle would decrease. In fact the bond–lone pair repulsion will also be lessened (since all the valency electrons of a S atom are held less tightly than those of an O atom); but generalization (*iv*) shows that this is usually of smaller importance than the lessening of the bond–bond repulsion. The remarkable thing is that the two effects so nearly balance each other, the inter-bond angle showing only a small change. If there are no lone pairs on the central atom, then of course the molecule remains linear whatever atom A. Incidentally, the fact that the inter-bond angle does not decrease below 90° [generalization (*i*)] does not lend any obvious support to theories that supposed hybridization of *s* and *p* with *d* orbitals is of great importance in molecules like H_2S, H_2Se and H_2Te.

REFERENCES

Allen, P. W. and Sutton, L. E. (1950) *Acta cryst., Camb.* **3,** 46

Beach, J. Y. (1950) *Annu. Rev. phys. Chem.* **1,** 189

Bunn, C. W. (1945) *Chemical Crystallography* Oxford University Press

Craig, D. P. (1950) *J. chem. Soc.* 2146

Cruikshank, D. W. J. and Viervoll, H. (1949) *Acta chem. scand.* **3,** 560

Debye, P. (1939) *Phys. Z.* **40,** 66, 404

Dieke, G. H. and Kistiakowsky, G. B. (1934) *Phys. Rev.* **45,** 4

Dunderman, F. V. and Bauer, S. H. (1946) *J. phys. Chem.* **50,** 32

Dunitz, J. D. and Hedberg, K. (1950) *J. Amer. chem. Soc.* **72,** 3108

Finbak, C. (1941) *Avh. norske VidenskAkad.* No. 7

— and Hassel, O. (1941) *Arkiv. Math. Natur. B.* **45,** No. 3

Garforth, F. M., Ingold, C. K. and Poole, H. G. (1948) *J. chem. Soc.* 508

Garner, W. E., Stone, F. S. and Tiley, P. F. (1952) *Proc. roy. Soc.* **A211,** 472

Gordy, W., Smith, W. V. and Trambarulo, R. F. (1953) *Microwave Spectroscopy* London, Chapman and Hall

Grison, E., Eriks, K., and de Vries, J. L. (1950) *Acta cryst., Camb.* **3,** 290

Harris, L. and King, G. W. (1940) *J. chem. Phys.* **8,** 755

Herzberg, G. (1945) *Infra-red and Raman Spectra* New York, Van Nostrand

Jeffrey, G. A. and Cruikshank, D. W. J. (1953) *Quart. Rev. chem. Soc., Lond.* **7,** 335

Karle, I. L. and Karle, J. (1949) *J. chem. Phys.* **17,** 1052

King, G. W. and Ingold, C. K. (1953) *J. chem. Soc.* 2725

Kohlrausch, K. W. F. and Wittek, H. (1942) *Ber. dtsch. chem. Ges.* **75,** 227

Lonsdale, K. (1948) *Crystals and X-Rays* London, Bell

Maxwell, L. R., Mosley, V. M. and Deming, L. S. (1934) *J. chem. Phys.* **2,** 331

Metropolis, N. (1941) *Phys. Rev.* **60,** 283

Mulliken, R. S. (1935) *J. chem Phys.* **3,** 720; (1942a) *Rev. mod. Phys.* **14,** 204; (1942b) *ibid* 265

Pauling, L. and Brockway, L. O. (1935) *J. Amer. chem. Soc.* **57,** 2684

Pirenne, M. H. (1946) *The Diffraction of X-rays and Electrons by Free Molecules* Cambridge, University Press

Ramsay, D. A. (1953) *J. chem. Phys.* **21,** 960

Shand, W. and Spurr, R. A. (1943) *J. Amer. chem. Soc.* **65,** 179

Sidgwick, N. V. (1950) *The Chemical Elements and their Compounds* Vol. 1, p. 691, Oxford University Press

Sponer, H. and Teller, E. (1941) *Rev. mod. Phys.* **13,** 75

Szasz, G. J. and Sheppard, N. (1953) *Trans. Faraday Soc.* **49,** 358

Townes, C. H. and Dailey, B. P. (1952) *J. chem. Phys.* **20,** 35

Vallance Jones, A. (1950) *J. chem. Phys.* **18,** 1263

Venkateswarlu, P. (1950) *Phys. Rev.* **77,** 676

Viervoll, H. (1947) *Acta chem. scand.* **1,** 120

— and Hassel, O. (1947) *ibid* **1,** 149

Walsh, A. D. (1947) *Disc. Faraday Soc.* **2,** 18; (1953a-j) *J. chem. Soc.* 2260, 2266, 2288, 2296, 2301, 2306, 2318, 2321, 2325, 2330

Wells, A. F. (1949) *Acta cryst., Camb.* **2,** 128

Wesson, L. G. (1948) *Tables of Electric Dipole Moments* Boston, M.I.T. Press

Whiffen, D. H. (1950) *Quart. Rev. chem. Soc., Lond.* **4,** 131

Wilson, A. J. C. *Structure Reports* International Union of Crystallography, Utrecht

2

THE CONFORMATIONS OF SIX-MEMBERED
RING SYSTEMS

W. Klyne

THE term 'conformations' denotes the different arrangements in space of the atoms in a single classical organic structure (configuration), the arrangements being produced by the rotation or twisting (but not breaking) of bonds.

I   II

An example is provided by the well-known ' chair ' and ' boat ' conformations of *cyclo*hexane (I and II).

The energy differences between two or more conformations of a compound determine which of them are stable. Even a small energy difference is sufficient to ensure that the unexcited molecules exist largely in the conformation of lowest energy content. A molecule can, however, and often does, take up a less favoured conformation when excited—*e.g.* in the course of reaction with other molecules. The ease of transformation from one conformation to another depends upon the height of the energy barriers between them. No case is yet known where the energy barriers are sufficiently high to permit the isolation of two separate conformations of the same ring system.

The general principle underlying all the work discussed in this chapter is that in six-membered ring systems, whether carbocyclic or heterocyclic, the most stable structures are built up of chair conformations carrying their substituents in equatorial positions (*i.e.* in the general plane of the ring, see p. 38).

In the present chapter only six-membered ring compounds are discussed. It is hoped to deal with five-membered rings and with acyclic compounds in a subsequent volume. The first part of the chapter deals with definitions and the geometrically possible conformations of simple systems. The next part deals with the more fundamental methods of investigating conformations. The third section considers the application of the concept of non-bonded energy to more complex systems. The fourth section deals with those chemical and physical properties which are a consequence of conformations; these properties often serve to provide circumstantial evidence regarding conformations, or, more often, the application of conformational principles to such evidence gained in the course of degradative and preparative studies helps in allotting configurations. Later sections of the chapter deal briefly with some more specialized aspects of the subject.

This review owes much to previous surveys by Barton (1953a; Tilden Lecture), Hassel (1953) and Angyal and Mills (1952).

DEFINITIONS AND POSSIBLE STRUCTURES

Conformation
This term, which has been defined in the introduction, was introduced by Haworth (1929). The alternative term ' constellation ' (introduced by Ebel, 1933) is used in many German and Swiss papers (Freudenberg, Prelog).

Chair and Boat Forms
Sachse (1890, 1892) and Mohr (1918) showed that a *cyclo*hexane ring can exist theoretically in two strainless forms in each of which all the C—C—C angles have the tetrahedral value of 109° 28′. These forms I and II are usually called ' chair ' and ' boat ' respectively (Ger. ' Sessel ' or ' Stufe ', and ' Wanne '; Fr. ' en chaise ' and ' en bateau '). They have also been called ' rigid ' ' staircase ' or ' Z ' (=chair) and ' movable ' ' bed ', ' cradle ', ' tub ', or ' C ' (=boat) forms.

The possible forms of tetrahydropyran rings have been discussed by Reeves (1950) in his studies of pyranoside sugars. Two chair forms (III, IV) and six boat forms are possible. The symbols ' C1 ' and ' 1C ' are those of Reeves.

III (C1)   IV (1C)

Equatorial and Axial Bonds
The C—H bonds in the chair conformation of *cyclo*hexane are of two different types; those which are perpendicular to the general plane of the ring (as in VA) and those which lie approximately in this plane (as in VB). The bonds in the boat conformation are considered later, p. 78).

VA   VB

The distinction between these two types of bonds was made first by Hassel in Norway (Hassel, 1943) and independently by Pitzer in California (Beckett, Pitzer and Spitzer, 1947)*. Pitzer and Beckett termed the two types of bond 'polar' (VA) and 'equatorial' (VB) (abbreviated p and e) and these terms came into general use in British and American literature. Hassel named the bonds ἑστήκως (upright, ϵ) and κείμενος, (prone, κ). The term 'polar' was an unfortunate choice, since it has another established meaning with reference to the electrical character of a bond; it became necessary therefore to speak of a substituent as being 'stereochemically polar'. After much discussion between interested chemists some of the leading authorities in the field have agreed to use 'axial' (abbreviated a) instead of 'polar' in the stereochemical sense (Barton, Hassel, Pitzer and Prelog, 1953). The term 'axial' will therefore be used in this review.

Monosubstituted cycloHexane Derivatives

A monosubstituted derivative can theoretically occur in two conformations, with the substitutent X equatorial (VI) and axial (VII)

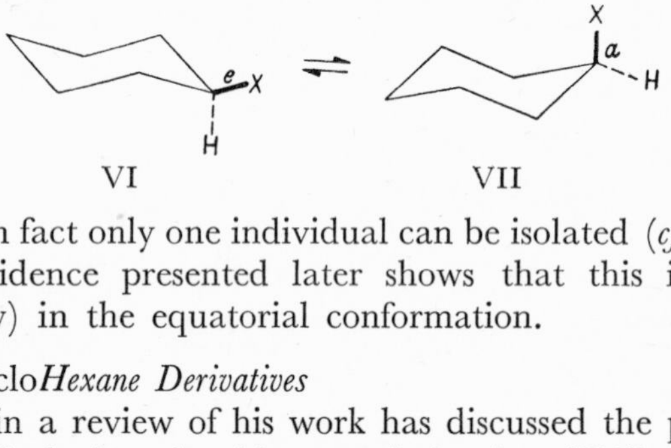

VI   VII

respectively. In fact only one individual can be isolated (cf Wightman, 1926), and evidence presented later shows that this individual is (predominantly) in the equatorial conformation.

Disubstituted cycloHexane Derivatives

Hassel (1950) in a review of his work has discussed the possible conformations of disubstituted cyclohexane derivatives $(C_6H_{10}X_2)$.

Configuration   Conformations
(classical formula)

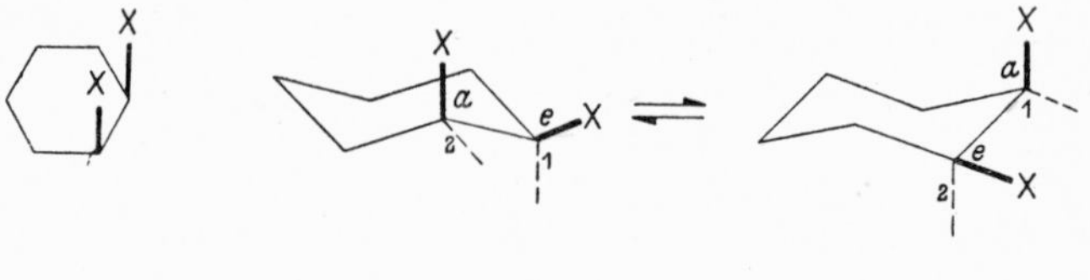

cis-1: 2
VIII

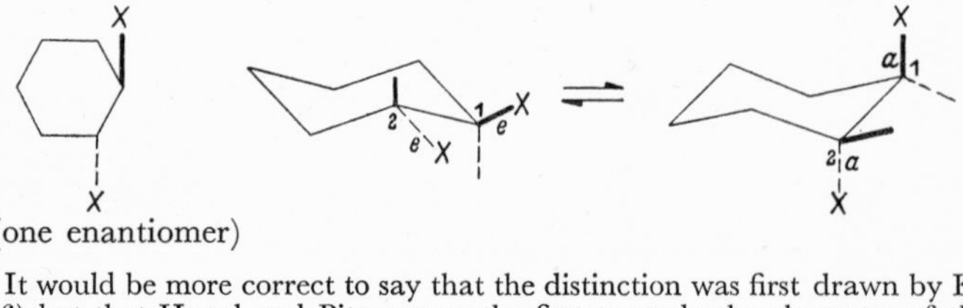

trans-1: 2
IX

(one enantiomer)

* It would be more correct to say that the distinction was first drawn by Kohlrausch et al (1936) but that Hassel and Pitzer were the first to study the character of the two types of bonds.

Configuration   Conformation
(classical formula)

cis-1:3
X

(one enantiomer)   trans-1:3
                                                                        XI

The *cis*-1:2 compound VIII must have one *e* and one *a* substituent. Conversion from one possible chair form to the other changes the *e* substituent into an *a* and vice-versa. On classical theory such a compound has a plane of symmetry and cannot be resolved. However the two chair conformations are mirror-images, and if the energy-barriers between them were high enough, resolution might be possible. Hassel has pointed out that so far no case is known—meaning that the energy barriers in the examples studied have not been high enough to stop interconversion. (Classical formulae should always be used in considering the number of possible isomers of a structure.)

The *trans*-1:3 compound (XI) exists in enantiomeric configurations in classical theory. For each enantiomer the two possible conformations are identical, each with one *e* and one *a* substituent.

The *trans*-1:2 and *cis*-1:3 compounds IX and X can each exist theoretically in conformations with both substituents equatorial (*e, e*), or with both substituents axial (*a, a*). For 1:4 disubstituted derivatives the picture is the same as for 1:2 derivatives. Hassel (1950) has considered some more complicated examples.

The interatomic distances between pairs of substituents in certain positions in chair and boat conformations are given in TABLE 1 (taken from Angyal and Mills, 1952). This table also includes the projected valency angles for 1:2-disubstituted compounds (Reeves, 1951); these are the angles between the two substituent bonds (C—X, C—Y) when projected on to a plane perpendicular to the bond C-1—C-2 (see XIII). The projection or star diagram (XIII) is often useful in considering reactions involving two ring-atoms.

A projected valency angle of 0° for *cis* configurations occurs only with boat forms of six-membered rings (and with five-membered rings). This may be called a ' true ' *cis* position. A projected valency angle of 60° is possible (in chair conformations) both for compounds which are (configurationally) *cis* and those which are (configurationally) *trans*.

39

A projected valency angle of 180° is possible in chair conformations only for *trans* compounds (' true ' *trans*-positions).

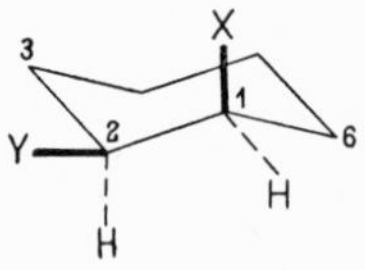

Perspective (XII)

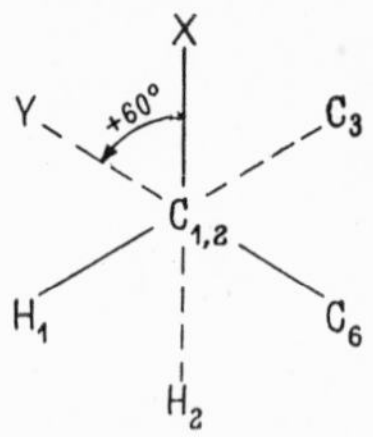

Projection (XIII)
Valencies of C-1, solid lines
Valencies of C-2, broken lines

In considering enantiomeric types of structure (Reeves 1951) the formulae are drawn with the ring to the right of the bond C-1—C-2; the angle is called positive if measured counter-clockwise (as in XIII) from the C-1 substituent to the C-2 substituent.

TABLE 1: DISTANCES BETWEEN ATOMS ATTACHED TO THE *cyclo*HEXANE RING AND PROJECTED VALENCY ANGLES

(From Angyal and Mills, 1952. Calculated by using the distances: C—C, 1·54; C—O, 1·42; C—H, 1·09 Å, and assuming tetrahedral angles throughout)

Position	Projected valency angles	Interatomic distances (Å)		
		H—H	O—O	C—C
Chair: 1*e*: 2*e* or 1*e*: 2*a*	60°	2·49	2·83	2·96
1*a*: 2*a*	180°	3·06	3·66	3·88
1*a*: 3*a*	—	2·51	2·51	2·51
Boat: ' sides ' (1*be*: 2*be*) or (1*ba*: 2*ba*)	0°	2·27	2·49	2·57
' bow and stern flagpoles ' (1*fp*: 4*fp*)	—	1·83	1·61	1·54

For *cis*- and *trans*-1:2-derivatives of *cyclo*pentane the projected valency angles are approximately 0° and 120° respectively. The projected valency angles for $O=C_1—C_2—X$ in 2-substituted *cyclo*-hexanones (chair conformation) are 15° if X is equatorial and 105° if X is axial (Cookson, 1954).

Decalins

Two decahydronaphthalenes (decalins) exist in which the two *cyclo*-hexane rings are *cis* and *trans* fused respectively (XIV and XV). Mohr (1918) suggested that these two structures were formed of two boats and two chairs respectively (XIVʙ and XVʙ). Hassel (1943; *cf* Wightman, 1925) pointed out that a two-chair form of *cis*-decalin was

40

possible (XIVc) and his subsequent work has shown that this is the preferred conformation (see p. 43). If this is rewritten as XIVd, its twofold axis of symmetry is obvious.

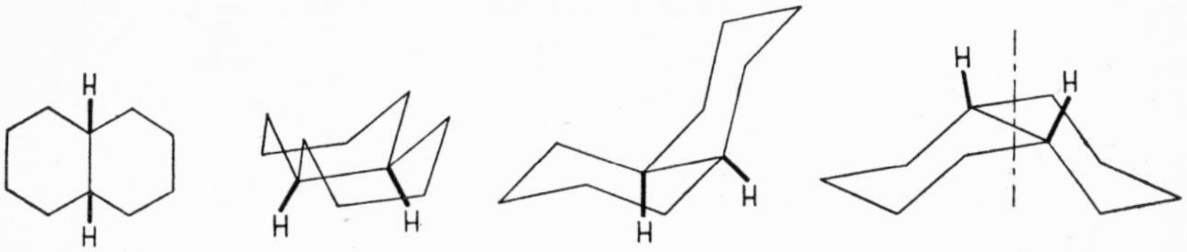

XIV

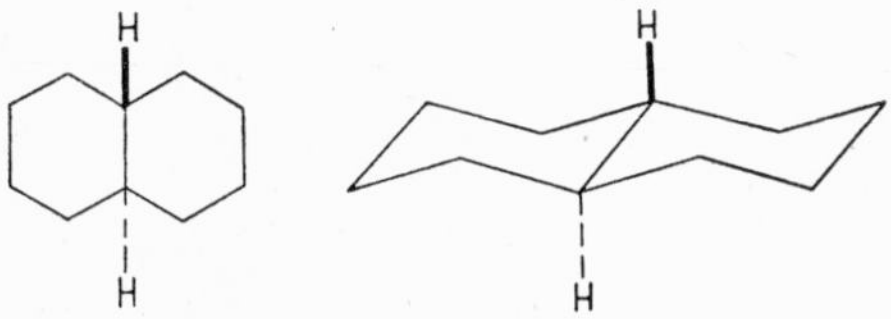

XV

Two two-chair conformations are possible for every *cis*-decalin and these may change freely into one another (Hassel, 1950; *cf* Mills, 1953; Cremlyn, Garmaise and Shoppee, 1953). As a result of this flexibility, 1- or 2- monosubstituted *cis*-decalins tend to exist in that conformation in which the substituent is equatorial, *e.g.* epimeric *cis*-1 decalyl derivatives (XVI A and B) each have the substituent X equatorial, although in A X at C-1 is *trans* to H at C-9, whilst in B it is *cis*.

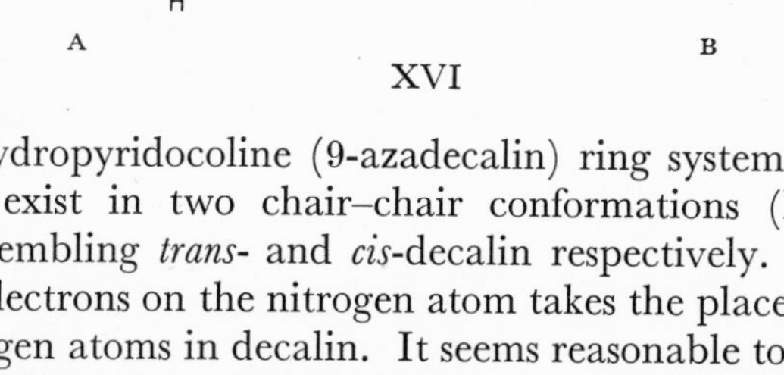

XVI

The octahydropyridocoline (9-azadecalin) ring system (XVII) can theoretically exist in two chair–chair conformations (XVIIIa and XVIIIb), resembling *trans*- and *cis*-decalin respectively. In these the lone pair of electrons on the nitrogen atom takes the place of one of the bridge-hydrogen atoms in decalin. It seems reasonable to suppose that the stable conformation of XVII is the *trans*-like XVIIIa (Cookson, 1953). This is true for the complex structure ' α '-*iso*sparteine which consists of two fused 9-azadecalin systems (Przyblyska and Barnes, 1953; see p. 44).

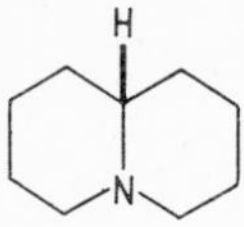

XVII 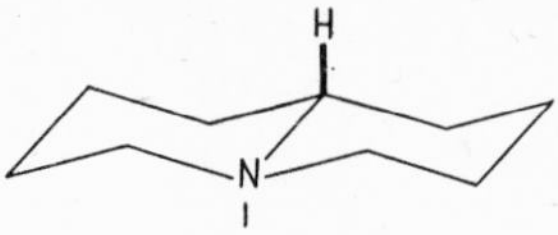   XVIII A 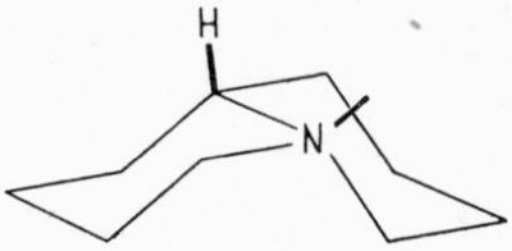   XVIII B

Polycyclic Systems

Angular fused systems such as perhydrophenanthrene and perhydro-chrysene are most stable in the *trans–anti–trans* forms XIX and XX (*cf* p. 50). These rather flat structures are the basis of two important groups

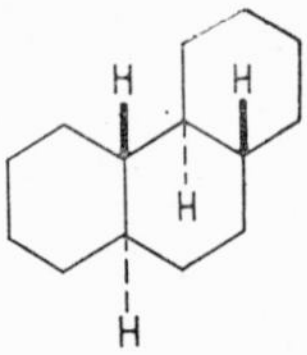

XIX 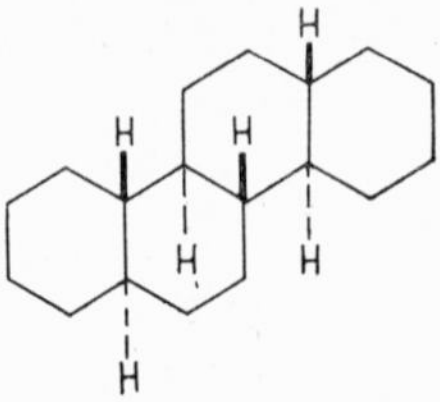   XX

of natural products, the steroids and the triterpenoids (*cf* Barton, 1950; Barton and Rosenfelder, 1951; Johnson, 1951). Angular structures with one of the terminal rings *cis*-fused can exist in all-chair forms which represent an extension of the *cis*-decalin (XIVc) structure of Bastiansen and Hassel (1946b). Polycyclic systems are considered further on p. 49.

FUNDAMENTAL METHODS OF INVESTIGATION

Electron Diffraction

The electron diffraction studies of Hassel and his colleagues on simple *cyclo*hexane derivatives and on the decalins in the vapour state and in solution represent perhaps the most fundamental method of investigating conformations (for reviews see Hassel, 1950, 1953). These studies, using the sector method for determining interatomic distance–distribution curves, are made in conditions in which the molecules are free from intermolecular forces. Formulae XXI and XXII show that the interatomic distances in the chair and boat forms of *cyclo*hexane are very different (see TABLE 1).

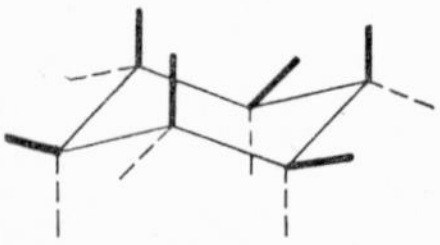

XXI 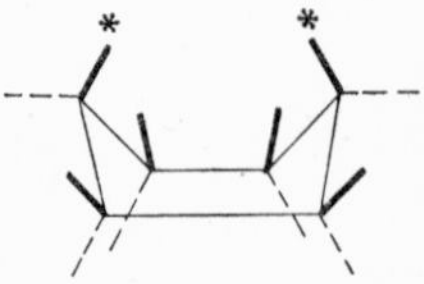   XXII

Hassel's studies indicate that *cyclo*hexane and all its simple derivatives exist preponderantly in the chair form (XXI). This is due to the fact that in the boat XXII the hydrogen atoms would come closer together than in XXI (especially the hydrogen atoms at the 'ends' of the boat**). In fact it may not be possible to maintain the tetrahedral valency angles in XXII.

In mono-substituted *cyclo*hexane derivatives (*e.g.* chloro*cyclo*hexane) the conformation in which the substituent is equatorial (XXIII) is present in much greater concentration than that in which the substituent is axial (XXIV).

XXIII   XXIV

(All hydrogen atoms omitted except those referred to in discussion.)

The instability of axial substituents such as X in XXIV is due to mutual repulsion between X and the two axial hydrogen atoms on the same side of the ring at C-3 and C-5. The equatorial substituent in XXIII is not subjected to such repulsion.

Di- and poly-substituted *cyclo*hexane derivatives usually take up that conformation in which a majority of the substituents are equatorial. Hassel (1950) has given a list of many compounds examined by his school. Slight deformations of the valency angles may take place to relieve strains, particularly in compounds carrying two large axial substituents on the same side of the ring (Hassel, 1950; van Vloten *et al*, 1950).

Electron diffraction studies of the two decalins are the principal direct evidence for the two-chair conformations XIVc and XVb (Bastiansen and Hassel, 1946b).

X-ray Diffraction

X-ray diffraction evidence has in many cases confirmed the two general principles deduced in the preceding section, *viz* that chair forms are more stable than boat and that equatorial substituents are more stable than axial. X-ray studies on solids, are, of course, open to the objection that conformations in the solid state are influenced by intermolecular forces. However, the x-ray evidence so far obtained agrees with that from electron diffraction and other methods on vapours or solutions. Many studies on simple *cyclo*hexane derivatives have been made by the Oslo school (for references see Hassel, 1950). The early studies by Hendricks and Bilicke (1926) and by Dickinson and Bilicke (1928) on 'β'-benzene hexachloride and hexabromide were the first positive evidence for the chair form of *cyclo*hexane.

Three important complete analyses of polycyclic structures, those of cholesteryl iodide (Carlisle and Crowfoot, 1945), the iodoacetate of methyl oleanolate (Abd El Rehim and Carlisle, 1954) and of lanosterol (Curtis, Fridrichsons and Mathieson, 1952) provide full details of the steroid and triterpenoid skeletons. Perspective views are given in XLIV (p. 56) and XLVI (p. 57) (cf Barton, 1950; Barton and Rosenfelder, 1951; Barton and Holness, 1952).

Examination of cellulose (Astbury and Davies, 1944) and of sucrose (Beevers and Cochran, 1946) has shown that the glucopyranoside rings in these compounds are of the chair form (III; type Cl, of Reeves). (For further references see Reeves, 1950.)

XXV   XXVI

X-ray analysis has shown that other saturated O-, S- and N-heterocyclic structures containing six-membered rings exist in chair conformations. Examples are NN'-dichloropiperazine (XXV) with the two chlorine atoms equatorial (Andersen and Hassel, 1949); 'aldehyde ammonia' (2:4:6-(e, e, e)-trimethyl-1:3:5–triazacyclohexane, Lund 1951), and—a more complex structure—'α'-isosparteine (XXVI), one of the fundamental ring structures of the lupin alkaloids which has four chair rings (Przybylska and Barnes, 1953). Cornubert, Delmas, Monteil and Viriot (1949) have given a useful summary of work on heterocyclic compounds by this and other methods. For an exhaustive catalogue of alicyclic structures which have been studied by x-ray diffraction, see Wyckoff (1953).

Dipole Moments

In structures containing at least two oriented dipoles, information concerning conformations can sometimes be obtained from measurement of dipole moments. Le Fèvre and Le Fèvre (1935) showed that cyclohexane-1:4-dione contained approximately 10 per cent of the boat conformation, the remainder being of the chair conformation. Nace and Turner (1953) have applied the same principles to a study of the steroid diketones, 5α- and 5β-androstane-3:17-dione (XXVII, XXVIII; the latter previously called aetiocholane-3:17-dione), which are trans and cis-2-decalones. Their results indicate that whilst the 5α (trans-) compound is 'all-chair', the 5β (cis-) compound probably contains about 15 per cent of the conformation in which the A ring is a boat (XXVIIIB).

44

The dipole moment of *trans*-1:2-dichloro*cyclo*hexane (Tulinskie, Di Giacomo and Smyth, 1953) indicates that it is a mixture of ($1e$, $2e$) and ($1a$, $2a$) conformations (IX), the former predominating (56 per cent in vapour, 72 per cent in benzene).

XXVII   XXVIII A   XXVIIIв

Previous work on steroids by Kumler (1945) cannot be interpreted at present because it deals with compounds in which non-oriented dipoles such as (C—)O—H are present; these are liable to rotation about the C—O bond.

Much work has been carried out on the isomeric benzene hexa-chlorides (Lind, Hobbs and Gross, 1950, and references there; Bastiansen, Ellefsen and Hassel, 1949) and this has recently been extended to cyclitol derivatives (Angyal and Angyal, 1952).

Infra-red and Raman Spectra

For simple structures such as *cyclo*hexane, dioxan and trioxan, the combined use of infra-red and Raman spectra provides valuable evidence for conformational studies. Different conformations may be distinguished on account of their different symmetries by the number of fundamental vibration frequencies permitted in the infra-red and Raman spectra. Chair conformations are indicated for *cyclo*hexane (Kohlrausch and Wittek, 1941; Gerding, Smit and Westrik, 1942; Rasmussen, 1943; Ramsay and Sutherland, 1947), 1:4-dioxan (Ramsay, 1947, Malherbe and Bernstein, 1952), and 1:3:5-trioxan (Ramsay, 1948). Larnaudie (1952, 1953) has examined the infra-red spectra of various mono- and di-substituted *cyclo*hexanes. Kozima and Yoshino (1953), using Raman spectra, have discussed the proportions of the a, a and e, e conformations of *trans*-1:4-dihalogeno*cyclo*hexanes present in various states.

Recent work on the infra-red spectra of hydroxy- and acetoxy-steroids has shown that there are useful empirical rules relating certain absorption maxima and the equatorial or axial nature of hydroxyl or acetoxyl groups in terminal rings (Jones *et al*, 1951; Cole *et al*, 1952; Fürst *et al*, 1952). This work is discussed in detail by Braude and Waight (this vol. p. 167).

Similar empirical relationships in the carbohydrate field, which may facilitate the distinction between α- and β-D-glucopyranosides (axial and equatorial linkages at C-1 respectively), have been reported briefly by Barker, Bourne, Stacey and Whiffen (1954). Other infra-red evidence is discussed on p. 83.

Thermodynamic Calculations

Aston, Pitzer and their colleagues have used a combination of thermodynamic and spectroscopic methods to show that *cyclo*hexane exists predominantly in the chair form. A comparison of the entropy determined from thermodynamic measurements with that calculated from spectroscopic data and known interatomic distances shows that *cyclo*hexane must have the symmetry number 6, and therefore exist almost entirely in the chair conformation at room temperature. (Aston *et al*, 1941, 1943; Pitzer and Beckett, 1947; Beckett, Pitzer and Spitzer, 1947). Hazebroek and Oosterhoff (1951) have shown that the proportion of the boat form increases with increasing temperature.

Pitzer and his colleagues showed that methyl*cyclo*hexane exists almost entirely in that conformation in which the substituent is equatorial, and that for the 1:2-, 1:3- and 1:4-dimethyl*cyclo*hexanes, the stereoisomer of lower energy content, entropy, density, refractive index and boiling point in each pair is the diequatorial one. This allotment of configuration agreed with previous arguments for the 1:2- and 1:4-compounds, but disagreed for the 1:3-compounds (see also Rossini and Pitzer, 1947; Haggis and Owen, 1953). Pitzer's allotment for the 1:3-isomers agrees with that found experimentally by Mousseron and Granger (1938); these authors had obtained the isomer of higher boiling point in optically active form, showing that it must be the *trans*-isomer.

The earlier allotments of configuration were based on the Auwers–Skita rules (Auwers, 1920; Auwers and Ottens, 1924; Skita, 1920; Skita and Schneck, 1922). The breakdown of these rules for 1:3 compounds is discussed fully by Haggis and Owen (1953). The reversal of configurations has been necessary in other cases, *viz* the 3-methyl-*cyclo*hexanols, 3-methyl*cyclo*hexylmethanols, 3-methyl*cyclo*hexanecarboxylic acids (Haggis and Owen, 1953; Goering and Serres, 1952; Noyce and Denney 1952; Siegel, 1953; Darling, Macbeth and Mills, 1953; and references there).

Heats of Combustion

Further evidence that *cyclo*hexane is an energetically favoured structure comes from the heats of combustion of the *cyclo*alkanes (Spitzer and Huffman, 1947) which are as follows (in kcal.mole^{-1} per CH_2 group): *cyclo*pentane, 158·7; *cyclo*hexane, 157·4; *cyclo*heptane, 158·3; *cyclo*octane, 158·6. The fact that *cyclo*hexane shows a minimum value, comparable with that for unbranched alkanes (157·0), supports the view that its non-bonded energy is less than that of other ring compounds.

Thermochemical studies of 2-alkyl*cyclo*hexanols (Skita and Faust, 1931) show that the *trans*-compounds, where both substituents can be equatorial, have lower heats of combustion than the *cis*-isomers (where one substituent must be axial). For other examples see Skita and Rossler (1939).

The study of secondary alcohols (whether polysubstituted *cyclo*hexane derivatives or polycyclic compounds) by equilibration methods, (p. 57) is an application of the same principles.

Seyer (1953) has suggested that certain anomalies in the specific heat of *cis*-decalin at 50° are due to a conformational change from two-chair (XIVc) to two-boat (XIVb). This seems an improbable explanation.

APPLICATIONS OF THE CONCEPT OF NON-BONDED INTER-ACTION ENERGY TO MORE COMPLEX COMPOUNDS

Calculations of Energy Differences

The importance of non-bonded strain energy in cyclic hydrocarbons was first discussed by Conn, Kistiakowsky and Smith (1939) following a suggestion by Schomaker. Pitzer (1945), using the value of 2·8 kcal. mole^{-1} for the rotation barrier about an ethane-like single C—C bond, calculated that the difference in strain energy between the boat and chair forms of a *cyclo*hexane ring would be 5·6 kcal. mole^{-1}. This value may be too low since it does not allow for the repulsion between the 'flag-pole' hydrogen atoms at the ends of the boat. Kumler (1945) suggested that the energy difference is probably 7–10 kcal. mole^{-1} (boat > chair). Shoppee (1946) estimated the height of the energy barrier for the transformation chair ⇌ boat ⇌ chair (ring conversion) to be 9–10 kcal.mole^{-1}; such a barrier can readily be surmounted as a result of thermal bombardment. Pitzer and Beckett (1947) calculated the energy difference for (*a*)-methyl*cyclo*hexane − (*e*)-methyl*cyclo*hexane as approximately 2 kcal.mole^{-1}.

Barton (1948) has calculated the interaction energies between nonbonded atoms in the 'chair' and 'boat' forms of *cyclo*hexane and in *trans*- and *cis*-decalin (the latter as two-boat and two-chair forms) using the equations applied by Dostrovsky, Hughes and Ingold (1946) and by Westheimer and Mayer (1946) in other cases. The values shown in TABLE 2 agree qualitatively with experimental evidence in that the stability order for *cyclo*hexane is chair > boat, and for the decalins, *trans* > *cis* (two-chair) > *cis* (two-boat); Barton points out, however, that the van der Waals radius for hydrogen and the correct form to be used for the repulsion term are uncertain. Furthermore the energy differences are not purely steric in origin.

TABLE 2. DIFFERENCES IN NON-BONDED ENERGY
Values in kcal.mole^{-1}

Compound	Stability order	Calculated differences in non-bonded energy	
		Semi-empirical*	Empirical†
cycloHexane	chair > boat	1·3–6·9	5·6
trans-Decalin and cis-Decalin (XIVc)	trans > cis	0·5–8·2	2·4‡
cis-Decalin (XIVc and B)	XIVc > XIVB	2·9–7·3	8·8
9-Methyl-trans- (and cis-) decalins	trans > cis	—	0·8

*Barton (1948)   † Turner (1952)
‡Difference in heats of combustion (experimental) 5 kcal.mole^{-1}

Turner (1952) has extended the empirical treatment of Pitzer (1945) and has calculated the steric energy of the cyclic hydrocarbons using values found by Pitzer (1940) and by Beckett *et al* (1947) for the energy differences between the eclipsed or opposed (XXIX), skew (gauche) (XXX) and staggered (stable) (XXXI) conformations of *n*-butane.

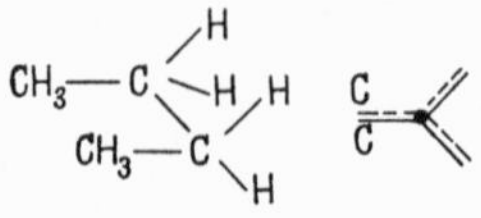

XXIX
Eclipsed

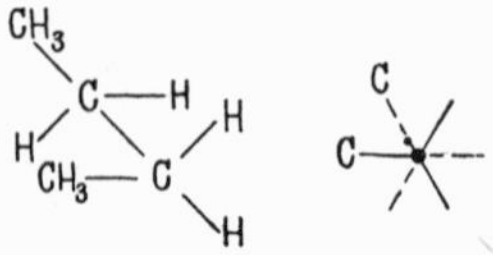

XXX
Skew

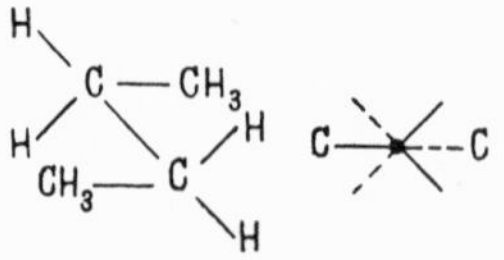

XXXI
Staggered

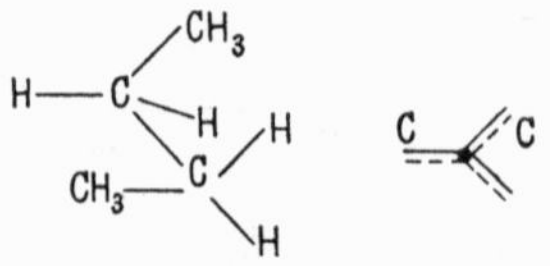

XXXII
120°

These values are as follows: XXX–XXXI, 0·8; XXIX–XXXI, 3·6 kcal.mole^{-1} (*cf* also Ito, 1953).

The energy differences calculated for various pairs of cyclic structures are given in TABLE 2. It is impossible to calculate a true value for the difference between ' two-chair '-*cis*-decalin and ' two-boat '-*cis*-decalin since the latter structure has two ' 120° ' interactions of type XXXII for which Pitzer's calculations give no value. (The value in TABLE 2 is a minimum value obtained by neglecting these unknowns.)

Introduction of an angular methyl group into *trans*- and *cis*-decalins (two-chair) reduces the calculated energy difference between them from 2·4 to 0·8 kcal.mole⁻¹. Bachmann, Ross, Dreiding and Smith (1954) have shown that for certain cyclic imides formally analogous to decalin (XXXIII), the introduction of an angle methyl group at R or R' actually makes the *cis*-compound (XXXIII) more stable than its isomer in which the two rings are *trans*-fused. They discuss in detail, with many references (*cf* Linstead *et al*, 1936, 1937), the effects of angle methyl groups on the stability of fused ring systems.

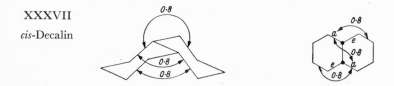

XXXIII	XXXIV	XXXV	XXXVI
	cis-anti-trans	*cis-syn-trans*	*trans-syn-trans*

The terms *syn*- and *anti*- are used here to designate the relative positions of adjacent bridge substituents *not* on the same bridge (atoms in heavy type in formulae XXXIV, XXXV and XXXVI)

Johnson (1953) has extended Turner's empirical method of calculation to all the possible perhydroanthracenes and perhydrophenanthrenes. His results are summarized in TABLE 3, and the method is illustrated by formulae XXXVII and XXXVIII.

XXXVII

cis-Decalin

Three skew interactions between pairs of bonds as shown. $\Delta E = 3 \times 0·8 = 2·4$ kcal. mole⁻¹.

XXXVIII

cis-syn-cis-

Perhydroanthracene

Two skew interactions $(2 \times 0·8 = 1·6$ kcal.) *plus* one (1:3*a,a*) interaction ($\sim 4·8$ kcal.) $= \sim 6·4$ kcal. mole⁻¹.

Linstead and Whetstone (1950) have shown experimentally that the *cis-syn-trans* perhydrophenanthrene ketone (XXXV) cannot be isomerized to the *trans-syn-trans* isomer (XXXVI) which would have to

TABLE 3. ENERGY RELATIONSHIPS IN PERHYDROANTHRACENES AND
PERHYDROPHENANTHRENES

(Johnson, 1953) ΔE values are relative to *trans-syn-trans* perhydroanthracene as zero. ΔE for $(1:3-a,a)$ interaction taken as $\sim 4\cdot8$ kcal. mole^{-1}.

Configuration	Interactions	ΔE (kcal.mole^{-1})
PERHYDROANTHRACENES		
trans-syn-trans	none	0
cis-syn-trans $(= trans-anti-cis)$	3 skew	2·4
cis-anti-cis	6 skew	4·8
trans-anti-trans (middle ring boat)	1 boat; 2 × ' 120° '	> 5·6
cis-syn-cis	2 skew; 1(1: 3-a: a)	~ 6·4
PERHYDROPHENANTHRENES		
trans-anti-trans	1 skew	0·8
trans-anti-cis	4 skew	3·2
cis-syn-trans	4 skew	3·2
cis-anti-cis	6 skew	4·8
cis-syn-cis	3 skew; 1(1: 3-a: a)	~ 7·2
trans-syn-trans	1 boat; + ?	> 5·6

For experimental work on perhydroanthracenes see Cook, McGinnis and Mitchell, 1944; perhydrophenanthrenes, Linstead *et al*, 1942; Linstead and Whetstone, 1950; polysubstituted dodecahydrophenanthrenes, Poos, Arth, Beyler and Sarett, 1953; Lukes and Sarett, 1954.

include one boat-ring (*cf* p. 79). Djerassi, Frick, Rosenkranz and Sondheimer (1953) and Bladon, Henbest, Jones *et al* (1953) have discussed examples in the steroid series which are complicated by the fusion of a five-membered ring to the perhydrophenanthrene system.

The recent discovery that the important tetracycline antibiotics aureomycin and terramycin have partially reduced naphthacene (2:3-benzanthracene) structures will stimulate interest in perhydroanthracene types (*cf* Hochstein *et al*, 1953). Heterocyclic analogues of this type are found in the yohimbine alkaloids (LVI, p. 60) which have been discussed by Janot, Goutarel, Le Hir, Amin and Prelog (1952) and by Cookson (1953) and the cevine group (Jacobs and Pelletier, 1953; Barton, Jeger, Prelog and Woodward, 1954).

Instability Factors

If the equatorial or axial nature of substituents is considered as a geometrical problem, and if it is accepted that every axial substituent is a factor making for instability, it is possible to calculate instability factors for polysubstituted *cyclo*hexane derivatives and related structures. This idea was introduced by Hassel and Ottar (1947) for the pyranose forms of carbohydrates and extended by Reeves (1949a, b,

1950, 1951). Any 1:3 (*a*,*a*)-disubstituted compound is strained and no monocyclic 1:3:5 (*a*,*a*,*a*)- trisubstituted compound is known.

Only one known isomer (γ) of hexachloro*cyclo*hexane (benzene hexachloride) has a pair of axial chlorine atoms in its normal conformation and here obvious deviations from the ideal structure occur, the (*a*,*a*) valencies being splayed outwards (van Vloten *et al*, 1950).

An axial CH_2OH group and an axial OH group on the same side of the ring produce a greater measure of instability than two axial OH groups on the same side (Hassel and Ottar, 1947). Reeves subsequently suggested that an axial hydroxyl on C-2 produced a large element of instability if the C—O valency at C-2 bisects the two C—O valencies of C-1 (Δ2 factor) (as in β-D-mannose, *cf* XXXIX).

XXXIX

TABLE 4 lists factors for the aldohexopyranoses and experimental data which show that predictions based on them closely represent the actual conformations (Reeves, 1950, 1951). Reeves summarized previous scattered references to the conformation of pyranoside rings (*e.g.* Pacsu, 1939; Scattergood and Pacsu, 1940).

If the two substituents of different sizes are in positions such that one must be equatorial and the other axial, it is logical to expect that the conformation which places the larger substituent equatorial will be preferred. Complications may be caused by dipoles of substituents (*e.g.* in *trans*-1: 2-dibromo*cyclo*hexane, *cf* p. 45).

Methyl–Carbonyl Interactions
No detailed calculations have yet been made regarding non-bonded interactions between substituents such as methyl in the 2 (or 6) position and the carbonyl oxygen of *cyclo*hexanone (*cf* Ames *et al*, 1953; comments by Dr T. G. Halsall). It may well be that the difference in non-bonded energy between axial and equatorial 2-methyl-*cyclo*-hexanones is much less than that between epimers carrying two univalent substituents, *e.g.* the 2-methyl-*cyclo*hexanols. The small projected valency angle $X—C_2—C_1 = O$ for X (equatorial), which is only 15°, is an unfavourable factor; for X (axial) this angle is 105° (Cookson, 1954).

TABLE 4. CONFORMATIONS OF PYRANOSIDES: INSTABILITY FACTORS
AND COMPLEXING BEHAVIOUR

Based on Reeves (1950, 1951). All compounds are D-pyranosides. Numbers
in columns 2 and 3 indicate axial substituents. H indicates the Hassel and
Ottar instability factor (CH_2OH a + OH a on same side of ring); **H** (in heavy
type) indicates CH_2OH a + two OH a; Δ 2 indicates Reeves's instability factor,
see p. 51. Complexing is considered on p. 75. ' Dextro–laevo ' means that the compound is thought to be a mixture of two conformations; ' compensating ' means
that the compound has two pairs of hydroxyl groups (one dextro, one laevo) in the
same conformation

Pyranoside		Instability factors		Conformation predicted from instability factors	Cuprammonium complex	Conformation deduced from complex	Equilibrium in free sugar. Preponderant anomer
		C1	1C				
Allose	α	1, 3	Δ2, 4, 5	C1	—	—	
	β	3	H, 1, 2, 4, 5	C1	—	—	—
Altrose	α	1, 2, 3	4, 5,	C1, 1C	dextro–laevo	C1⇌1C	
	β	Δ2, 3	H, 1, 4, 5	C1, 1C	dextro–laevo	C1⇌1C	—
Glucose	α	1	H, Δ2, 3, 4, 5	C1	compensating	C1	} β
	β	None	**H**, 1, 2, 3, 4, 5,	C1	compensating	C1	
Mannose	α	1, 2	H, 3, 4, 5	C1	dextro	C1	} α
	β	Δ2	**H**, 1, 3, 4, 5	C1, 1C	dextro	C1	
Gulose	α	1, 3, 4	Δ2, 5	C1, 1C	dextro	C1	—
	β	3, 4	H, 1, 2, 5	C1	—		
Idose	α	1, 2, 3, 4	5	1C	compensating	1C	
	β	Δ2, 3, 4	H, 1, 5	C1, 1C	compensating	—	—
Galactose	α	1, 4	H, Δ2, 3, 5	C1	laevo	C1	} β
	β	4	**H**, 1, 2, 3, 5	C1	laevo	C1	
Talose	α	1, 2, 4	H, 3, 5	C1, 1C	—	—	} α
	β	Δ2, 4	**H**, 1, 3, 5	C1, 1C	—	—	

Multi-substituted cycloHexanes

Compounds with equatorial substituents are in general more stable
than their isomers with axial substituents. Anomalies in the behaviour
of certain degradation products of diterpenoids and triterpenoids led
Barton (1953a, footnote 64; 1953b) to consider more closely the
different types of multi-substituted cyclohexanes. The symbols (1:2-
X: Y) and (1:3-X: Y) are used to denote repulsive non-bonded interactions between substituents X and Y attached to adjacent—and
adjacent but one—carbon atoms in a cyclohexane ring.

In a monosubstituted derivative the significant interactions are, in
the axial conformation, 4(1: 2-H: H) + 2(1: 2-X: H) + 2(1: 3-X: H)

and, in the equatorial conformation $2(1:2\text{-H}:H) + 4(1:2\text{-X}:H) + 2(1:3\text{-H}:H)$. Since experiment shows that the X(e) conformation is more stable than X(a), the repulsions in X(a) must be greater than in X(e). Therefore

$$(1:2\text{-H}:H) + (1:3\text{-X}:H) > (1:2\text{-X}:H) + (1:3\text{-H}:H) \dots\dots\dots(1)$$

From the behaviour of 1X-2: 2-R: R-trisubstituted derivatives, where X(e) is more stable than X(a), it may be deduced that

$$(1:2\text{-H}:H) + (1:2\text{-R}:H) + 2(1:3\text{-X}:H) >$$
$$(1:2\text{-X}:H) + (1:2\text{-R}:X) + 2(1:3\text{-H}:H) \dots\dots\dots\dots(2)$$

In 1:2 : 2: 6: 6-pentasubstituted compounds the usual stability order is inverted, *i.e.* the conformation with the substituent X at C-1 axial is more stable than that with X equatorial.

This is in accordance with the facts cited above. Adding the inequalities 1 and 2 together gives

$$(1:2\text{-R}:X) + (1:3\text{-H}:H) > (1:2\text{-R}:H) + (1:3\text{-X}:H) \dots\dots(3)$$

which is a condition required for the X(a) conformation of (XL, Y = R) to be more stable than X(e).

The two inequalities 1 and 3 together can be applied to all other types of 2:6-substituted *cyclo*hexane derivatives. The results show that only in following types is the usual stability order inverted, *i.e.* X(a) is more stable than X(e):

$$1X\text{-}2(a):6(a)\text{-RR}; \quad 1X\text{-}2(e):2(a):6(a)\text{-RRR};$$
$$\text{and } 1X\text{-}2(e):2(a):6(e):6(a)\text{-RRRR}.$$

The general type is shown by XL, in which the two groups Y may be either hydrogen or a substituent.

XL

These principles were applied to certain degradation products of the sesquiterpenoids eudesmol and selinene by Barton (1953b), who showed that these compounds must be *trans*-decalin derivatives; this is supported by rotational evidence (Klyne, 1953).

The ' 4 : 5-Effect' in Perhydrophenanthrenes
Another special factor which has recently been suspected is the non-bonded interaction between two equatorial substituents in the 4 : 5-positions in *trans-anti-trans*-perhydrophenanthrene types (*e.g.* between 1β- and 11α-substituents in XLVI). As a result of such repulsions an axial substituent may in certain cases be more stable than its equatorial epimer. Ames, Beton, Bowers, Halsall and Jones (1954) have discussed

certain 19-methyl- (and 19-hydroxyl-)18α-triterpenoids (*cf* XCVII for numbering) where it appears that the more stable epimer is probably the 19β (axial) one; here one of the deciding factors may be repulsion of a 19α-substituent group by the 12β-hydrogen atom. This factor is associated with the ' γ-carbon effect' in the steric hindrance of ketones, referred to by Barton (1953a).

The Effect of Strong Electrostatic Forces

The original body of evidence on which was based the general principle —that chair conformations carrying equatorial substituents are the most stable—was drawn largely from compounds carrying methyl and hydroxyl groups as substituents. These substituents, which are generally unstable when in the axial conformation, are not strongly polar in the electrostatic sense. (Note the confusion which would be caused here if the term ' polar' were used in a stereochemical sense also.)

The picture may be quite different when substituents are present which show strong electrostatic interactions. *trans*-1: 2-Dichloro- and dibromo-*cyclo*hexane exist as a mixture of the (*e,e*) and (*a,a*) forms, the latter being about one-third to one-half of the total (Hassel and Ottar, 1947; Tulinskie *et al*, 1953). Even the corresponding *trans*-1: 2-diol contains an appreciable proportion of the (*a,a*) conformation (Ottar, 1947).

Corey (1953 a, b, c) has discussed the conformations of α-halocyclanones. Jones, Ramsay, Herling and Dobriner (1952) had indicated from limited evidence that the effect of an α-bromine atom on the infra-red carbonyl frequency (Δν) of steroid ketones depends on the angle between the C═O and C—Br valencies. If these valencies are nearly co-planar (Br, *e*), Δν is 13 to 25 cm^{-1}; if the valencies are far from co-planar (Br, *a*), Δν is small, ∼5 cm^{-1}. Their reference values were for 11-bromo-12-oxosteroids where the conformations were fixed by ring-fusion. Corey then used this finding to study α-bromo*cyclo*hexanones and other α-halocyclanones including steroid derivatives. He showed that for 2-bromo-*cyclo*hexanone (XLI, R = H) Δν = 4, indicating that the bromine atom is axial (XLI в).

B   A   C

XLI

In 2-bromo-4: 4-dimethyl*cyclo*hexanone, Δν = 16, indicating that the preferred conformation is that in which the bromine is equatorial

(XLI c); an axial bromine atom would suffer strong steric repulsion by the axial methyl group at C-4. Calculations of the steric and electrostatic energy differences between XLIB and XLIc (R = H) also indicated that the axial conformation for Br should be the more stable when R = H. (For further discussions on steroids, see Fieser *et al*, 1953; Holysz, 1953; Jones, 1953; Beereboom, Djerassi, Ginsburg and Fieser, 1953; see also Braude and Waight this volume, p. 169.)

In the kinetically controlled bromination of a polycyclic ketone the axial α-bromoketone predominates (Corey, 1953d, 1954). This rule depends on the preferential enolization of a carbonyl group towards an axial hydrogen and preferential attack on the enol by axially situated bromine. Corey has applied these ideas to all positions in the steroid nucleus, and has indicated for each position which of the two epimeric α-bromo-oxosteroids is formed under kinetic and thermodynamic control respectively.

Cookson (1954) has shown that the shift in the position of the ultraviolet absorption maximum of a ketone produced on substitution of a halogen for an α-hydrogen atom is a function of the angle between the carbonyl group and the carbon–halogen bond. This shift ($\Delta\lambda$) for an equatorial α-bromo*cyclo*hexanone is about $-5m\mu$, and for an axial one $+28m\mu$.

The Distortion of Chair Conformations

It is sometimes necessary to consider the distortions to which chair conformations may be subjected in the course of reaction. Angyal and McDonald (1952) (*cf* Kuhn, 1952) have produced a rational explanation of the fact that *cis*- (*a,e*)-1:2-diols will give *iso*propylidene derivatives whilst *trans*- (*e,e*)-1:2-diols will not except in some special cases. Each type of compound has a projected valency angle of 60° between the two hydroxyl groups, and it might be thought that they should react with acetone with equal readiness. However, such a reaction involves the movement of the two hydroxyl groups to more nearly co-planar positions. Movement about the bond C-1—C-2 in the *cis*-diol (XLII) to bring this about increases the distances between the axial groups and flattens the puckered ring; it is reasonable to suppose that little energy is required for this deformation.

XLII   XLIII

In the *trans*-diol (XLIII) however, rotation about C-1—C-2 to bring the two hydroxyl groups closer together will make the ring more puckered and will crowd the axial groups together. This would require much energy, and the *trans*-glycols do not, as a rule, condense with acetone.

THE CONSEQUENCES OF DIFFERENT CONFORMATIONS

Many sets of facts regarding the stability and reactivity of epimeric alicyclic compounds can be explained in terms of the equatorial or axial conformations of the groups concerned. These ideas were introduced by Barton (1950) and have since been developed by him and his colleagues, and widely applied by other workers in the field of alicyclic chemistry.

Apart from questions of stability, the effects of conformations on the course and rate of reactions are of two kinds—those due to accessibility (steric hindrance or steric compression), and those due to particular steric requirements of an individual reaction.

A selection of examples illustrating the principles enunciated by Barton is given in TABLE 5. Examples in which the configurations were known beforehand—and which provided the evidence for the principles—are distinguished from examples where the application of the principles has provided the whole or part of the evidence in allotting configurations.

XLIV Steroid, *trans* A/B series (5α)

Note that in 'two-chair'-*cis*-decalins each bridgehead substituent is equatorial with respect to one ring and axial with respect to the other

XLV Steroid, *cis* A/B series (5β)

The more rigid *trans*-decalin type systems, and particularly polycyclic systems such as are found in the steroids and triterpenoids (XLIV–XLVI), provide both literally and metaphorically a firmer foundation for the consideration of conformational effects than the mobile monocyclic *cyclo*hexane systems (examples are provided in connection with reaction mechanisms, pp. 68–73).

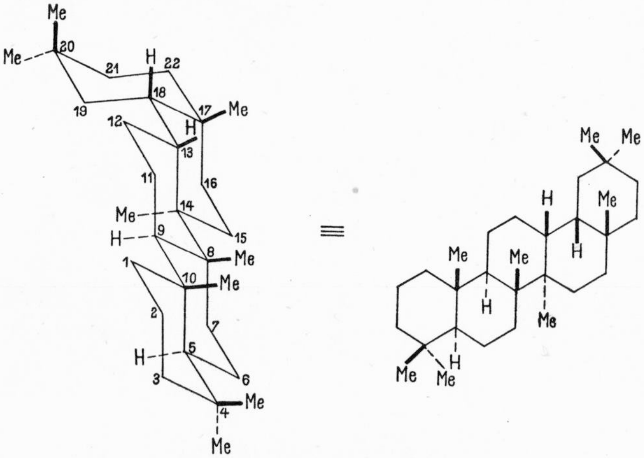

XLVI Triterpenoid (18 β-oleanane, β-amyrin series)
(New numbering, as steroids)

Stability of Epimers

Equatorial hydroxyl groups are more stable than axial; therefore when a polycyclic secondary alcohol is equilibrated with alkali, the isomer which preponderates in the reaction mixture will be that which has an equatorial hydroxyl (Barton, 1950, 1953a). This equilibration involves an oxidation–reduction reaction in which a trace of ketone is necessary (Doering and Aschner, 1949; *cf* Hückel and Naab, 1931).

As a corollary, when secondary alcohols are prepared by reduction of polyclic ketones with sodium and alcohol, the equatorial secondary alcohol predominates.

XLVII

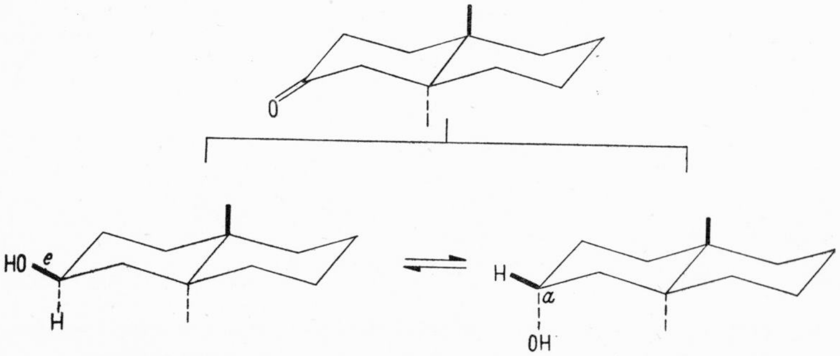

XLVIII
(Predominant)

XLIX

57

TABLE 5. RELATIONSHIPS BETWEEN CONFORMATION OF SUBSTITUENTS AND CHEMICAL
PROPERTIES IN STEROIDS AND TRITERPENOIDS

Types of evidence are indicated by the following abbreviations:
Elim   Elimination (ionic); (a) substituent eliminates with antiparallel (a)
          hydrogen atom.
Eq   Equilibration; (e) preponderates.
Est   Esterification; (e) less hindered than (a).
H   Hydrolysis of esters; (e) less hindered than (a).
Ox   Oxidation; (e)-H less hindered than (a)-H; i.e. (a)-hydroxy compound
          less hindered.
Pyr   Elimination (pyrolytic)—requires cis-substituents.
Red   Reduction of ketones by sodium and alcohols; (e) preponderates.
Rt   Rearrangement of ring system—involves (e) substituent, see p. 70.
S   1: 2 Shift of (a) substituent accompanying elimination. See p. 69.

Compounds referred to are alcohols (or their carboxylate esters) unless indicated
otherwise.

Examples used by Barton (1950) and by Barton and Rosenfelder (1951) as evidence
for the principles relating conformation and activity are marked * in the last column.
For references to previous experimental work, see Barton (1950, 1953).

References given in the last column are the chief references to work where the
application of the principles has been of value in allotting configurations.

REFERENCES

Page references are to this review

a Barton, 1950
b Barton and Rosenfelder, 1951
c Shoppee and Summers, 1952
d Ellis and Petrow, 1952; see also p. 69
e Greenhalgh, Henbest and Jones, 1952
f Hirschmann, Snoddy and Wendler, 1952; see also p. 71
g Miescher and Kägi, 1949; see also p. 69
h Elks and Shoppee, 1953
i See discussion on pp. 69 and 71
j Goldberg, Sicé, Robert and Plattner, 1947
k Evans and Shoppee, 1953
l Bridgwater and Shoppee, 1953
m Cole, 1952
n Ruzicka, Montavon and Jeger, 1948; see also p. 70
o Barton and Holness, 1952
p Halsall, Jones et al, 1952; see also p. 70
q Barnes, Barton et al, 1953
r Halsall, Hodges and Jones, 1953
s Barton and Thomas, 1953
t Budziarek, Johnston, Manson and Spring, 1951
u Barton and Brooks, 1951

† Conformations relative to ring C
§ 17-Hydroxyl groups not equilibrated by alkali (ref. h)
‖ Ursane and lupane series similar in rings A and B
‖? 24-Methyllanostane.

58

TABLE 5

Series	Position	Conformation and configuration of substituent		Types of evidence	References
		(e)	(a)		
STEROIDS					
5α	2	α	β	Red, H	*
	3	β	α	Eq, H, Ox, Elim (OTs)	*
	4	α	β	Red, H, Elim, Pyr	a, b
	5	–	α	Eq (Br), Elim (Cl)	*
	6	α	β	Eq (Br), Red, H, Elim (OH, Br), Ox	* c
	10	–	β	S	d
5α and 5β	7	β	α	Red, H, Elim, Ox,	* e
	11	α	β	Eq, Elim, (OH, Br; 11:12 Br₂), Est, Ox	*
	12	β	α	Eq, Ox, Elim, Rt	* f
	17†	β†	α†	H, S, (Eq§), Eq, COCH₃; CO₂Me	g, h
5α and 5β; D-homo	17	α	β	Rt	i
	17a	β	α	H, S	i, j
5β	3	α	β	Eq, H, Ox, Elim (OTs)	* k, l
Lumistane 5α: 8β: 9α: 10α	3	α	β	Eq	m

TRITERPENOIDS
(Numbers in parentheses are the 'old' numbers for positions used in the literature up to 1953)

Series	Position	(e)	(a)	Types of evidence	References
Oleanane ‖	3 (2)	β	α	Eq, H, Rt, Elim	a, n
	6 (7)	α	β	Est, Elim	a
	11	α	β	Elim	o
	12	β	α	Est, Red	o
	16	β	α	Est, Red	o
Oleanane (18α)	19	α	β	Elim, Rt	p
(18β)	19	β	α	Est, Elim	o
Lanostane and eburicane ‖?	3 (2)	β	α	Eq, Red, Rt, Elim	q, r
	7 (8)	β	α	Red, Est, Elim	q, s
	11	α	β	Red, Est	q
	12	β	α	Red (LiAlH₄)	r
	17†	β†	α†	Eq (COCH₃)	q

Regarding ring-junctions 9, 13, 14, 18 and 19 in oleanane series, see refs. o, t, u.
Regarding ring-junctions 8, 9 in lanostane series, see refs. q, s.

59

In monocyclic compounds the stable isomer is the one with the larger number of equatorial substituents (*i.e.* the *trans* isomer for 1:2- and 1:4- disubstituted derivatives of *cyclo*hexane and the *cis* isomer for 1:3-derivatives) (*cf* pp. 38–9).

The equilibrium between the α- and β-pyranose anomers of an aldose is a similar problem. The proportions of the anomers are qualitatively those which would be expected from a consideration of stability factors. Thus glucose, after mutarotation, has a rotation consistent with the existence of a mixture containing 63 per cent β-D-glucopyranose (L;1-OH, *e*) and 37 per cent α-D-glucopyranose (LI;1-OH *a*). (For further examples see TABLE 4.)

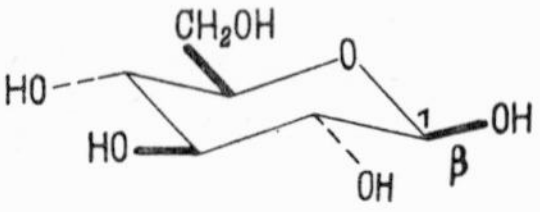

L 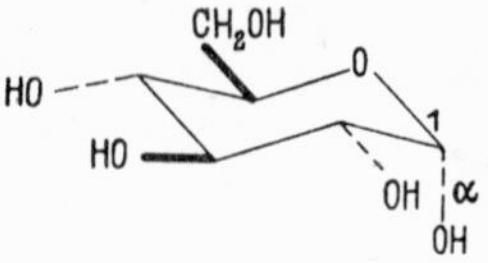   LI

Carboxyl Groups

Compounds with equatorial carboxyl (or alkoxycarbonyl) groups are more stable than their axial epimers. Examples are not as numerous as for hydroxycompounds, but the following may be mentioned. 3:4-*seco*-Dicarboxylic acids (LII), obtained by opening ring *A* of 5β steroids, are partly epimerized at C-5 on treatment with alkali, the 5α-carboxyl group (axial with respect to ring *B*) being inverted to give a 5β(*e*) group. (For references see Elsevier's *Encyclopaedia of Organic Chemistry*, **14**, 215, 218; also discussion by Klyne, 1953.) Methyl lupininate (LIII, X = CO₂Me), obtained by oxidation of lupinine

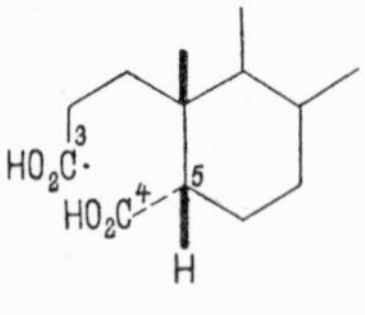

LII 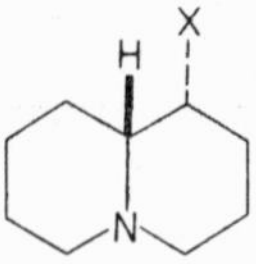   LIII

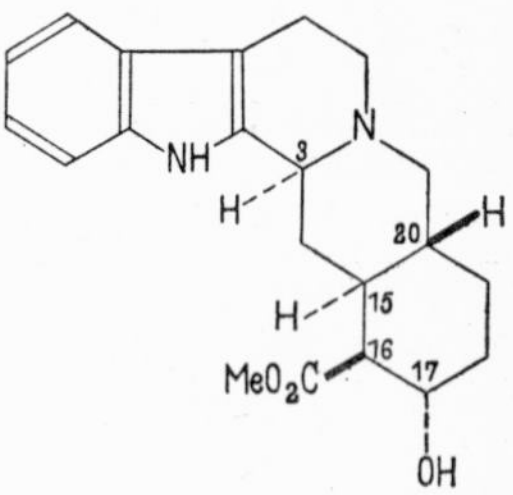

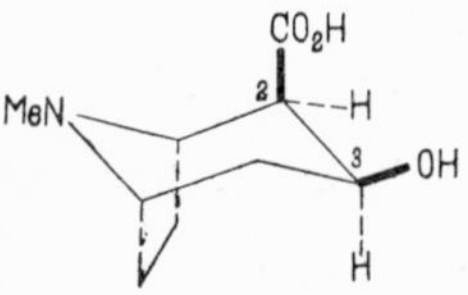

LIV 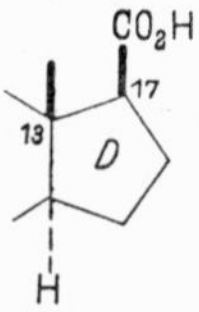   LV   LVI

(LIII, X = CH₂OH), is isomerized by alkali and therefore presumably has an axial carboxyl group (Cookson, 1953). Ecgonine,

$2\beta(a)$-carboxytropan-$3\beta(e)$-ol (LIV) is isomerized by alkali to ψ-ecgonine, the $2\alpha(e)$ isomer* (Findlay, 1953).

A special case in the steroid field is that of the etianic acids (androstane-17-carboxylic acids) (LV) where the group is attached to a five-membered ring. Here the pseudo-equatorial 17β-acid is more stable than the pseudo-axial 17α-isomer.

The alkaloid corynanthine (LVI) on treatment with alkali is hydrolysed and the carboxyl group epimerized; Janot *et al* (1952) and Cookson (1953) used this as evidence for the axial nature of the methoxycarbonyl group in corynanthine.

Acetals of Polyhydric Alcohols

The preferential formation of certain ring-types in the acetals of polyhydric alcohols has been discussed by Barker and Bourne (1952) and Barker, Bourne and Whiffen (1952). They base their arguments on the principle that the most stable conformation of a polyhydric alcohol is that in which the carbon skeleton possesses a planar zigzag structure. If their results are considered in terms of the cyclic product, instead of the acyclic starting material, they are in agreement with the general principles of conformational analysis. The first preference, according to Barker *et al*, is for a so-called 'β-C' ring (a six-membered ring formed from two hydroxyl groups on the same side of a Fischer projection). Such a ring (LVII) is a dioxa*cyclo*hexane with two equatorial substituents. The 'β-T' ring (LVIII) which is not so readily formed, has one equatorial and one axial substituent. Turning to five-membered rings, Barker *et al* have pointed out that 'αC' rings (LIX), which are unknown, would have an eclipsed conformation of four carbon atoms of the chain. These and other more complex examples are considered by Mills (1954).

LVII   LVIII   LIX

Steric Hindrance

Axial hydroxyl or acyloxy groups are more subject to steric hindrance (by the erected hydrogen atoms or substituents on the β-carbon atoms) than the corresponding equatorial groups. The axial compounds therefore are esterified (or hydrolysed) slower than the equatorial compounds†.

* These configurations are not known relative to glyceraldehyde.
† This is an empirical generalization. Few if any kinetic studies have been made of these reactions with polycyclic compounds, and their mechanisms can only be assumed by analogy with reactions of simpler compounds (*cf* Ingold, 1953b, Chap. 14). The esters considered are carboxylates; Dr P. B. D. de la Mare has pointed out to the reviewer that the behaviour of toluene-p-sulphonates might be quite different.

In the monosubstituted derivatives LX and LXI the non-bonded interactions between the groups shown in heavy type hindering the substituents R are as follows (Barton, 1953): for an equatorial substituent as in LX, $4(1:2\text{-R}:\text{H})$ interactions; for an axial substituent as in LXI, $2(1:2\text{-R}:\text{H}) + 2(1:3\text{-R}:\text{H})$ interactions. If R is OH, or a similar group, the $1:3$ distances are shorter than the $1:2$ distances,

LX   LXI

and therefore the hindrance factors for the axial substituent are greater than for the equatorial substituents. This treatment may be applied to the relative degrees of steric hindrance of 2α-, 2β-, 3α- and 3β-hydroxyl derivatives of 5α-cholestane (Barton, 1953; cf Fürst and Plattner, 1949). Barton (1953) has discussed similarly the steric hindrance of keto groups in cyclohexane rings.

Eliel (1953) has suggested that the slower reaction of axial-substituted compounds may be due to one of two causes. Either the axial substituent stays in this position during reaction and non-bonded interference by other axial groups slows down the reaction (Path A), or the molecule may be forced into another conformation in which the reacting group is equatorial, and the slower rate is due to the extra energy required to change the conformation (Path B). Evidence from

the rates of esterification of the menthols (Read and Grubb, 1934) and the hydrolysis of the decalyl hydrogen phthalates (Hückel et al, 1937) suggests that the reactions take place by Path B, involving conformational rearrangements.

Steric hindrance of amino groups has been discussed by Macbeth, Mills and Robertson (1951); whilst both equatorial and axial amino groups will condense with phthalic anhydride to give phthalamic acids ($R \cdot NH \cdot CO \cdot C_6H_4 \cdot CO_2H$), only equatorial amino groups will condense further to give substituted phthalimides

$$R \cdot N \Big\langle \begin{matrix} CO \\ CO \end{matrix} \Big\rangle C_6H_4.$$

Presumably 1:3-interactions hinder the formation of these cyclic derivatives from axial amino-compounds.

Differences in reactivity of carboxyl groups are exemplified by the diterpenoid resin acids, dehydroabietic acid (LXII; CO_2H e; readily esterified) and podocarpic acid (LXIII; CO_2H a; close to Me(a) at C-12; seriously hindered). (See Fieser and Fieser, 1949; Simonsen and Barton, 1952.)

LXII   LXIII

Regarding the effect of conformation on the dissociation constants and esterification rates of carboxyl groups, see Barton and Schmeidler, (1948, 1949), Smith and Byrne (1950) and Siegel and Morse (1953). Regarding partition coefficients of steroid alcohols and their behaviour on chromatography, see Savard (1953), Brooks, Klyne and Miller (1953).

Oxidations
In the oxidation of secondary alcohols by chromic acid or by hypobromous acid, the rate-determining step is the attack on the C—H bond (*cf* Westheimer *et al*, 1949–1952). Compounds carrying equatorial hydroxyl groups are in fact oxidized more slowly than their epimers carrying axial hydroxyl groups. These facts are consistent with the view that relative rates of oxidation are dependent on steric hindrance of the hydrogen atom of the carbinol group (axial hydrogen in LXIV more hindered than equatorial hydrogen in LXVI).

LXIV   LXV   LXVI

Reactions with Particular Geometrical Requirements

Elimination Reactions

Bimolecular ionic elimination reactions (*E*2) take place most readily when the four centres concerned lie in one plane (Hughes, Ingold *et al*, 1948; Ingold 1953a. See de la Mare, this volume, p. 112). In *cyclo*-hexane derivatives this arrangement is found only in compounds where the two substituents to be eliminated are *trans* and are both axial (one on each opposite side of the ring system) (LXVII→LXVIII).

LXVII   LXVIII

Many examples in the monocyclic and polycyclic series have been summarized by Hückel, Tappe and Legutke (1940), Hughes, Ingold *et al* (1948) and Barton (1950), and the principle of *trans*-elimination has been much used in recent years in structural problems. Examples are included in TABLE 5.

LXIXA   LXIXB

Compounds which are *trans* with both substituents held equatorial (LXIXA) do not undergo such elimination reactions. Excellent examples are provided by the debromination of steroid dibromides with iodide ion (Barton and Rosenfelder, 1951; Barton and Miller, 1950). The idea of *trans*-elimination in this reaction was implied by Young, Pressman and Coryell (1939) and by Winstein, Pressman and Young (1939). *cis*-Compounds (one substituent axial, the other equatorial, LXIXB) react slowly or not at all.

Other reactions which in the alicyclic series are kinetically *E*1 (Hughes, Ingold *et al*, 1948) show a similar geometrical specificity favouring *trans*-elimination. Presumably this means that elimination is completed before the heterolysed group X has receded far enough to leave a planar carbonium ion (Ingold, 1953a, b).

These reactions include the solvolysis of toluene-*p*-sulphonates (Hückel *et al*, 1940, Hückel, 1944), the acid-catalysed dehydration of alcohols (Hughes, Ingold *et al*, 1948) and the deamination of primary amines (Mills, 1953). The need for true *trans*-geometry in such eliminations is shown by the fact that *β*-benzene hexachloride, with all chlorine substituents equatorial (Cristol, 1947), and certain bridge-head halides (see *e.g.* Cristol and Hause, 1952) lose hydrogen halide with alkali only with great difficulty (*cf* de la Mare, this volume, pp. 96 and 113, also Hughes, Ingold and Pasternak, 1953).

The stereochemistry of the substituents in ring *E* of the alkaloid yohimbine (LXX) provides an excellent example of the use of conformational analysis in determining configuration (Janot, Goutarel, le Hir, Amin and Prelog, 1952; Cookson, 1953).

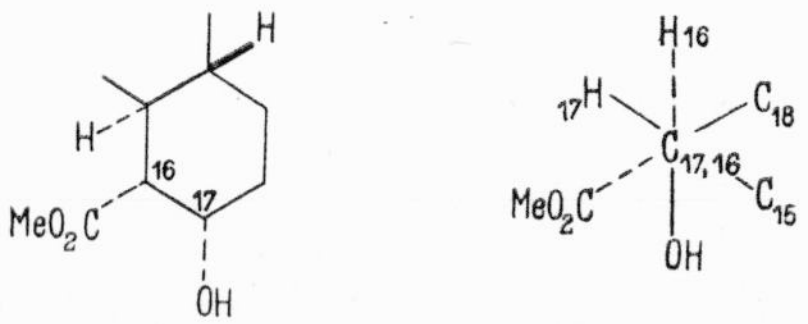

LXX

The behaviour of the C_{16}-epimeric esters yohimbine and corynanthine on alkaline hydrolysis shows that the methoxycarbonyl group in yohimbine is equatorial (16α), and in corynanthine axial (16β). The dehydration of the two compounds as their 17-sulphuric acid esters confirms this and indicates that the hydroxyl group at C-17 is α (axial) in both alkaloids. The yohimbine derivative is dehydrated very easily by alkali indicating that the hydrogen at C-16 and hydroxyl at C-17 are *trans* and both axial (LXX). The corynanthine derivative in similar conditions suffers dehydration and decarboxylation, giving the so-called *apo*corynanthol (yohimb-16-ene).

Thermal Decompositions

The thermal decompositions of esters to give olefins require a planar transition state (LXXI) in which the *O*-acyl group and a *cis* hydrogen atom on the neighbouring carbon atom are co-planar (Barton, 1949). The homogeneous unimolecular nature of the reaction, which is the theoretical justification for assuming *cis* specificity, has been proved for menthyl benzoate (Barton, Head and Williams, 1953) and for xanthates (O'Connor and Nace, 1952).

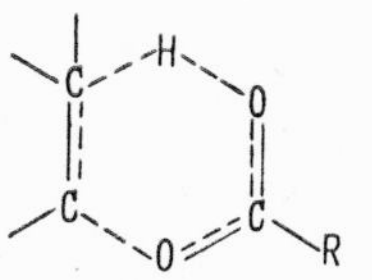

LXXI

cis-(*a*,*e*)-1: 2-Substituents will form such a transition state readily; *trans*-(*e*,*e*)-1: 2-substituents will not (see p. 55).

Substitution Reactions

Bimolecular substitution reactions (S_N2) always involve inversion of configuration at the carbon atom concerned, in *cyclo*hexane derivatives as in acyclic systems. An axial substituent can undergo such a change (LXXII), though with difficulty, but if there is an axial hydrogen atom on an adjacent carbon atom, elimination can occur (*cf* LXVII) and usually preponderates (Angyal and Mills, 1952).

LXXII   LXXIII   LXXIV

A good example is provided by the 3-chloro-cholestanes (Shoppee, 1946) and -coprostanes (Bridgwater and Shoppee, 1953), which undergo inversion accompanied by much elimination. If an axial substituent is conveniently placed on the β-carbon atom, rearrangement may occur (see p. 69).

An equatorial substituent cannot easily undergo an S_N2 reaction because the opposite face of the carbon atom is shielded by the rest of the ring (*cf* Bartlett and Rosen, 1942).

In S_N1-type reactions with acyclic compounds, the stereochemical result is generally racemization—with some inversion due to shielding by the departing anion. In *cyclo*hexane systems conformational factors may have an important effect, as *e.g.* in the deamination of amines with nitrous acid (Mills, 1953, see also Bose, 1952, 1953). The last stage of this reaction in the alicyclic series is the unimolecular decomposition of a diazonium ion. In *cyclo*hexane derivatives if the amino group (and hence the diazonium ion) is axial, the result of the reaction is elimination (LXXIII) and, to a lesser extent, formation of the alcohol of opposite configuration. The elimination presumably occurs because the electrons of an adjacent *trans*-hydrogen atom are suitably placed to move over to form a double bond before the diazonium ion has moved away.

If the amino group (and hence the diazonium ion group) is equatorial, the result is chiefly retention, *i.e.* formation of an alcohol of the same configuration as the original amine. Here elimination does not occur, since the hydrogen atoms on adjacent carbon atoms (*e.g* H* in LXXIV) are not suitably placed for participation in a concerted elimination. Mills suggests a pyramidal transition state as shown in LXXIV which is favoured by the geometry of the *cyclo*hexane ring. This is geometrically similar in a formal sense to the pyramidal transition state postulated in the S_Ni mechanism for reaction of alcohols with thionyl chloride. Similar results are found in the treatment of some

66

equatorial hydroxy-compounds with hydrogen chloride or phosphorus pentachloride; thus (−)-menthol in certain conditions yields (−)-menthyl chloride (retention) (Hückel and Pietrzok, 1939) although the equatorial 3-hydroxysteroids undergo inversion with phosphorus pentachloride (Shoppee 1946; Bridgwater and Shoppee, 1953).

Only an axial substituent on the β-carbon atom is able to play the part of a neighbouring group in substitution reactions of *cyclo*hexyl compounds (*cf* de la Mare; this volume, Chapter 3, p. 99). Examples have recently been studied by Alt and Barton (1954); $2\beta(a)$-bromo-cholestan-$3\alpha(a)$-ol on treatment with hydrobromic and acetic acids gives $2\beta(a) : 3\alpha(a)$-dibromocholestane via a bromonium ion (*cf* the diaxial opening of epoxide rings, p. 74). The corresponding diequatorial compound (2α-bromocholestan-3β-ol) is unreactive.

(Axial and equatorial substituents are shown by vertical and diagonal lines respectively.)

Comparison of cyclo*Hexyl and* cyclo*Pentyl Compounds*

Brown and his colleagues have offered an explanation of the slowness of reaction of *cyclo*hexyl compounds—as compared with *cyclo*pentyl and other compounds—in S_N2 and S_N1 reactions by their concept of I-strain (Brown, Fletcher and Johannesen, 1951; Brown and Borkowski, 1952 ; *cf* de la Mare, this volume p. 104). They point out that in a chair-form *cyclo*hexane ring with a covalency of four at every carbon atom, non-bonded interactions are at a minimum since there are no opposed butane configurations. If such a compound undergoes an S_N2 or S_N1 reaction this ideal situation is disturbed ; in the transition state of an S_N2 reaction (LXXII) the valency diagram for groups attached to C-1 and C-2 becomes (approximately) as LXXV. Furthermore, the valency angle C-2—C-1—C-6 is strained from the tetrahedral angle to 120°. The transition state is therefore not energetically favoured.

LXXV   LXXVII   LXXVIII   LXXIX

In a *cyclo*pentane ring (LXXVII), however, each side of the regular pentagon involves an opposed butane configuration (LXXVIII), relieved slightly by puckering of the ring (Aston *et al*, 1943). The S_N2

transition state, approximately as LXXIX, formed from this is more favoured from the point of view of non-bonded energy than the transition state LXXV for a *cyclo*hexane ring.

Conversely, Brown *et al* point out that reactions involving a change in covalency state of a ring carbon atom from 3 to 4 (carbonyl→ cyanhydrin, *etc*) should take place more easily for *cyclo*hexanones than for *cyclo*pentanones—as in fact they do. (For further examples of the application of the concept of I-strain see Friess and Franckenburg, 1952; Kuivila and Becker, 1952.)

Brown, Brewster and Schechter (1954), in an important paper on the chemical behaviour of five- and six-membered ring compounds, have suggested as a general rule that *exo* double bonds stabilize a five-membered ring and destabilize a six-membered ring. Reaction occurs in such a manner as to favour the formation or retention of an *exo* double bond in a five-membered ring and to avoid the formation or retention of such a bond in a six-membered ring. Many examples from both homocyclic and heterocyclic chemistry were discussed.

1: 2-Shifts

1: 2-Shifts of many kinds which proceed through a carbonium ion intermediate require *trans* geometry as a rule between the group which is lost (X) and the migrating group (R).

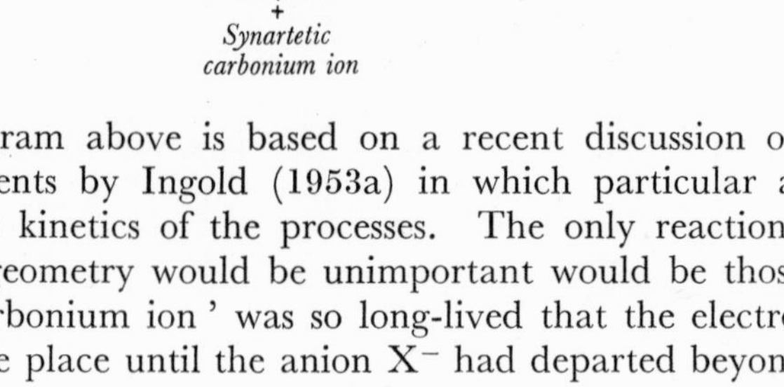

The diagram above is based on a recent discussion of saturated rearrangements by Ingold (1953a) in which particular attention is paid to the kinetics of the processes. The only reactions in which molecular geometry would be unimportant would be those in which the ' 1st carbonium ion ' was so long-lived that the electron shift (*b*) did not take place until the anion X⁻ had departed beyond shielding range.

Two main classes of rearrangement which occur with *cyclo*hexane derivatives are (*i*) the 1: 2-shift of a substituent R, without alteration in ring-size, and (*ii*) change in ring-size when a ring-bond serves as the migrating group R. These two types of reaction have different conformational requirements. They will be discussed first using examples from rigid polycyclic structures, and then for monocyclic compounds.

Shifts without Ring Contraction

If a substituent R attached to a *cyclo*hexane ring is to undergo a 1:2-shift, it, and the group X which is displaced from the molecule, must both be axial and antiparallel, LXXX (Barton, 1950, 1953).

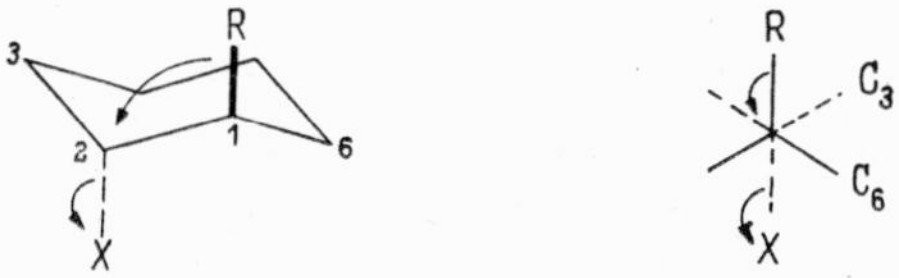

LXXX

Two examples of such rearrangements in the steroid series involving an axial hydroxyl group and an antiparallel axial methyl group are the formation of ' Westphalen's diol ' (LXXXII) from cholestane-3β: 5α: 6β-triol (as diacetate) (LXXXI) (Westphalen, 1915; Ellis and Petrow, 1952, previous references there; Bladon, Henbest and Wood, 1952) and of ψ-androstene derivatives (LXXXIV) by dehydration of androstan-17α-ols (LXXXIII) (Miescher and Kägi, 1949). In the latter reaction the axial angular methyl group at C-13 moves over to C-17 giving a 17β-methyl-13-nor-steroid.

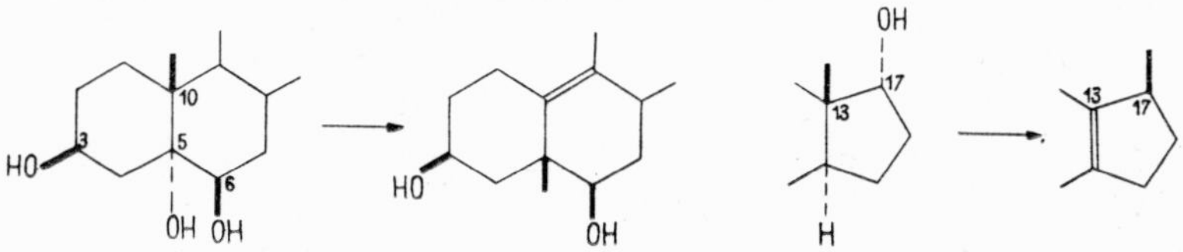

LXXXI   LXXXII   LXXXIII   LXXXIV

The epimeric 17β-amino-17a-hydroxy-17a-methyl-*D*-homosteroids give, on treatment with nitrous acid, products characteristic of *trans*-rearrangement (Prins and Shoppee, 1946; Klyne and Shoppee, 1952; Cremlyn, Garmaise and Shoppee, 1953). The 17$a\alpha$- and 17β-groups are the two axial groups involved in each case.

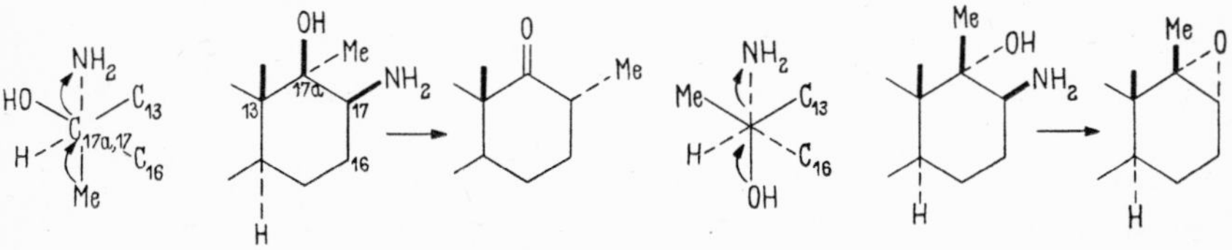

LXXXV   LXXXVI   LXXXVII   LXXXVIII

In LXXXV the 17$a\alpha$-methyl shifts to give a 17α-methyl-17a-ketone (LXXXVI) ('uranolone') (Klyne, 1950); in LXXXVII a pair of electrons of the 17$a\alpha$-oxygen atom move over to form an epoxide ring (Ruzicka and Meldahl, 1941) (LXXXVIII).

69

Ring Contraction

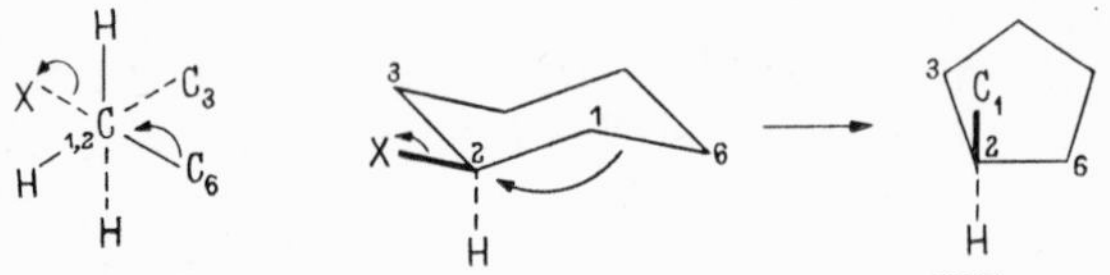

LXXXIX   XC

Reactions where a *cyclo*hexane ring contracts in size to a *cyclo*pentane ring (XC) are 1 : 2-shifts in which a ring-bond plays the part of the migrating group R.   Reference to formula (LXXXIX) and the accompanying valency diagram shows that only an equatorial substituent X can form part of the *trans*-system necessary for such a 1 : 2-shift to occur (Barton, 1950).   Expressed in other ways, the substituent X and three ring carbon atoms must be co-planar, or the projected valency angle C-6—C-1—C-2—X must be 180°.

3β-Hydroxytriterpenoids (XCI; OH,*e*) rearrange on treatment with phosphorus pentachloride to give *A*-nor-hydrocarbons XCII (Ruzicka, Montavon and Jeger, 1948 and earlier references there).   The 3α-hydroxy epimers (XCIII; OH,*a*) on similar treatment are dehydrated

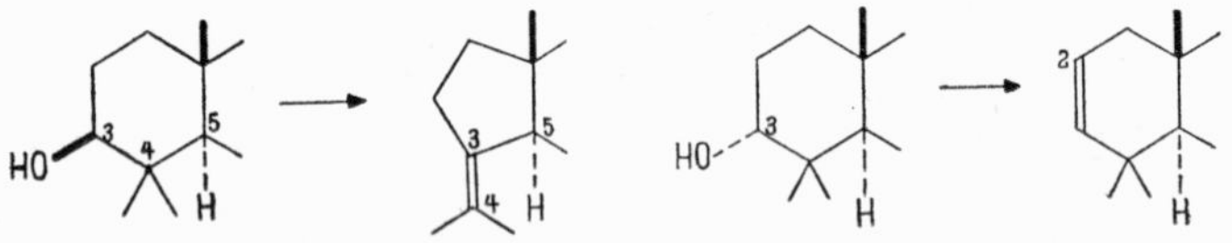

XCI   XCII   XCIII   XCIV

normally to give Δ^2-unsaturated compounds (XCIV) without re-arrangement.   The abnormal Hofmann elimination reaction of the quaternary hydroxide from *trans*octahydroindole (King, Bovey, Mason and Whitehead, 1953) probably involves a similar ring-contraction (McKenna, 1954).

A similar example from the other end of the triterpenoid molecule is provided by the 19-substituted derivatives of the 18-*iso*-β-amyrin (18α-oleanane) series.   Halsall, Jones *et al* (1952) have shown that the 19α-chloro compound XCV (Cl,*e*), on treatment with silver acetate, rearranges to give lupeol (XCVI) in which the *E*-ring is five-membered; 19α-hydroxy compounds rearrange with phosphorus oxychloride to XCVI.   On the other hand, the 19β-hydroxy compounds (XCVII; OH,*a*) dehydrate normally to give olean-18-enes (XCVIII).

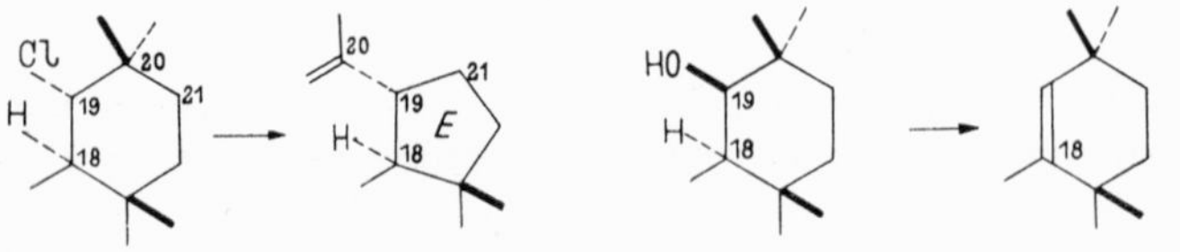

XCV   XCVI   XCVII   XCVIII

70

The 17α(e)-amino-17a-hydroxy-D-homosteroids, analogous to the 17β(a)-amino-compounds discussed on p. 69, have been studied by Cremlyn *et al* (1953). The 17α(e)-NH$_2$:17$a\beta$(e)-OH compound (XCIX)

XCIX	C	CI	LXXXVIII
			(+ a little C)

undergoes ring contraction by a *trans*-1:2-shift, giving the 17α-20-ketone with a five-membered D-ring (C). The 17$a\alpha$(a) OH compound (CI) yields chiefly the epoxide (LXXXVIII) with a little of the ring-contracted product (C). The epoxide arises presumably because the oxygen of the 17$a\alpha$ hydroxyl group is in a suitable position to take part in a pyramidal transition state as the diazonium group departs—similar to the transition state (LXXIV) proposed by Mills (1953) to account for the behaviour of simple equatorial amines on treatment with nitrous acid (p. 66). (For a discussion of reaction mechanisms, see Cremlyn *et al*, 1953.)

Hirschmann, Snoddy and Wendler (1952) have described a most interesting rearrangement by solvolysis of the methanesulphonate of a 12β-hydroxysapogenin (rockogenin) (CII) to give a C-nor-D-homo compound (*i.e.* a compound in which the six-membered C-ring has contracted and the five-membered D-ring has expanded, CIII).

CII   CIII
(Ms = CH$_3$.SO$_2$)

Here the four co-planar centres involved in the rearrangement are C-12, C-13, C-14 and the β-oxygen atom at C-12. The discovery of this rearrangement occured most opportunely since the C-nor-D-homo-steroid skeleton (CIV) has recently been suggested for the alkaloid jervine by Fried, Wintersteiner *et al* (1951). The toluene-p-sulphonate of the 12α-epimer of CII eliminated normally to give a Δ^{11}-steroid.

CIV

Barton (1953a) has pointed out that in all these rearrangements the rupture of the C—C bond, which is essential for the rearrangement, yields a tertiary carbonium ion.

Behaviour of Monocyclic Compounds

When we turn to monocyclic compounds of the *cyclo*hexane series the picture is not so simple, since the single ring can readily change from one chair conformation to the other under the influence of the reagents used.

The pinacolic rearrangements of 2-amino-*cyclo*hexanols have been discussed by Pollak and Curtin (1950) and by McCasland (1951). The possible conformations of the *cis* and *trans* compounds are shown in CV and CVI.

The groups which are arranged antiparallel to N and *trans* with respect to the bond C-1—C-2 are as follows:

Case	Configuration		Conformation	Group antiparallel to N	Expected rearrangement
1	CVA	*cis*	OH *a* NH$_2$*e*	C-6	Ring contraction
2	CVB	*cis*	NH$_2$*a* OH *e*	H(C-1)	*cyclo*Hexanone
3	CVIA	*trans*	OH *e* NH$_2$*e*	C-6	Ring contraction
4	CVIB	*trans*	OH *a* NH$_2$*a*	OH	Epoxide formation

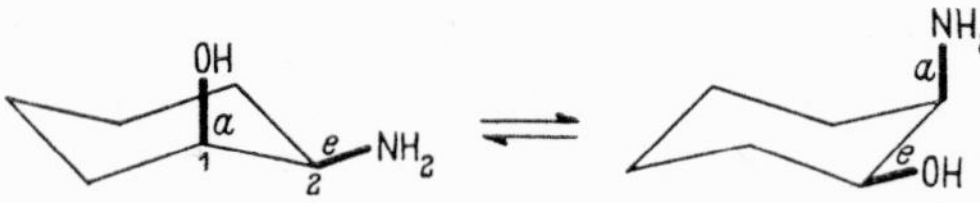

CV

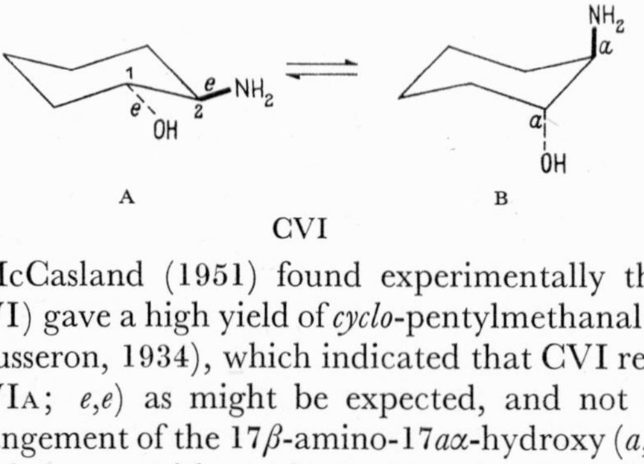

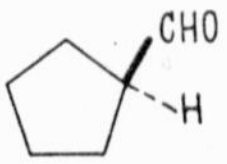

CVI

McCasland (1951) found experimentally that the *trans* compound (CVI) gave a high yield of *cyclo*-pentylmethanal (CVII) (*cf* Godchot and Mousseron, 1934), which indicated that CVI reacts in the conformation (CVIA; *e,e*) as might be expected, and not (CVIB; *a,a*). The rearrangement of the 17β-amino-17α-hydroxy (*a,a*) steroid (LXXXVII), which occurs without ring contraction (p. 69), illustrates the value of polycyclic systems in providing us with fairly rigid conformations of types which are not favoured in the mobile monocyclic systems. The *cis* 2-amino*cyclo*hexanol (CV) on treatment with nitrous acid yielded a mixture of the rearranged aldehyde CVII and *cyclo*hexanone, indicating that it reacts partly as CVA and partly as CVB (one *e*, one *a* substitutent in each conformation).

Recent work by Schmukler and Curtin (1953) on the 2-amino-1-phenyl*cyclo*hexan-1-ols shows the effect of a single large substituent in favouring the conformation in which this substituent (phenyl) is equatorial, and the hydroxyl therefore axial. The products of reaction

72

with nitrous acid are chiefly those indicated in cases 1 and 4 above; the *cis*-hydroxyamine undergoes ring contraction, the *trans*-hydroxy-amine gives products which are presumed to arise via the epoxide.

The related pinacolic dehydrations of 1 : 2-dimethyl*cyclo*hexane-1 : 2-diols with acid have been studied by Bartlett, Meerwein and their co-workers. The *trans*-diol (CIX) gives about 80 per cent of 1-acetyl-1-methyl*cyclo*pentane (CXI) (Bartlett and Pöckel, 1937). The diol (CIX) presumably reacts here in the conformation CIXA (two methyl groups *a*; two hydroxyl groups *e*). If it reacted as CIXB (hydroxyl groups *a*) the product would be the epoxide CXII*. The *cis*-diol CVIII

—⊢► *Reaction does not occur*

also gives chiefly the ring-contracted *cyclo*pentane derivative CXI, though less rapidly than the *trans*-isomer (Meerwein, 1939; Bartlett, unpublished observations, *cf* Bartlett, 1953). This must be formed by migration of the C-3—C-2 bond to C-1 (as shown in CVIIIB); movement of an axial methyl group (as shown in CVIIIA) would give 2 : 2-dimethyl*cyclo*hexanone (CX). Bartlett and Pöckel (1937) reported the occurrence of this latter reaction, but later work has not confirmed this. (The reviewer is indebted to Professor P. D. Bartlett, Harvard, for details of this unpublished work.)

In the *cyclo*pentane series the rearrangement proceeds without ring contraction giving the 2 : 2-dimethylketone; the *cis*-diol, which is more favourably situated, reacts faster than the *trans*-diol which gives much tarry product.

Dependence of the course of reaction on configuration is found also in the pyrolysis of *cyclo*hexanediol sulphites (Price and Berti, 1954).

Ring Opening

Another interesting example where the course of reaction depends on conformation is provided by the reactions of the isomeric steroid 3 : 5-diols (as their 3-toluene-*p*-sulphonyloxy derivatives) with alkali. Clayton and Henbest (1953) have shown that the 3β : 5α-compound

---

* Dr. A. Nickon has pointed out that this epoxide may indeed be formed; in aqueous acid the oxide ring would open again to regenerate the *trans*-glycol.

yields as its chief product the 3α : 5α-epoxide by S_N2 reaction at C-3; a minor product was an unsaturated ketone in which ring A had been opened, 4 : 5-*seco*cholest-3-en-5-one. Alkaline treatment of the 3α : 5β-diol gave the unsaturated ketone as the sole product. The formation of this unsaturated ketone is explained by a concerted process in which the electrons of the C-4—C-5 bond move over to give a double bond between C-3 and C-4, whilst the toluene-p-sulphonyloxy group moves away from C-3.

Both epoxide-formation and ring-opening depend on the fact that ring A is fixed by fusion with ring B, and the acyloxy group is held equatorial. In the monocyclic series *trans*-elimination takes place from the other conformation where the toluene-p-sulphonyloxy group is axial, yielding *cyclo*hex-1-en-3-ol.

Conformational Factors in other Reactions

Reduction of Ketones

Catalytic hydrogenation of carbonyl groups in acid solution, which is rapid, gives axial hydroxy-compounds. Hydrogenation in neutral solution, which is usually slow, reduces unhindered carbonyl groups to equatorial hydroxyl groups, but hindered carbonyl groups to axial hydroxyl groups (Barton, 1953a). These generalizations replace the previous rule of Auwers (1920) and Skita (1920) (*cf* Skita and Faust, 1931). Similar regularities are found in the reduction of oximes to amines (Barton, 1953a). Lithium aluminium hydride and sodium borohydride give the same products as catalytic hydrogenation in neutral solution. Meerwein–Ponndorf reduction of unhindered ketones gives a larger proportion of the axial epimer than do the metal hydrides; since this reaction is a slow equilibration, the proportion of axial epimer decreases as the time of reaction increases. The reduction of ketones with sodium and alcohol (giving predominantly equatorial hydroxyl groups) has been discussed on p. 57.

Opening of Epoxide Rings

When steroid epoxide rings (CXIV) are opened by reaction with hydrogen (or lithium aluminium hydride), hydrogen halides or aqueous acid, the products have their substituents in axial positions (Fürst and Plattner, 1951; Fürst and Scotoni, 1953a, b; Schmidlin and Wettstein, 1953: a table is given by Barton, 1953a).

Mills (unpublished suggestion quoted by Newth and Homer, 1952), Bose, Chaudhuri and Bhattacharyya (1953), Newth (1953) and Cookson (1954b) have discussed the extension of this rule to sugar epoxides.

CXIII   CXIV   CXV

Carbanion Reduction Processes

Many reductions which proceed through carbanions give products carrying the added hydrogen atoms in the more stable configurations (Barton and Robinson, 1954). These include the reduction of $\alpha\beta$-unsaturated ketones and halogen substitution products with alkali metals and liquid ammonia, and the reduction of conjugated dienes and trienes with sodium and alcohol.

The process is most easily rationalized by assuming that in the carbanion the lone pair of electrons takes up the most stable position and a proton then adds on to them. Professor C. W. Shoppee (Symposium on 'Dynamic Stereochemistry', Manchester, March, 1954) drew attention to the fact that the carbonation of cholestan-3α- and -3β-yl Grignard reagents gives the equatorial (3β) carboxylic acid, no matter what the configuration of the original halogen substituent (cf Corey and Sneen, 1953).

Complexing of Cyclic Glycols

The geometry of 1:2-glycol groupings on six-membered rings has been discussed by Reeves (1951) and an abridged form of his results has been presented on p. 40 (in TABLE 1).

Reeves (1944, 1949a, b, 1950, 1951) has studied intensively the complexing of carbohydrates with cuprammonium solutions and has discovered some important relations between the projected valency angles of the glycol groups and the properties of their cuprammonium derivatives. These are summarized in TABLE 6.

TABLE 6. CYCLIC GLYCOLS: PROJECTED VALENCY ANGLES AND RELATED PROPERTIES
(Based on Reeves, 1951)

Ring	Configuration and conformation of 1:2-OH groups	Projected valency angle	Reaction with $Pb(OAc)_4$	Behaviour with cuprammonium	
				Change in specific resistance	Optical effect (ΔCu)
5-membered	cis	0°	instant	large	small
	trans	120°	slow	no reaction	—
6-membered (chair)	cis (e,a)	60°	rapid	medium*	v. large
	trans (e,e)	60°	slow	small*	v. large
	trans (a,a)	180°	slow	no reaction	—
6-membered (boat)	cis†	0°	instant	large	small

* Difference between these types not very marked
† These figures apply to pairs of OH groups at the 'sides' of the boat. Those at the 'ends' are like glycol groups on chair-form rings.

Cuprammonium complexes formed from 1: 2-glycols with a projected valency angle of $\pm 60°$ show very large molecular rotation differences from the free glycols (ΔCu values). Boat forms are improbable for pyranosides whenever a chair form is geometrically possible. If this argument is accepted, then for certain bridged ring pyranosides only *one* chair conformation is possible *e.g.* the 1:6-anhydro-β-D-pyranose (CXVI) must have the 1C form. It is now possible to say which of the two possible 60° types of complex has a large $+\Delta$Cu value and which has a large $-\Delta$Cu value.

CXVI   CXVII
                    D-Galactosan; 1:6-anhydro-
                      β-D-galacto-pyranose

The only pair of hydroxyl groups with a 60° valency angle in D-galactosan is the 3: 4-diol group, the geometry of which is shown in CXVII (1: 6 bridge omitted for the sake of clarity). This compound has a large positive ΔCu value which may therefore be associated with a projected valency angle of $+60°$; conversely D-mannosan, which has a projected valency angle of $-60°$, has a large negative ΔCu value.

Similar evidence can be obtained from a consideration of substituted D-glucopyranosides. If the 1C conformation were favoured the projected valency angles for 2: 3- and 3: 4-diol groups would each be 180°, and complexing would not be expected. In the C1 conformation the projected valency angles are $-60°$ for the 2: 3-diol group and $+60°$ for the 3: 4-diol group. In fact D-glucopyranosides (CXVIII) in which only

CXVIII

the 2:3- or 3: 4-diol groups are free (*e.g.* the 4-O-methyl and 2-O-methyl derivatives) have large negative and positive ΔCu values respectively.

It is now possible to use the ΔCu values of other pyranosides to see whether their conformations agree with those predicted from the instability factors of Reeves and of Hassel and Ottar (1947). The results, some of which are collected in TABLE 4 (p. 52; *cf* Reeves, 1951), show that the complexing behaviour in nearly every case supports the conformations allotted from instability factors.

1β: 6-Anhydride formation is geometrically possible only for hexopyranosides in the 1C conformation, *cf* CXVI. Reeves (1949, 1951)

76

has pointed out that only those hexoses which from a consideration of instability factors would be expected to exist in the 1C form do in fact readily give 1β: 6-anhydro-compounds, *viz* altrose and idose.

Reference has been made above (p. 55) to the complexing of *cyclo*-hexane-1: 2-diols with acetone (Angyal and Macdonald, 1952). Complexing with boric acid appears to be impossible for compounds with a projected valency angle of $60°$ (Boëseken and Giffen, 1920).

Transient Intermediates

The conformations of transient intermediates may also be important in determining the course of reactions. Wendler (1953) has discussed an excellent example, *viz* the N $\longrightarrow$ O acyl migrations in the isomeric 3-amino-1: 3-diphenylpropan-1-ols, which involve six-membered ring intermediates.

Natural Occurrence and Biological Activity

Angyal and Mills have pointed out (1952) that among the aldohexo-pyranoses and their glycosides, and among the cyclitols, only those isomers occur commonly in nature which have no $1a$: $3a$ grouping in either of their possible conformations.

In the steroid series the distribution of equatorial and axial substituents among natural products is of interest. Most naturally-occurring steroids have the common 3-hydroxyl group in an equatorial position (3β in A/B *trans* and Δ^5-steroids; 3α in A/B *cis* steroids, *cf* XLIV, XLV). The important exceptions are the cardiac glycosides and toad poisons (nearly all) and the sapogenins (an important minority)—in which there is a 3β-hydroxyl in an A/B *cis* structure. Many of the hydroxyl groups in other positions, which are characteristic of the different classes of steroids, and may be responsible for their physiological activity, are axial (*e.g.* the 11β- and 17α-hydroxyl groups of the adrenal steroids; 7α- and 12α-hydroxyl groups of the bile acids).

Among triterpenoids the common 3-hydroxyl group (formerly called 2) is β in nearly all compounds whose structure has so far been elucidated. It is now known, however, that at least three naturally occurring compounds have 3α-hydroxyl groups, *viz* polyporenic acid A (Halsall, Hodges and Jones, 1953) and ' α ' and ' β ' boswellic acids (Ruzicka and Wirz, 1940, 1941; for other references see Klyne and Stokes, 1954).

Shoppee (1952b) has discussed the relationship between stereochemistry and physiological activity in the steroids with special reference to the molecular profile.

Magasanik and Chargaff (1948) have discovered a most interesting correlation between the conformations of the cyclitols and their liability to oxidation by *Acetobacter suboxidans*, *viz* that only axial hydroxyl groups are oxidized. In a subsequent paper Magasanik, Franzl and

Chargaff (1952) suggested that the carbon atom in the 3-position (counterclockwise) to this group (as shown in CXIX) must carry an equatorial hydroxyl group, but exceptions to this second rule are known. Posternak and Reymond (1953) have extended this work and shown that the rules do not apply to substances with few hydroxyl groups (*cf* also Anderson, Tomita, Kussi and Kirkwood, 1953).

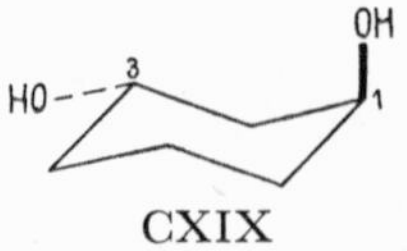

CXIX

The review on enzyme specificity by Gottschalk (1950) might well be reconsidered in terms of conformations.

BOAT FORMS

The preceding sections of this chapter have dealt chiefly with chair-form *cyclo*hexane rings. It is now necessary to consider some special cases where boat forms do or may exist. A brief review has been given by Shoppee (1952a). Many claims of the isolation of *cyclo*hexane derivatives in boat and chair forms have been made, but further work has shown them to be unfounded (for references, see Raphael, 1953, p. 132).

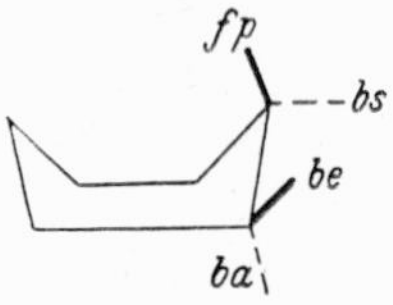

CXX

The four types of bonds attaching substituents to a boat-form *cyclo*hexane ring are shown in CXX. Those at the ' ends ' of the boat are different in stereochemical character from the bonds in chair form; they may be called ' flagpole ' (*fp*) (Angyal and Mills, 1952) and ' bowsprit ' (*bs*) respectively. The two types at the ' sides ' of the boat resemble the equatorial and axial bonds of a chair; they may be called boat-equatorial (*be*) and boat-axial (*ba*) respectively.

The dipole moment of *cyclo*hexane-1: 4-dione indicates that this probably exists to the extent of about 10 per cent in the boat form (CXXI) (Le Fèvre and Le Fèvre, 1935). Apparently no fundamental investigations of *cyclo*hexanone have been undertaken; it is possible that this compound may have a small but appreciable percentage of the boat form (CXXII) in its equilibrium mixture. 3-Oxosteroids of the 5β-series probably exist with their *A* rings partly in the boat conformation (p. 44).

Simple geometry demands that the middle rings of some polycyclic structures must be boat form (Johnson, 1951, 1953). The *trans-syn-trans* perhydrophenanthrene CXXIII must have a boat conformation

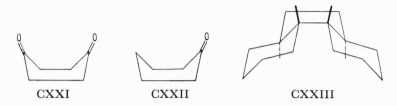

CXXI	CXXII	CXXIII

for its middle ring. The *cis-syn-trans* ketone CXXIV, which can exist in a three-chair form does not, therefore, rearrange to the *trans-syn-trans* isomer (Linstead and Whetstone, 1950).

The ease with which chair forms can be turned into boat forms under the influence of a suitable reagent is exemplified by the formation of

CXXIV	CXXV	CXXVI

3: 9-epoxides (CXXVI) from 3α-hydroxy-$\Delta^{9(11)}$-steroids of the 5β (*A/B cis*) series (CXXV) (Kendall *et al*, 1946). In these epoxides the *A* ring is a boat form.

Bridged-ring Boat Forms

The chemistry of boat forms can best be studied in bridged-ring structures in which the six-membered ring is locked in a boat conformation by being tied across its ends as in structures of type (CXXVII) and (CXXVIII).

CXXVII	CXXVIII	CXXIX

In the *bicyclo*-(1: 2: 2)-heptane (norcamphane) series, *exo*-norborneol (CXXIX; X = OH,*be*; Y = H) is more stable than the *endo* isomer (Y = OH, *ba*; X = H) (Alder and Stein, 1934, 1936). Evidence from

79

steric hindrance and rearrangements agrees with this assignment of configuration (Winstein and Trifan, 1952b, c; Roberts, Bennett and Armstrong, 1950).

In camphane derivatives, however, the position is more complicated due to the *gem*-dimethyl group on the bridge atom (Shoppee, 1952a). Borneol (CXXX, OH, *ba*) is more stable (Asahina, Ishidate and Sone,

CXXX   CXXXI

1936) and less hindered sterically (Vavon, 1931; Lipp and Bund, 1935; Bode, 1937) than its 'boat-equatorial' isomer *iso*borneol (CXXXI; OH, *be*). If the left-hand *cyclo*pentane ring (C1-4, C-7) is considered in the latter compound, there is a 1: 3-*cis*-repulsion between the hydroxyl and one of the *gem*-methyl groups, shown in heavy type in CXXXI.

However, *iso*borneol undergoes 1: 2-shifts of the type indicated in CXXXII much more readily than borneol, because its geometry is favourable (*cf* Shoppee 1952a; Brown, Hughes, Ingold and Smith, 1951; Winstein, Trifan *et al*, 1952; Ingold, 1953a; de la Mare, this vol. p. 107).

CXXXII   CXXXIII   CXXXIIIA

Bridged boat-form rings are found in some carbohydrate derivatives. Reeves (1949, 1951) points out that 2: 6-anhydropyranosides must have a bridged boat-form *e.g.* methyl 2: 6-anhydro-α-D-altropyranoside (CXXXIII). Here the 3: 4-glycol grouping has the ' true *cis* ' form with a projected valency angle of 0°. This compound reacts readily with cuprammonium giving a large increase in specific resistance and a small rotational shift (+ 470), and it reacts instantaneously with lead tetra-acetate. Another type of bridged boat is represented by the 1 : 4-anhydropyranoses, *e.g.* 2: 3 : 6-tri-*O*-methyl-1 : 4-anhydro-α-D-glucopyranose CXXXIIIA (Freudenberg and Braun, 1928).

A number of papers have recently appeared on the stereochemistry of the heterocyclic alcohols tropine (tropan-3α-ol; CXXXIV; X = H, Y = OH) and ψ-tropine (tropan-3β-ol; CXXXIV; X = OH, Y = H).

The configurations shown are indicated by the following evidence : dipole moments and infra-red absorption (Zenitz *et al*, 1952); acyl migrations, (Nickon and Fieser, 1952; Fodor and Nadór, 1952, 1953); stability of epimers to alkali (Cookson, 1953); dipole moments (Clemo and Jack, 1953); oxazoline bridge formation (Hardegger and Ott, 1953) ; Sparke, 1953 ; x-ray examination of tropine hydrobromide (Visser *et al*, 1954) (*cf* Chapter 4, p. 171, and the work on ecgonine referred to on p. 61).

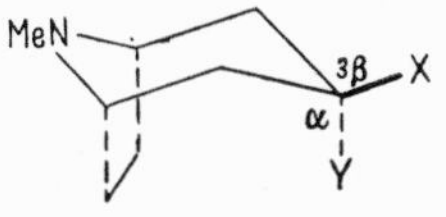

CXXXIV

The pinocampheols (derivatives of *bicyclo*[3 : 1 : 1]-heptane) provide an interesting field for study.   Here one of the two six-membered rings must be a chair and the other a boat (Schmidt, 1944).

UNSATURATED SIX-MEMBERED RINGS

There has been little discussion in the literature of the stereochemistry of *cyclo*hexene rings.   Brief notes have recently been published by Raphael and Stenlake (1953) and Barton, Cookson, Klyne and Shoppee (1954).   The two carbon atoms of the double bond (1 and 2) and the two carbon atoms attached to them (3 and 6) must be in or nearly in the same plane.   The two remaining carbon atoms 4 and 5 take up a puckered or ' half-chair ' conformation (as CXXXV and CXXXVI), although the evidence for this is not extensive.

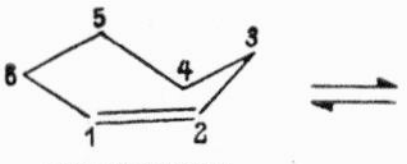

CXXXV 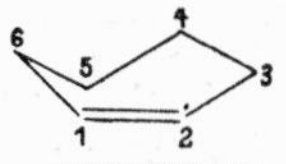   CXXXVI 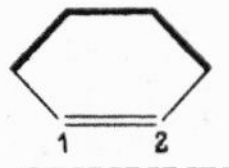   CXXXVII

These may be drawn schematically:

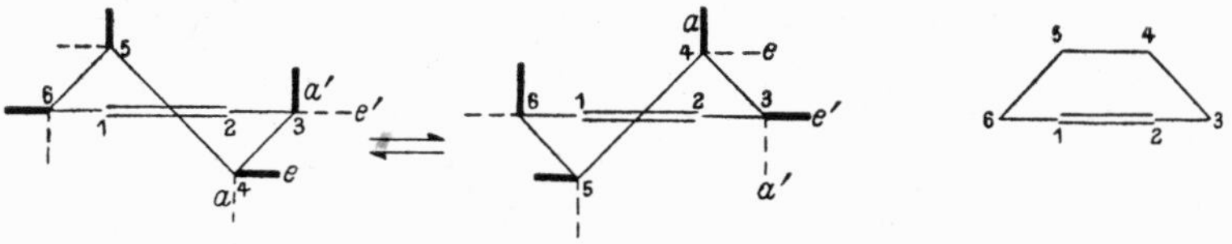

Beckett, Freeman and Pitzer (1948) calculated that this conformation (first suggested by Lister, 1941) would be more favourable energetically than the ' half-boat ' conformation CXXXVII by 2·7 kcal. mole^{-1}.   Dr S. J. Angyal (personal communication) has calculated that the distances between the ends of the half-rings CXXXVIII (butene), CXXXIX (half-chair) and CXL (half-boat) are 2·88Å;

2·94Å; and 2·56Å respectively. Obviously the butene unit will fit the half-chair unit better than the half-boat.

Unless fixed in some way by fusion with other rings, the two half-chair conformations CXXXV and CXXXVI are interconvertible like the two chair forms of a *cyclo*hexane ring. The valencies of C-3, and C-6 are in what might be called ' quasi-equatorial ' (e') and ' quasi-axial ' (a') positions as shown. The valencies of C-4 and C-5 are equatorial and axial. Barton *et al* (1954) have listed a number of examples showing that in, 3: 4-, 3: 5-, and 3: 6-disubstituted *cyclo*hexenes, that isomer which can take up a diequatorial conformation is the more stable.

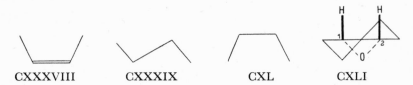

CXXXVIII   CXXXIX   CXL   CXLI

X-ray and electron diffraction studies on the benzene tetrachlorides (3: 4: 5: 6-tetrachloro*cyclo*hexenes) (Bastiansen and Markali, 1952; Bastiansen, 1952; Orloff *et al*, 1953) and one of the pentachloro*cyclo*-hexenes (Pastenak, 1951) have shown that these compounds should be represented as ' half-chair ' conformations.

1: 2-Epoxy*cyclo*hexane has been shown by electron diffraction to have a ' half-chair ' conformation (CXLI) (Ottar, 1947), although it might have been expected that the six-membered ring would be a half-boat, since C-1 and C-2, which are common to the three-membered ring, must be in the eclipsed conformation.

Arguments similar to those given for *cyclo*hexene may be applied to tetrahydronaphthalene (tetralin) derivatives where the benzenoid ring is fused at C-1 and C-2 of formulae CXXXV and CXXXVI. Lasheen (1952) has shown by x-ray analysis that ' naphthalene tetrachloride ' has a puckered alicyclic ring with two chlorine atoms in axial and two in equatorial positions (CXLII).

CXLII

However, Saksena (1938) claimed on the basis of Raman spectra that the *cyclo*hexene ring of tetralin has a ' half-boat ' conformation as CXXXVII.

Taylor (1954) has attempted to apply similar ideas to a consideration of the relative stabilities of 1- and 2-octalins; *cis*-1-octalin is more stable than *cis*-2-octalin, whilst *trans*-2-octalin is more stable than *trans*-1-octalin. 3-Oxosteroids of the 5α-series enolize preferentially to give a 2 : 3-double bond; those of the 5β-series give a 3 : 4-double bond.

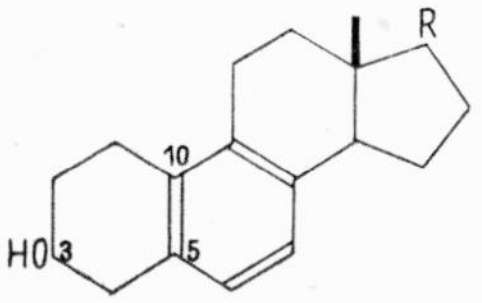

CXLIII

Infra-red measurements have recently been made on the 3-epimeric neoergosterols (CXLIII; hydroxyl at C-3, α and β respectively) by Mosettig and Scheer (1952) and independently by Dr. I. D. P. Wootton in London, using material kindly provided by Dr. E. Mosettig (Bethesda, Md.). Both alcohols show a band at 1044 cm⁻¹ characteristic of an equatorial hydroxyl group (*cf* p. 167) and the spectra from 1200–900 cm⁻¹ are almost identical. This may be explained if the *A* ring takes up two different conformations in the two epimers such that in each case the hydroxyl group is equatorial (CXLIV and CXLV).

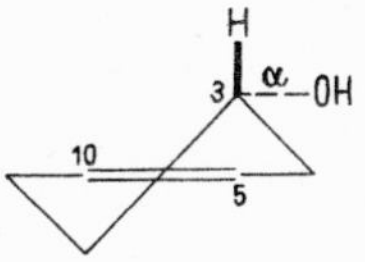

CXLIV 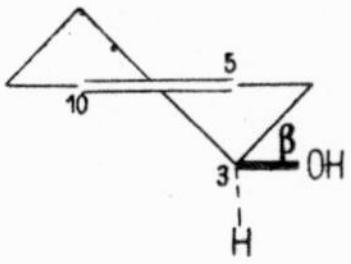   CXLV

The complex stereochemistry of the lysergic acids, which involves a double bond, a hetero-atom (N) and a carboxyl group in a very rigid fused ring system, has been discussed by Cookson (1953) and Stenlake (1953).

Conclusion

In this chapter the reviewer has tried to show how the study of conformations, based on physico-chemical measurements which are the province of the specialist, has within the last five years developed into a method which may be of value in all structural problems of alicyclic chemistry. It is hoped that the next few years will see the extension of this concept to the more difficult field of acyclic compounds.

The writer is indebted to Professor D. H. R. Barton, F.R.S., Dr P. de Mayo and Dr A. Nickon (Birkbeck College, London) for many helpful comments on the manuscript.

REFERENCES

Abd El Rehim, A. M. and Carlisle, C. H. (1954) *Chem. & Ind.* 279

Alder, K. and Stein, G. (1934) *Liebigs Ann.* **514,** 211; (1936) *ibid* **525,** 183

Alt, G. H. and Barton, D. H. R. (1954) in preparation. (Results briefly discussed by Prof. D. H. R. Barton at the Symposium on Dynamic Stereochemistry in Manchester, March, 1954.)

Ames, T. R., Beton, J. L., Bowers, A., Halsall, T. G. and Jones, E. R. H. (1954) *J. chem. Soc.* 1905 *cf* (1953) *Chem. & Ind.* 847, 1386

Andersen, P. and Hassel, O. (1949) *Acta chem. scand.* **3,** 1180

Anderson, L., Tomita, K., Kussi, P. and Kirkwood, S. (1953) *J. biol. Chem.*, **204,** 769

Angyal, C. J. and Angyal, S. J. (1952) *J. chem. Soc.* 695

— and Macdonald, C. G. (1952) *ibid* 686

— and Mills, J. A. (1952) *Rev. pure appl. Chem.*, *Aust.* **2,** 185

Asahina, Y., Ishidate, M. and Sano, T. (1936) *Ber. dtsch. chem. Ges.* **69,** 343

Astbury, W. T. and Davies, M. M. (1944) *Nature, Lond.* **154,** 84

Aston, J. G., Fink, H. L. and Schumann, S. C. (1943) *J. Amer. chem. Soc.* **65,** 341

— Schumann, S. C., Fink, H. L. and Doty, P. M. (1941) *ibid* **63,** 2029

Auwers, K. von (1920) *Liebigs Ann.* **420,** 91

— and Ottens, B. (1924) *Ber. dtsch. chem. Ges.* **57,** 437

Bachmann, W. E., Ross, A., Dreiding, A. S. and Smith, P. A. S. (1954) *J. org. Chem.* **19,** 222

Barker, S. A. and Bourne, E. J. (1952) *J. chem. Soc.* 905, *cf Advanc. Carbohydr. Chem.* **7,** 138

— — Stacey, M. and Whiffen, D. H. (1954) *J. chem. Soc.* 171

— — and Whiffen, D. H. (1952) *ibid* 3865

Barnes, C. S., Barton, D. H. R., Fawcett, J. S. and Thomas, B. R. (1953) *ibid* 576

Bartlett, P. D. (1953) in *Organic Chemistry*, vol. 3, p. 1, ed. H. Gilman, New York, Wiley

— and Pöckel, I. (1937) *J. Amer. chem. Soc.* **59,** 820

— and Rosen, L. J. (1942) *ibid* **64,** 543

Barton, D. H. R. (1948) *J. chem. Soc.* 340; (1949) *ibid* 2174; (1950) *Experientia* **6,** 316; (1953a) *J. chem. Soc.* 1027; (1953b) *Chem. & Ind.* 664

— and Brooks, C. J. W. (1951) *J. chem. Soc.* 257

— — and Holness, N. J. (1951) *ibid* 277

— Cookson, R. C., Klyne, W. and Shoppee, C. W. (1954) *Chem. & Ind.* 21

— Hassel, O., Pitzer, K. S. and Prelog, V. (1953) *Nature, Lond.* **172,** 1096, *cf Science* (1954) **119,** 49

— Head, A. J. and Williams, R. J. (1953) *J. chem. Soc.* 1715

— and Holness, N. J. (1952) *ibid* 78

— Jeger, O., Prelog, V. and Woodward, R. B. (1954) *Experientia*, **10,** 81

— and Miller, E. (1950) *J. Amer. chem. Soc.* **72,** 1066

— and Robinson, C. H. (1954) in preparation (*cf* Alt and Barton, 1954) see also G. E. Arth *et al* (1954) *J. Amer. chem. Soc.* **76,** 1715

— and Rosenfelder, W. J. (1951) *J. chem. Soc.* 1048

— and Schmeidler, G. A. (1948) *ibid* 1197; (1949) *ibid* S 232

— and Thomas, B. R. (1953) *ibid* 1842

Bastiansen, O. (1952) *Acta chem. scand.* **6,** 875

— Ellefsen, Ø. and Hassel, O. (1949) *ibid* **3,** 918

— and Hassel, O. (1946a) *Tidsskr. Kemi Bergv.* **6,** 96; (1946b) *Nature, Lond.* **157,** 765; (1951) *Acta chem. scand.* **5,** 1404

— and Markali, J. (1952) *ibid* **6,** 442

Beckett, C. W., Freeman, N. K. and Pitzer, K. S. (1948) *J. Amer. chem. Soc.* **70,** 4227

— Pitzer, K. S. and Spitzer, R. (1947) *ibid* **69,** 2488

Beereboom, J. J., Djerassi, C., Ginsburg, D. and Fieser, L. F. (1953) *ibid* **75,** 3500

Beevers, C. A. and Cochrane, W. (1946) *Nature, Lond.* **157,** 872

THE CONFORMATIONS OF SIX-MEMBERED RING SYSTEMS

Bijvoet, J. M. (1948) *Rec. Trav. chim. Pays-Bas* **67,** 777
Bladon, P., Henbest, H. B., Jones, E. R. H., *et al* (1953) *J. chem. Soc.* 2921
— — and Wood, G. W. (1952) *ibid* 2737
Bode, H. (1937) *Ber. dtsch. chem. Ges.* **70,** 1167
Boëseken, J. and Giffen, J. V. (1920) *Rec. Trav. chim. Pays-Bas* **39,** 186
Bose, A. K. (1952) *Experientia* **8,** 458; (1953) *ibid* **9,** 256
— and Chaudhuri, D. K. R. (1953) *Nature, Lond.* **171,** 652
— — and Bhattacharyya, A. K. (1953) *Chem. & Ind.* 869
Bridgwater, R. J. and Shoppee, C. W. (1953) *J. chem. Soc.* 1709
Brooks, R. V., Klyne, W. and Miller, E. (1953) *Biochem. J.* **54,** 212
Brown, F., Hughes, E. D., Ingold, C. K. and Smith, J. F. (1951) *Nature, Lond.* **168,** 65
Brown, H. C. and Borkowski, M. (1952) *J. Amer. chem. Soc.* **74,** 1894
— Brewster, J. H. and Schechter, H. (1954) *ibid* **76,** 467
— Fletcher, R. S. and Johannessen, R. B. (1951) *ibid* **73,** 212
Budziarek, R., Johnston, J. D., Manson, W. and Spring, F. S. (1951) *Chem. & Ind.* 478
Carlisle, C. H. and Crowfoot, D. M. (1945) *Proc. roy. Soc. A,* **184,** 64
Clayton, R. B. and Henbest, H. B. (1953) *Chem. & Ind.* 1315
Clemo, G. R. and Jack, K. H. (1953) *Chem. & Ind.* 195
Cole, A. R. H. (1952) *J. chem. Soc.* 4969
— Jones, R. N. and Dobriner, K. (1952) *J. Amer. chem. Soc.* **74,** 5571
Conn, J. B., Kistiakowsky, G. B. and Smith, E. A. (1939) *ibid* **61,** 1868
Cook, J. W., McGinnis, N. A. and Mitchell, S. (1944) *J. chem. Soc.* 286
Cookson, R. C. (1953) *Chem. & Ind.* 337; (1954a) *J. chem. Soc.* 282; (b) *Chem. & Ind.* 223
Corey, E. J. (1953a, b, c) *J. Amer. chem. Soc.* **75,** 2301, 3297, 4832; (1953d) *Experientia* **9,** 329; (1954) *J. Amer. chem. Soc.* **76,** 175
— and Sneen, R. A. (1953) *J. Amer. chem. Soc.* **75,** 6234
Cornubert, R. (1953) *Bull. Soc. chim. Fr.* M. 42
— Delmas, R., Monteil, S. and Viriot, J. (1949) *ibid* [v], **16,** 819
Cremlyn, R. J. W., Garmaise, D. L. and Shoppee, C. W. (1953) *J. chem. Soc.* 1847
Cristol, S. J. (1947) *J. Amer. chem. Soc.* **69,** 338
— and Hause, N. L. (1952) *ibid* **74,** 2193
Curtis, R. G., Fridrichsons, J., and Mathieson, A. McL. (1952) *Nature, Lond.* **170,** 321
Darling, L. H., Macbeth, A. K. and Mills, J. A. (1953) *J. chem. Soc.* 1364
Dickinson, R. G. and Bilicke, C. (1928) *J. Amer. chem. Soc.* **50,** 764
Djerassi, C., Frick, W., Rosenkranz, G. and Sondheimer, F. (1953) *ibid* **75,** 3496
Doering, W. von E. and Aschner, T. C. (1949) *ibid* **71,** 838
Dostrovsky, I., Hughes, E. D. and Ingold, C. K. (1946) *J. chem. Soc.* 173
Ebel, F. (1933) in *Stereochemie*, ed. K. Freudenberg, p. 825 Leipzig and Vienna, Deuticke
Eliel, E. L. (1953) *Experientia* **9,** 91
Elks, J. and Shoppee, C. W. (1953) *J. chem. Soc.* 241
Ellis, B. and Petrow, V. (1952) *ibid* 2246
Evans, D. D. and Shoppee, C. W. (1953) *ibid* 540
Fieser, L. F. and Dominguez, X. A. (1953) *J. Amer. chem. Soc.* **75,** 1704
— and Ettore, R. (1953) *ibid* **75,** 1700
— and Fieser, M. (1949) *Natural Products related to Phenanthrene,* 3rd ed. New York, Reinhold
— Huang, W. Y. (1953) *J. Amer. chem. Soc.* **75,** 4837
Findlay, S. P. (1953) *ibid* **75,** 4624
Fodor, G. and Kovács, O. (1953) *J. chem. Soc.* 724
— and Nádor, K. (1952) *Nature, Lond.* **169,** 462; (1953) *J. chem. Soc.* 721
Freudenberg, K. and Braun, E. (1928) *Liebigs Ann.* **460,** 288
Fried, J., Wintersteiner, O., Moore, M., Iselin, B. M. and Klingsberg, A. (1951) *J. Amer. chem. Soc.* **73,** 2970

Friess, S. L. and Frankenburg, P. E. (1952) *ibid* **74**, 2679
Furberg, S. and Hassel, O. (1950) *Acta chem. scand.* **4.** 597
Fürst, A., Kuhn, H. H., Scotoni, R. Jr. and Günthard, H. H. (1952) *Helv. chim. acta* **35**, 951
— and Plattner, P. A. (1949) *ibid* **32**, 275; (1951) *12th Int. Congr. Chem. Abstr.*, 409
— and Scotoni, R. Jr. (1953a, b) *Helv. chim. acta* **36**, 1332, 1410
Gerding, H., Smit, E. and Westrik, R. (1942) *Rec. Trav. chim. Pays-Bas* **61**, 561
Godchot, M. and Mousseron, M. (1934) *C. R. Acad. Sci., Paris*, **198**, 2000
Goering, H. L. and Serres, C. Jr. (1952) *J. Amer. chem. Soc.* **74**, 5908
Goldberg, M. W., Sicé, J., Robert H. and Plattner, P. A. (1947) *Helv. chim. acta*. **30**, 1441
Gottschalk, A. (1950) *Advanc. Carbohydr. Chem.* **5**, 49
Greenhalgh, C. W., Henbest, H. B. and Jones, E. R. H. (1952) *J. chem. Soc.*, 2375
Haggis, G. A. and Owen, L. N. (1953) *ibid* 389, 399, 404, 408
Halsall, T. G., Hodges, R. and Jones, E. R. H. (1953) *ibid* 3019
— Jones, E. R. H. *et al* (1952) *ibid* 2862, 2868
Hardegger, E. and Ott, H. (1953) *Helv. chim. acta* **36**, 1186
Hassel, O. (1943) *Tidsskr. Kemi. Bergv.* **3**, 32; (1950) *Research, Lond.* **3**, 504; (1953) *Quart. Rev. chem. Soc., Lond.* **7**, 221.
— and Lunde, K. (1950) *Acta chem. scand.* **4**, 1597
— and Ore, S. (1946) *Tidsskr. Kemi. Bergv.* **6**, 72
— and Ottar, B. (1947) *Acta chem. scand.* **1**, 929
— and Viervoll, H. (1943) *Tidsskr. Kemi. Bergv.* **3**, 35; (1947) *Acta chem. scand.* **1**, 149
Haworth, W. N. (1929) *The Constitution of Sugars*, p. 90, London, Arnold
Hazebroek, P. and Oosterhoff, L. J. (1951) *Disc. Faraday Soc.* **10**, 87
Hendricks, S. B. and Billicke, C. (1926) *J. Amer. chem. Soc* **48**, 3007
Herzog, H. L., Oliveto, E. P., Jernik, M. A. and Herschberg, E. B. (1952) *ibid* **74**, 4470
Heusser, H., Anliker, R. and Jeger, O. (1952) *Helv. chim. acta* **35**, 1537
Hirschmann, R., Snoddy, C. S., Jr. and Wendler, N. L. (1952) *J. Amer. chem. Soc.* **74**, 2693, *cf* (1953) *ibid* **75**, 5136; also Elks, J. *et al* (1953) *Chem. & Ind.* 1387
Hochstein, F. A., Stephens, C. R., Conover, L. H., Regna, P. P., Pasternak, R., Gordon, P. N., Pilgrim, F. J., Brunings, K. J. and Woodward, R. B. (1953) *J. Amer. chem. Soc.* **75**, 5455
Holysz, R. P. (1953) *ibid* **75**, 4432
Hückel, W. (1934) *Ber. dtsch. chem. Ges.* **67**, 129; (1937) *Liebigs Ann.* **533**, 1; (1944) *Ber. dtsch. chem. Ges.* **77**, 805
— Havekoss, H., Kumetat, K., Ullmann, D. and Doll, W. (1937) *Liebigs Ann.* **533**, 128
— and Kümmerle, K. (1942) *Ber. dtsch. chem. Ges.* **75**, 115
— and Naab, H. (1931) *ibid* **64**, 2137
— and Pietrzok, H. (1939) *Liebigs Ann.* **540**, 250
— Tappe, W. and Legutke, G. (1940) *ibid* **543**, 191
Hughes, E. D., Ingold, C. K. *et al* (1948) *J. chem. Soc.* 2093, 2117
— — and Pasternak, R. (1953) *ibid* 3832
Ingold, C. K. (1953a) *Structure and Mechanism in Organic Reactions*, London, Bell; (1953b) *J. chem. Soc.* 2845
Ito, K. (1953) *J. Amer. chem. Soc.* **75**, 2430
Jacobs, W. A. and Pelletier, S. W. (1953) *J. org. Chem.* **18**, 765
Janot, M. M., Goutarel, R., Le Hir, A., Amin, A. and Prelog, V. (1952) *Bull. Soc. chim. Fr.* 1085, *cf* also (1953) *ibid* 1023, 1027
Johnson, W. S. (1951) *Experientia* **7**, 315; (1953) *J. Amer. chem. Soc.* **75**, 1498
Jones, R. N. (1953) *ibid* **75**, 4839
— Humphries, P., Herling, F. and Dobriner, K. (1951) *ibid* **73**, 3215

Jones, R. N., Ramsay, D. A., Herling, F. and Dobriner, K. (1952) *ibid* **74,** 2828
Kendall, E. C. *et al* (1946) *J. biol. Chem.* **162,** 565, 571; **164,** 569
King, F. E., Bovey, D. M., Mason, ·K G. and Whitehead, R. L. St. D. (1953) *J. chem. Soc.* 250
Klyne, W. (1950) *Nature, Lond.* **166,** 559; (1953) *J. chem. Soc.* 3027
— and Shoppee, C. W. (1952) *Chem. & Ind.* 470
— and Stokes, W. M. (1954) *J. chem. Soc.* 1979
Kohlrausch, K. W. F., Reitz, A. W. and Stockmair, W. (1936) *Z. phys. Chem. B* **32,** 229
— and Wittek, H. (1941) *ibid B*, **48,** 177
Kozima, K., and Yoshino, T. (1953) *J. Amer. chem. Soc.* **75,** 166
Kuhn, L. P. (1952) *ibid* **74,** 2492
Kuivila, H. G. and Becker, W. J. (1952) *ibid* **74,** 5329
Kumler, W. D. (1945) *ibid* **67,** 1901
Larnaudie, M. (1952) *C. R. Acad. Sci., Paris* **235,** 154; (1953) *ibid* **236,** 909
Lasheen, M. A. (1942) *Acta cryst., Camb.* **5,** 593
Le Fèvre, C. G. and Le Fèvre, R. J. W. (1935) *J. chem. Soc.* 1696
Lind, E. L., Hobbs, M. E. and Gross, P. M. (1950) *J. Amer. chem. Soc.* **72,** 4474
Linstead, R. P. *et al* (1936) *J. chem. Soc.* 470, 478; (1937) *ibid* 1140; (1942) *J. Amer. chem. Soc.* **64,** 1985 and succeeding papers
— and Whetstone, R. R. (1950) *J. chem. Soc.* 1428
Lipp, M. and Bund, E. (1935) *Ber. dtsch. chem. Ges.* **68,** 249
Lister, M. W. (1941) *J. Amer. chem. Soc.* **63,** 143
Lukes, R. M. and Sarett, L. H. (1954) *ibid* **76,** 1178
Lund, E. W. (1951) *Acta chem. scand.* **5,** 678
Macbeth, A. K., Mills, J. A. and Robertson, W. G. P. (1951) *J. chem. Soc.* 3968
McCasland, G. E. (1951) *J. Amer. chem. Soc.* **73,** 2293
McKenna, J. (1954) *Chem. & Ind.* 406
Magasanik, B. and Chargaff, E. (1948) *J. biol. Chem.* **174,** 173
— Franzl, R. E. and Chargaff, E. (1952) *J. Amer. chem. Soc.* **74,** 2618
Malherbe, F. E. and Bernstein, H. J. (1952) *ibid* **74,** 4408
Meerwein, H. (1939) *Liebigs Ann.* **542,** 123
Miescher, K. and Kägi, H. (1949) *Helv. chim. acta* **32,** 761
Mills, J. A. (1953) *J. chem. Soc.* 260; (1954) *Chem. & Ind.* 633
Mohr, E. (1918) *J. prakt. Chem.* **98,** 315
Mosettig, E. and Scheer, I. (1952) *J. org. Chem.* **17,** 764
Mousseron, M. and Granger, R. (1938) *Bull. soc. chim. Fr.* **5,** 1618
Nace, H. R. and Turner, R. B. (1953) *J. Amer. chem. Soc.* **75,** 4063
Newth, F. H. (1953) *Chem. & Ind.* 1257
— and Homer, R. F. (1953) *J. chem. Soc.* 989
Nickon, A. and Fieser, L. F. (1952) *J. Amer. chem. Soc.* **74,** 5566
Nowak, R., Jeger, O. and Ruzicka, L. (1949) *Helv. chim. acta* **32,** 323
Noyce, D. S. and Denney, D. B. (1952) *J. Amer. chem. Soc.* **74,** 5912
O'Connor, G. L. and Nace, H. R. (1952) *ibid* **74,** 5454
Orloff, H. D., Kolka, A. J., Calingaert, G., Griffing, M. E. and Kerr, E. R. (1953) *ibid* **75,** 4243; *cf* (1954) *ibid* **76,** 1244
Ottar, B. (1947) *Acta chem. scand.* **1,** 283
Pacsu, E. (1939) *J. Amer. chem. Soc.* **61,** 2669
Pastenak, R. S. (1951) *Acta cryst., Camb.* **4,** 316
Pitzer, K. S. (1940) *Chem. Rev.* **27,** 39; (1945) *Science,* **101,** 672
— and Beckett, C. W. (1947) *J. Amer. chem. Soc.* **69,** 977
Pollak, P. I. and Curtin, D. Y. (1950) *ibid* **72,** 961
Poos, G. I., Arth, G. E., Beyler, R. E. and Sarett, L. H. (1953) *ibid* **75,** 422
Posternak, T. and Reymond, D. (1953) *Helv. chim. acta* **36,** 260

Price, C. C. and Berti, G. (1954) *J. Amer. chem. Soc.* **76,** 1211
Prins, D. A. and Shoppee, C. W. (1946) *J. chem. Soc.* 494
Przybylska, M. and Barnes, W. H. (1953) *Acta cryst., Camb.* **6,** 377
Ramsay, D. A. (1947) *Proc. roy. Soc. A* **190,** 562; (1948) *Trans. Faraday Soc.* **44,** 289
— and Sutherland, G. B. B. M. (1947) *Proc. roy. Soc. A* **190,** 245
Raphael, R. A. (1953) in *The Chemistry of Carbon Compounds*, ed. E. H. Rodd, vol. II *A*, Amsterdam, Elsevier
— and Stenlake, J. B. (1953) *Chem. & Ind.* 1286
Rasmussen, R. S. (1943) *J. chem. Phys.* **11,** 249 and references there
Read, J. and Grubb, W. J. (1934) *J. chem. Soc.* 1779
Reeves, R. E. (1944) *J. biol. Chem.* **154,** 49; (1949a, b) *J. Amer. chem. Soc.* **71,** 215, 2116; (1950) *ibid* **72,** 1499; (1951) *Advanc. Carbohydr. Chem.* **6,** 108
Roberts, J. D., Bennett, W. and Armstrong, R. (1950) *J. Amer. chem. Soc.* **72,** 3329
Rosenkranz, H., Milhorat, A. T. and Farber, M. (1952) *J. biol. Chem.* **195,** 509
Rossini, F. D. and Pitzer, K. S. (1947) *Science,* **105,** 647
Ruzicka, L. and Gubser, H. (1945) *Helv. chim. acta* **28,** 1054
— Montavon, M. and Jeger, O. (1948) *ibid* **31,** 819
— and Meldahl, H. F. (1941) *ibid* **24,** 1321
— and Wirz, W. (1940) *ibid* **23,** 132; (1941) *ibid* **24,** 248
Sachse, H. (1890) *Ber. dtsch. chem. Ges.* **23,** 1363; (1892) *Z. phys. Chem.* **10,** 203
Saksena, B. D. (1938) *Proc. Ind. Acad. Sci. A* **8,** 73
Savard, K. (1953) *J. biol. Chem.* **202,** 457
Scattergood, A. and Pacsu, E. (1940) *J. Amer. chem. Soc.* **62,** 903
Schmidlin, J. and Wettstein, A. (1953) *Helv. chim. acta* **36,** 1241
Schmidt, H. (1944) *Ber. dtsch. chem. Ges.* **77,** 544
Schmukler, S. and Curtin, D. Y. (1953) *Amer. chem. Soc. Abstr.* 124*th Meeting* 18–O
Seyer, W. F. (1953) *J. Amer. chem. Soc.* **75,** 616
Shoppee, C. W. (1946) *J. chem. Soc.* 1138; (1952a) *Chem. & Ind.* 86; (1952b) 2*nd Int. Congr. Biochem., Symposium on Steroids* 5, Paris
— and Summers, G. H. R. (1952) *J. chem. Soc.* 3361
Siegel, S. (1953) *J. Amer. chem. Soc.* **75,** 1317
— and Morse, J. G. (1953) *ibid* **75,** 3857
Simonsen, J. L. and Barton, D. H. R. (1952) *The Terpenes*, vol. 3. Cambridge University Press
— and Owen, L. N. (1947) *ibid* vols. 1 and 2
Skita, A. (1920) *Ber. dtsch. chem. Ges.* **53,** 1792
— and Faust, W. (1931) *ibid* **64,** 2878; (1939) *ibid* **72,** 1127
— and Rossler, R. (1939) *ibid* **72,** 265
— and Schneck, A. (1922) *ibid* **55,** 144
Smith, H. A. and Byrne, F. P. (1950) *J. Amer. chem. Soc.* **72,** 4406
Sparke, M. B. (1953) *Chem. & Ind.* 749
Spitzer, R. and Huffman, H. M. (1947) *J. Amer. chem. Soc.* **69,** 211
Stenlake, J. B. (1953) *Chem. & Ind.* 1089
Taylor, D. A. H. (1954) *ibid* 250
Tulinskie, A., Di Giacomo, A. and Smyth, C. P. (1953) *J. Amer. chem. Soc.* **75,** 3552
Turner, R. B. (1952) *ibid* **74,** 2118
van Vloten, W., Kruissink, C. A., Strijk, B. and Bijvoet, J. M. (1950) *Acta cryst., Camb.* **3,** 139
Vavon, G. (1931) *Bull. Soc. chim. Fr.* [iv] **49,** 937
— and Anziani, P. (1937) *ibid* [v] **4,** 1080
— and Jacubowicz, B. (1933) *ibid* [iv] **53,** 581
— and Peignier, P. (1925) *ibid* [iv] **37,** 823; (1926) *ibid* [iv] **39,** 924
Visser, J. W., Manassen, J. and de Vries, J. L. (1954) *Acta cryst., Camb.* **7,** 288
Wendler, N. L. (1953) *Experientia,* **9,** 416

Westheimer, F. H. (1949) *Chem. Rev.* **45,** 419
— *et al* (1949) *J. Amer. chem. Soc.* **71,** 25; (1951) **73, 65;** (1952) **74,** 4383, 4387
— and Mayer, J. E. (1946) *J. chem. Phys.* **14,** 733
Westphalen, T. (1915) *Ber. dtsch. chem. Ges.* **48,** 1064
Wightman, W. A. (1925) *J. chem. Soc.* **127,** 1421; (1926) *ibid* 2541
Winstein, S. and Trifan, *et al* (1952a, b, c) *J. Amer. chem. Soc.* **74,** 1127, 1147, 1154
— Pressman, D. and Young, W. G. (1939) *ibid* **61,** 1645
Wyckoff, R. W. G. (1953) *Crystal Structures*, vol. 3, chap. XV, New York, Interscience
Young, W. G., Pressman, D. and Coryell, C. D. (1939) *J. Amer. chem. Soc.* **61,** 1640
Zenitz, B. L., Martini, C. M., Priznar, M. and Nachod, F. C. (1952) *ibid* **74,** 5564

3

STEREOCHEMICAL FACTORS IN REACTION MECHANISMS AND KINETICS

P. B. D. de la Mare

STEREOCHEMICAL PROBLEMS enter immediately into studies of reaction mechanisms, since the aim in any such investigation is to discover the detailed path of the reaction, and therefore to determine the geometry of those intermediate states through which the system passes as the reactants are transformed into the products. The past twenty years have seen great developments in this field; in the present chapter, space is available for the discussion only of selected topics, and even these have not been dealt with exhaustively. Among the subjects which have been omitted, despite their intrinsic interest and importance, are included the stereochemical aspects involved in aromatic substitution, in studies of acid and base strength, and in *cis–trans*-isomerizations.

STEREOCHEMISTRY OF NUCLEOPHILIC SUBSTITUTION

Introduction

Unimolecular and Bimolecular Mechanisms
Heterolytic nucleophilic substitution reactions are those in which a reagent Y, carrying a pair of electrons, displaces a group X from a molecule RX, leaving with X the electron-pair originally associated with the RX bond, as in the example: $R \cdot Cl + OEt^- \rightarrow R \cdot OEt + Cl^-$. It has been established by kinetic methods, largely as a result of the extensive work of the school of Hughes and Ingold (*cf* Hughes, 1941a) that two mechanisms exist for such processes. In the first (bimolecular, S_N2), the reagent attacks the organic molecule and displaces the group X from it in a synchronous, or concerted process, in which the C—Y bond is being formed at the same time as the C—X bond is being broken. In the second (unimolecular, S_N1), the rate-determining stage of the reaction is the slow heterolytic fission of the C—X bond; this is followed by the rapid reaction of the resulting carbonium cation with substances in the environment, as may be written, for a typical example:

$$Me_3C \cdot Cl \xrightarrow{\text{slow}} Me_3C^+ + Cl^-; \qquad Me_3C^+ + Y^- \xrightarrow{\text{fast}} Me_3C \cdot Y$$

Steric Hindrance

Bimolecular nucleophilic substitution requires, in the transition state of the reaction, the presence of five groups bonded or partly bonded to the carbon atom at which substitution is occurring. When these groups are bulky, therefore, repulsions between them may make the transition state of the reaction difficult to attain, with the result that the reaction is hindered sterically. An example of particular interest is *neo*pentyl bromide, which, under conditions conducive to bimolecular displacements (*e.g.* with sodium ethoxide in ethanol) is many powers of ten less reactive than ethyl bromide. Dostrovsky, Hughes and Ingold (1946) surveyed in some detail the reactions of *neo*pentyl and other alkyl halides with nucleophilic reagents. They also made calculations, as far as these were possible, of the contributions to the energies of activation which might be expected from consideration of steric hindrance. These calculations referred to the symmetrical exchange reaction, $RBr + Br^{*-} \rightleftharpoons RBr^{*} + Br^{-}$, with a transition state of the

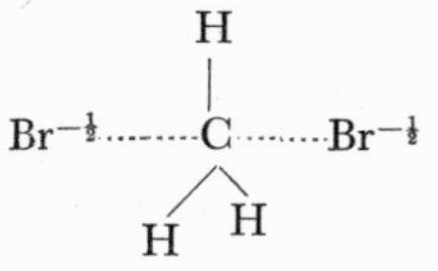

$$
\begin{array}{ccc}
& & \text{Me} \\
& & | \\
\text{H} & \text{Me} & \text{Me}-\text{C}-\text{Me} \\
| & | & | \\
\text{Br}^{-\frac{1}{2}}\cdots\text{C}\cdots\text{Br}^{-\frac{1}{2}} & \text{Br}^{-\frac{1}{2}}\cdots\text{C}\cdots\text{Br}^{-\frac{1}{2}} & \text{Br}^{-\frac{1}{2}}\cdots\text{C}\cdots\text{Br}^{-\frac{1}{2}} \\
\diagup\diagdown & \diagup\diagdown & \diagup\diagdown \\
\text{H} \quad \text{H} & \text{Me} \quad \text{Me} & \text{H} \quad \text{H} \\
\text{I} & \text{II} & \text{III}
\end{array}
$$

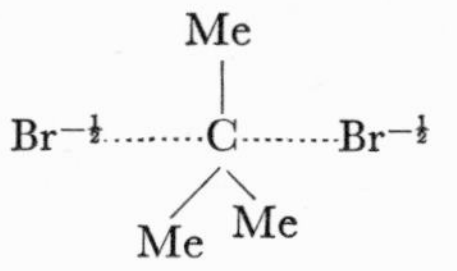

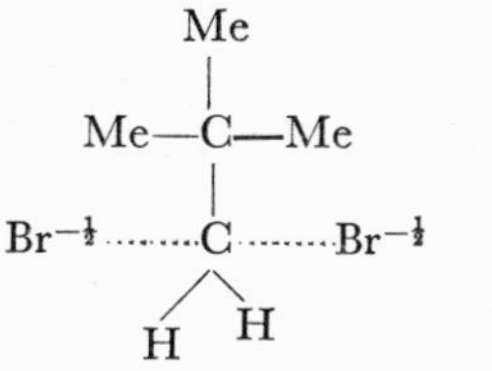

form shown in the diagrams I, II and III. In the next section (p. 95) evidence for this particular geometrical arrangement will be developed.

In TABLE 1 are given some of their experimental and calculated values, together with results obtained more recently by Hughes, Ingold, and the writer, which have as yet been published only in summary [*cf* de la Mare, England, Fowden, Hughes and Ingold (1948), de la Mare (1948, 1950a)].

The calculations of Dostrovsky, Hughes and Ingold (1946) should be followed through in detail by those who wish to gain a fuller insight into the methods used in this type of computation. In brief, the following energy terms were calculated:

(*i*) The energy required to stretch the C—Br bond to a length *r* using a Morse curve, the constants for which were obtained conventionally from spectroscopic data.

(*ii*) The energy required to bring a bromide ion to a distance *r* from the central carbon atom, using an expression for the energy required to compress two atoms together, obtained from measurements on the compressibility of ionic crystals, together with the proper van der Waals and electrostatic energy terms.

(*iii*) The energy of interaction between the groups R and Br, as a function of *r*, and calculated as in (*ii*).

TABLE 1. RATES AND ARRHENIUS PARAMETERS FOR THE REACTIONS OF ALKYL BROMIDES (RBr) WITH ANIONS

The parameters E (kcal. mole^{-1}) and $\log_{10}B$ (l. mole^{-1} sec^{-1}) are taken from the equation k_2 (l. mole^{-1} sec^{-1}) $= Be^{-E/RT}$

R	Me	MeCH$_2$	Me$_2$CH	Me$_3$C	Me·CH$_2$·CH$_2$	Me$_2$CH·CH$_2$	Me$_3$C·CH$_2$
RBr+Br$^-$in acetone at 25°C							
$k_2 \times 10^5$	13,000	170	1·8	0·51	110	5·7	0·003
E	15·8	17·5	19·7	21·8	17·5	18·9	22·0
$\log_{10} B$	10·7	10·1	9·7	10·7	9·8	9·6	8·5
RBr+OEt$^-$ in EtOH at 55°C							
$k_2 \times 10^5$	3440	195	—	—	54·7	5·8	8·3 × 10^{-4}
E	20·0	21·0	—	—	—	22·8	26·2
$\log_{10} B$	11·9	11·3	—	—	—	11·0	9·4
Calc. steric contribution to E	0·0	0·7	1·4	2·2	0·7	2·3	11·7

These three energy terms were all expressed using infinite separation as the arbitrary zero of energy; they were summed, to give the total energy of the system, the minimum value of which defined the energy and the C—Br separation in the transition state. From this treatment it appeared, for methyl bromide (I), that there is virtually no contribution to the energy from steric compressions between the H and Br atoms. The minimum for *tert.*-butyl bromide (II), lay 2·2 kcal. mole^{-1} higher. This was taken as an estimate of the contribution made by steric hindrance to the energy of activation of the reaction, and the fact that the experimental value [$E(\text{Bu}^t\text{Br}) - E(\text{MeBr})$ = 6 kcal. mole^{-1}] was higher, was taken as evidence that other (polar) influences increase this energy-difference.

For *neo*pentyl bromide (III), the contribution from steric hindrance to the energy of activation of the reaction, calculated in similar fashion, was 11·7 kcal. mole^{-1}. In this case the bulky *tert.*-butyl group must force the entering and leaving bromine atoms away from collinearity with the central carbon atom, thus relieving some of the steric strain allowed for in the calculation. In fact, the measured energy-difference for this compound is 6 kcal., indicating that considerable accommodation to the steric strain involved in attaining the transition state is achieved by a bending of the Br—C—Br system.

A further point of interest in regard to steric effects is illustrated by the values for the non-exponential Arrhenius parameter, or 'B-factor'.

This, considered from the point of view of the collision theory of reactions, provides a measure of the probability that a collision able to provide the energy of activation will in fact result in reaction. It is not necessarily reduced by steric effects, which appear characteristically in the energy of activation. Thus, for the reactions of the compounds RBr, the B-factor decreases steadily with increasing steric hindrance in the series R = Me, Et, n-Pr, isoBu, neopentyl; but in the series R = Me, Et, isoPr, $tert$.-Bu, although steric hindrance also increases, the B-factor passes through a minimum, and, of all the compounds investigated, $tert$.-butyl bromide has a B factor nearest to that of the unhindered reference compound, methyl bromide. It seems likely that, when the energetically favoured configuration of the transition state requires bending of the Br—C—Br bond ($e.g.$ $Me_3C \cdot CH_2Br$), the probability that a collision of sufficient energy will cause reaction is less than in cases in which the transition state has a more symmetrical arrangement (CH_3Br, CMe_3Br). A similar view of such variations in the Arrhenius B-factors has been expressed by Ivanoff and Magat (1950).

Steric Acceleration

Unimolecular substitutions involve, in the rate-determining stage of the reaction, the separation of the displaced group, without requiring the simultaneous attack of a reagent. Steric hindrance becomes of much smaller importance in reactions proceeding by this mechanism. For example, neopentyl bromide, the bimolecular reactions of which are heavily hindered sterically, undergoes unimolecular solvolyses at rates very similar to those of such analogous compounds as ethyl bromide.

If, on the other hand, a sufficiently large number of bulky groups accumulate round the reaction-centre, the possibility arises that ionization may relieve steric strains present in the original molecule. The reaction may then appear to be accelerated sterically. Brown and his co-workers (cf Brown and Fletcher, 1949), and also Hughes (1951a, b), and Bartlett (1951) have been particularly concerned to establish the reality of this effect in regard to the rates of unimolecular solvolyses of $tert$.-halides.

It has been pointed out, however (cf especially Hughes, 1951a, b), that it is difficult to distinguish effects due to steric acceleration from those for which other structural influences are responsible, particularly when small rate-differences are being considered. Experimentally, it appears that considerable complexity of structure is required before the rates of reaction begin to show any significant increases which may be attributed to steric acceleration.

Hughes (1951a) has summarized some of the available data as follows. Large increases in the rate of reaction only appear in the most highly branched compounds, and it seems likely that, in primary and secondary halides, effects due to steric acceleration are usually negligible.

Compound	CMe_3Cl	$CMeEt_2Cl$	CEt_3Cl	CEt_2Pr^iCl
Relative rate of unimolecular solvolysis	1	2·4	2·8	2·0
Compound	$CMePr^i_2Cl$	CEt_2Bu^tCl	CBu^t_3Cl	
Relative rate of unimolecular solvolysis	14	48	600	

The Walden Inversion

The Walden inversion is most simply demonstrated by the conversion of an optically active compound into either of two enantiomorphic derivatives by the use of specific reagents, e.g.:

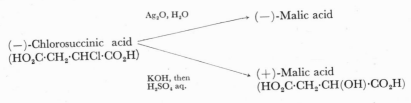

$$\text{(−)-Chlorosuccinic acid} \quad (HO_2C \cdot CH_2 \cdot CHCl \cdot CO_2H)$$

Ag$_2$O, H$_2$O → (−)-Malic acid

KOH, then H$_2$SO$_4$ aq. → (+)-Malic acid (HO$_2$C·CH$_2$·CH(OH)·CO$_2$H)

Inversion of configuration must have occurred in one of the two reactions. An independent method is, however, required of relating configuration with sign of rotation before it can be deduced in which process the inversion has occurred.

Prior to 1937, this problem had been approached by methods which, although they had some success, particularly in the hands of Frankland (1913), and of Kenyon, Phillips and their co-workers (cf Kenyon and Phillips, 1930), yet were ambiguous in many crucial cases. The establishment that nucleophilic substitution may occur by at least two mechanisms enabled Hughes, Ingold, and their collaborators to initiate a kinetic approach (cf Hughes, 1938) which has resulted in considerable clarification of the situation.

Bimolecular Nucleophilic Substitution (S_N2)

Bimolecular nucleophilic substitutions are considered to proceed with inversion of stereochemical configuration. The experimental evidence on which this view is based comes from studies of symmetrical exchange reactions, such as the reaction of sec.-octyl iodide with iodide ions (Hughes, Juliusberger, Scott, Topley and Weiss, 1936; Cowdrey, Hughes, Nevell and Wilson, 1938). The rate of racemization and the rate of uptake of radioactive ions into the organic molecule were studied under the same conditions, and the relationship between the two rates showed that a Walden inversion accompanied every substitution in which a radioactive atom entered the organic molecule.

The case in which a nucleophilic anion attacks a carbon directly attached to an atom bearing a positive charge, as in the displacement reactions of tetra-alkyl ammonium or tri-alkylsulphonium salts, is of some special interest. These reactions are held to proceed with inversion of configuration (*cf* Cowdrey, Hughes, Ingold, Masterman and Scott, 1937), but it has proved difficult to provide a test of mechanism associated with the necessary analysis of products. The example of the decomposition of (−)-trimethyl piperityl ammonium hydroxide (Read and Walker, 1934), usually quoted as demonstrating inversion in such a case, is, according to Dr. J. A. Mills (personal communication, 1953), rendered of doubtful validity by recent work of Macbeth and Shannon (1952). It has been shown, however, by Harvey, Hoye, Hughes, and Ingold (personal communication from Professor E. D. Hughes, 1952; *cf* Ingold, 1953a, p. 380) that the bimolecular reactions of anions with the α-phenylethylsulphonium group in the α-phenylethylsulphonium cation (Ph·CHMe·+SR$_2$) gives predominant configurational inversion.

It may be concluded, therefore, that the transition state of a bimolecular substitution is better represented by such diagrams as IV or VI than by their counterparts V or VII. Electrostatic arguments, on the other hand, would clearly favour VII as the preferred configuration for the displacement of an SEt$_2$ group by an anion; and the experimental result in contradiction of this is given a quantum-mechanical explanation by Cowdrey, Hughes, Ingold, Masterman and Scott (1937). According to these authors, there will be less repulsion between the electrons of the 'split' bond (*e.g.*, Y·······C·······X, where X is the group displaced) and those of the C—R bonds in states IV and VI than in states V and VII, since the surface of minimum electron-density of the Y·······C·······X bond conforms better in the former cases with the positions of the groups R. Gillespie (1952) has made calculations concerning the two possible types of configuration, using the rather different approach that the d-orbitals of carbon contribute to the bonding forces in these transition states, and has made it plausible that the shapes of the orbitals available for binding would favour inversion of configuration.

The conclusion, supported by experiment and theory, that bimolecular substitutions of this type are accompanied invariably by configurational inversion, has been of the greatest importance in establishing the relationships between the configurations of optically

IV   V   VI   VII

(Delocalization of the formal charges is neglected)

active compounds. Thus (+)-α-bromopropionic acid (VIII) has been converted (a) by a bimolecular reaction between its anion and hydroxide ion into (+)-lactic acid (IX) (Cowdrey, Hughes and Ingold, 1937); and (b) by a bimolecular reaction with azide ion into an α-azidopropionic acid (X), which on catalytic reduction, not affecting the asymmetric centre, gave (+)-alanine (XI) (Brewster, Hughes, Ingold and Rao, 1950—see SCHEME 1). Further use of arguments of this type is discussed in Chapter 5 (p. 194).

SCHEME 1

The symbol —$\xrightarrow{\Omega}$ implies substitution with inversion of configuration.

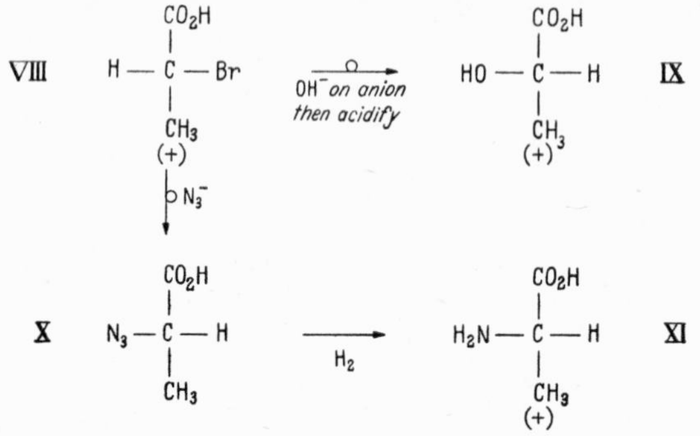

Unimolecular Nucleophilic Substitution (S_N1)

Substitution with racemization—If a carbonium ion C^+R_3 produced in a reaction has sufficient life to be regarded as a completely free entity, then the groups R will be able to attain their preferred arrangement, distributed trigonally in the same plane as the central carbon atom. The approach to coplanarity is of considerable assistance to ionization; for, whereas tert.-butyl halides react very readily with hydroxylic solvents, yet the tertiary halides 4-chlorocamphane (XII), 1-chloro-apocamphane (XIII), and 1-bromotriptycene (XIV), in which the bridged ring-structure holds the substituents in their tetrahedral positions, are very unreactive* (Bartlett and Knox, 1939; Bartlett and Lewis, 1950; Bartlett, 1951; Doering and Schoenewaldt, 1951).

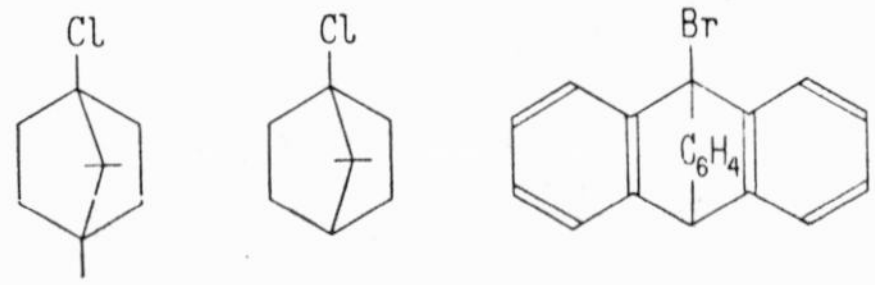

XII   XIII   XIV

* Bartlett (1951) has pointed out that the reactivity may also be inhibited, in such structural situations as XII–XIV, by the steric hindrance to solvation provided by the large size of the reacting molecule. The writer discounts this as a major contributor to the extraordinary lack of reactivity of the halogen in these compounds, particularly in view of the opposite effect of greatly enhanced reactivity, discussed above, of highly branched tert.-halides, such as $Bu^t_3C \cdot Cl$, in which steric hindrance to solvation, if it exists, might be expected to appear also.

The attainment of planarity destroys the optical asymmetry at the ionizing carbon atom. Hence it is to be expected that, if the reaction proceeds by way of such a carbonium ion, the product of substitution will be racemized, to an extent which will be determined by the freedom from the influence of the leaving group achieved by the ion. The experimental facts accord with these expectations. Provided that the groups R do not interact (other than through the C—R bond) with the positive centre produced in the heterolysis, unimolecular substitution is accompanied by racemization, which is often extensive. The amount of racemization is determined by those factors which would be expected to determine the stability of the ion. The more ionizing the solvent, for example, the greater the racemization; and structural features which favour coplanarity and long life in the ion have also a marked effect, as is shown by the fact that *sec.*-alkyl iodides, on undergoing unimolecular substitution, are racemized to the extent of about 30 per cent, whereas α-phenylethyl halides, in which the phenyl group stabilizes the ion in its planar configuration, are almost completely racemized on solvolysis in aqueous alcohol. That fraction of the product which is not racemized is found in these cases to have the inverted structure (*cf* Hughes, Ingold, Martin and Meigh, 1950), since the approaching nucleophilic reagent tends to be diverted away from the neighbourhood of the leaving group.

Substitution with retention of configuration—Hydrolysis of such a compound as $Me \cdot CHBr \cdot CO_2^-$ by the unimolecular mechanism was shown by Cowdrey, Hughes and Ingold (1937) to give substantial retention of configuration, in striking contrast with the behaviour of the *sec.*-alkyl halides. Cowdrey, Hughes, Ingold, Masterman and Scott (1937) suggested, to explain this result, that the carboxylate-ion substituent would be oriented away from the eliminated group, and that the pyramidal configuration (XV) thus produced would tend to be maintained until the new group entered, and would therefore favour retention of the original optical configuration*.

XV

Winstein and his co-workers have extended the scope of this original observation (for summary *cf* Winstein, 1951). Finding that many groups, situated β to the centre of substitution, have the effect of promoting retention of configuration, they use the term ' neighbouring

* There has not yet been recorded any experimental distinction between this view and the alternative, discussed by Winstein and Lucas (1939) and by Grunwald and Winstein (1948) that the intermediate carbonium ion is in this case an α-lactone. A related problem is discussed on p. 117.

97

group effect', and symbolize the path of the reaction as in SCHEME 2. If the neighbouring group R is, for example, O^-, OR, SR, or NR_2, then the cyclic intermediate (XVII) is an ethylene oxide, oxonium ion, sulphonium ion, or immonium ion respectively. Again if the neighbouring group is $O \cdot CO \cdot CH_3$ or Br, the cyclic intermediate is considered to be of the analogous type XX or XXI; the last of these had earlier

SCHEME 2

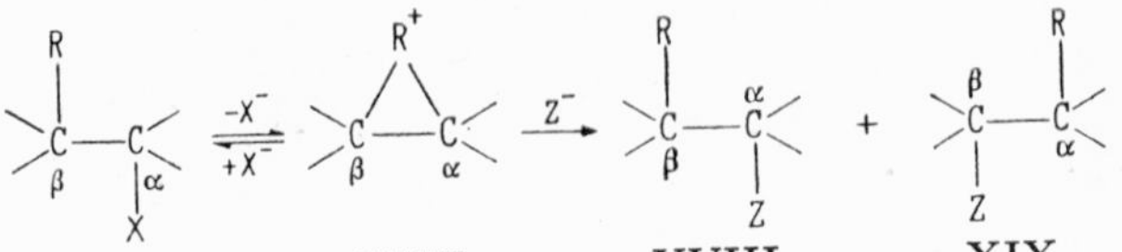

been proposed by Roberts and Kimball (1937) to explain the predominating *trans*-addition of halogens to olefinic substances, as is discussed on p. 115. All these structures are regarded as resonance hybrids, in

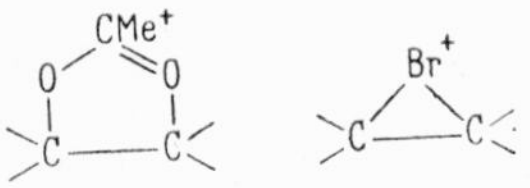

which charge is to a greater or less degree distributed over the atoms of the ring.

TABLE 2, taken from a more complete summary given by Winstein (1951), illustrates cases in which retention of optical configuration has been observed as the result of unimolecular substitution, and has been ascribed to a neighbouring group effect.

TABLE 2.   RETENTION OF CONFIGURATION DUE TO THE PARTICIPATION OF NEIGHBOURING GROUPS IN THE REACTION OF $Me \cdot CHR \cdot CHX \cdot Me$

Neighbouring group (R)	Replaced group (X)	Entering group (Z)	Reagent
I	OH	Br, Cl	HBr, HCl
Br	Br	OAc	AgOAc
OH	Br	OAc	AgOAc
Cl	OH	Cl	$SOCl_2$
OAc	$O \cdot SO_2R$	OAc	AcOH, KOAc
OMe	Br	OAc	AgOAc

Intermediates preserving the characteristic cyclic structure have been isolated in certain instances. The formation of compounds related to ethylene oxide from chlorohydrins is, of course, a well-known procedure. Intermediates derived from type XX have been obtained by Winstein, Hess and Buckles (1942). Their results for the

98

solvolysis in acetic acid of *trans*-2-acetoxy-*cyclo*hexyl toluene-*p*-sulphonate are set out symbolically in SCHEME 3 ; the intermediate XXVI was isolated as a product of partial reaction.

SCHEME 3

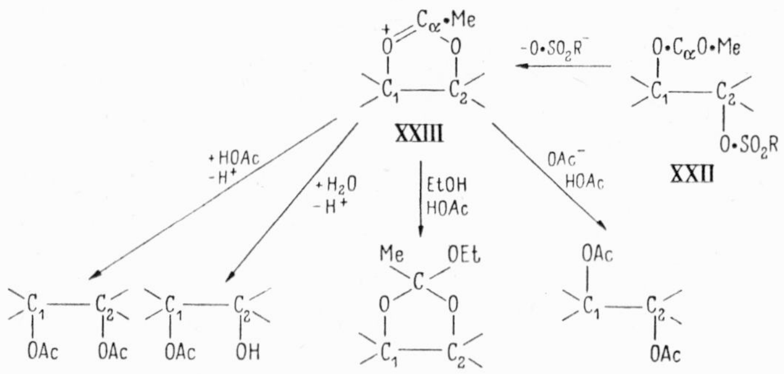

In a similar way, crystalline salts of a cyclic intermediate cation (XXVIII) were isolated by Winstein, Goodman and Boschan (1950) from the solvolysis of *trans*-2-benzamido-*cyclo*hexyl toluene-*p*-sulphonate (XXIX):

SCHEME 4

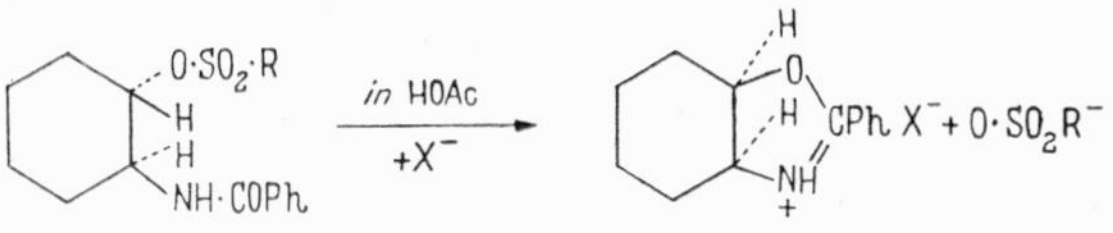

XXIX   XXVIII

$R = p\text{-}CH_3 \cdot C_6 H_4$

It might be expected that the participation of a neighbouring group in the displacement of a nucleophilic substituent would result in an enhanced rate of reaction, since in the transition state the leaving group would be ' helped-off ' by the nucleophilic entry of the electron-pair from the participating substituent. This aspect has been investigated particularly by Winstein, Grunwald and their collaborators (Winstein, Hanson and Grunwald, 1948; Winstein, Grunwald and Ingraham, 1948; Winstein and Grunwald, 1946).

The following results illustrate the rates of solvolysis in acetic acid, shown kinetically in representative cases to involve rate-determining ionization, of *trans*-2-substituted *cyclo*-hexyl benzenesulphonates. Effects due particularly to the stereochemistry of the *cyclo*hexyl ring are considered later (p. 106).

2-Substituent:	I	H	OAc	Br	OMe	Cl
Relative rate:	1770	1·0	0·24	0·10	0·06	0·0046

For certain groups, rough estimates, as shown below, were made of the 'driving force' (*i.e.* of the lowering of the activation energy of heterolysis) provided by various substituents, correcting, in an approximate way, for the electrostatic effect that these groups would have had in the absence of participation.

Neighbouring group:	$S \cdot CH_2 \cdot CH_2OH$	I	NH_2	O^-	Br	OH	Cl
Corrected driving force: (kcal. mole^{-1})	13	9	8	6	5	1	~ 0

These refer to β-substituted ethyl compounds, $R \cdot CH_2 \cdot CH_2 \cdot X$, and it was shown experimentally that the influence of any particular group was reduced by the presence of conjugating or hyperconjugating substituents (such as phenyl or alkyl) in the α-position, and increased by the same types of substituent in the β-position.

Rearrangements accompanying Unimolecular Substitution

It is indicated in SCHEME 2 (p. 98) that the participation of a β-substituent in heterolytic reactions which follow such a route introduces the possibility that the final ring-opening will give a rearranged product. There are many well-known examples of this behaviour (*cf* Fuson, Price and Burness, 1946; Winstein and Ingraham, 1952). Rearrangements of the Wagner type have a certain structural similarity in that they involve migration of an alkyl group to an adjacent carbon atom, as is exemplified by the conversion of *neo*pentyl bromide into *tert.*-amyl ether and trimethylethylene, on unimolecular solvolysis in ethyl alcohol (Dostrovsky and Hughes, 1946).

SCHEME 5

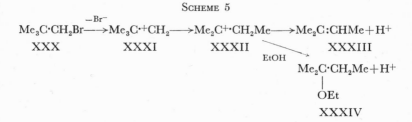

Kinetic Features of the Wagner Rearrangement

The rate of solvolysis of *neo*pentyl bromide ($k_1 = 1 \cdot 5 \times 10^{-6}$ sec^{-1} for solvolysis at 95° in wet formic acid) is of the same order of magnitude as that of the corresponding reaction of ethyl bromide ($k_1 = 2 \cdot 7 \times 10^{-6}$ sec^{-1}). It was presumed by Brown, Hughes, Ingold and Smith (1951) that, in such a rearrangement, in which the migration of a group to an adjacent carbon atom does not accelerate the reaction, the two ions XXXI and XXXII, which are presumed to be intermediate in the solvolysis, are separated by an energy-barrier, and are capable of separate existence.

In the case of tritylmethyl chloride ($Ph_3C\cdot CH_2Cl$), however, a different situation arises. This compound reacts unimolecularly to give completely rearranged products, and its solvolysis in wet formic acid is estimated (Charlton, Dostrovsky and Hughes, 1951) to proceed some 50,000 times more rapidly than the corresponding reaction of *neo*-pentyl chloride. In this case, the migrating group evidently contributes a considerable driving force to the ionization. It is assumed, therefore, that there exists, not a pair of ions separated by an energy barrier, but a single ion, more stable than either of the classical structures, symbolized by Brown, Hughes, Ingold and Smith, as shown in XXXV. These authors have used the terms ' synartetic ion ' and ' synartetic acceleration ' for situations such as this, in which they consider (Ingold, 1953a, b; and personal communication), that the new hybrid structure is formed entirely by redistribution of shared σ-electrons.

| XXXV | XXXVI |

Stereochemical Consequences of the Wagner Change

A Wagner rearrangement, in which a group R migrates from C_β to C_α, may be represented as in XXXVI. Since the migrating group moves with its bonding electrons, it must necessarily, if it is optically active, retain its asymmetry. The stereochemistry at the carbon atoms undergoing substitution and rearrangement (C_α, C_β) are matters of some interest, and important examples have recently been studied by Cram (1949, 1952). He examined the solvolyses of the toluene-*p*-sulphonyl and *p*-bromobenzenesulphonyl derivatives of the stereo-isomers of 3-phenylbutan-2-ol, in acetic acid as solvent; the sequence of reactions suggested to explain the results is shown, with slight modification, in SCHEME 6.

Esters of structure XXXVII, or of its enantiomorph XXXVIII, give racemized mixtures of derivatives XLV and XLVI. Since the rate of disappearance of optical activity of XXXVII, for example, is found to be greater than that of the appearance of the ion OR⁻ in the medium, it follows that there must be a route from XXXVII to XXXVIII involving inversion at both asymmetric centres (' internal return '). Since kinetic evidence showed that the ion OR⁻ did not in the process of this rearrangement become liberated into the environment, it was deduced that an internally compensated, bridged ' phenonium ion-pair ' XLI was an intermediate. The racemized acetate, XLV + XLVI, formed as final product of the acetolysis, must also come from an internally compensated intermediate, such as the ' phenonium ion ' XLIII, or its equivalent, a pair of unsymmetrical (' classical ')

SCHEME 6.   SOLVOLYSES IN ACETIC ACID OF DIASTEREOISOMERIC TOLUENE-*p*-SULPHONATES OF 3-PHENYLBUTAN-2-OL

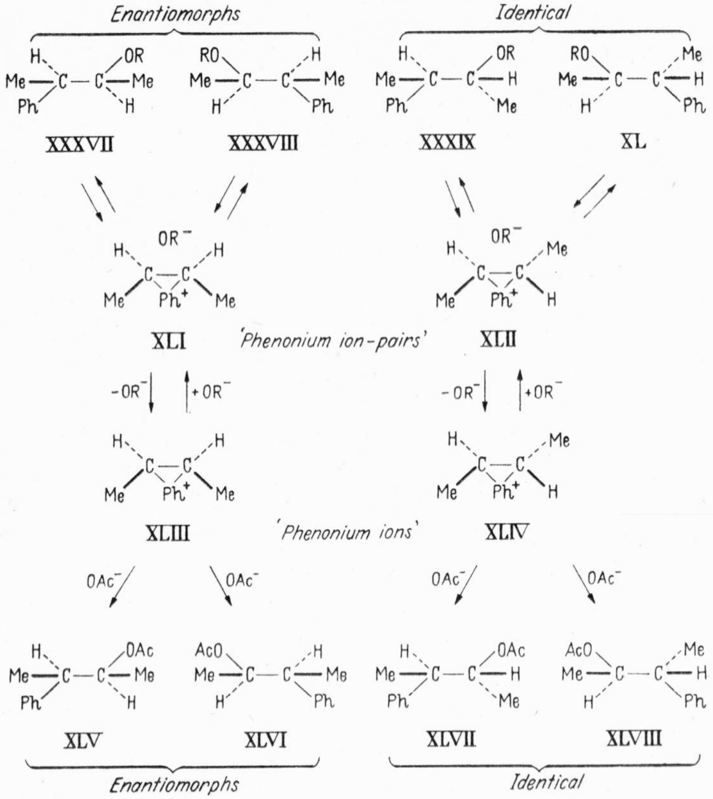

Enantiomorphs   *Identical*

H,   OR   RO,   H   H,   OR   RO,   Me

Me—C—C—Me Me—C—C—Me Me—C—C—H Me—C—C—H

Ph   H   H   Ph   Ph   Me   H   Ph

XXXVII   **XXXVIII**   **XXXIX**   **XL**

H, OR⁻ H   H, OR⁻ Me

C—C   C—C

Me Ph⁺ Me   Me Ph⁺ H

XLI   *'Phenonium ion-pairs'*   **XLII**

−OR⁻ | +OR⁻   − OR⁻ | +OR⁻

H,   H   H,   Me

C—C   C—C

Me Ph⁺ Me   Me Ph⁺ H

XLIII   *'Phenonium ions'*   **XLIV**

OAc⁻ /   \ OAc⁻   OAc⁻ /   \ OAc⁻

H,   OAc   AcO,   H   H,   OAc   AcO,   Me

Me—C—C—Me Me—C—C—Me Me—C—C—H Me—C—C—H

Ph   H   H   Ph   Ph   Me   H   Ph

XLV   **XLVI**   **XLVII**   **XLVIII**

Enantiomorphs   *Identical*

For discussions of the detailed structure of the intermediates, the cited original papers of Winstein, Cram, Roberts, Hughes, Ingold, and their collaborators should be consulted.

carbonium ions in equilibrium. It should be noted that the diastereo-isomeric structure **XXXIX** (identical with **XL**), when undergoing the corresponding reaction-sequence, forms an intermediate **XLII**, which is not internally compensated, and consequently the product of 'internal return', or of acetolysis, has the same configuration as the starting material, and does not become racemized.

A small, but significant part of the reaction involves the formation, from **XXXVII** for example, of derivatives of the diastereoisomeric structure **XXXIX**. This is evidence that classical carbonium ionic intermediates are in fact formed during the acetolyses of these compounds. That this represents a general feature of such ionizations is confirmed by more recent work on the solvolyses of the chlorides and bromides of 1 : 2-diphenylpropan-1-ol. In these reactions, substitution occurs with no rearrangement, but with partial racemization at the centre of substitution. The work of Roberts and Regan (1953) seems to confirm this point. They studied the reactions of p-X·C$_6$H$_4$·CH$_2$·^{14}CH$_2$·NH$_2$ with nitrous acid; these are presumed to proceed through carbonium ions (*e.g.* p-X-C$_6$H$_4$·CH$_2$·^{14}C$^+$H$_2$), which might rearrange through a phenonium ion or ion-pair. Experimentally, the product contained more or less of the product of rearrangement, p-X·C$_6$H$_4$·^{14}CH$_2$·CH$_2$·Y (Y = OH,OAc), depending on the solvent and the group X. Thus with X = NO$_2$, there was only about 5 per cent of rearrangement, and in this case the reaction of the solvent with the ' classical ' carbonium ion must be more rapid than the rearrangement of the latter. Winstein and Morse (1952) showed in an analogous way, that the solvolysis of ($-$)α-phenyl-*neo*-pentyl chloride in acetic acid involves the classical carbonium ion Me$_3$C·$^+$CHPh. In this case, if the bridged ion had been an intermediate from which the non-rearranged product arose, then any residual optical activity would have corresponded with retention of configuration. Experimentally, the unrearranged acetate had a residual rotation corresponding with inversion of configuration.

Rearrangements related to the Wagner change—Various other rearrangements, in which groups migrate to an adjacent atom (1 : 2-shifts; *cf* Whitmore, 1932; Wheland, 1949), are to be classified with the Wagner change, and have similar stereochemical consequences. Thus, in the Hoffman, Curtius, Lossen, Wolff and Beckmann rearrangements, the migrating group, if it is optically active, retains its configuration during transfer, as has been shown particularly by the work of Kenyon and his school (*cf* Arcus and Kenyon, 1939; Kenyon and Young, 1941; Campbell and Kenyon, 1946) and of Wallis and his co-workers (*cf* Lane and Wallis, 1941).

With regard to the stereochemistry at the atom to which the group migrates, the situation is again governed by the principles which have been exemplified for the Wagner change. Thus group-migration may contribute a driving force to the pinacol migration (*cf* Winstein, 1951), assisting in the acid-catalysed removal of the hydroxy-group in what may be termed an internal nucleophilic displacement. Completion of this process to give the rearranged product results, therefore (*cf* Bartlett and co-workers, 1937, 1940), in stereochemical inversion at the atom to which the group migrates; in this particular rearrangement, of course, any asymmetric centre existing originally at the β-carbon atom is destroyed by the formation there of the carbonyl group. Thus, in the transformation of XLIX to L, there is retention of configuration within R, inversion at C$_\alpha$, and destruction of asymmetry at C$_\beta$.

XLIX   L

Substitutions in Cyclic Systems

So far, this account has been most concerned with the reactions of aliphatic compounds. Cyclic structures introduce additional complications.

Bimolecular Reactions

Fierens and Verschelden (1952) have recently examined in detail the reactivities of some *cyclo*alkyl bromides with iodide ions in acetone, and their values are given below.

$$[CH_2]_n : CHBr + I^- \text{ in acetone}$$

$n=$	1	2	3	4	5	6	7
$10^5 k_2 (25°; \text{ l. mole}^{-1}\text{sec}^{-1})$	~0·3*	0·00†	0·010	2·1	0·013	1·3‡	0·4
$E(\text{kcal. mole}^{-1})$	—	—	24·5	20·4	23·5	20·4‡	21·2

* From data of Juvala (1930). † From data of Roberts and Chambers (1951). ‡ Almost identical values were recorded for *iso*propyl bromide.

The relatively small reactivity of *cyclo*hexyl bromide is probably the result of the fact that it has one particular stable conformation (see Chapter 2, pp. 43 and 46), and that in this conformation (LI), the remainder of the ring inhibits sterically the attack of a nucleophilic reagent (*cf* Easty, 1949). This additional differential stability between the initial and transition state is not so marked in the more nearly planar *cyclo*pentyl bromide, and is partially lost in the more strained *cyclo*heptyl bromide, but increases again as the ring becomes still larger. Thus may be made plausible the sequence in reactivity, *cyclo*pentyl > *cyclo*hexyl < *cyclo*heptyl > *cyclo*octyl > *cyclo*pentadecyl, the last comparison being made by reference to the work of van Straten, Nicholls and Winkler (1951).

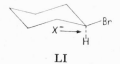

LI

It is tempting, following Roberts and Chambers (1951) to ascribe the decreasing reactivity in the series *cyclo*pentyl > *cyclo*butyl > *cyclo*propyl to the increasing power of the ring to simulate the properties of an unsaturated system. The classical analogy of this type has been discussed in more modern terms by Walsh (1949). In a similar way, Bergstrom and Siegel (1952) have interpreted the ultra-violet spectra of compounds in which ring-systems are 'hyperconjugated' with a double link as indicating that the tendency of a *cyclo*propane ring to hyperconjugate in this way may be considerable, though not as great as that of an ethylenic link itself. It does not seem possible, however, to treat the results of bimolecular substitution entirely in this way, because vinyl bromide seems to be rather reactive as compared with *cyclo*propyl bromide. Brown, Fletcher and Johannesen (1951) have suggested that, in the latter compound, the ring-valencies attached to the attacked carbon atom are displaced in the transition state from the position which they would prefer in the absence of ring strain (120°) to a considerably strained position (60°), and that this displacement is greater than in the initial state, when the unstrained angle between the valencies is 109°. Thus these workers consider that there is an increase of internal steric strain on going from the initial to the transition state of such a bimolecular reaction, and that this contributes to an increase in the activation energy of the reaction.

Unimolecular reactions—The solvolyses, under ionizing conditions, of *cyclo*alkyl compounds have been examined by Roberts and Chambers (1951), and by Winstein and co-workers (*cf* Winstein, Morse, Grunwald, Jones, Corse, Trifan and Marshall, 1952) as is shown in TABLE 3. For this reaction, as for the solvolyses of the

TABLE 3. RATES, ACTIVATION ENERGIES AND PRODUCTS OF SOLVOLYSES OF
*cyclo*ALKYLTOLUENE-*p*-SULPHONATES, RX, IN ACETIC ACID

R	Rel. rate $(Me_2CHX=1)$	E (kcal. mole^{-1})	Products
*cyclo*Propyl	2×10^{-5}	34	Allyl acetate
*cyclo*Butyl	14	~ 30	*cyclo*Propylcarbinyl acetate (65%)
			*cyclo*Butyl acetate (22%)
			Allylcarbinyl toluene-*p*-sulphonate (13%)
*cyclo*Pentyl	16	28	*cyclo*Pentyl acetate (61%)
			*cyclo*Pentene (39%)
*cyclo*Hexyl	1	28	*cyclo*Hexyl acetate (15%)
			*cyclo*Hexene (85%)

corresponding halides, it is the *cyclo*hexyl compound which resembles in rate most closely the corresponding *iso*propyl derivative. It is considered by these authors, as also by Brown, Fletcher and Johannesen (1951), that the approximate planarity of the ring introduces, in *cyclo*pentyl derivatives, a strain (the hydrogen atoms being eclipsed rather than in their preferred staggered relationship) which may be partially relieved in the transition state. On this view, the reactivity of *cyclo*pentyl derivatives under ionizing conditions is an example of steric acceleration.

The increased reactivity of *cyclo*butyl compounds, taken in conjunction with the extensive rearrangement of the carbon skeleton occurring in the solvolysis, is evidence of the intermediate formation of a hybrid ion (*cf* Roberts and Mazur, 1951), which gains stability by distribution of its charge. SCHEME 7 gives one possible formulation of this reaction.

The extraordinary unreactivity of *cyclo*propyl compounds under ionizing conditions is probably to be ascribed, partly to the analogy with the corresponding vinyl derivative, and partly to the relative increase of steric strain in the transition state, as discussed by Brown, Fletcher and Johannesen (1951).

SCHEME 7

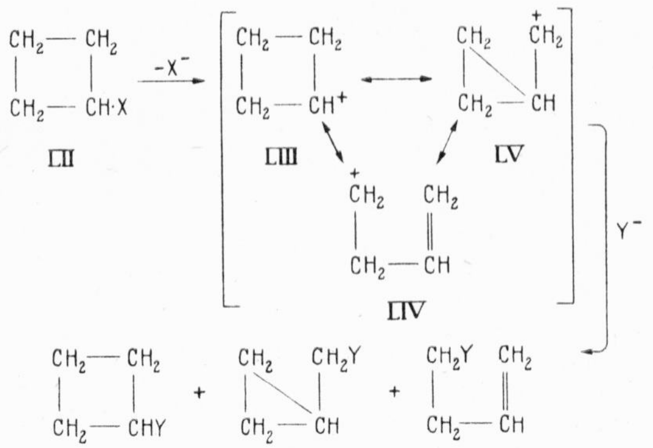

$$
\begin{array}{ccc}
\underset{\text{CII}}{\begin{array}{c} CH_2 — CH_2 \\ | \qquad | \\ CH_2 — CH \cdot X \end{array}}
& \xrightarrow{-X^-} &
\left[\begin{array}{ccc}
\underset{\text{CIII}}{\begin{array}{c} CH_2 — CH_2 \\ | \qquad | \\ CH_2 — CH^+ \end{array}}
& \longleftrightarrow &
\underset{\text{CV}}{\begin{array}{c} CH_2 \quad \overset{+}{CH_2} \\ | \diagdown | \\ CH_2 — CH \end{array}} \\
& \underset{\text{CIV}}{\begin{array}{c} \overset{+}{CH_2} \quad CH_2 \\ | \qquad \| \\ CH_2 — CH \end{array}}
\end{array}\right]
\end{array}
\quad Y^-
$$

$$
\begin{array}{ccccc}
CH_2 — CH_2 \\ | \qquad | \\ CH_2 — CHY
& + &
\begin{array}{c} CH_2 \quad CH_2Y \\ | \diagdown | \\ CH_2 — CH \end{array}
& + &
\begin{array}{c} CH_2Y \quad CH_2 \\ | \qquad \| \\ CH_2 — CH \end{array}
\end{array}
$$

Stereochemical requirements for effective participation of neighbouring groups in displacements—For the ionizing system LVI, the participation of R in the displacement of X is similar electronically to a bimolecular nucleophilic displacement of X by the migrating electron-pair of the group R. It is for this reason that reactions which involve participation of a neighbouring group in an ionization are sometimes termed 'internal S_N2' reactions; this usage should strictly be confined to the first stage of the over-all substitution. For effective participation, therefore, the groups R and X must be so placed that the electrons of the partial bonds attaching R and X to C_α are separated as far as possible. Alicyclic systems differ from their aliphatic analogues in that this restriction cannot be accommodated automatically. That a restriction of this type can become of dominant importance in determining reactivity is shown by the fact that *trans*-2-acetoxy-*cyclo*hexyl toluene-*p*-sulphonate undergoes solvolysis in acetic acid some 500 times more rapidly than its *cis*-isomer (Winstein, Grunwald, Buckles and Hanson, 1948).

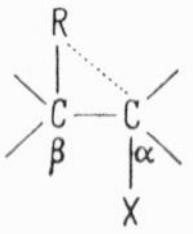

LVI

Parallel investigations by the schools of Winstein and of Hughes and Ingold have led to clarification of effects observed in the more complex ring-structures. Thus the acetolyses of bornyl and *iso*bornyl and of *endo*- and *exo*-norbornyl toluene-*p*-sulphonates have been examined and the rates compared with those of simpler related structures (Winstein and Trifan, 1952; Winstein, Morse, Grunwald, Jones, Corse, Trifan and Marshall, 1952). The values are given below (*cyclo*hexyl toluene-*p*-sulphonate = 1).

Toluene-*p*-sulphonate: Relative rate:

*iso*bornyl	*exo*norbornyl	bornyl	*endo*norbornyl
(LVII)	(LVIII)	(LIX)	(LX)
3.5×10^5	500	1·4	1·4

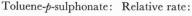

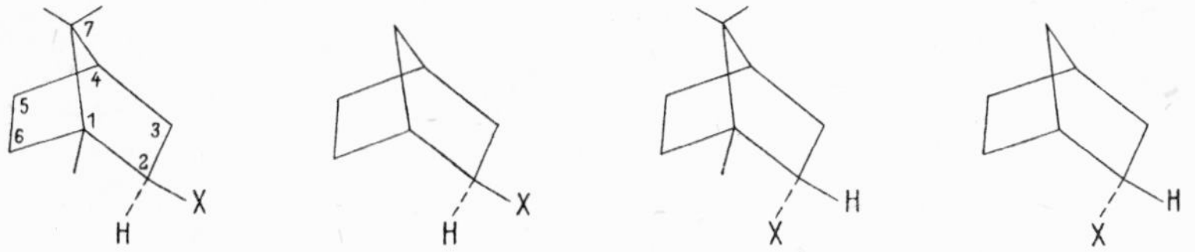

*endo*Norbornyl toluene-*p*-sulphonate gives entirely the *exo*-derivative on solvolysis; when the starting material is optically active, the product is found to be entirely racemized, and the racemization proceeds at the same rate as the solvolysis. The simplest explanation of these facts is that the reaction proceeds through a transition state (LXI) appropriate to ionization without rearrangement or neighbouring-group-participation. The resulting carbonium ion, when it is completely free from the influence of the leaving group, is a resonance-hybrid of structures LXII and LXIII; the latter structure is identical with (LXIV), which is the mirror-image of (LXII). In this compound, the group displaced is not sterically situated in such a way that

SCHEME 8

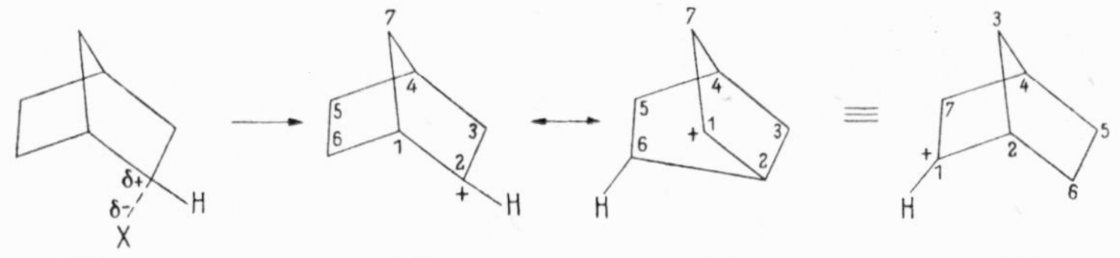

CXI LXII LXIII LXIV

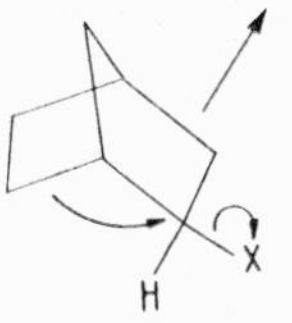

LXV

the electrons of the migrating bond can help the reaction. The *exo*-isomer, on the other hand, also gives derivatives of the *exo*-structure, and, if optically active, racemizes at a rate which is more rapid than that of the solvolysis. The route, in this case, must be directly to the hybrid ion; additional driving force, and hence increased rate, is provided by synchronous ionization and bond-shift, which in this case is sterically permissible (LXV). Racemization results from the uptake of acetate ion at C-1 and C-2 to give enantiomorphic products (*cf* LXII and LXIV). The fact that the racemization proceeds at a rate

107

more rapid than that of the solvolysis is thought to indicate an internal migration of the ester-group by partial ionization, possibly to an ion-pair (*cf* Cram, 1949, 1952).

The still more striking difference in reactivity between bornyl and *iso*bornyl derivatives, as shown above, and also in the work of Brown, Hughes, Ingold and Smith (1951) has been discussed in similar terms by both groups of workers. Rearrangements to derivatives of camphene hydrate are also observed in certain reactions of bornyl and *iso*bornyl chloride, and this leads us to a consideration of camphene hydrochloride (LXVI), which is very reactive in solvolysis. In non-hydroxylic solvents, it undergoes a rearrangement, catalysed by hydrochloric acid, to form, in the first place, *iso*bornyl chloride (LXIX). A further, much slower, isomerization occurs, on prolonged treatment, provided that the solvent has a sufficiently ionizing character, to give bornyl chloride (LXX), which is the isomer which preponderates in the equilibrium mixture. In the course of the rearrangement of camphene hydrochloride, it undergoes exchange with chloride ions, at a rate which is more rapid than that of the rearrangement to *iso*bornyl chloride.

It has long been realized, on the basis of this evidence (*cf* Nevell, de Salas, and Wilson, 1939 ; Bateman, Cooper, Hughes and Ingold, 1940) that the reaction was one involving ionization; and the demonstration by Brown, Hughes, Ingold and Smith (1951) that the solvolysis of camphene hydrochloride in dry ethanol at 0° is some six thousand times faster than that of *tert.*-butyl chloride led these authors to ascribe the enhanced reactivity to the joint effects of steric and synartetic

SCHEME 9

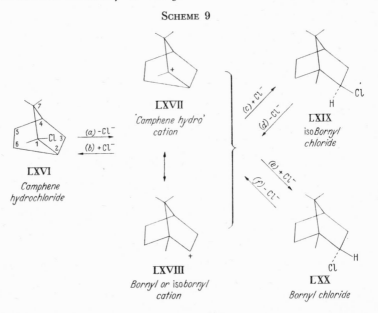

LXVII
'Camphene hydro'
cation

LXIX
iso*Bornyl*
chloride

LXVI
Camphene
hydrochloride

LXVIII
Bornyl or isobornyl
cation

LXX
Bornyl chloride

acceleration. SCHEME 9 represents the course of the rearrangements occurring in non-hydroxylic solvents. The intermediate ion is presumably a hybrid of structures LXVII and LXVIII; and the rates of halide-exchange and of the rearrangements indicate that the hybrid reacts with chloride ions most rapidly by path *b*, and least rapidly by path *e*.

For reactions in hydroxylic solvents, the relationships between the product and the mechanism of the reaction do not appear to have been established satisfactorily. Camphene hydrochloride on hydrolysis with water, and bornyl or *iso*bornyl chloride on hydrolysis with aqueous calcium hydroxide, give camphene hydrate (Aschan, 1908 ; *cf* Simonsen and Owen, 1949, pp. 346–9), as would be expected if a hybrid ion were produced, and if this still reacted preferentially at C-1 (SCHEME 9). On the other hand, camphene hydrochloride with methyl alcohol gives *iso*bornyl methyl ether, and *iso*bornyl chloride with acetic acid gives *iso*bornyl acetate. It is not clear whether these substances arise during the heterolysis or, as seems more likely, from rearrangement of the product under the influence of acid in the medium; it is recorded (Simonsen and Owen, 1949, pp. 317–320) that ' camphene methyl ether ' does in fact rearrange to *iso*bornyl methyl ether when mixed with a methyl-alcoholic solution of hydrogen chloride.

Unsaturated systems as neighbouring groups—It has been considered by various workers (for an early discussion, *cf* Shoppee, 1946) that unsaturated centres might act as neighbouring groups in displacement reactions, causing retention of configuration at the carbon atom undergoing substitution. Winstein, Brown, Schreiber, and Schlesinger (1952) have shown, for example, that benzylmethylcarbinyl toluene-*p*-sulphonate undergoes solvolysis in formic acid to give 85 per cent retention of configuration, though in ethyl alcohol it gives predominating inversion. It has also been shown by Davies, Hughes and Ingold (*cf* Hughes, 1951b; Brewster, Hiron, Hughes, Ingold and Rao, 1950) that the presence of an allyl group attached to the reaction-centre favours replacement with retention of configuration.

In cyclic systems (*cf* Shoppee, 1946) a suitably placed double bond may interact with a developing carbonium ionic centre sufficiently to cause retention of configuration. Thus cholesteryl chloride on solvolysis in methyl alcohol gives cholesteryl methyl ether. The acetolysis of cholesteryl toluene-*p*-sulphonate in acetic acid has been studied kinetically by Winstein and Adams (1948). Since the reaction was unimolecular, and proceeded more rapidly than the corresponding acetolysis of *cyclo*hexyl toluene-*p*-sulphonate, it was regarded as a case in which a double bond participates in the ionization of an adjacent substituent, and as a model for the *i*-cholesteryl rearrangement. This reaction has recently been discussed in some detail by Shoppee (1951;

cf also Shoppee and Summers, 1952), who considers that the intermediate ion produced in the solvolysis of cholesteryl derivatives reacts with nucleophilic reagents to form derivatives of *i*-cholesterol. Thus

SCHEME 10

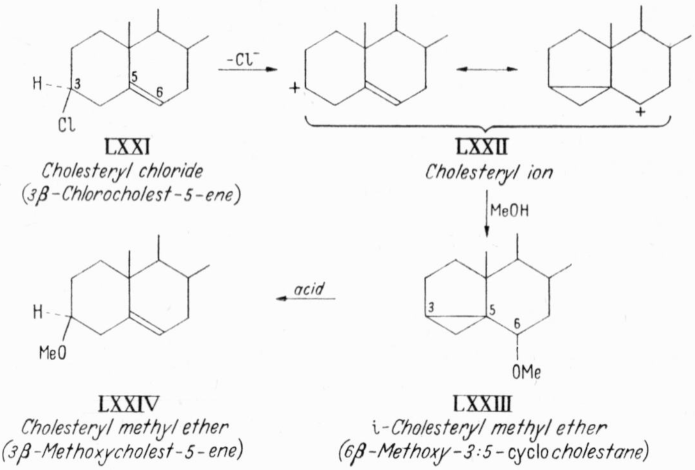

LXXI
Cholesteryl chloride
(3β-Chlorocholest-5-ene)

LXXII
Cholesteryl ion

LXXIV
Cholesteryl methyl ether
(3β-Methoxycholest-5-ene)

LXXIII
i-Cholesteryl methyl ether
(6β-Methoxy-3:5-cyclocholestane)

under slightly basic conditions, cholesteryl chloride reacts with methyl alcohol to form *i*-cholesteryl methyl ether, which rearranges under slightly acidic conditions to form cholesteryl methyl ether.

Intramolecular Replacements in Nucleophilic Substitutions

Certain substitution reactions involve cyclic transition states of a type rather different from those yet considered. Thionyl chloride, for example, often reacts with alcohols to form halides of retained configuration, even when no ' neighbouring group ' exists in the alcohol. Thus Shoppee (1946) has recorded that a 3β-hydroxyl group in a saturated steroid nucleus is replaced by chlorine with inversion of configuration by PCl_5, but with retention when $SOCl_2$ is used as the reagent. It is supposed, in such cases (*cf* Hughes, 1938) that the reaction involves the formation of an ester-halide, which then undergoes an intramolecular nucleophilic rearrangement with retention of configuration ($S_N i$). Variants and elaborations of this mechanism have recently been discussed by Cram (1953). Some of the reactions of alkyl hydrogen phthalates (*cf* Hughes, 1941) may involve intramolecular displacements of analogous kinds.

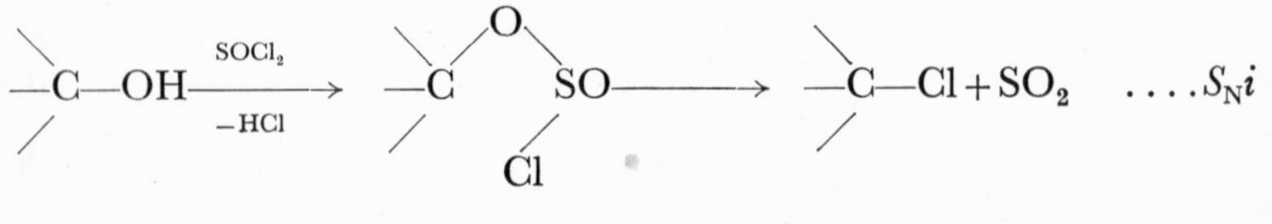

ESTER-HYDROLYSIS AND ESTERIFICATION

The formation and the hydrolysis of esters proceed by two distinct classes of mechanism, according to the two possibilities of fission in the system M·CO·O·R (Day and Ingold, 1941):

(a) Acyl-oxygen fission: M·CO·O·R + H·O·H——→M·CO·O·H + H·O·R

(b) Alkyl-oxygen fission: M·CO·O·R + H·O·H——→M·CO·O·H + H·O·R

Acyl-oxygen fission is the more common class of reaction among carboxylic esters, and, when this route is followed, the group R, if it is optically active, necessarily retains its configuration, since the O—R bond attached to the asymmetric carbon atom is not broken. Thus Holmberg (1912) showed that the acid-catalysed hydrolysis of O-acetyl-malic acid proceeds with retention of configuration; this is taken to be an example of bimolecular acidic hydrolysis with acyl-oxygen fission. Similarly, the acid-catalysed esterification of octan-2-ol gives a product with retained configuration (Hughes, Ingold and Masterman, 1939). Both bimolecular and unimolecular variants of these mechanisms are known (cf Day and Ingold, 1941).

The many reactions already discussed of esters of toluene-p-sulphonic acid will have made it clear that compounds of the type R·OSO$_2$·Ar react characteristically by alkyl-oxygen fission, and resemble the alkyl halides in undergoing both unimolecular and bimolecular displacement reactions of this type. Alkyl-oxygen fission is, on the whole, a less common route in the reactions of carboxylic esters, but Kenyon, Balfe, and their co-workers have examined a number of cases which they classified as following this mechanism. Thus Balfe, Doughty, Kenyon and Poplett (1942) have shown that the alkaline hydrolysis of p-methoxybenzhydryl hydrogen phthalate gives almost completely racemized p-methoxybenzhydrol (p-MeO·C$_6$H$_4$·CH(OH)·Ph). It is presumed that racemization results from the ionization of the ester to form the p-methoxybenzhydryl cation (p-MeO·C$_6$H$_4$·C$^+$HPh). A similar case, the acid-catalysed hydrolysis of methylethylisohexyl-carbinyl acetate has been studied kinetically by Bunton, Hughes, Ingold and Meigh (1950), and shown to involve racemization accompanied by some excess of inversion, thus exemplifying the analogy between the reactions of esters, when they undergo alkyl-oxygen fission, and alkyl halides, for which similar effects have been demonstrated. The analogous bimolecular process has been exemplified by the hydrolysis, in dilute acid solution, of β-malolactonic acid, which proceeds with fission at the point indicated (LXXV), and consequently with inversion of configuration (cf Cowdrey, Hughes, Ingold, Masterman and Scott, 1937).

HO$_2$C·CH—CH$_2$
\
CO
/
O

LXXV

111

STEREOCHEMISTRY OF NUCLEOPHILIC ELIMINATION

For 1 : 2-eliminations there exist two mechanisms, corresponding with those available for nucleophilic substitutions. The first (bimolecular, $E2$) involves attack by the nucleophilic reagent (Z) on the β-group removed (usually H) synchronous with the removal of the displaced group Y, as may be formulated:

$$Z + H—CR_2—CR_2—Y \longrightarrow ZH^+ + CR_2 : CR_2 + Y^- \quad \dots (E2)$$

The second (unimolecular, $E1$), involves the slow heterolysis of the organic compound, followed by the rapid removal of the proton, thus:

$$H—CR_2—CR_2—Y \xrightarrow{\text{slow}} H—CR_2—^+CR_2 + Y^-;$$
$$H—CR_2—^+CR_2 \longrightarrow H^+ + CR_2 : CR_2 \quad \dots (E1)$$

Reviews of the kinetic and structural evidence concerning these mechanisms have been given by Hughes and Ingold (1941), by Dhar, Hughes, Ingold, Mandour, Maw and Woolf (1948), and by the writer (1950b). An example relevant to the present discussion is the following. Bimolecular elimination from 2-iodo-3-methyl-butane results in the formation in predominating amount of the olefin in which elimination has occurred towards the methine group, that is, towards the most alkylated carbon atom, according to the principle first enunciated by Saytzeff (1875):

$$
\begin{array}{ccc}
Me_2CH & Me_2C & Me_2CH \\
\diagdown & \diagdown & \diagdown \\
CH—I \xrightarrow[\substack{-EtOH \\ -I^-}]{OEt^-} & CH\ (82\%) \quad + & CH\ (18\%)\ (E2) \\
\diagup & \diagup & \diagup\!\!\diagup \\
CH_3 & CH_3 & CH_2
\end{array}
$$

A similar result is obtained for unimolecular elimination from the corresponding sulphonium salt:

$$
\begin{array}{ccc}
Me_2CH & Me_2C & Me_2CH \\
\diagdown & \diagdown & \diagdown \\
CH\cdot^+SMe_2 \xrightarrow[\substack{-Me_2S \\ -H^+}]{} & CH\ (91\%) \quad + & CH\ (9\%)\ (E1) \\
\diagup & \diagup & \diagup\!\!\diagup \\
CH_3 & CH_3 & CH_2
\end{array}
$$

Hyperconjugation of the methyl groups with the developing double bond, stabilizing preferentially the transition state leading to elimination towards the methine group, is considered to be the structural feature which determines the direction of these eliminations.

By analogy with the form of the transition state preferred for substitution, it might be expected that, for facile bimolecular elimination, the electrons released from the separating hydrogen atom should enter the octet of the carbon atom on the side remote from the departing group. Hückel, Tappe and Legutke (1940) recognized that the restriction must be of importance in cyclic structures, and exemplified it, though

112

without a kinetic investigation, in the following way. *neo*Menthyl chloride (LXXVI) with ethoxide ions undergoes elimination in the expected direction towards the methine group, because for this compound the displaced hydrogen atom is *trans*- to the displaced chlorine (SCHEME 11).

SCHEME 11

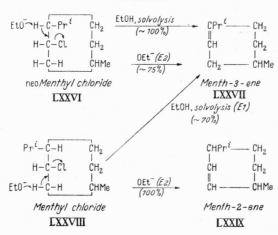

With menthyl chloride (LXXVIII) on the other hand, *trans*-elimination cannot occur towards the methine group, and, rather than undergo *cis*-elimination, this compound undergoes elimination towards the methylene group, contrary to the Saytzeff rule.

Unimolecular elimination is not restricted to the same degree ; to a first approximation, unimolecular elimination should not be influenced by stereochemical considerations of this sort, since in principle the distinction between the two structures disappears in the free cation. It is indeed found that menthyl chloride undergoes solvolysis to give a preponderating amount of menth-3-ene, in contrast to its behaviour in bimolecular reaction. Hughes, Ingold and Rose (1953) have shown, however, that *neo*menthyl chloride gives under solvolytic conditions a considerably greater proportion of menth-3-ene than does menthyl chloride. They explained this difference as determined by the bimolecular reaction of *neo*menthyl chloride with ethanol ; but alternatively, it may be that the carbonium ionic centre, as it develops in this compound, is not completely free to undergo elimination in the required direction.

Another example of the difficulty of *cis*-elimination has been studied by Cristol, Hause and Meek (1951), and also by Hughes, Ingold and Pasternak (1953). These two groups of workers have shown that, of the geometric isomers of hexachloro*cyclo*hexane (' benzene hexachloride '), the least reactive with alkali, by a factor of many

113

thousands, is the β-isomer (LXXX) in which no hydrogen atom is *trans*- to an adjacent chlorine atom. The activation energy for the reaction is also higher for this than for its isomers, and the entropy of activation is found to be abnormally large.

LXXX   LXXXI

Various workers (*cf* Dostrovsky, Hughes and Ingold, 1946 ; Cristol, Hause and Meek, 1951) have interpreted similarly the fact that halogeno-ethylenes are dehydrohalogenated to form acetylenic compounds most readily when they contain a hydrogen atom *trans*- to the eliminated halogen. Examples of this behaviour are well known (*cf* Chavanne, 1912; Martin and Bruylants, 1951).

In a recent kinetic investigation, Miller and Noyes (1952) have shown that *cis*-dihalogenoethylenes such as LXXXI, from which hydrogen halide can be eliminated in the *trans*-sense, react with sodium methoxide much more rapidly than their *trans*-isomers. These authors, and also Cristol, Hause and Meek (1951), considered that the abnormal Arrhenius parameters, sometimes observed in cases in which *cis*-elimination must occur, indicated that this type of reaction, unlike *trans*-elimination, is a two-stage process, of the general type discussed by Hughes, Ingold and Patel (1933), in which the removal of a proton to form a carbanion determines the rate of the reaction. Since, however, the products of these reactions have not been satisfactorily investigated, the cause of the anomalies is not yet certainly established. Recently Cristol and Fix (1953) have shown that the unchanged reactant recovered after partial reaction of β-benzene hexachloride (LXXX) with sodium ethoxide in deuterated ethanol, contained some deuterium, and have claimed on this basis that at least part of this *cis*-elimination proceeds through a carbanion.

The above considerations apply only to heterolytic processes. Barton (1949), and also Barton, Head and Williams (1952), have emphasized that homolytic thermal decompositions of the unimolecular type require *cis*-elimination, but lack of space precludes discussion of this point.

STEREOCHEMISTRY OF ADDITION REACTIONS

Reviews of the addition of halogens to olefinic substances have been given by Williams (1941), and more recently by de la Mare (1949, 1950b). Electrophilic attack by the halogenating agent is most

114

commonly the first stage of the reaction, and, in hydroxylic solvents, extraneous nucleophilic reagents compete with halide ions in completing the reaction, as has often formally been represented :

SCHEME 12

$$R \cdot CH:CH_2 + Br_2 \longrightarrow R \cdot^+ CH \cdot CH_2Br + Br^- \qquad \dots\, (1)$$

$$R \cdot^+ CH \cdot CH_2Br + Br^- \longrightarrow R \cdot CHBr \cdot CH_2Br \qquad \dots\, (2a)$$

$$+ X^- \longrightarrow R \cdot CHX \cdot CH_2Br \qquad \dots\, (2b)$$

$$+ R'OH \longrightarrow R \cdot CH(OR') \cdot CH_2Br + H^+ \qquad \dots\, (2c)$$

This representation accords with the three established characteristics of these reactions, namely, (*i*) that the halogen acts as an electrophilic reagent, as the result of the attack on which (*ii*) there is developed on one of the olefinic carbon atoms a carbonium ionic centre, for which (*iii*) any nucleophilic reagents present in the medium will compete in the final stages of the reaction. Under all but strongly ionizing conditions, however, the kinetics of halogen addition reveal that the actual process is more complex (*cf* de la Mare and Robertson, 1950).

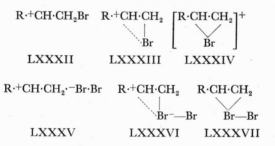

Structures such as LXXXV–LXXXVII have been postulated, for example, to interpret the kinetics of addition of bromine in such solvents as acetic acid and chloroform (*cf* especially White and Robertson, 1939; Williams, 1941). Considerable physical evidence has also accumulated to confirm the view that, when halogens and olefinic substances interact, the first result is the formation of a 1:1-molecular complex (*cf* Freed and Sancier, 1952). It is not known whether this type of species is sometimes responsible for the determination of the nature and stereochemistry of the products of these reactions, and hence, for simplicity, the following discussion will be based on the more conventional structures LXXXII–LXXXIV.

Halogens often add to olefinic substances in the *trans*-sense. Thus maleic acid adds bromine to form ($\pm$)-dibromosuccinic acid, whereas fumaric acid forms the *meso*-diastereoisomer. Roberts and Kimball (1937) interpreted such observations as showing that structures such as may be represented by LXXXIV contributed to the state of the ionic intermediate. This view implies that the first halogen atom, which initiates the addition, acts as a ' neighbouring group ' to hold the configuration of the intermediate and allow *trans*-addition. It is of interest to consider the parallel conclusions that may be reached from studies of substitution reactions in which halogen atoms act as neighbouring groups. In such cases, intermediates of a similar hybrid structure have been proposed (Winstein and Lucas, 1939); and Bateman, Church, Hughes, Ingold and Taher (1940) considered that, when an intermediate cation is preserved in configuration by an α-bromine atom, the symmetry of the system converts, through resonance, what would have been a dipole with one covalent and one electrostatic bond into a ring with two equivalent bonds which are partly covalent and partly electrostatic.

With regard to the neighbouring chlorine substituent, Winstein and Grunwald have concluded that usually no ' driving force ' is provided by this group in ionization reactions. These authors concluded that the rate-determining ionizations proceed, in these cases, by the formation of the classical carbonium ion, rather than by the direct formation of a cyclic intermediate. Addition reactions, when they are considered to involve similar intermediates, should, for consistency, be regarded also as proceeding through classical carbonium ions. It is necessary, at the same time, to accommodate *trans*-addition, established for chlorine by Lucas and Gould (1941), just as it is necessary to explain retention of configuration caused by neighbouring chlorine groups in substitution reactions. There exists a perfectly adequate way of doing this. The C—Cl bond differs from the C—Me and C—Ph bonds in that it is considerably dipolar in the sense $C^{\delta+}$—$Cl^{\delta-}$. A carbonium ionic centre on the carbon atom adjacent to the dipole will have a considerable electrostatic attraction for its negative end, and must therefore distort the C—Cl link towards the cyclic configuration, as is indicated, for bromine, in LXXXIII (and similarly in LXXXVI). Yet it is not necessary that the configuration should become cyclic in the sense of structure LXXXIV with equivalent bonds between the halogen atom and the two carbon atoms. It will be remembered, by way of analogy, that many hydrogen-bonded complexes (*cf* LXXXVIII) have hydrogen atoms

$$
\begin{array}{ccc}
 & \text{O} \cdots\cdots \text{H–O} & \\
 & \diagup \qquad \quad \diagdown & \\
\text{R—C} & & \text{C—R} \\
 & \diagdown \qquad \quad \diagup & \\
 & \text{O–H} \cdots\cdots \text{O} & \\
\end{array}
$$

LXXXVIII

held between two oxygen atoms by electrostatic forces worth several kcal. mole^{-1} per bond, and yet have the hydrogen atoms unequally bonded between the two oxygen atoms.

The experimental facts seem, therefore, to allow an alternative to the view of halogen-addition usually associated with the names of

116

Roberts and Kimball (1937). Such an alternative seems to have been envisaged by Winstein (*cf* Winstein and Morse, 1952, p. 1134), in the statement that the stereochemical results corresponding to the formation and opening of a bridged intermediate may in some cases be simulated by a dynamic pair of isomeric cations, as has been discussed also by Ingold (1953a, p. 662). In the analogous case of the electrostatic, as compared with the ' α-lactone ' representation of the S_N1-hydrolysis of the α-bromopropionate ion, discussed above (p. 97), no experimental distinction between the two possibilities has yet been achieved.

For addition reactions, however, there exists evidence which leads the writer to consider that the two possibilities are distinct, and have independent ranges of validity. Ross (1947) has presented acceptable grounds for the belief that cyclic immonium ions are cleaved by bases as shown:

$$Me{\cdot}CH{\cdot}CH_2 \quad \xrightarrow{\text{OH}^-} \quad Me{\cdot}CH{\cdot}CH_2OH$$

Me·CH·CH$_2$	OH$^-$	Me·CH·CH$_2$OH
\/	$\longrightarrow$	|
$^+$NEt$_2$		NEt$_2$
LXXXIX		XC

On the other hand, intermediates supposed to be of the analogous cyclic type, appearing in halogen addition reactions, cleave in the opposite direction. Thus it would be usual to write as follows the addition of iodine chloride to propylene studied by Ingold and Smith (1931):

Me·CH:CH$_2$ + ICl $\longrightarrow$ Cl$^-$ + Me·CH·CH$_2$ $\longrightarrow$ Me·CHCl·CH$_2$I

\/

I$^+$

XCI	XCII
' Roberts and Kimball '	Major product
intermediate	

It would appear, therefore, that the analogous intermediates LXXXIX and XCI cleave in opposite directions. Dewar (1947, 1951a) regards this discrepancy as proving that the intermediates involved in addition are of a special type, in which the halogen atom and the ethylenic centre are linked by a so-called ' π-bond '. A much more reasonable explanation is that the halogen atom which leads the electrophilic attack does not in the first stage of the addition reaction become equivalently bonded to the two olefinic carbon atoms. The preferred view is shown in SCHEME 13.

The appearance of XCV as a minor product of the reaction is suggestive that, although XCIII, the first intermediate in the reaction, is destroyed most readily to form XCII, yet there is an alternative path, rather less energetically favourable, by a 1:2 shift through XCI and perhaps XCIV, giving the minor product XCV. Little is known concerning the energy relationships between the intermediates XCIII, XCI, and XCIV; nor is it even known whether XCI can ever be of

SCHEME 13

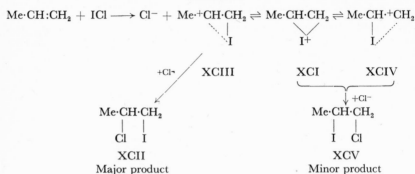

XCII
Major product

XCV
Minor product

Note: Addition of iodine chloride to olefinic compounds is stoichiometric, leaving no free iodine in the solution when excess of iodine chloride is used. Hence addition is unlikely to proceed through the dissociation $2ICl \rightleftharpoons I_2 + Cl_2$; nor is it likely that any significant reaction occurs by the alternative polarization $Cl^{\delta +}{-}I^{\delta -}$. Further investigation is, however, necessary to prove beyond doubt that the minor product is formed by the route suggested. If the minor product is in this case actually formed by another mechanism, the argument that reaction through the intermediate XCI is not the most favourable path for addition would be even further reinforced.

Roberts and Regan (1953) discuss, in a manner which appears to be essentially similar, the function of the phenyl group when a carbonium ionic centre develops on an adjacent carbon atom.

sufficient life to be classified as an intermediate (*cf* Dewar, 1951b), rather than as a transition state separating the other two possible intermediate carbonium ions.

When the electrophilic part of the addendum does not readily undergo a 1:2 shift of the type indicated, addition may entirely follow the normal route. Thus, addition of hydrogen chloride to propylene gives entirely $Me \cdot CHCl \cdot CH_3$ (Kharasch, Kluger and Mayo, 1939). Similarly, addition of hypochlorous acid to propylene gives 90 per cent of the expected addition product, $Me \cdot CH(OH) \cdot CH_2Cl$ (Smith, 1919). Although all the quoted results for addition of HCl, $Cl \cdot OH$, and $I \cdot Cl$ were obtained without knowledge of the kinetics and mechanisms of the reactions studied (and hence the conclusions which we may draw can only be tentative), it is significant that the amount of observed 'abnormal' addition product increases in the order $X = H < Cl < I$, where X is the electrophilic portion of the adding reagent ; this is the order in which these substituents participate in displacement reactions (p. 100).

It has been suggested also to the writer by Professor P. W. Robertson that group-migration of this sort is likely to occur with particular ease in cases in which the olefinic centre, at which addition is completed by a nucleophilic reagent, is sterically congested. The results obtained by Barton and Miller (1950) and by Ziegler and Shabica (1952) for the additions of halogens to derivatives of cholesterol are of interest in this connection. Chlorine, bromine chloride, and bromine give initially, under polar conditions, $5\alpha : 6\beta$ derivatives of cholesterol obtained by *trans*-addition. The dichloride and bromo-chloride thus obtained are stable, but the dibromide (XCVI), on standing in solution, undergoes spontaneous change to an equilibrium mixture, which contains a preponderance of the isomeric $5\beta:6\alpha$ compound (XCVIII).

Cholesterol   XCVI   XCVII   XCVIII

The former, one may presume, is produced by kinetically controlled addition, directed in the *trans*-sense by the electrostatic effect of the neighbouring bromine atom. The latter is produced by a subsequent isomerization, which, since it is intramolecular (Grob and Winstein, 1952), presumably proceeds through an intermediate of the form XCVII. Since the position of the equilibrium indicates that XCVII is transformed more rapidly into XCVIII than into XCVI, it cannot be the intermediate concerned in the original addition of halogen, because this process leads predominantly to XCVI.

Bromine chloride, supplied by *N*-bromosuccinimide and HCl, reacts in the sense $Br^{\delta+}$—$Cl^{\delta-}$; yet the product obtained in the reaction of bromine chloride with cholesterol was the 5α-bromo-6β-chloro-derivative (Ziegler and Shabica, 1952). It might have been presumed that $Br^{\delta+}$ would initiate addition at the 6-position, for two reasons: (*a*) by analogy with addition to propylene, in which attack is predominantly at the least substituted carbon atom, as is usually formulated $\overrightarrow{Me \cdot CH \overset{\frown}{:} CH_2}$; and (*b*) from the confirmatory fact that cholesterol adds hydrogen chloride in the expected fashion the hydrogen becoming attached to C-6 and the chlorine to C-5. It is reasonable to conclude, therefore, that the entering bromine atom, though attacking the 6-position, migrates from there to the 5-position through the 'symmetrical' intermediate (such as LXXXIV) before completion of the reaction. Barton, Miller and Young (1951) adopting the formulation of Roberts and Kimball (1937), prefer to speak of ' non-Markownikow ' attack on the three-membered ring, thereby focusing attention on the completion, rather than on the initiation, of the reaction.

It is interesting to note, as has been pointed out by Waters, Caverhill and Robertson (1947) that *trans*-addition of halogens is not a universal rule. Thus Barton and Miller (1950) showed that $PhICl_2$ reacts with derivatives of cholesterol to form the $5\alpha:6\alpha$-dichlorides, obtained evidently by *cis*-addition. On the other hand the 1:4-addition of

119

chlorine to butadiene does not appear to involve a cyclic intermediate such as XCIX or C, as is shown by the demonstration (Mislow and Hellmann, 1951) that the 1:4-addition of chlorine to butadiene leads exclusively to the formation of 1:4-dichlorobut-*trans*-2-ene.

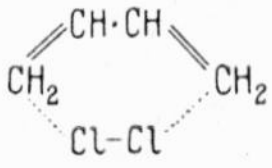

XCIX 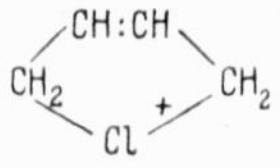   C

STERIC EFFECTS IN RACEMIZATION OF DERIVATIVES OF DIPHENYL

Many derivatives of diphenyl can exist in enantiomorphic forms as the result of the presence of *ortho*-substituents which restrict rotation about the link joining the two rings. Other systems in which molecular asymmetry can arise as the result of restricted rotation about a single bond are also well known.

In the early work of Adams and his school (summarized by Adams and Yuan, 1933; Shriner, Adams and Marvel, 1943), the ease of racemization of many of these compounds was compared, in a semi-quantitative fashion, and it was shown that *ortho*-substituents could be arranged in the following sequence of decreasing effectiveness in preventing racemization : $Br > Me > Cl > NO_2 > CO_2H > OMe > F$. From models, it was shown that this sequence agreed fairly well with what would be expected on purely steric grounds, the 'interference values' of these groups decreasing in very nearly the same order.

The data in TABLE 4 show how substituents in other positions in the diphenyl nucleus affect the rate of racemization of compounds of type CI. Substituents in the 4' and 5' positions have little effect on

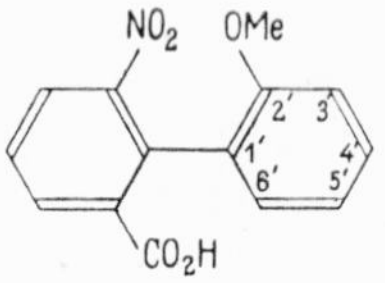

CI 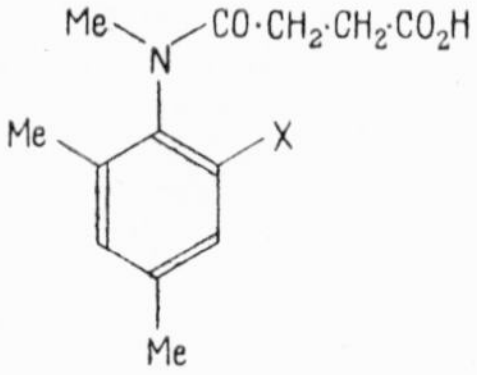   CII

TABLE 4. HALF-LIVES FOR THE RACEMIZATION OF DERIVATIVES OF 6-CARBOXY-2'-METHOXY-2-NITRODIPHENYL (CI)
(Values are $t_{\frac{1}{2}}$ in min. at 25°)

Substituent:	NO_2	Br	Cl	Me	MeO
Position: 3'	1905	827	711	331	98
4'	115	25	12	2·5	3·6
5'	35	32	31	12	11

the rate of the reaction, but any substituent in the 3' position, adjacent to the 2'-methoxy group, causes an increase in the optical stability. This result can be accommodated on steric grounds, seeing that a group adjacent to the methoxy-group may be expected to have a 'buttressing' effect, preventing the methoxy-group from bending away from the *ortho*-substituents in the other ring, and thus increasing the steric strain in the planar configuration required for racemization. The abnormal effect of the nitro-group, considering its size, in preventing racemization when introduced into the 3' and 4'-positions, does not seem to be thoroughly understood. It sometimes happens that the nitro-group has the reverse effect, as in the following example of type CII studied by Adams and Sundholm (1948) and by Adams and Gordon (1950):

TABLE 5. HALF-LIVES FOR THE RACEMIZATION OF COMPOUNDS OF TYPE CII
(Values are $t_{\frac{1}{2}}$ in h)

X	I	Br	Cl	OMe	NO$_2$
$t_{\frac{1}{2}}$ (117°)	21·5	3·1	0·6	—	—
$t_{\frac{1}{2}}$ (57°)	—	—	63	2·7	0·6

Here optical activity is allowed by virtue of the restricted rotation about the link between the aromatic ring and the nitrogen atom. The usual result, that groups become less effective in preventing racemization as their size decreases, is shown by the series $I > Br > Cl > OMe$; but the *ortho*-nitro-group permits abnormally rapid racemization, which, it has been proposed, is favoured in this case by the development of coplanarity, presumably by the contribution to the structure of the molecule of structures such as CIII.

CIII

It is unfortunate for the quantitative development of this subject that reliable determinations of the activation energy required for racemization have been made for very few of the compounds which have been resolved into enantiomorphs. Arrhenius parameters are available for the racemization of diphenyl derivatives from the work of Kuhn and Albrecht (1927), Li and Adams (1935), Kistiakowsky and Smith (1936), Adams and Kornblum (1941), and Rieger and Westheimer (1950) ; and for other cases of hindered rotation from Jamison and Turner (1938), Mills and Elliott (1928), and Mills and Kelham (1937). Unfortunately, not all of these determinations are equally reliable. The Arrhenius B-factors seem mostly to be of the order 10^{11} sec^{-1}. It is reasonable that a value rather smaller than that (10^{13}) usually regarded as typical of unimolecular reactions should be obtained for this type of process, since it is necessary for successful racemization that the energy of activation be distributed in a particular manner among the deformed bonds, thus restricting the positions and vibrations of the atoms in the transition state, with a resulting lowering in the entropy of activation. The data are, however, too diverse to make profitable a more close discussion of the recorded differences, and such a treatment as has been attempted by Cagle and Eyring (1951) should, in the writer's opinion, await a considerable extension of the existing information.

Westheimer and Mayer (1946) first outlined a method for calculating the energies of activation of racemization in sterically hindered derivatives of diphenyl. In subsequent work (Westheimer, 1947; Rieger and Westheimer, 1950) the energies of activation for the racemization of CIV and CV (21·6 and 28·0 kcal. mole^{-1} respectively) were determined and compared with the calculated values (21·4 and 28·6 respectively, using a particular set of assumptions).

CIV   CV

Confirmation is thus given of the view that the effect of the extra iodine atoms in compound CV is due to the ' buttressing effect ' already mentioned.

In making calculations of this sort, the main uncertainty (always provided that the geometry of the transition state is approximately known, as in this case it is) arises from the difficulty in choosing suitable expressions for the energy as a function of the positions of the groups brought into proximity in the reaction. The data are obtained from spectroscopic values for the energy of stretching and bending of the bonds, and from values for the compressibility of atoms and groups in the molecule, often derived from virial coefficients of simple gaseous substances. The good agreement between theory and experiment in the example studied by Rieger and Westheimer is evidence for the approximate validity of the assumptions made in these calculations; a fruitful approach to the difficult task of determining the mutual interaction in a molecule of groups not directly bonded is likely to come from a more extensive study of the energies of activation of this type of racemization, in which one is not concerned with the additional difficulty of the energetics of breaking old bonds and forming new ones.

REFERENCES

Adams, R. and Gordon, J. R. (1950) *J. Amer. chem. Soc.* **72,** 2454
— and Kornblum, N. (1941) *ibid* **63,** 189
— and Sundholm, N. K. (1948) *ibid* **70,** 2667
— and Yuan, H. C. (1933) *Chem. Rev.* **12,** 261
Arcus, C. L. and Kenyon, J. (1939) *J. chem. Soc.* 916
Aschan, O. (1908) *Ber. dtsch. chem. Ges.* **41,** 1092
Balfe, M. P., Doughty, M. A., Kenyon, J., and Poplett, R. (1942) *J. chem. Soc.* 605
Bartlett, P. D. (1951) *Bull. Soc. chim. Fr.* (5) **18A,** C100
— and Brown, R. F. (1940) *J. Amer. chem. Soc.* **62,** 2927
— and Knox, L. H. (1939) *ibid* **61,** 3184
— and Lewis, E. S. (1950) *ibid* **72,** 1005
— and Pöckel, I. (1937) *ibid* **59,** 820
Barton, D. H. R. (1949) *J. chem. Soc.* 2174
— Head, A. J. and Williams, R. J. (1952) *ibid* 453
— and Miller, E. (1950) *J. Amer. chem. Soc.* **72,** 370, 1066
— — and Young, H. T. (1951) *J. chem. Soc.* 2598
Bateman, L. C., Church, M. G., Hughes, E. D., Ingold, C. K. and Taher, N. A. (1940) *ibid* 979
— Cooper, K. A., Hughes, E. D. and Ingold, C. K. (1940) *ibid* 925
Bergstrom, C. G. and Seigel, S. (1952) *J. Amer. chem. Soc.* **74,** 145
Brewster, P., Hiron, F., Hughes, E. D., Ingold, C. K. and Rao, P. A. D. (1950) *Nature, Lond.* **166,** 179
— Hughes, E. D., Ingold, C. K. and Rao, P. A. D. (1950) *ibid* **166,** 178
Brown, F., Hughes, E. D., Ingold, C. K. and Smith, J. B. (1951) *ibid* **168,** 65
Brown, H. C. and Fletcher, R. S. (1949) *J. Amer. chem. Soc.* **71,** 1845
— — and Johannesen, R. B. (1951) *ibid* **73,** 212 .
Bunton, C. A., Hughes, E. D., Ingold, C. K. and Meigh, D. F. (1950) *Nature, Lond.* **166,** 680
Cagle, F. W. and Eyring, H. (1951) *J. Amer. chem. Soc.* **73,** 5628
Campbell, A. and Kenyon, J. (1946) *J. chem. Soc.* 25
Charlton, J. C., Dostrovsky, I. and Hughes, E. D. (1951) *Nature, Lond.* **167,** 986
Chavanne, G. (1912) *Bull. Soc. chim. Belg.* **26,** 287
Cowdrey, W. A., Hughes, E. D. and Ingold, C. K. (1937) *J. chem. Soc.* 1208
— — — Masterman, S. and Scott, A. D. (1937) *ibid* 1256, 1264
— — Nevell, T. P. and Wilson, C. L. (1938) *ibid* 209
Cram, D. J. (1949) *J. Amer. chem. Soc.* **71,** 3863; (1952) *ibid* **74,** 2129, 2159; (1953) *ibid* **75,** 332.
Cristol, S. J. and Fix, D. D. (1953) *ibid* **75,** 2647
— Hause, N. L. and Meek. J. S. (1951) *ibid* **73,** 674
Day, J. N. E. and Ingold, C. K. (1941) *Trans. Faraday Soc.* **37,** 686
de la Mare, P. B. D. (1948) Thesis, University of London; (1949) *Quart. Rev. chem. Soc., Lond.* **3,** 126; (1950a) *Industr. chim. belge* **15,** 789; (1950b) *Annu. Rep. Progr. Chem.* **47,** 133, 134
— England, B. D., Fowden, L., Hughes, E. D. and Ingold, C. K. (1948) *J. Chim. phys.* **45,** 236
— and Robertson, P. W. (1950) *J. chem. Soc.* 2838
Dewar, M. J. S. (1947) *Disc. Faraday Soc.* **2,** 75 ; (1951a) *Bull. Soc. chim. Fr.* (5), **18A,** C71; (1951b) *Annu. Rep. Progr. Chem.* **48,** 118
Dhar, M. L., Hughes, E. D., Ingold, C. K., Mandour, A. M. M., Maw, G. A. and Woolf, L. I. (1948) *J. chem. Soc.* 2093
Doering, W. von E. and Schoenewaldt, E. F. (1951) *J. Amer. chem. Soc.* **73,** 2333
Dostrovsky, I. and Hughes, E. D. (1946) *J. chem. Soc.* 157
— — and Ingold, C. K. (1946) *ibid* 173

Easty, G. M. (1949) Thesis, University of London
Fierens, P. J. C. and Verschelden, P. (1952) *Bull. Soc. chim. Belg.* **61,** 427, 609
Frankland, P. F. (1913) *J. chem. Soc.* **103,** 713
Freed, S. and Sancier, K. M. (1952) *J. Amer. chem. Soc.* **74,** 1273
Fuson, R. C., Price, C. C. and Burness, D. M. (1946) *J. org. Chem.* **11,** 475
Gillespie, R. J. (1952) *J. chem. Soc.* 1002
Grob, C. A. and Winstein, S. (1952) *Helv. chim. acta* **35,** 782
Grunwald, E. and Winstein, S. (1948) *J. Amer. chem. Soc.* **70,** 841
Holmberg, B. (1912) *Ber. dtsch. chem. Ges.* **45,** 2997
Hückel, W., Tappe, W. and Legutke, G. (1940) *Liebigs Ann.* **543,** 191
Hughes, E. D. (1938) *Trans. Faraday Soc.* **34,** 202 ; (1941a, b) *ibid* **37,** 603, 725 ;
    (1951a) *Bull. Soc. chim. Fr.* (5) **18A,** C39; (1951b) *Quart. Rev. chem. Soc., Lond.*
    5, 245; (1951c) in *Chemistry of Carbon Compounds,* Ed. E. H. Rodd, Vol. 1A,
    p. 192, New York, Elsevier
—   and Ingold, C. K. (1941) *Trans. Faraday Soc.* **37,** 657
—   —   Martin, R. J. L. and Meigh, D. F. (1950) *Nature, Lond.* **166,** 679
—   —   and Masterman, S. (1939) *J. chem. Soc.* 840
—   —   and Pasternak, R. (1953) *ibid* 3832
—   —   and Patel, C. S. (1933) *ibid* 526
—   —   and Rose, J. B. (1953) *ibid* 3839
—   Juliusberger, F., Masterman, S., Topley, B. and Weiss, J. (1935) *ibid* 1525
—   —   Scott, A. D., Topley, B. and Weiss, J. (1936) *ibid* 1173
Ingold, C. K. (1953a) *Structure and Mechanism in Organic Chemistry,* London, Bell;
    (1953b) *J. chem. Soc.* 2845
—   and Smith, H. G. (1931) *ibid* 2742
Ivanoff, N. and Magat, M. (1950) *J. Chim. phys.* **47,** 914
Jamison, M. M. and Turner, E. E. (1938) *J. chem. Soc.* 1646
Juvala, A. (1930). *Ber. dtsch. chem. Ges.* **63,** 1989
Kenyon, J. and Phillips, H. (1930) *Trans. Faraday Soc.* **26,** 451
—   and Young, D. P. (1941) *J. chem. Soc.* 263
Kharasch, M. S., Kluger, S. C. and Mayo, F. R. (1939) *J. org. Chem.* **4,** 428
Kistiakowsky, G. B. and Smith, W. R. (1936) *J. Amer. chem. Soc.* **58,** 1043
Kuhn, R. and Albrecht, O. (1927) *Liebigs Ann.* **455,** 272; **458,** 221
Lane, J. F. and Wallis, E. S. (1941) *J. Amer. chem. Soc.* **63,** 1674
Li, C. C. and Adams, R. (1935) *ibid* **57,** 1565
Lucas, H. J. and Gould, C. W. (1941) *ibid* **63,** 2541
Macbeth, A. K. and Shannon, J. S. (1952) *J. chem. Soc.* 2852
Martin, F. and Bruylants, A. (1951) *Bull. Soc. chim. Belg.* **60,** 259
Miller, S. I., and Noyes, R. M. (1952) *J. Amer. chem. Soc.* **74,** 629
Mills, W. H. and Elliott, K. A. C. (1928) *J. chem. Soc.* 1291
—   and Kelham, R. M. (1937) *ibid* 274
Mislow, K. and Hellmann, H. M. (1951) *J. Amer. chem. Soc.* **73,** 244
Nevell, T. P., de Salas, E. and Wilson, C. L. (1939) *J. chem. Soc.* 1188
Read, J. and Walker, J. (1934) *ibid* 308
Rieger, M. and Westheimer, F. H. (1950) *J. Amer. chem. Soc.* **72,** 19, 28
Roberts, I. and Kimball, G. E. (1937) *J. Amer. chem. Soc.* **59,** 947
Roberts, J. D. and Chambers, V. C. (1951) *ibid* **73,** 5034
—   and Mazur, R. H. (1951) *ibid* **73,** 3542
—   and Regan, C. M. (1953) *ibid* **75,** 2069
Ross, S. D. (1947) *J. Amer. chem. Soc.* **69,** 2982
Saytzeff, A. (1875) *Liebigs Ann.* **179,** 296
Shoppee, C. W. (1946) *J. chem. Soc.* 1138, 1147; (1951) *Bull. Soc. chim. Fr.* (5), **(18A),**
    C120
—   —   and Summers, G. H. R. (1952) *J. chem. Soc.* 3361

Shriner, R. L., Adams, R. and Marvel, C. S. (1943) in *Organic Chemistry*, Ed. H. Gilman, 2nd ed. pp. 347 *et seq*, New York, Wiley

Simonsen, J. L. and Owen, L. N. (1949) *The Terpenes* Vol. II, Cambridge University Press

Smith, L. (1919) *Z. phys. Chem.* **93**, 59

Straten, S. F. van, Nicholls., R. V. V. and Winkler, C. A. (1951) *Canad. J. Chem.* **29**, 372

Walsh, A. D. (1949) *Trans. Faraday Soc.* **45**, 179

Waters, H. D. C., Caverhill, A. R. and Robertson, P. W. (1947) *J. chem. Soc.* 1168

Westheimer, F. H. (1947) *J. chem. Phys.* **15**, 252

— and Mayer, J. E. (1946) *ibid* **14**, 733

Wheland, G. W. (1949) *Advanced Organic Chemistry* New York, Wiley, pp. 475-534

White, E. P. and Robertson, P. W. (1939) *J. chem. Soc.* 1513

Whitmore, F. C. (1932) *J. Amer. chem. Soc.* **54**, 3274

Williams, G. (1941) *Trans. Faraday Soc.* **37**, 749

Winstein, S. (1951) *Bull. Soc. chim. Fr.* (v) **18C**, 55

— and Adams, F. (1948) *J. Amer. chem. Soc.* **70**, 838

— Brown, M., Schreiber, K. C. and Schlesinger, A. H. (1952) *ibid* **74**, 1140

— Goodman, L. and Boschan, R. (1950) *ibid* **72**, 2311, 4669

— and Grunwald, E. (1946) *ibid* **68**, 536; (1948) *ibid* **70**, 828, 841, 846

— — Buckles, R. E. and Hanson, C. (1948) *ibid* **70**, 816

— — and Ingraham, L. L. (1948) *ibid* **70**, 821

— Hanson, C. and Grunwald, E. (1948) *ibid* **70**, 812

— Hess, H. V. and Buckles, R. E. (1942) *ibid* **64**, 2796

— and Ingraham, L. L. (1952) *ibid* **74**, 1160

— and Lucas, H. J. (1939) *ibid* **61**, 1576

— and Morse, B. K. (1952) *ibid* **74**, 1133

— — Grunwald, E., Jones, H. W., Corse, J., Trifan, D. and Marshall, H. (1952) *ibid* **74**, 1127, 1130

— and Schreiber, K. C. (1952) *ibid* **74**, 2165

— and Trifan, D. S. (1949) *ibid* **71**, 2953; (1952) *ibid* **74**, 1147, 1154

Ziegler, J. B. and Shabica, A. C. (1952) *ibid* **74**, 4891

4

THE RELATIONSHIPS BETWEEN THE STEREOCHEMISTRY AND SPECTROSCOPIC PROPERTIES OF ORGANIC COMPOUNDS

E. A. Braude and E. S. Waight

THE study of molecular spectra has contributed in very considerable measure to the development of stereochemistry during the last forty years. The modern era of spectroscopy may be said to begin with Bohr's interpretation of the spectrum of atomic hydrogen (Bohr, 1913), and during the following two decades, the principles by which the spectra of small molecules can be analysed on the basis of quantum theory were also established. Spectroscopy thus became the first method to provide accurate data concerning the dimensions of gaseous molecules, and the determination of bond lengths and bond angles in simple structures such as H_2O, H_2S, NH_3, CO_2, C_2H_2, and C_2H_4 undoubtedly represents the first major contribution of spectroscopy to stereochemistry. Admirable accounts of this phase may be found in a number of text-books, particularly those of Kronig (1935) and of Herzberg (1950). Owing to its mathematical complexity, the precise analysis of vibrational and rotational spectra is generally limited to molecules containing between two and about eight atoms (or perhaps twice that number in exceptional cases embodying special features of symmetry) and although such work is still being actively carried on in several centres of research, it may be said that the pioneering period ended in the nineteen thirties and that the last twenty years have been a period of consolidation and refinement rather than of fundamental advance in this field. Very recently, however, the rapid development of microwave spectroscopy, made possible by the perfection of radar technique during the second world war, has made an additional wavelength range experimentally accessible, and has given fresh impetus to the study of rotational spectra of small molecules and to the determination of bond lengths and angles from moments of inertia (Wilson, 1951, 1952; Strandberg, 1953; Gordy, Smith and Trambarulo, 1953).

Since about 1935, the spectra of larger molecules which defy exact mathematical analysis have received increasing attention. Purely empirical use of ultra-violet and visible light absorption properties, *e.g.* for the distinction between geometrical isomers, was made over forty years ago by Hantzsch (1910) and others, but it is only during the last twenty years that such correlations have been put on at least a qualitative theoretical basis. Most of the problems of geometrical isomerism were, of course, solved by other physical or by chemical methods before spectroscopy was applied to them, but in a number of cases, notably in the polyenes (Zechmeister, 1944) and other extended conjugated systems, electronic spectra have provided guiding information concerning configuration about double bonds. An essential pre-requisite is an understanding of the relations between the *two*-dimensional shape of a conjugated system and the energy and probability of its characteristic electronic transitions, and several wave-mechanical approximation methods, which consider only the unsaturation electrons, have been shown to lend themselves to a reasonably simple treatment of this problem (for references, see p. 175 A and B*). It has also been shown (Braude, 1950) that an extremely simple relationship exists in electronic spectra between the absorption intensity, the transition probability and the cross-sectional area of the absorbing structure, so that if the transition probability can be taken as unity, molecular dimensions can be deduced from the observed extinction coefficients and vice versa. Of greater import from the point of view of stereochemistry, however, is the application of electronic spectra to questions of steric configuration about single bonds, which originated with the demonstration that restricted rotation about the central bond in ortho-substituted diphenyls is apparent in the near-ultra-violet spectra (Pickett *et al.*, 1936; O'Shaughnessy and Rodebush, 1940). Although the theory of the relation between the *three*-dimensional shape of conjugated systems and their electronic transitions is as yet in a comparatively elementary state (Guy, 1949; Klevens and Platt, 1949; Braude *et al.*, 1949, 1952, 1954), the spectroscopic method has the threefold advantage of being applicable to dilute solutions, as well as experimentally simpler and more sensitive than other methods such as optical resolution, or x-ray or electron diffraction. Numerous examples of steric inhibition of conjugation have been discovered within the last ten years from spectroscopic investigations in the ultra-violet and visible regions, and it seems highly probable that this subject will grow to become the second major contribution of spectroscopy to stereochemistry.

The preoccupation of chemical spectroscopists with fairly complex organic molecules since about 1935 has also extended to the near-infra-red region and no other physical method of determining structure has developed as rapidly of late as infra-red absorption and Raman spectroscopy. Infra-red spectra possess the intrinsic advantages over near-ultra-violet and visible spectra of being exhibited by every type of compound, and of being more specifically related to structure, but

* Where numerous related references occur they have been collected together at the end of the chapter to avoid long lists of names in the text.—ED.

they also possess the consequential disadvantages of greater complexity and of being much less amenable to theoretical treatment by approximation methods. In fact, the application of infra-red spectroscopy to the qualitative structural analysis of complex molecules has been almost entirely empirical. From the stereochemical point of view, the most prominent uses have been in the distinction between geometrical isomers in unsaturated systems (p. 156) and between conformational isomers in alicyclic systems (p. 164), and in special problems, such as hydrogen-bonding (*cf* Chapter 6). A recent development which holds considerable promise is the use of polarized infra-red radiation in the study of the stereochemistry of solid macromolecules, such as proteins, which is discussed in Chapter 7.

As has been indicated, recent progress amongst the various topics mentioned has been most marked in the elucidation of the stereochemistry of unsaturated compounds, and of alicyclic systems; these have therefore been selected for more detailed discussion in the following sections.

VISIBLE AND ULTRA-VIOLET LIGHT ABSORPTION IN
RELATION TO GEOMETRICAL ISOMERISM ABOUT
DOUBLE BONDS

The electronic spectra associated with isolated double bonds, *e.g.* $C=C$, $C=N$ *etc* lie in the far-ultra-violet region which is not readily accessible to quantitative measurements by the instruments at present available. For this reason, the usefulness of electronic spectra in stereochemical problems of complex molecules is largely confined to conjugated systems containing two or more unsaturated centres and exhibiting selective absorption above 2000 Å (see Braude, 1945). With neutral molecules, intense absorption in this region arises from transitions from a predominantly homopolar ground state to a predominantly dipolar excited state, *e.g.* $C=C-C=C \rightarrow C^+ - C=C-C^-$. Normally transitions of this kind (termed N→V transitions by Mulliken) are only influenced in a secondary degree by non-conjugating substituents directly attached to the double bond system and little diagnostically useful information concerning geometrical isomerism due to such substituents can be gained from the near-ultra-violet spectra. Thus, for example, *cis*- and *trans*-piperylene (I and II) (Braude and Coles, 1951) and *cis*- and *trans*-propenylacetylene (Allan and Whiting,

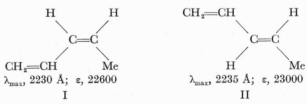

λ_{max}, 2230 Å; ε, 22600 λ_{max}, 2235 Å; ε, 23000

I   II

128

1953) exhibit almost identical absorption in solution. In the presence of larger saturated substituents, however, steric effects do appear but they arise from changes in conformation about the single bonds joining the unsaturated groups, rather than from configuration about the multiple bonds, and will be discussed separately in the next section.

Multi-conjugated Systems

A different situation arises in tri-conjugated and more extended systems in which one unsaturated group is flanked by two others. The effective over-all length of the conjugated system will be greater when the two flanking groups are *trans*-orientated than when they are *cis*-orientated and this difference is in itself sufficient to cause marked changes in the electronic spectrum. The classical example is stilbene; the band associated with the tri-conjugated system appears at longer wavelengths and is of higher intensity in the *trans*- (IV) than in the *cis*-isomer (III).

H   H
 \   /
  C═C
 /   \
Ph   Ph
λ_{max}, 2800 Å; ε, 10500
III

Ph   H
 \   /
  C═C
 /   \
H   Ph
λ_{max}, 2955 Å; ε, 29000
IV

The same relationship is usually observed in other multi-conjugated systems (TABLE 1), though there are certain exceptions, *e.g.* the *cis*- and *trans*-azobenzenes.

TABLE 1. ULTRA-VIOLET ABSORPTION OF *cis*- AND *trans*-ISOMERS IN CONJUGATED SYSTEMS

Compound	Isomer	'Partial-chromophore' band		'Full-chromophore' band		Ref.*
		λ_{max} Å	ε	λ_{max} Å	ε	
Ph·CH:CH·Ph	*cis*	2240	24400	2800	10500	a
	trans	2285	16400	2955	29000	
Ph·CH:CH·CH:CH$_2$	*cis*	<2200	—	2650	14000	b, c
	trans	2230	12000	2800	28300	
Ph·CH:CH·CO·Ph	*cis*	2470	14000	2890	8900	d
	trans	2250	12200	2980	23700	
Ph·CH:CH·CO$_2$H	*cis*	2220	23000	2800	13500	e
	trans	2260	15000	2950	27000	e
Ph·N:N·Ph	*cis*	—	—	3240	15000	e
	trans	—	—	3190	20000	

* References: *a* Beale and Roe, 1953; *b* Braude, Jones and Stern, 1947; *c* Grummitt and Cristoph, 1951; *d* Kuhn, Lutz and Bauer, 1950; *e* Braude, 1945.

The problem of the relationship between the geometry of conjugated systems and their electronic spectra was first examined theoretically by Mulliken*, and several other treatments, using different forms of molecular orbital theory in various stages of refinement have since been carried out. All are based on idealized models in which the unsaturation electrons are regarded as moving in the electrical field due to the constituent atoms, an approximation which is taken to extremes in the free electron gas model assuming a uniform potential (Bayliss). Absorption causes electronic motion along the axis of the system and wavelength and intensity are governed by the number (n) of ' mobile ' electrons and by the effective path length (l) of the electronic oscillation. Various functions have been proposed connecting l with λ and ε; those favoured by the simplest models (references p. 175, A) take the forms $\lambda^2 \propto l$ and $\varepsilon \propto l^2$ at low values of n, indicating that λ is a very much less sensitive function of l than is ε, but that transition energy decreases and transition probability increases, the more elongated the system. This is qualitatively, though not quantitatively, in agreement with the experimental data (cf TABLE 1) which show a smaller dependence of λ on l, and a greater dependence of ε on l than predicted by the above expressions. Thus, assuming that l in the stilbene can be equated with the distance between the $p{:}p'$-positions, the expected ratios $\lambda_{max}(trans)/\lambda_{max}(cis)$ and $\varepsilon (trans)/\varepsilon (cis)$ are 1·15 and 1·74, respectively while those observed are 1·06 and 2·76†. There are other indications that λ is a rather insensitive function of the planar geometry of a conjugated system (cf the polyenes, discussed below) and, according to the majority of the more refined theories, λ should, in fact, be independent of l and a function of the number n of unsaturation electrons alone (for references see p. 175, B). If this be true, such differences in λ as are observed between cis- and $trans$-isomers must be due to other factors. One of these will be a change in the submerged vibrational structure of the electronic bands, which may easily cause displacements of the order of 50 Å in the highest point of the band envelope, and the direction of which is difficult to predict. The small differences in λ_{max} between the stereoisomeric azobenzenes and their derivatives may well be due to this effect, but it can hardly account for the much larger differences found in the ethylenic systems. There can be little doubt that, in the latter, the most important contributory factor is steric hindrance to a co-planar arrangement of the conjugated system in the cis-isomer, as was first clearly recognized by Lewis (Lewis and Calvin, 1939; Lewis, Magel and Lipkin, 1940) and by R. N. Jones (1943). In the case of cis-stilbene (FIGURE 1) this will result in an equilibrium configuration

---

* See p. 175, References A.

† There is some ambiguity about the choice of λ_{max} in $trans$-stilbene and other compounds showing a broad band which exhibits vibrational structure but the general argument is not affected.

in which the planes of the phenyl rings are rotated by an appreciable angle with respect to the plane of the ethylenic double bond and the effect on the ultra-violet spectrum may be interpreted in the following way. The long-wavelength absorption in the stilbenes may be ascribed to electronic oscillations over the whole length of the molecule (see above), or in a different terminology, to transitions from ground states in which dipolar structures, *e.g.* $^+Ph{=}CH{-}CH{=}Ph^-$, make a relatively small contribution, to excited states in which such structures make relatively large contributions. Since the dipolar structures require a uniplanar arrangement of the double bond and the phenyl

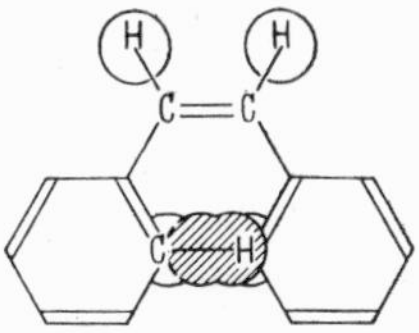

cis-Stilbene 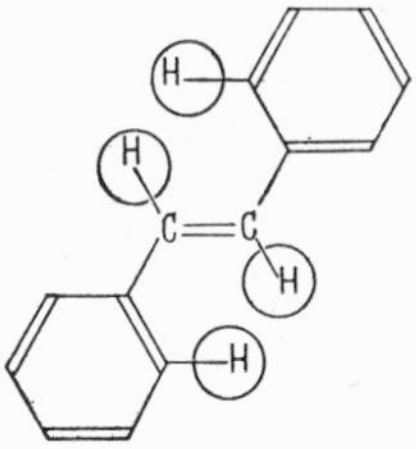   *trans*-Stilbene

FIGURE 1

rings, steric hindrance to such an arrangement will raise the potential energy of the excited state more than that of the ground state, and the transition energy will be increased, *i.e.* λ_{max} will be decreased. Assuming that the wavelength shift of 150 Å from *trans*- to *cis*-stilbene is wholly due to steric hindrance, the differential de-stabilization amounts to $\sim$ 6 kcal. mole^{-1}, a value remarkably close to the resonance energy of *trans*-stilbene (Wheland, 1944).

The absence of a comparable hypsochromic shift in the azobenzenes is not due to lack of a steric effect since the intensity ratio is similar to that observed in other cases and since *cis*-azobenzene is also appreciably non-planar in the crystalline state (Hampson and Robertson, 1941). It seems that the difference in behaviour must be conditioned by subtler differences between the electronic or steric properties of —CH= and —N=; valency-angle distortions may be less costly in repulsion energy, or deviations from uniplanarity less costly in resonance-energy, when nitrogen replaces carbon.

In addition to their long-wavelength bands near 2800 Å, stilbene, phenylbutadiene, cinnamic acid and benzylidene acetone all exhibit shorter-wavelength bands near 2300 Å which may be ascribed to the ' partial ', di-conjugated styryl (Ph—C=C) chromophore. The *cis–trans* wavelength shift of the di-conjugate bands is much smaller than with the tri-conjugate bands, while the intensity relationships are reversed, ε being invariably greater in the *cis*- than in the *trans*-isomers. It is tempting to explain this by the fact that steric hindrance in a

131

system such as *cis*-stilbene can be relieved not only by the rotation of *both* terminal groups by a medium angle, but also by the rotation of *one* terminal group through a large angle, leaving the other phenyl group co-planar with the ethylenic bond. Thus the transition energy of the partial styryl chromophore is little altered, but the transition probability in the *cis*-isomer is much increased relative to that of the full chromophore.

Polyenes

Early observations on the occurrence of geometrical isomerism in the carotenoid polyenes were made by several investigators (see Karrer and Jucker, 1950), but the major advances were not achieved until ultra-violet and visible absorption spectroscopy was applied to this problem, first by Gillam (1936) and later, more extensively, by Zechmeister (1944). When solutions of β-carotene in petrol are kept at an elevated temperature, treated with iodine, or illuminated, small but definite changes in the highly characteristic absorption curve take place; the visible band near 4600 Å shifts to shorter wavelengths by ~ 100Å and decreases in intensity, while the weak ultra-violet band near 3400 Å increases in intensity. The spectral changes are qualitatively similar to, though quantitatively less pronounced, than those associated with *cis–trans*-isomerism in tri-conjugate systems, and a number of isomeric β-carotenes, which are different from the position-isomers α- and γ-carotene, can be isolated from the solution by careful chromatography. Similar observations were made with other carotenoids isolated from natural sources, the largest number of isomers (6) being obtained from lycopene (V). There is no doubt that these represent geometrical isomers and it has become generally accepted that the stablest members of each series, which are also those with the most intense absorption bands in the visible region, possess all-*trans* configurations, while the others have one or more ethylenic bonds which are *cis*-substituted with respect to the carbon chain.

A detailed assignment of the geometrical configuration of *cis*-carotenoids which rests almost entirely on an interpretation of the

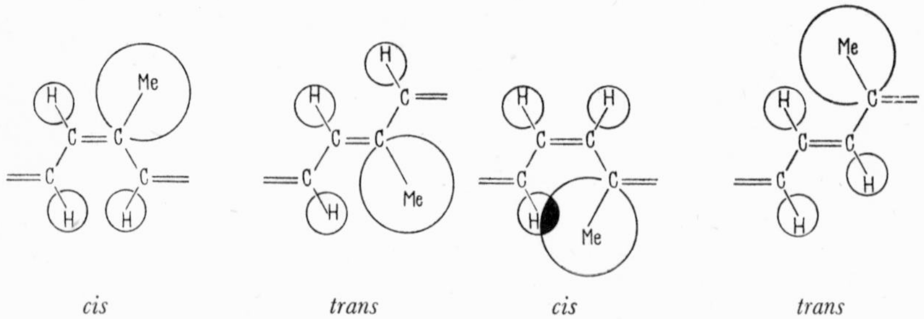

cis	*trans*	*cis*	*trans*
$=$CH—CH$=$CMe—CH$=$		$=$CH—CH$=$CH—CMe$=$	

FIGURE 2

132

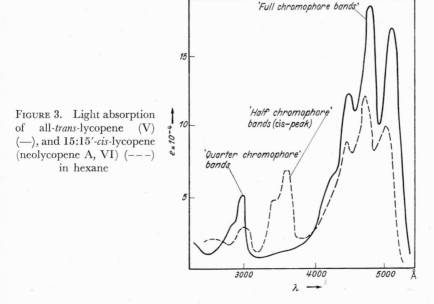

FIGURE 3. Light absorption of all-*trans*-lycopene (V) (—), and 15:15′-*cis*-lycopene (neolycopene A, VI) (– – –) in hexane

visible and ultra-violet spectra was made by Pauling (1939, 1949) and Zechmeister (1944) (*cf* Zechmeister *et al.*, 1943). Their main assumptions and postulates are the following: (1) The visible bands are due to transitions involving electronic oscillations from end to end of the conjugated polyene chain. (2) The ultra-violet bands near 3400 Å are associated with the partial 'half-length' chromophores consisting of ∼ 6 conjugated ethylenic bonds and are due to electronic oscillations from the ends to the middle of the chain; these bands are of very low intensity in the all-*trans* isomers because the dipoles of the two half-oscillations are in opposition so that the over-all moment vanishes and the transition is 'forbidden'. (3) The ultra-violet bands near 2900 Å are associated with the partial 'quarter length' chromophores consisting of ∼ 3 conjugated ethylenic bonds. (4) Only those ethylenic groups which are flanked by two unsubstituted —CH= units, *i.e.* those contained in the systems =CH—CH=CH—CH= and =CH—CMe=CH—CH=, but not those contained in the system =CH—CH=CH—CMe= will be able to assume a stable *cis*-configuration, owing to steric repulsion (FIGURE 2). On this basis, a *cis*-bond will have the largest effect when located in the centre of the chain; the total chromophore length will be decreased by a factor of cos 30° and the intensity of the visible bands by a factor of $\cos^2 30°$ assuming Mulliken's relation $\varepsilon \propto l^2$ (see above)*, while the intensity of the half-chromophore band will be increased to a maximum since the

---

* Pauling (1939, 1949) and Zechmeister *et al.*, (1943) actually used cos 27° in their calculations which were based on a value of 125° for the C—C=C angle, but it is now known that this value is nearer 120°.

133

transition will have a resultant dipole moment at right angles to the centre bond. Neolycopene A, which exhibits the most intense ' *cis*-peak ' amongst the six known stereoisomers of the lycopene series (FIGURE 3) is therefore regarded as 15:15'-*cis*-lycopene (VI). Convincing confirmation for this assignment has recently been provided by the total synthesis of 15:15'-*cis*-β-carotene (VIII) (Inhoffen *et al.*, 1950, 1951) in which the central *cis*-ethylenic link was introduced in the final step by catalytic semihydrogenation of an acetylenic link so that the position is not in doubt. The spectral relationships between all-*trans*-β-carotene (VII) and 15:15'-*cis*-β-carotene, and between (natural) all-*trans*-lycopene and neolycopene A are in close agreement

TABLE 2. VISIBLE AND ULTRA-VIOLET LIGHT ABSORPTION OF *cis*- AND *trans*-CAROTENOIDS (HEXANE SOLUTIONS)

Compound	' Full-chromophore ' band		' Half-chromophore ' band (' *cis* '-peak)		Ref.*
	λ_{max} Å	ε	λ_{max} Å	ε	
All-*trans*-lycopene (V)	4730	186000	3630	14000	a
15:15'-*cis*-lycopene (VI) (Neolycopene A)	4650	122000	3610	68000	a
All-*trans*-β-carotene (VII)	4520	152000	3380	8000	b
15:15'-*cis*-β-carotene (VIII)	4490	92500	3380	52000	b
All-*trans*-dimethylcrocetin (IX)	4200	134000	3140	8000	c
8:8'-*cis*-dimethylcrocetin (X)	4190	105000	3140	40000	c

* References: *a* Zechmeister *et al.*, 1943; *b* Inhoffen *et al.*, 1950, 1951; *c* Inhoffen *et al.*, 1953.

(TABLE 2). Similar relationships also hold for all-*trans*-dimethylcrocetin (IX) and synthetic 8:8'-*cis*-dimethylcrocetin (X) (Inhoffen *et al.*, 1953). It may be noted that the hypsochromic shifts of the visible bands are relatively small, but that the ratios of ε for the *cis*- and *trans*-isomers are either close to, or larger than, the factor $\cos^2 30°$ (1·33). Intensity differences unaccompanied by any significant wavelength displacements have also been observed recently in synthetic geometrical isomers of diene and triene carboxylic acids (references p. 175, c), and of cinnamaldazine and phenylpentadienaldazine (Dale and Zechmeister, 1953).

By an extension of the arguments outlined above, Pauling and Zechmeister and their colleagues have attempted to assign geometrical configuration to other isomers of lycopene and other carotenoids. These are much less securely founded, however, and yet remain to be confirmed; the complexity of the problem may be gauged from the fact that a symmetrical polyene containing twelve double bonds can give rise to 2080 geometrical isomers, and even if only seven double

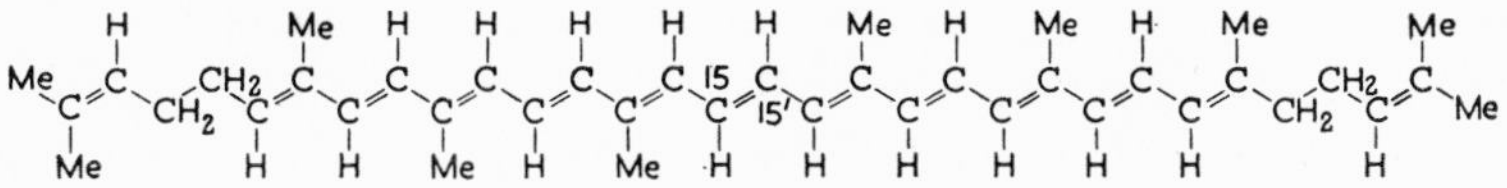

V

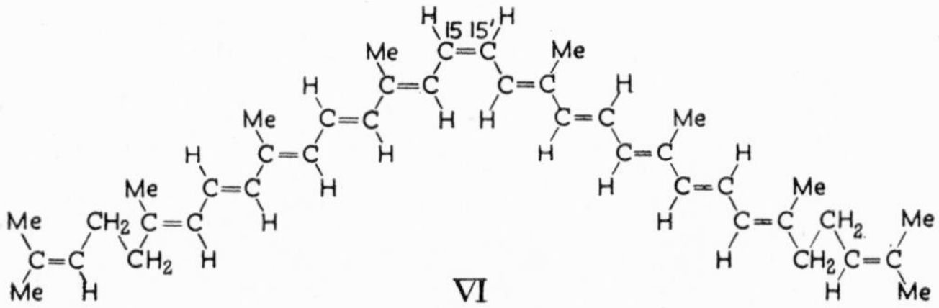

VI

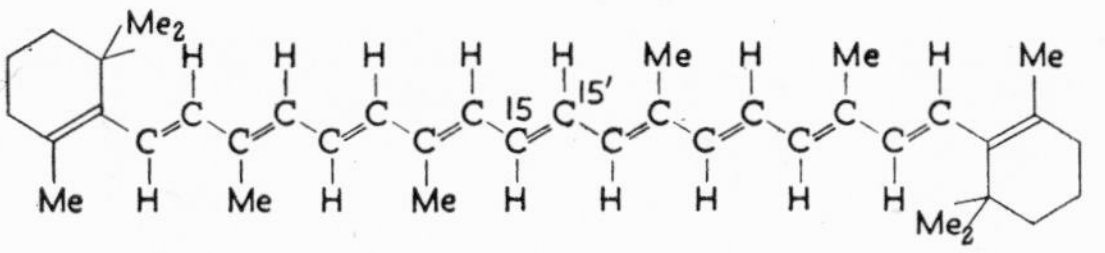

VII

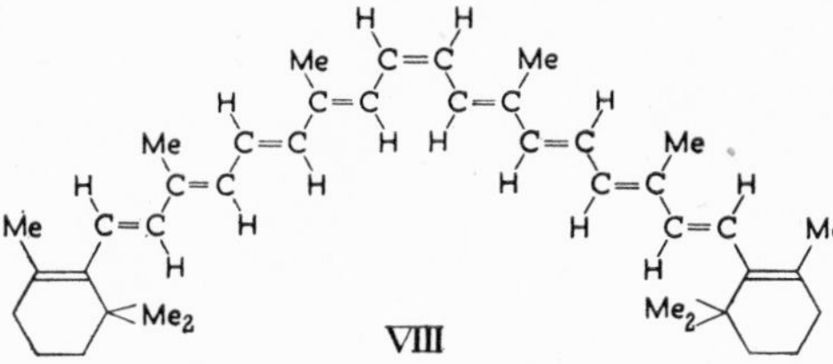

VIII

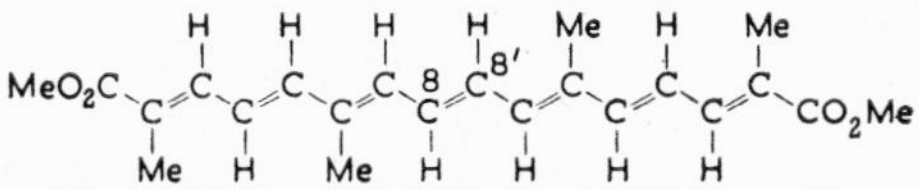

IX

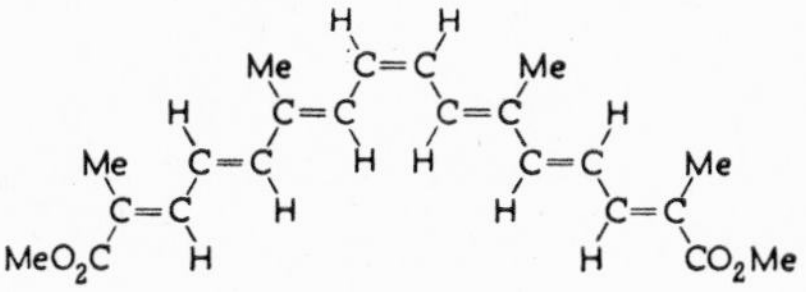

X

135

bonds are stereochemically effective, the number of isomers is still 72. The assumption that double bonds of the type $=CH-CH=CH-CMe=$ are stereochemically ineffective is, moreover, in doubt, as reasonably stable synthetic polyenes which, according to the methods of preparation, contain such *cis*-groupings have recently been obtained (Garbers *et al.*, 1952, 1953; Oroshnik *et al.*, 1952; Zechmeister and Wallcave, 1953) and found to show spectral and chemical differences from the *trans*-isomers comparable to those observed with $=CH-CH=CH-CH=$ systems. There are also certain other difficulties with the details of the Pauling-Zechmeister theory, such as the behaviour of the presumed ' quarter '-chromophore bands which do not show the increase in intensity which might be expected in poly-*cis*-polyenes. These uncertainties do not detract from the great value of electronic spectra as a means of detecting and identifying geometrical isomers in multi-conjugate systems, nor from the considerable achievement of having established the geometrical configuration of several complex molecules by an experimentally very simple method.

ULTRA-VIOLET LIGHT ABSORPTION IN RELATION TO STERIC CONFORMATION ABOUT SINGLE BONDS IN CONJUGATED SYSTEMS

Our knowledge of the relationships between the stereochemical fine-structure of unsaturated compounds and their ultra-violet and visible light absorption has developed very rapidly during the last ten or fifteen years. This is partly the result of the increasing use made of absorption spectroscopy as a tool for the elucidation of the structure of organic compounds in general, and partly to a widespread interest in the theory and subtler structural aspects of conjugated systems, stimulated by the presence of such systems in many important types of natural products.

Dienes

In the preceding discussion of the relations between geometrical isomerism about double bonds and electronic spectra, use has already been made of the concept that the electronic potential energy of a conjugated system of double bonds is at a minimum in a uniplanar arrangement. This concept is derived in resonance theory from the postulate of contributing resonance structures in which conventional single bonds assume partial double bond character, and in molecular orbital theory from the principle of maximum overlap which requires a parallel orientation of interacting electron orbitals. The electronically preferred uniplanarity of conjugated systems has another important consequence, namely the possible existence of geometrical isomerism about single bonds. This was first discussed in relation to spectral properties by Mulliken who introduced the term *s–cis–trans*-isomerism (*s* denoting *single* bond, reference, p. 175, A). Butadiene, 1:4-pentadiene (piperylene, see p. 128) and most other open-chain dienes exhibit K-bands* of much higher intensity than cyclic dienes in which the conjugated system is necessarily cisoid (TABLE 3) and the observed ε ratios correspond well to those predicted by the relation $ε ∝ l^2$, assuming an *s–trans*-form† for the acyclic dienes. Such a result is in agreement with the theoretical expectation that the most elongated form of a conjugated system will be electronically the most stable. The conclusion that butadiene exists predominantly in the *s–trans*-form at room temperature is also in agreement with the results of electron-diffraction and Raman spectroscopic studies (Schomaker and Pauling, 1939; Bradacs and Kahovec, 1940; Szasz and Sheppard, 1953). An experimental estimate by Aston *et al.* (1946) of the energy difference between the *s–cis*- and *trans*-forms of butadiene and of the rotational barrier between them has given values of $2·6$ kcal. mole^{-1} and $2·3$ kcal. mole^{-1}, respectively, and a more recent calculation of Parr and Mulliken (1950) is in good agreement with these data. It may be noted in passing that the rotational barrier for the central bond in butadiene is actually somewhat smaller than for the central bond in butane (~ 3 kcal. mole^{-1}) where the non-bonded atom interactions are much larger.

The characteristic absorption of butadiene not only has much higher ε than that of monocyclic dienes, but is also situated at much shorter wavelengths. That the wavelength difference, unlike the intensity difference, is not due to the difference in *s–cis–trans*-form is shown by the fact that bicyclic cisoid dienes containing the two double bonds in different rings absorb at similar wavelengths to acyclic transoid dienes (Barton and Brooks, 1951; Bailey and Golden, 1953)§. The bathochromic shift in monocyclic dienes must, therefore, be due to some other factor and was attributed by Mulliken to hyperconjugation of the diene system with the C—H bonds of the cyclic methylene groups, which is also indicated by the chemical properties of *cyclo*pentadiene. This can hardly be the complete explanation, however, for λ shows a marked dependence on ring size and is at a maximum in *cyclo*hexadiene (Pesch and Friess, 1950; Pullman and Berthier, 1950, 1951). It seems probable that in the six- and higher membered rings hyperconjugation

---

* For descriptive purposes, the longest-wavelength bands due to N→V transitions of conjugated systems, are often referred to as K-bands (from the German *Konjugation*) following Burawoy (1939).

† The terms ' configuration ', ' conformation ' and ' constellation ' have all been employed to denote isomerism arising from restricted rotation about single bonds. The potential barriers to which such isomerism is due vary in magnitude from a fraction of a kilocalorie to over 10 kcal. mole^{-1} and the ease of interconversion correspondingly varies from extreme lability to complete stability under ordinary conditions. The simple designation ' form ', which has the advantage of brevity, will be used here to cover the general phenomenon.

§ Lack of information on this point led Sugden and Walsh (1945) to the opposite conclusion.

of the diene system with the C—C bonds is also involved, similar to that observed in certain other cases (Braude, 1949); such interaction would be at a maximum in cyclohexadiene which can assume some pseudo-benzenoid character, as has also been suggested by Woodward (1942). Although most acyclic dienes exhibit K-bands of high intensity ($\varepsilon > 15000$) corresponding to their existence entirely or at least predominantly in the s–trans-form under ordinary conditions, two highly

TABLE 3. ULTRA-VIOLET LIGHT ABSORPTION OF ACYCLIC AND MONOCYCLIC DIENES (HEXANE OR ETHANOL SOLUTIONS)

Compound	λ_{max} Å	ε	Ref.*
CH₂:CH·CH:CH₂	2170	21000	a
CHMe:CH·CH:CH₂	2230	23000	a
CH:CMe·CH:CH₂	2200	24000	a
CHMe:CH·CH:CHMe	2270	23000	a
CH₂:CMe·CMe:CH₂	2250	21000	a
CMe₂:CH·CH:CMe₂	2410	23000	b
CMe₂:CH·CMe:CH₂	2320	8500	c
	2385	3400	a
	2560	8000	a
	2480	7400	d
	2280	5600	d
	2200	10000	e

* References: a Booker, Evans and Gillam, 1940; b Braude and Timmons, 1950; c Lunt and Sondheimer, 1950 (data independently confirmed by Timmons and Braude); d Pesch and Friess, 1950; Cope and Estes, 1950; e Bailey and Golden, 1953.

significant exceptions on record are 1:1:3-trimethyl butadiene and some of its derivatives which show $\lambda_{max} = 2280$ Å, $\varepsilon \sim 8500$ (TABLE 3; also Braude and Coles, 1952) and 3-chloro-1 : 1-dimethylbutadiene which exhibits λ_{max}, 2330Å, ε, 8100 (Braude and Evans, 1954). There is considerable overlap between two of the methyl substituents in a planar s–trans-form of 1:1:3-trimethylbutadiene and the low intensity could be ascribed to a predominance of the s–cis-form for this reason. Projection diagrams (FIGURE 4) show, however, that almost equal steric hindrance exists in the planar s–cis form. On balance,

138

therefore, an *s–trans*-form partly twisted about the central single bond is the most likely and the low ε value is to be ascribed to non-planarity of the chromophoric system.

One example of this general effect has already been mentioned (*cis*-stilbene) and most of the remainder of this section will be devoted to a discussion of others. The case of 1:1:3-trimethylbutadiene is

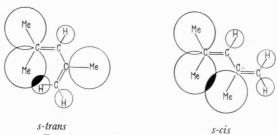

s-trans   *s-cis*

FIGURE 4. 1:1:3-Trimethylbutadiene

particularly instructive, however, in that it illustrates a fundamental ambiguity in interpreting electronic spectra in terms of steric con-formation of conjugated systems about single bonds: *s–cis–trans*-isomerism and non-planarity can have closely similar spectral con-sequences. It should also be remembered that the competing energy factors which govern the choice of conformation are not large (usually less than 3 kcal. mole^{-1}) and that differences can easily become so small (*i.e.* less than 1 kcal. mole^{-1}) that equilibria between two or more forms will exist under ordinary conditions.

Diphenyls and other Diaryls

Data illustrating the fact that the near-ultra-violet light absorption characteristic of conjugated systems can, under certain circumstances, be profoundly influenced by substituents, such as methyl groups, which normally have only small spectral effects in this region, can be found in the literature from about 1930 onwards. The first definite suggestion that this phenomenon may arise from steric hindrance to uniplanarity appears to have been made by Kistiakowsky (1936) in connection with the spectra of *o*-substituted diphenyls, which were subsequently investigated and discussed in some detail by Rodebush and others (Lewis and Calvin, 1939; Calvin, 1939; O'Shaughnessy and Rodebush, 1940; Williamson and Rodebush, 1941; Friedel *et al.*, 1948; Braude, Sondheimer and Forbes, 1954). Diphenyl exhibits a K-band near 2500 Å which may be ascribed to the transitions from the homopolar ground state to a dipolar excited state represented as $^{+}$Ph=Ph^{-}. Rodebush found that whereas *m:m'*- and *p:p'*-ditolyl absorb similarly to diphenyl, in *o-o'*-ditolyl the K-band has almost completely vanished and the absorption closely resembles that of toluene (FIGURE 5). The two uniplanar forms (XIA and XIB) of

139

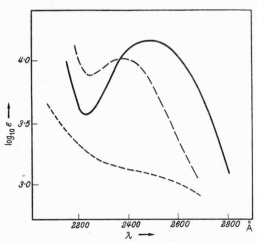

FIGURE 5.   Absorption curves of diphenyl (——),
o-methyldiphenyl (— — —) and *o*:*o'*-dimethyl-
diphenyl (– – – –) in ethanol

o:*o'*-ditolyl are related like *s–cis–trans*-forms one of which is much less
hindered than the other, but even in (XIA) there is considerable overlap between the *o*-methyl groups and the *o'*-hydrogen atoms, as shown
by the projection diagrams*.   The steric hindrance to uniplanarity is
evidently sufficient to cause the benzene rings to be rotated at a large
angle with respect to one another, so that conjugation is ineffective and

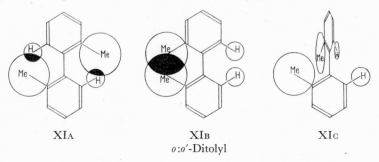

XIA   XIB   XIC
o:*o'*-Ditolyl

the two chromophores absorb almost independently.   The equilibrium
state of the molecule must be intermediate between the planar '*s–trans*'-
form (XIA) and the form (XIC) in which the rings are at right angles.

o-Methyldiphenyl, in which steric hindrance to uniplanarity is
approximately half as great as in *o*:*o'*-ditolyl, also shows a large spectral
difference (Friedel *et al.*, 1948;   Braude, Sondheimer and Forbes,
1954), but the K-band is still observable though it has been displaced
by 120 Å towards *shorter* wavelength as compared with diphenyl
(FIGURE 5).   The shift corresponds to a change in transition energy
of 5 kcal. mole^{-1} and represents the amount by which the potential

* The dimensions used in the diagrams are discussed on p. 146.

TABLE 4. ULTRA-VIOLET LIGHT ABSORPTION OF DIPHENYL AND SUBSTITUTED DIPHENYLS (ETHANOL SOLUTIONS)

Compound	λ_{max} Å	ε	Ref.*
XII (diphenyl)	2490	15000	a
XIII (Me-substituted)	2370	10500	a
XIV (Et-substituted)	2330	9000	a
XV (Me Me-substituted)	<2200	—	b
XVI (CH_2–CH_2 bridge)	2650	17000	c, d
XVII (MeO OMe, CH_2–CH_2 bridge)	2720	13500	d
XVIII (CH_2–O–CH_2 bridge)	2500	16500	d
XIX (MeO OMe, CH_2–O–CH_2 bridge)	2530	8700	d
XX (MeO HO OMe, CH_2/CH_2, CH_2/CHPh, NMe)	2800	6300	e

* References: a Braude et al., 1954; b O'Shaughnessy and Rodebush, 1940; c Jones, R.N., 1941; Braude, 1949; d Beaven et al., 1952; e Robinson, 1947; Bentley and Robinson, 1952. For similar diphenyl derivatives with an o:o' bridge, see Cookson and Mann, 1949; Beeby et al., 1950; Bergmann and Pelchowitz, 1953.

energy of the more rigid excited state has been raised in excess of that of the ground state (FIGURE 6). The replacement of the o-methyl substituent by ethyl, n-propyl or n-butyl has only a small effect, as might be expected since a longer alkyl chain can take up a position in which it contributes little additional overlap (Braude *et al.*, 1954). In contrast to $o:o'$-ditolyl, 9:10-dihydrophenanthrene (XVI), 2:7-dihydrodibenzoxepin (XVIII) and similar derivatives of diphenyl in which the $o:o'$-positions are bridged by a short two- or three-membered chain, exhibit K-bands in the same region as diphenyl or displaced to *longer* wavelength as a result of the normal substituent effects (TABLE 4; references there). In spite of some strain in the non-benzenoid ring, the two phenyl groups in these molecules must be held in approximately uniplanar positions such that the angle between them is little greater than in diphenyl itself* (Braude, 1951). On the other hand, phenyl-dihydrothebaine (XX) which contains a five-membered $o:o'$-bridge, exhibits no diphenyl-type absorption and must be highly non-planar; indeed, it was the abnormal optical properties which provided Robinson (1947, *cf* Bentley and Robinson, 1952) with the clue to the structure of this much-investigated compound.

Numerous other examples of spectral indications of steric hindrance in o-substituted diphenyls and related systems have been described during the last ten years (Krumholz, 1951; King *et al.*, 1951; Phillips and Graham, 1952). A suitably fused ring acts like an o-substituent; thus the spectrum of 2-phenylnaphthalene gives strong evidence of conjugation between the two aryl groups, whereas the spectrum of 1-phenylnaphthalene corresponds very nearly to a summation of benzene and naphthalene absorption (Friedel *et al.*, 1948). Similar effects have been noted in 9-arylated anthracene derivatives (Jones, 1941, 1947; Hirshberg, 1948) and 1-arylated anthraquinones (Braude, Fawcett and Webb, 1954).

In those systems (*e.g.* o-methyldiphenyl) which exhibit a displaced K-band, provided the assignment has been correctly made, it is possible in principle to calculate the angle of twist from the magnitude of the shift. In practice, however, this cannot at present be done reliably because the functional relation between interplanar angle (θ) and resonance energy (ΔE_R) is not known. Theoretically, the simplest functions which pass through the fixed points when $\theta = 0$ (max.) or $90°$ (min.) are $\Delta E_R = k$ (cos θ) and $\Delta E_R = k$ (cos θ)^2 which predict that as θ increases ΔE_R will at first fall quite slowly to $\sim 0.9\ E_R$ when $\theta = 25°$ and then increasingly rapidly (Guy, 1949). The relatively slight loss of

---

* The generally accepted correlation between conjugation and planarity has been challenged by Beaven, Hall, Lesslie and Turner (1952) on the grounds that atomic models indicate an angle of $20°$ between the planes of the benzene rings in 9:10-dihydrophenanthrene XVI, but an angle of $50°$ in dihydrodibenzoxepin XVIII. Rigid models, however, cannot afford a reliable *quantitative* indication of the fine-structure of a complex molecule and the interplanar angle deduced in this particular instance is almost certainly too large.

resonance interaction at small interplanar angles is made more probable by the fact that diphenyl itself, though uniplanar in the crystalline state (Dhar, 1932), is reported from electron diffraction measurements to deviate from planarity by $\sim 40°$ in the gaseous phase (Karle and Brockway, 1944; Bastiansen, 1949). Thus, it is more accurate to

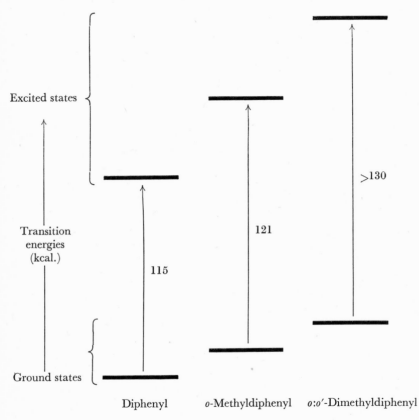

Excited states

Transition energies (kcal.)

>130

121

115

Ground states

Diphenyl   o-Methyldiphenyl   o:o'-Dimethyldiphenyl

FIGURE 6. Schematic representation of the K-band transitions in diphenyl and o-alkylated diphenyls

speak of near-planarity rather than uniplanarity as a condition of effective conjugation.

The steric effects which have such marked influence on the electronic spectra of substituted diphenyls are, of course, of the same type as those responsible for the longer-known occurrence of optical asymmetry in such systems (see Adams and Yuan, 1933 ; Adams and Finger, 1939) and realization of this fact materially assisted in interpreting the spectral phenomena. Quite apart from the fact that they are independent of the conditions of asymmetry, electronic spectra are, however, a much more sensitive index of restricted rotation than optical resolvability for two reasons. First, the existence of isolable optical isomers with life-times of the order of hours or days requires energy barriers of ~ 15 kcal. mole^{-1} or more (so as to prevent rapid racemization by thermal excitation), whereas the smallest significant wavelength displacements (~ 50 Å) correspond to energy increments of only about 1 or 2 kcal. mole^{-1} in the near-ultra-violet region. Secondly, optical resolvability is a function of the molecular ground state alone, whereas the spectral properties are conditioned by both the ground and excited electronic levels; and the excited levels are, as has already been discussed, particularly subject to steric effects. For this reason, a much higher degree of steric overlap is needed to produce optical resolvability than spectral phenomena; mono- and di-o-substituted diphenyls are only resolvable if the groups are very large, whereas even one o-methyl substituent brings about a large change in the spectrum.

Acetophenones

The substituted diaryls discussed in the preceding section provide typical examples of conjugated systems in which steric hindrance to near-planarity results either in a hypsochromic shift or in a complete disappearance of the characteristic K-band. A second, related class of steric effects, which is less common and has only been recognized more recently, involves a decrease in the K-band intensity alone, without any significant wavelength displacement. This class of steric effects has been studied most fully in aromatic and ethylenic ketones (O'Shaughnessy and Rodebush, 1940; Braude *et al.*, 1949, 1950, 1954; Ramart-Lucas and Hoch, 1952).

Benzaldehyde and acetophenone exhibit intense bands near 2400 Å which are ascribed to an allowed transition of the benzoyl chromophore which may be represented by Ph—C$=$O$\rightarrow$$^+Ph=$C—O$^-$. Methyl substituents in any of the three ring-positions cause only the normal, small bathochromic displacements ($+\Delta\lambda\simeq50$ Å); in the benzaldehydes, these are unaccompanied by any pronounced changes in intensity although closer inspection reveals that whereas m- and p-methyl groups increase ε slightly, o-methyl groups produce a small but definite decrease. In the acetophenones, m- and p-methyl groups also increase ε slightly ($+\Delta\varepsilon\simeq1,000$), but o-methyl groups produce a very marked decrease. The ratios of the observed ε to that expected (ε_0) on the assumption that, in the absence of a special ' ortho '-effect, o-methyl groups would increase ε by a similar amount as in other positions, range from 0·8 to 0·2 (TABLE 5)*. The fact that $\varepsilon/\varepsilon_0$ is much smaller

---

* The fact that the observed intensities of the K-bands of acetophenone and 2:4-dimethylacetophenone are almost equal led O'Shaughnessy and Rodebush (1940) to conclude that *two* o-methyl substituents are needed to produce steric effect in this system. Only when the increments in ε normally expected for methyl substituents are taken into consideration does the *ortho*- effect in 2:4-dimethylacetophenone become apparent (Braude *et al.*, 1954); the values of $\varepsilon/\varepsilon_0$ for this compound and for 2-methylacetophenone, where the effect is obvious, are in fact similar.

TABLE 5. ULTRA-VIOLET LIGHT ABSORPTION OF SUBSTITUTED BENZALDEHYDES AND ACETOPHENONES (HEXANE SOLUTIONS)*

Compound	λ_{max} (Å)	ε	$\varepsilon/\varepsilon_0$
BENZALDEHYDES			
Unsubstituted	2420	14000	1·00
4-Methyl	2510	15000	1·00
2-Methyl	2510	13000	0·87
2:6-Dimethyl (XXI)	2510	12500	0·78
2:4:6-Trimethyl	2640	14500	0·85
ACETOPHENONES			
Unsubstituted	2420	13000	1·00
4-Methyl	2520	15000	1·00
2-Methyl	2420	8500	0·58
2:4-Dimethyl	2510	13000	0·76
2:5-Dimethyl	2450	10000	0·59
2:6-Dimethyl (XXII)	2510	5500	0·32
2:4:6-Trimethyl	2420	3500	0·18

*Braude, Sondheimer and Forbes, 1954

for the ketones than for the aldehydes, and much smaller in the presence of two than in the presence of one *o*-substituent, excludes the possibility that hydrogen-bonding between the carbonyl and ring-methyl groups or similar phenomena might be responsible for the *ortho*-effects. The spectral differences between the substituted aldehydes and ketones are, however, explicable in terms of steric hindrance, which will be much more severe with the acetyl- than with the formyl-group. Projection diagrams (FIGURE 7) of the uniplanar structures, employing covalent

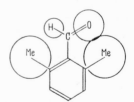

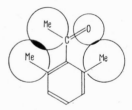

2:6-Dimethylbenzaldehyde (XXI)   2:6-Dimethylacetophenone (XXII)

FIGURE 7

radii (except for hydrogen, where a value of 0·6 Å is used), indicate no steric overlap of an *o*-methyl substituent with the hydrogen atom of the formyl group and only slight overlap with the oxygen atom, but very appreciable overlap with the acetyl–methyl group.

A few remarks concerning the choice of dimensions in scale-diagrams may be interpolated at this point. Steric overlap is commonly represented by the use of van der Waals' radii which are based on the equilibrium distances between non-bonded atoms in crystals. For the purpose of dealing with structural problems of liquid and gaseous substances, however, van der Waals' radii generally represent an excessively large measure of interatomic forces between non-bonded atoms within one molecule. The repulsion energies between atoms are highly exponential functions of distance and the magnitude of suitably representative interference radii will be closely dependent on the physical property under investigation. Absorption of ultra-violet light corresponds to energy increments of the order of 100 kcal. mole^{-1} and, as has already been mentioned, the smallest wavelength displacements ($\sim$50 Å) which are significant in the electronic spectra of organic compounds in solution represent energy differences of $\sim$ 1–3 kcal. mole^{-1}. Potential energy curves for the approach between non-bonded atoms are not yet accurately known except for a few atom pairs (Evans, 1946; Hill, 1948), but it is certain that interpenetration energies reach the order of 1–3 kcal. mole^{-1} at interatomic distances much nearer to the sum of the covalent radii (*i.e.* bond distances) than to the sum of the van der Waals radii. The fact that van der Waals' radii are too large a parameter for the present purpose is confirmed by the fact that many compounds in which appreciable steric overlap is indicated on a van der Waals scale (*e.g.* *o*-tolualdehyde) exhibit no, or only very slight, spectral anomalies. For these reasons, the projection diagrams in this chapter have been drawn using mainly covalent radii, which represent a minimum measure of steric interference properties (Braude, Jones *et al.*, 1949). The onset of spectrally detectable effects actually occurs somewhere between covalent and van der Waals' overlap, and this has been allowed for in the case of hydrogen to which an interference radius of 0·6 Å, intermediate between the covalent (0·3 Å) and van der Waals' (1·2 Å) radii, has been empirically assigned.

Returning now to the main theme, the fact that the K-bands of *o*-alkylated acetophenones show no abnormal wavelength displacements greater than 50 Å means that the steric effects in this system amount to less than 3 kcal. mole^{-1} and that the transition energy, and the spacings of the ground and excited electronic levels are not significantly altered. Since the nature of the transition remains unaltered, the transition moment associated with any individual absorption act must also be unchanged, yet the decrease in ε shows that the macroscopic transition probability is reduced. Such a phenomenon is not inherent in classical theory, but the following interpretation has recently been put forward by Braude, Sondheimer and Forbes (1954). In the ground electronic state of hindered acetophenones, the levels of torsional vibration about the Ph—CO link will be of the type indicated in FIGURE 8, giving a preferred angle θ_1 between the planes of the phenyl and carbonyl groups such that θ_1 lies between

$0°$ and $90°$. In the excited electronic state, in which the double bond character of the Ph—CO link is greatly increased owing to greater contributions from $^+$Ph=C—O$^-$, the preferred interplanar angle will have a smaller value θ_2. Now, the spacings of the torsional levels in a polyatomic molecule such as acetophenone are quite small (much less than 3 kcal. mole^{-1}) and several of the lower torsional levels will be

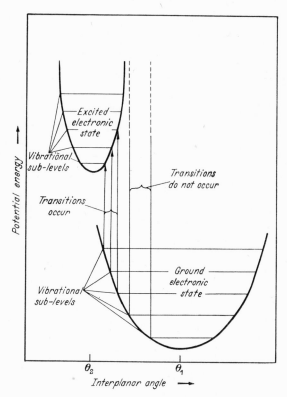

FIGURE 8. Electronic transitions between a non-planar ground state and a near-planar excited state

occupied by different molecules at room temperature. However, since the motion of electrons is very much faster than that of atomic nuclei (the Franck-Condon principle), the actual interplanar angle θ existing in any individual molecule at the moment of absorption cannot change during an electronic transition and only those molecules in which $\theta \simeq \theta_2$ will be able to undergo the transition. The fraction r of molecules fulfilling this condition will, on the simplest possible assumptions, be given by $\cos(\theta_1 - \theta_2)$. If the further assumption (which will be justified later) is made that $\theta_2 \simeq 0$, $i.e.$, that the chromophoric system must be almost truly uniplanar in the excited state, then $r \simeq \cos \theta_1$. But r is also given by $\varepsilon/\varepsilon_0$ where ε_0 is the value for the unhindered compound

147

in which $\theta_1 = 0$. Hence $\varepsilon/\varepsilon_0 \simeq \cos \theta_1$. The values of θ_1 derived in this way are given in TABLE 6 and indicate that one o-methyl substituent results in a mean interplanar angle of about 50°, and two o-methyl substituents in an angle of about 75° between the phenyl and carbonyl groups in the ground electronic state of acetophenones. If $\cos^2 \theta$ instead of $\cos \theta$ functions are used, the derived values of θ are reduced by 10–15°.

TABLE 6. INTERPLANAR ANGLES IN o-ALKYLATED ACETOPHENONES CALCULATED FROM DIPOLE MOMENTS AND ULTRA-VIOLET SPECTRA
(Braude, Sondheimer and Forbes, 1954)

Compound	μ_{obs} (D)	μ_0 (D)	θ_1°*	θ_1°†
ACETOPHENONE				
Unsubstituted	2·96	2·96	0	0
2-Methyl	—	2·86	—	55
2:4-Dimethyl	2·95	3·13	58	41
2:5-Dimethyl	2·85	2·96	61	54
2:6-Dimethyl	—	2·96	—	71
2:4:6-Trimethyl	2·81	3·03	78	80

* Calculated from μ † Calculated from ε

If these conclusions are correct, they should also be borne out by other physical properties strongly influenced by electronic interaction. One such property is the dipole moment. The values (μ_{obs}) determined for acetophenones by Bentley, Everard, Marsden and Sutton (1949) are shown in TABLE 6, together with the values (μ_0) calculated by vector addition of group moments for the uniplanar structures. The interplanar angle θ_1 is given by $\cos \theta_1 \simeq (\mu_{obs} - \mu_{90})/(\mu_0 - \mu_{90})$ where μ_{90} is the moment for the completely deconjugated system ($\theta_1 = 90$), taken to be the same as that of a saturated ketone (2·75D, the value for acetone). For the three compounds for which both spectral and dipole moment data are available, the values of θ_1 derived in this way are in good agreement, considering the approximations made and the sensitivity of the calculated value of θ_1 to uncertainties in μ. Moreover, since dipole moments are conditioned by the molecular ground states alone, this supports the assumption made above that $\theta_2 \simeq 0$.

We may thus distinguish clearly between two types of spectral effects arising from the steric hindrance to near-planarity in conjugated systems. Type 1 which is exemplified by the o-alkylated diphenyls and occurs when steric hindrance is strong, causes a change in both wavelength and intensity of a K-band and is associated with transitions between non-planar ground states and non-planar excited states. Type 2, which is exemplified by the o-alkylated acetophenones and occurs when steric hindrance is relatively weak, causes a decrease in absorption intensity alone and is associated with transitions between non-planar ground states and near-planar excited states.

Ethylenic Ketones

Steric effects of the type observed in acetophenones also occur in the alicyclic analogues, *i.e.* acetyl*cyclo*hexenes, as well as in open-chain ethylenic ketones. In these systems, matters are rendered somewhat more complicated than in the aromatic compounds by the possible incidence of *s–cis–trans*-isomerism, as well as of deviations from uni-planarity. The operation of dual steric effects both of which primarily influence absorption intensity has already been briefly mentioned in the case of acyclic dienes (p. 138).

Conjugated mono-ethylenic aldehydes and ketones exhibit strong K-bands in the 2200–2500 Å region which are ascribed to the allowed transition $C{=}C{-}C{=}O \rightarrow {}^+C{-}C{=}C{-}O^-$ and the exact location of which is controlled in a well-understood manner by the normal bathochromic influence of alkyl substituents. In open-chain ethylenic aldehydes, *e.g.* crotonaldehyde (**XXIII**) which have been shown by dipole moment (Bentley *et al.*, 1949) and electron-diffraction measurements (Mackle and Sutton, 1951) to exist predominantly in the *s–trans*-form at ordinary temperatures, the K-bands have ε-values of 16000–18000 (Evans and Gillam, 1943). Intensities of the same order are shown by cyclic ethylenic ketones with an enforced *s–trans*-form, whereas ketones with an enforced *s–cis*-form have ε-values of approximately 5000–10000, as expected from the relation $\varepsilon \sim l^2$ (*cf* p. 130) (Turner and Voitle, 1951; French and Wiley, 1949). Acyclic ketones, on the other hand, exhibit intermediate intensities (Braude, Jones *et al.*, 1949; Evans and Gillam, 1941) and the question arises whether this is due to *s–cis–trans*-isomerism or non-planarity or both. Dipole moment measurements indicate that mesityl oxide (**XXV**) exists entirely in the *s–cis*-form (Bentley *et al.*, 1949); this is understandable since the planar *s–trans*-form is strongly hindered, whereas the *s–cis*-form is unhindered and will be favoured in spite of its intrinsically lower resonance stabilization. No independent evidence is available for ethylidene acetone (**XXIV**), 1-formyl*cyclo*hexene (**XXVI**) and 1-acetyl*cyclo*hexene (**XXIX**) which have ε values almost identical with mesityl oxide (TABLE 7) although *s–trans*-forms of these compounds would be expected to be unhindered. It is, of course, possible that ε is structure-dependent owing to other factors than those considered, or that the compounds exist as mixtures of *s–cis* and *s–trans*-forms. (In that case, ε should be temperature-dependent, but this may not be readily detectable since the expected energy difference between *s–cis*- and *s–trans*-forms is quite small, ~ 3 kcal. mole^{-1}.)

Methyl substitution of the 2- or 6-positions of formyl*cyclo*hexene, as of benzaldehyde (p. 144), produces hardly any spectral abnormalities. On the other hand, alkylation of acetyl*cyclo*hexene causes very marked effects, similar to those observed in the acetophenones. However, whereas the two *o*-positions in the benzenoid system are equivalent

149

Formula	Compound	λ_{max} (Å)	ε	Ref.†
XXIII	MeCH:CH·CHO	2170	15600	a
XXIV	MeCH:CH·COMe	2240	9700‡	b
XXV	Me₂C:CH·COMe	2310	12000	c
XXVI		2290	12000	d
XXVII		2420	11000	d
XXVIII		2490	11600	d
XXIX		2320	12500	d
XXX		2450	6500	d
XXXI		2320	12000	d
XXXII		2430	1400	e
XXXIII		2240	12000	f
XXXIV		2520	6500	g

TABLE 8. ULTRA-VIOLET LIGHT ABSORPTION OF DIENONES AND TRIENONES OF THE β-IONONE TYPE (ETHANOL SOLUTIONS)§

Formula	Compound	Full chromophore 'Dienone' band		Partial chromophore 'Enone' band	
		$\lambda_{max}(\text{Å})$	ε	$\lambda_{max}(\text{Å})$	ε
XXXV	CH:CHCOMe (ring)	2810	20800	—	—
XXXVI	Me Me CH:CHCOMe (ring)	2810	13000	2280	4000
XXXVII	Me Me CH:CHCOMe Me (ring)	2960	10700	2230	6500
XXXVIIA	Me Me CH:CMeCOMe Me (ring)	2780	4500	2280	11600
		'Trienone' band		'Dienone' band	
XXXVIII	(CH:CH)₂COMe (ring)	3200	37500	—	—
XXXVIIIA	Me Me (CH:CH)₂COMe (ring)	3260	15500	2800	18500

§ Braude *et al.*, 1949, 1950, 1952.

* Ethanol is unsuitable for measurements on aldehydes owing to hemi-acetal formation.

† References: *a* Evans and Gillam, 1943; *b* Evans and Gillam, 1941; *c* Gray *et al.*, 1947; *d* Braude, Jones *et al.*, 1949; *e* Henbest and Woods, 1952; *f* Rigby, 1949; *g* French and Wiley, 1949.

‡ The low ε value for this compound may be due, in part, to admixture with the unconjugated isomer CH₂:CH·CH₂COMe.

(assuming no double bond fixation in the ring), the 2- and 6-positions in the *cyclo*hexene system are not equivalent and a 2-methyl substituent results in a much larger decrease in ε than two 6-methyl substituents. The effective interference dimensions in the two positions should be nearly the same, since one of two 6-methyl substituents must be ' quasi-equatorial ' and lie nearly in the plane of the ring (*cf* Chapter 2, p. 81), and several different interpretations of the data are possible. The most probable appears to be that 1-acetyl*cyclo*hexene and 6:6-dimethyl-1-acetyl*cyclo*hexene are mainly unhindered *s–trans*, that 2-methyl-1-acetyl*cyclo*hexene is hindered *s–trans*, and that 2:6:6-tri-methylacetyl*cyclo*hexene is strongly hindered *s–trans* or *s–cis*.

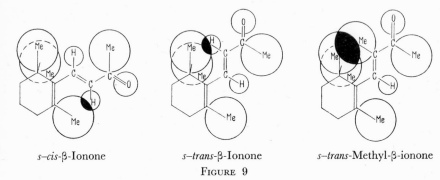

| *s–cis*-β-Ionone | *s–trans*-β-Ionone | *s–trans*-Methyl-β-ionone |

FIGURE 9

Somewhat similar observations have been made with diethylenic and triethylenic ketones of the β-ionone type, but here methyl substituents in the 6-position have a much larger effect than in the 2-position (for references, see TABLE 8). Moreover, in addition to the disappearance of the full-chromophore dienone or trienone bands, the simultaneous appearance of ' side-chain '-chromophore enone or dienone bands is observed (TABLE 8). These facts are best explained by assuming that alkyl substitution results in progressively non-planar *s–trans*-forms (FIGURE 9) rather than in changes from *s–trans* to *s–cis*. It appears that in these systems, the loss in resonance stabilization due to such a change would be greater than the loss in stabilization due to non-planarity in the *s–trans*-form. The conclusion that β-ionone derivatives exist in the hindered *s–trans*-form has recently been confirmed in the case of crystalline β-ionylidenecrotonic acid by an x-ray diffraction analysis (MacGillavry, Kreuger and Eichhorn, 1951). The spectra of vitamin A_1 and A_2 and of the corresponding aldehydes (retinene$_1$ and retinine$_2$) can be interpreted in a similar way (Oroshnik, Karmas and Mebane, 1952; Farrar, Hamlet, Henbest and Jones, 1952).

The importance of taking account of steric effects in the interpretation of the ultra-violet absorption of conjugated systems is illustrated very forcibly by the case of methylionone. The structure (XXXVIIA) assigned to this compound by Köster (1947) has been questioned by

Lusskin and Winston (1949) because of the virtual absence of a dienone band, but it is, in fact, fully compatible (Braude and Jones, 1950) with the spectral data since the methyl substituent in the side-chain will greatly enhance steric hindrance to uniplanarity as compared with β-ionone (*cf* FIGURE 9).

Interesting steric effects are also exhibited by ketonic derivatives of the acetyl*cyclo*hexene and β-ionone series (Braude, Jones *et al.*, 1949). Semicarbazones behave similarly to the ketones, but 2:4-dinitrophenyl-hydrazones, which absorb at much longer wavelengths, exhibit changes in band positions rather than intensities. This difference in behaviour is due to the fact that in the 2:4-dinitrophenylhydrazones, the characteristic chromophore band is centred in the dinitrophenyl group rather than in the diene system (Braude and Jones, 1945) and the partial chromophore band due to the side chain is located very close to the full chromophore band and is of almost identical intensity. As a result, the two bands effectively overlap and non-planarity of the *cyclo*hexene ring with the side-chain merely produces a small wavelength shift.

Other Conjugated Systems

In addition to those discussed in the two preceding sections, spectral effects ascribable to steric hindrance to near-planarity have been observed in many other types of conjugated systems and several hundred individual cases have been recorded during the last ten years. Only a few of these can be briefly mentioned here.

The conjugation between chromophores contained in medium-size (*i.e.* 7 to 12-membered) alicyclic rings is usually inhibited owing to the non-planarity of such structures. A good example is *cyclo*octatetraene which exhibits neither tetraene- nor aromatic-type absorption (Eccleston, Coleman and Adams, 1950), in agreement with its staggered ' crown '-structure (Person, Pimentel and Pitzer, 1952). Less complete de-conjugation is found in cyclic ethylenic ketones (Prelog *et al.*, 1948, 1949) and in α-diketones and their derivatives (Leonard *et al.*, 1950, 1953).

Steric hindrance in benzene derivatives containing unsaturated side-chains is very common. In addition to the acetophenones, reference has already been made to the stilbenes. Other cases of this type include substituted styrenes, benzoic acids and esters, aromatic nitro-compounds and azo-dyes (for references, see p. 175, D).

Steric effects somewhat analogous to those observed in diaryls have also been noted in condensed polycyclic benzenoid hydrocarbons (Badger *et al.*, 1950; Brockmann *et al.*, 1951, 1952; Newman and Wolf, 1952). In 4:5-dimethylphenanthrene and its derivatives, for example, the two substituents cannot be accommodated in the plane of the ring, and x-ray diffraction studies on related systems (Donaldson and Robertson, 1953) have indicated that the strain is relieved partly by an out-of-plane displacement of the substituents and partly by a distortion of the aromatic nucleus. Intra-molecular crowding of this type leads to a marked loss in vibrational fine-structure of the benzenoid absorption.

Steric Effects in π–p and π–σ Conjugation

Most of the examples so far mentioned involve steric inhibition of what may be termed π–π conjugation, *i.e.* interaction between two or more multiple bonds. Examples are also known of steric inhibition of π–p conjugation, *i.e.* interaction between multiple bonds and the unshared electron pairs of atoms such as nitrogen, and of steric inhibition of π–σ conjugation, *i.e.* interaction between multiple bonds and non-adjacent single bonds. Steric inhibition of π–p conjugation is well exemplified by substituted N-dialkylanilines (Remington, 1945; Platt and Klevens, 1949). The introduction of o-substituents results in the disappearance of a band near 2500 Å ascribed to the Ph—N̈ chromophore, and the decrease in intensity can be correlated with the size of the substituent. Similar effects have been noted in o-alkylated anisoles in which the band near 2700 Å associated with the Ph—Ö chromophore is weakened (Burawoy and Chamberlain, 1952).

Steric inhibition of π–σ conjugation has been observed in alkylated sorbyl and cinnamyl alcohols (Braude and Timmons, 1950; Braude and Coles, 1951). In the unhindered compounds, the —CH_2OH group has a well-defined bathochromic effect ascribed to interaction of the type $C{=}C{-}CR_2{-}OH \rightarrow {}^+C{-}C{=}CR_2$ OH^-. Such interaction is at a maximum when the C—O bond is at *right angles* to the plane of the C=C-bond (note the difference from π–π-conjugation) and is easily destroyed when the required orientation is subject to steric hindrance. This is well illustrated by the comparison of styryldimethylcarbinol (XXXIX) and α-methylstyryldimethylcarbinol (XL).

XXXIX   XL

The former compound exhibits a band at 2510Å (ε, 17,500) which is considerably displaced and intensified as compared with that of styrene at 2440Å (ε, 12,000). (That this displacement is mainly due

154

to the hyperconjugative effect of the hydroxyl rather than of the methyl substituents follows from the fact that there is much less difference in absorption between styrene and α- or β-methylstyrene, and between cinnamyl alcohol, $PhCH=CH \cdot CH_2OH$, and styryldimethylcarbinol.) By contrast, the absorption of the carbinol (XL) ($\lambda_{max.}$ 2450Å, ε, 11,500) is almost identical with that of styrene, evidently because of steric interference between the α-methyl and the other two methyl substituents, which prevents the —CMe_2OH grouping from taking up the most favourable conformation (that shown in the scale diagram) for hyperconjugative interaction.

Charge-resonance Systems

A further type of conjugation subject to steric effects occurs in charge-resonance systems such as represented by triphenylmethane dyes (Newman and Deno, 1951) and cyanine dyes (Brunings and Corwin,

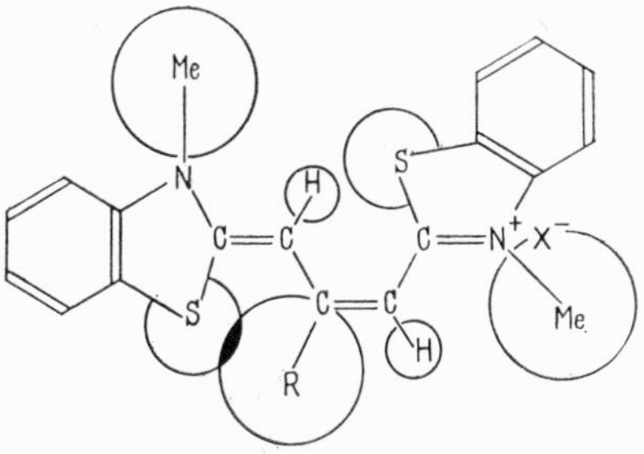

XLI

1942; Brooker *et al.*, 1947, 1953; Kiprianov *et al.*, 1950, 1952). In the latter, non-planarity results in a decrease in the intensity of the characteristic band accompanied by a displacement to *longer* wavelengths if the dye is highly symmetrical (TABLE 9; see last line). These are the only cases known in which non-planarity produces a bathochromic shift and although the effect is evidently related to the symmetry properties of the system, its detailed theoretical interpretation presents considerable difficulties.

TABLE 9. VISIBLE LIGHT ABSORPTION OF THIOCARBOCYANINES (XLI) IN METHANOL[*]

9-Substituent	λ_{max}(Å)	$\varepsilon \times 10^{-3}$
H	5550	149
Me	5380	122
Et	5425	118
Pr^i	5450	94
Bu^t	5875	21

[*] Brooker *et al.*, 1953

INFRA-RED LIGHT ABSORPTION IN RELATION TO
GEOMETRICAL ISOMERISM ABOUT DOUBLE BONDS

The application of infra-red spectroscopy to structural problems in complex molecules depends on the fact that, although a complete or exact analysis of the spectra is seldom feasible, it is nevertheless possible to assign prominent absorption bands to vibrational excitations of particular groups of atoms or bonds ('infra-red chromophores'). Such assignments are generally based on one or more of four methods. In the first, which is entirely empirical and the most widely used, the spectra of a large number of molecules containing a common structural unit are compared and bands of approximately constant frequency recurring in each spectrum are assigned to the common unit. The success of this procedure depends on the circumstance that vibrational energies and frequencies are primarily determined by atomic masses and by the relatively large forces between two atoms joined by a bond and between bonds joined to the same atom, whereas they are influenced to a smaller extent by the much weaker interaction between non-bonded atoms and non-adjacent bonds. Thus, although, strictly speaking, each vibration involves the molecule as a whole, the mechanical coupling between different bonds is often sufficiently weak to allow particular vibrations to be associated with particular bonds or groups. In the second method, which is semi-empirical and an extension of the first, the spectrum of a complex molecule is compared with that of a very simple molecule containing an identical structural feature and amenable to proper mathematical treatment, and the assignment of bands which correspond is made on this basis. A third method consists of comparing the infra-red and Raman spectra of the same molecule; the selection rules for the absorption and scattering processes are different, and vibrations excited by one often do not participate (are 'forbidden') in the other. Absorption can only take place if it is accompanied by a change in electrical polarization and the intensity of the band is related to the change in dipole moment, whereas Raman scattering must be accompanied by a change in molecular polarizability. The symmetry properties of the responsible structural unit can often be deduced in this way, and further information can be obtained by determining the degree of optical polarization of the Raman lines. A fourth method, which is the least widely used but has the soundest theoretical basis, is to compare the spectrum of the molecule with that of isotopic isomers. The replacement of one atom by an isotope (*e.g.* H by D) involves a known change in atomic mass but no significant change in interatomic forces, and the resulting frequency alterations can be easily calculated and identified.

Since geometrical isomerism about multiple bonds normally involves no changes in bond type, differences between the infra-red spectra of

geometrical isomers arise mainly from differences in symmetry properties and, to a lesser extent, from changes in non-bonded atom
and non-adjacent bond interactions. The first two methods of assignment mentioned above have been used most frequently in the interpretation of the spectra of geometrical isomers, but the Raman method
has also been applied, particularly with ethylenic compounds which
have been by far the most thoroughly investigated by spectroscopic
means from this point of view.

Ethylenic Compounds
Ethylene possesses twelve normal modes of vibration (FIGURE 10)

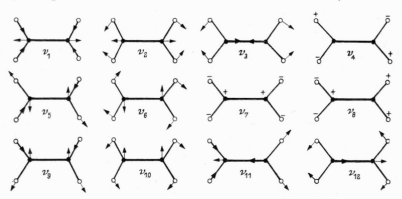

FIGURE 10. Normal vibrational modes of the ethylene molecule

which may be classified as (i) C—H stretching (ii) C=C stretching
(iii) C—H in-plane bending (iv) C—H out-of-plane wagging (v) CH_2
twisting. In the spectra of substituted ethylenes the number of bands
resulting from these modes is reduced according to the number of
ethylenic hydrogen atoms replaced by other groups, but in addition
there are bands due to vibrations of the substituent groups. In

TABLE 10. C=C STRETCHING FREQUENCIES IN ALKYLETHYLENES
(from Sheppard and Simpson, 1952)

Type	Frequency (cm^{-1})	Absorption Intensity
CHR^1:CH$_2$	1645	Medium
CHR^1:CHR^2 (*trans*)	1675	Weak
CHR^1:CHR^2 (*cis*)	1660	Medium
CR^{1}R^2:CH$_2$	1650	Medium
CR^{1}R^2:CHR^3	1670	Medium
CR^{1}R^2:CR^{3}R^4	1670	Very weak

symmetrically substituted ethylenes, C=C stretching involves no
change in dipole moment and hence does not give rise to infra-red

absorption; in other cases a weak or medium intensity band can be observed, the position of which is dependent on the substitutional pattern (TABLE 10). The molecular polarizability of the C=C group, on the other hand, is high so that C=C stretching vibrations give rise to strong Raman lines.

The C—H stretching frequencies occur in the range 3100–2950 cm^{-1} and are of medium intensity in infra-red absorption. The differences in these frequencies for *cis*- and *trans*-substituted ethylenes are generally too small, however, to render them of use for distinguishing between geometrical isomers.

Ethylenic C—H in-plane deformations give rise to medium intensity infra-red bands in the region 1450–1100 cm^{-1}, which have occasionally been employed in identifying substitution patterns, but they are less valuable for this purpose than the out-of-plane frequencies, which give rise to strong infra-red absorption (TABLE 11). As has already been

TABLE 11. ETHYLENIC C—H OUT-OF-PLANE DEFORMATION FREQUENCIES IN ALKYL ETHYLENES
(from Sheppard and Simpson, 1952)

Type	Frequency (cm^{-1})	Absorption Intensity
CHR^1:CH$_2$	990, 910	Strong
CHR^1:CHR^2 (*trans*)	965	Strong
CHR^1:CHR^2 (*cis*)	730–675	Usually strong
CR^{1}R^2:CH$_2$	890	Strong
CR^{1}R^2:CHR^3	830–800	Strong

mentioned, differences in the vibrational spectra of geometrical isomers are mainly due to symmetry differences. These are especially large in di-substituted ethylenes and it is in such systems, both acyclic (*e.g.* hex-3-ene, FIGURE 11) and alicyclic (*e.g. cyclo*decene) that infra-red light absorption has been most valuable (Blomquist *et al.*, 1952; Cope *et al.*, 1953). The use of infra-red spectra is, of course, not limited to the qualitative identification, but includes the quantitative analysis of mixtures of isomers (Barnes, Liddell and Williams, 1943; Anderson and Seyfried, 1948).

Me   CH$_2$Cl   Me   H

C=C   C=C

H   H   H   CH$_2$Cl

(XLIIA)   (XLIIB)

The infra-red frequencies characteristic of alkyl-substituted ethylenes undergo little or no change when atoms other than carbon and hydrogen are attached to carbon atoms removed from the double

158

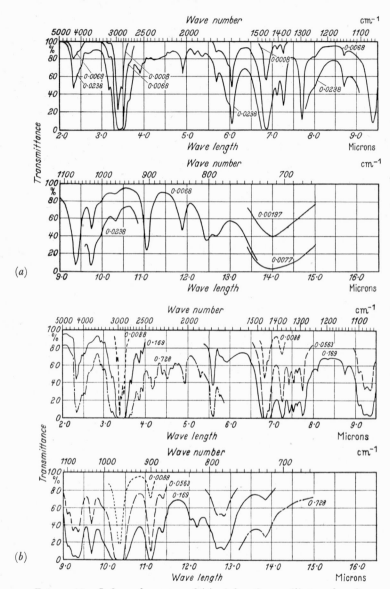

FIGURE 11. Infra-red spectra of (a) *cis*-hex-3-ene, (b) *trans*-hex-3-ene (American Petroleum Institute, Infra-red Spectra Nos. 1059 and 705)

bond; thus, the *cis*-isomer of crotyl chloride (XLIIA) has a band at 1660 cm^{-1}, while the *trans*-isomer (XLIIB) shows bands at 1675 and 960 cm^{-1} (Hatch and Nesbitt, 1950). In unsaturated carboxylic acids, the very strong C=O band overlaps the C=C stretching frequency which appears only as a shoulder, but esterification results in a shift of the C=O band to higher frequencies, thus enabling the C=C stretching frequency to be determined with more certainty. The

159

ethylenic C—H out-of-plane deformation frequency near 700 cm^{-1} in *cis*-isomers is often difficult to locate, but it is usually safe to make the assignment by showing that the medium intensity C=C stretching band near 1660 cm^{-1} is not accompanied by a strong band near 965 cm^{-1}, indicative of a *trans*-disubstituted isomer. In pure *trans*-dialkylethylenes, this band has an apparent molecular extinction coefficient (ε) of $\sim$150. The *cis*-isomers often have bands near this frequency but ε is rarely >20 (but see Allan and Whiting, 1953). In this way, it has been possible, for example, to confirm the *cis*-structures assigned to the naturally occurring isomers of 'leaf alcohol' (hex-3-en-1-ol), jasmone (**XLIII**), cinerolone (**XLIV**), selachyl

CMe:C·CH$_2$·CH:CH·CH$_2$Me $\qquad$ CMe:C·CH$_2$·CH:CH·Me

$\diagup$ CH$_2 \qquad\qquad\qquad\qquad$ HO·CH

$\diagdown$ CH$_2$—C:O $\qquad\qquad\qquad\qquad$ CH$_2$—C:O

$\qquad$ XLIII $\qquad\qquad\qquad\qquad\qquad$ XLIV

alcohol (D-α-oleyl glycerol ether) and oleic and linoleic acids and esters, all of which show a medium strength band near 1660 cm^{-1}, but only weak absorption near 965 cm^{-1}. The synthetically prepared *trans*-isomers of these compounds, the naturally occurring steroids containing the ergost-22-ene side chain, vaccenic acid and sphingosine, the common basic component of the sphingolipids on the other hand, have a strong band near 965 cm^{-1} and weak absorption near 1670 cm^{-1} (for references, see p. 176, E).

The differences in the spectra of stereoisomeric trialkylethylenes are much less marked (Barnard *et al.*, 1950; Cram, 1952 ; Dreiding and Pratt, 1954). Saunders and Smith (1949) have noted, however, that 3-methylpent-*cis*-2-ene, nerol (2:6-dimethylocta-*cis*-2:6-dienol) and hevea rubber (*cis*-polyisoprene) all show a band at 1640 cm^{-1} which is not present in 3-methylpent-*trans*-2-ene, geraniol and gutta percha. The *cis*- and *trans*-structures for hevea rubber and gutta percha have been confirmed by determining the polarization characteristics of the C=C stretching band (see also Sutherland and Vallance Jones, 1950).

In ethylenes in which atoms such as chlorine, oxygen and sulphur are attached directly to the double bond considerable shifts to lower frequencies occur in both the C=C stretching and the =C—H out-of-plane deformation bands, presumably as a consequence of resonance interaction (TABLE 12). In simple molecules of this type, the molecular geometry can be readily deduced from the infra-red and Raman spectra by a consideration of symmetry properties. Thus in the symmetrical *trans*-1:2-dichloroethylene the C=C stretching vibration appears as a strong line at 1576 cm^{-1} in the Raman spectrum, but

TABLE 12.   CHARACTERISTIC INFRA-RED FREQUENCIES (IN cm^{-1}) OF HALOGENATED
AND OTHER SUBSTITUTED ETHYLENES

The following symbols are used in TABLES 12 and 13: ν(C=C), stretching frequency; δ'(=C—H), out-of-plane deformation frequency; s, strong; m, medium; w, weak; *, not recorded or identification uncertain.

Compound	cis-Isomer		trans-Isomer		Ref.*
	ν(C=C)	δ'(=C—H)	ν(C=C)	δ'(=C—H)	
CH$_3$·CH:CH·Cl	1640; s	675; s	1650; s	930; s	a
CH$_2$Cl·CH:CH·Cl	1625; s	*	1625; s	938; s	b, c
CF$_3$·CH:CH·Cl	*	*	1650; s	935; s	b
CHCl:CHCl	1590; s	697; s	—	895; s	d
CH$_3$·CH:CH·Br	1614	685	1614	930; s	b, e
CH$_2$Br·CH:CH·Br	1595	680	1595	933; s	e
CF$_3$·CH:CH·Br	*	*	1645	934; s	b
CF$_3$·CH:CH·I	*	*	1613	940; s	b
C$_2$H$_5$·CH:CH·O·C$_4$H$_9$	1660; s	733; s	1665 ⎱ 1655 ⎰ ; s	933; s	f
CH$_3$·CH:CH·S·Ph	*	(710)†; s	*	938; s	g

* References: a Rasmussen, 1948; b Haszeldine, 1951, 1952; c Wolfe, et al., 1954; d Bernstein and Ramsay, 1949; e Hatch and Harwell, 1953; f Hall, et al., 1951; g Tarbell and McCall, 1952.
† From the spectrum of the sulphilimine.

TABLE 13.   CHARACTERISTIC INFRA-RED FREQUENCIES (IN cm^{-1}) OF ETHYLENES
CONTAINING CONJUGATED UNSATURATED GROUPS

Compound	cis-Isomer		trans-Isomer		Ref.*
	ν(C=C)	δ'(=C—H)	ν(C=C)	δ'(=C—H)	
CH$_3$·CH:CHPh	1653; w	769 (?); s	1667; m	962; s	a
CH$_3$·CH(OH)·CH:CH·Ph	1645; w	*	1655; w	970; s	b
Ph·CH:CH·Ph	*	*	—	964; s	c
CHBr:CH·Ph	*	770(?); s	*	935; s	d
CH$_3$·CH:CH·C⋮CH	1623; w	723; s	1634; w	956; s	e
CH$_3$·CH:CH·CHO	*	*	1645; m	970; s	f
(C$_4$H$_9$)$_n$·CH:CH·CO$_2$H	1642	*	1652	984; s	g
C$_7$H$_{15}$·CH:CH·CO NH·C$_4$H$_9$	1660	*	1671	977; s	g

* References: a Mixer, et al., 1953; b Philpotts and Thain, 1950; Braude and Coles, 1951; c Thompson, et al. 1950, Brackman and Plesch, 1952; d Grovenstein and Lee, 1953; e Allan and Whiting, 1953; f Rasmussen, 1948, Hall, et al., 1951, cf Sondheimer, 1952; g Crombie, 1952, see also Sinclair, et al., 1952; Freeman, 1953.

there is no band near this frequency in the infra-red spectrum.   In the cis-isomer, on the other hand, the C=C stretching vibration gives rise to a strong infra-red band at 1590 cm^{-1} as well as to a strong Raman line at 1587 cm^{-1} (references, p. 176, F).   Similar differences appear in the spectra of the fully deuterated isomers.   Although trans-1:2-dichloropropene is not symmetrical, the change in dipole moment resulting from C=C stretching is small and gives rise to weak absorption, as compared with the strong band at 1615 cm^{-1} due to this vibration

in the *cis*-isomer. Using similar arguments, structures can be assigned
to the isomeric forms of 2:3-dichlorobut-2-ene, 1:2:3-trichloropropene
and 2:3-dichloro-1-hydroxypropene (reference, p. 176, F).
The effect of conjugated unsaturated groups on the infra-red absorption associated with ethylenic bonds has been investigated in some
detail (TABLE 13). Conjugated phenyl groups produce only small shifts
in the ethylenic C—H out-of-plane deformation frequencies. A band
near 970 cm⁻¹ appears in the spectra of the *trans*-isomers of β-methylstyrene (Mixer *et al.*, 1953), styrylmethylcarbinol (Braude and Coles,
1951; Philpotts and Thain, 1950) and of stilbene (Thompson *et al.*, 1950),
thus enabling them to be distinguished from the *cis*-isomers, which have
weaker absorption in this region but stronger bands near 1660 cm⁻¹ (see
also Brackman and Plesch, 1952). Conjugation with carbonyl groups,
on the other hand, results in more marked deviations of the characteristic
ethylenic frequencies from the values found for simple olefins. The
C=C stretching band moves to lower, and the C—H out-of-plane
deformation band, to higher frequencies. Similarly, conjugation with
an acetylenic bond, as in pent-2-en-4-yne, has a marked effect (Celmer
and Solomons, 1953; Allan and Whiting, 1953).
In conjugated dienes, the C=C stretching vibrations are coupled,
resulting in two frequencies, the mean of which is considerably lower
than the values characteristic of unconjugated double bonds.
Depending on the symmetry of the molecule, one or both of the
frequencies, which are usually near 1655 and 1600 cm⁻¹, may be
observed in the infra-red spectrum (Sheppard and Simpson, 1952).
The ethylenic C—H out-of-plane deformation frequencies are again
extremely useful in identifying stereoisomers as they show characteristic
differences for the three possible structures (TABLE 14).

TABLE 14. ETHYLENIC C—H OUT-OF-PLANE DEFORMATION FREQUENCIES (IN cm⁻¹)
FOR COMPOUNDS OF THE TYPE R·CH:CH·CH:CH·R*

Configuration	Frequency	Intensity
trans–trans	990	Very strong
cis–trans	{985 950	}Strong
cis–cis	{985 950	}Medium

* References: Jackson *et al.*, 1952; Privett *et al.*, 1953; Celmer and Solomons, 1953; Crombie, private
communication.

Crombie (1952) has confirmed the structures of the isomeric
*N-iso*butylundeca-1:7-diene- and *N-iso*butylnona-1:5-diene- carboxy-
amides, synthesized in an attempt to determine the structures of the
naturally-occurring insecticides herculin and pellitorine, from their
infra-red spectra. The isolated double bonds give rise to bands at the
same frequencies as simple olefins, but the bands associated with the

162

conjugated double bonds show shifts similar to those of the model compounds in TABLE 13. As in simpler structures (*cf* p. 161), the ethylenic C—H out-of-plane deformation frequency in the *cis*-isomers is difficult to identify, although a band at 825 cm^{-1} has been associated with this vibration in *cis*-octadeca-2-enoic acid (Sinclair *et al*, 1952).

Similar differences characterize the ethylenic C—H out-of-plane deformation frequencies of conjugated trienes (Paschke, Tolberg and Wheeler, 1953). Thus β-eleostearic acid (octadeca-*trans*-9:*trans*-11: *trans*-13-trienoic acid) and pseudoeleostearic acid (the corresponding *trans*-10:*trans*-12:*trans*-14-isomer) show single very strong bands at 993cm^{-1}, whereas α-eleostearic acid (the *cis*-9:*trans*-11:*trans*-13-isomer), has two bands at 991 and 963 cm^{-1}, of strong and medium intensity respectively. Another octadeca-9:11:13-trienoic acid, punicic acid, shows bands at 991 and 941 cm^{-1} and also contains *cis*- and *trans*-substituted bonds.

Azo- and Azomethine Derivatives
Geometrical isomerism is common in compounds containing C=N and N=N groups and the symmetry differences between the *cis*- and *trans*-isomers are similar to those found in ethylenic systems, but no systematic infra-red investigation has yet been carried out.

Tetlow (1950) has shown that the *cis*- and *trans*-isomers of azobenzene have markedly different infra-red spectra, characteristic bands being shown at 1157, 970 and 755 cm^{-1} by the *cis*-isomer and at 1300 and 1225 cm^{-1} by the *trans*-isomers. The two forms also show differences in the 6 μ region, but have no bands that may be attributed to N—H stretching vibrations near 3300 cm^{-1} which refutes the suggestion of Hodgson (1948) that the *cis*-(unstable) isomer is a mixture of hydrazobenzene and azoxybenzene. It may be noted that the N=N stretching vibration probably occurs near 1580 cm^{-1} (Le Fèvre *et al*., 1953).

Anderson, Le Fèvre and Savage (1947) have found that the unstable *cis*-isomers of diazocyanides show a characteristic pattern of bands, the origin of which is uncertain, in the region 900–800 cm^{-1}, whereas

XLV   XLVI

XLVII

163

no such bands are observed in the stable *trans*-isomers. By this means, it was shown that the stable form of diphenyl-4:4'-bisdiazocyanide, which exists in only two of the three possible stereoisomeric forms (XLV, XLVI and XLVII), contains no *cis*-azo-groups and hence must have the *trans–trans*-structure (XLVII) in agreement with dipole moment evidence (Le Fèvre and Vine, 1938).

Hendricks, Wulf, Hilbert and Liddel (1936) have elucidated the stereochemistry of *o*-hydroxyphenyl derivatives of the type $2\text{-HO·C}_6\text{H}_4\text{·X=N·Y}$ where X is carbon or nitrogen and Y is carbon, nitrogen or oxygen, by determining whether the hydroxyl group is inter- or intra-molecularly hydrogen-bonded. Only the *trans*-isomers can undergo intramolecular bonding involving the unshared electron pair of the nitrogen atom and therefore fail to show the first overtone of the O—H stretching frequency, whereas this appears in the spectra of dilute solutions of the *cis*-isomers as a sharp band in the region $7500\text{–}6200\ \text{cm}^{-1}$.

INFRA-RED LIGHT ABSORPTION IN RELATION TO THE CONFORMATION OF ALICYCLIC RINGS

Although the possible existence of ' chair ' and ' boat ' forms of *cyclo*-hexane was already recognized by Sachse in 1890, the problem of the ' labile ' stereochemistry of alicyclic ring systems has only been seriously tackled within the last decade (*cf* Chapter 2). Rapid progress has been possible as the result of the simultaneous application of several modern physical methods of structural investigation and infra-red spectroscopy has made important contributions to these developments.

The infra-red spectrum of *cyclo*hexane itself is amenable to mathematical analysis as a result of the high degree of symmetry of the molecule, and it has been pointed out by Rasmussen (1943) that the number of bands which have been observed place the molecule in the D_{3d} symmetry group as required by the ' chair ' structure. Ramsay and Sutherland (1947) subsequently calculated the vibrational frequencies for a model consisting of six points of equal mass arranged in a puckered regular hexagon in the chair form and found them to be in satisfactory agreement with the experimentally determined values. The Raman spectrum of *cyclo*hexane has also been examined and provides information concerning the spatial arrangement of the constituent atoms. The degree of optical polarization of the scattered light is dependent on the symmetry properties of the vibrations concerned and it was first reported that this indicates a planar structure for *cyclo*hexane. Subsequent investigations have shown, however, that polarization data for the Raman spectrum support the predominance of the ' chair form ' (Langseth and Bak, 1940; Kohlrausch and Wittek, 1941; Gerding *et al.*, 1942).

Substituted cycloHexanes

It was pointed out by Hassel (1943) that in the chair-form of *cyclo*-hexane, six of the C—H bonds lie roughly in the general plane of the ring while the other six are oriented perpendicular to it (*cf* Chapter 2). The two types of bonds have been referred to as ' κ ' and ' ε ' or ' equatorial ' and ' polar ' (now ' axial ', *cf* p. 38). Mono-substituted *cyclo*hexanes can exist in two forms in which the substituent occupies either of the possible positions and which should exhibit different vibrational spectra. An assignment can often be made from the fine-structure shown by the vibrational bands when measured in the vapour-phase and which is due to the existence of a series of rotational states associated with each vibrational level. The rotational pattern depends on the relative orientations of the transition moment of the vibration and on the principal moments of inertia of the molecule, and although it is fully resolved only in small, symmetrical structures, useful information can be obtained from the band-contours of quite large molecules provided they possess some symmetry (Gerhard and Dennison, 1933; Badger and Zumwalt, 1938). In this way, Larnaudie (1952) has assigned the bands at 2146 and 2174 cm^{-1} in monodeutero*cyclo*hexane to the C—D stretching vibrations of the axial (*a*) and equatorial (*e*) forms, respectively; the bands are of equal intensity, indicating roughly equal amounts of the two forms. In monohalogeno*cyclo*hexanes, on the other hand, the C—halogen stretching bands attributed to the equatorial forms are considerably stronger than those attributed to the axial form, while in the case of methyl*cyclo*hexane it is concluded that the equatorial form is present exclusively.

Larnaudie (1953) also examined the infra-red spectra of a number of disubstituted *cyclo*hexanes $C_6H_{10}X_2$; the values of the C—X stretching frequencies and the assignments are shown in TABLE 15.

TABLE 15. C—X STRETCHING FREQUENCIES IN DISUBSTITUTED *cyclo*HEXANES ($C_6H_{10}X_2$)

Compound	ν_{C-X}(cm^{-1})	Conformation
trans-1:2-$C_6H_{10}(OH)_2$	1072, 1081	Diequatorial chair
trans-1:2-$C_6H_{10}Cl_2$	707	Diequatorial chair
	738, 745	Diaxial chair
trans-1:2-$C_6H_{10}Br_2$	651, 663·5	Diequatorial chair
	685·5, 697	Diaxial chair
trans-1:4-$C_6H_{10}Cl_2$	760	Diequatorial chair
	783	Diaxial chair
trans-1:4-$C_6H_{10}Br_2$	729	Diequatorial chair
	740	Diaxial chair
cis-1:4-$C_6H_{10}Br_2$	630, 638	Equatorial, axial chair
	712, 734	Boat
cis-1:4-$C_6H_{10}Cl_2$	754, 758, 773, 781,	$\int$ Equatorial, axial chair
	660(?), 681(?), 716(?)	$\big\{$ and boat

The data indicate that while *trans-cyclo*hexane-1:2-diol exists entirely in the diequatorial chair form, the corresponding dichloro- and dibromo-*cyclo*hexanes are equilibrium mixtures of diequatorial and diaxial chair forms in agreement with evidence from dipole moments (Tulinskie *et al.*, 1953). The existence of similar equilibria in *trans*-1:4-dichloro- and dibromo-*cyclo*hexanes is indicated by the observation that the relative intensities of the bands vary according to the state of the sample. Kozima and Yoshino (1953) similarly concluded, from Raman data, that *trans*-1:4-dichloro- and dibromo-*cyclo*hexanes exist as equilibrium mixtures of $1a:4a$ and $1e:4e$-forms in solution, but that the $1a:4a$-form is the more stable in solution, whereas only the $1e:4e$-form can be detected in the solid. These conclusions may well be correct, but the assignments should not be regarded as completely certain in the absence of corroborative evidence since the frequencies may be somewhat dependent on intermolecular influences.

The conformations of *cyclo*hexanediols have been deduced by Kuhn (1952) from a study of the effects of hydrogen-bonding on the O—H stretching frequencies. Intermolecular hydrogen-bonding is readily detected by observing the dependence of the relative intensities of the sharp band associated with an unbonded and the broad band associated with a bonded OH group on the concentration of the diol in a suitable non-polar solvent. If hydrogen-bonding is entirely intramolecular, the relative intensities are independent of concentration and the difference in frequency of the two bands is a measure of the distance between the oxygen atoms. It is found that intramolecular hydrogen-bonding occurs only if the separation of the oxygen atoms of the two hydroxyl groups does not exceed about 3·3 Å. Thus, in *trans-cyclo*hexane-1:2-diol, which exhibits intramolecular bonding, the hydroxyl groups must be equatorial (O—H . . . O distance = 2·34 Å, assuming the ring to be in the chair form) and not axial (O—H . . . O distance > 3·3 Å), in agreement with Larnaudie's results, whereas in *cis-cyclo*hexane-1:3-diol, the hydroxyl groups must be axial (O—H . . . O distance = 1·64 Å) and not equatorial (O—H . . . O distance > 3·3 Å).

The infra-red and Raman spectra of the five isomeric hexachloro-*cyclo*hexanes and of certain more highly substituted derivatives have also been analysed (Milone and Borello, 1953; Riemschneider, 1953; Zbinden, 1953).

Fused Alicyclic Ring Systems
Whereas substituted *cyclo*hexanes can exist in labile stereoisomeric forms, alicyclic systems containing two or more fused rings give rise to stable conformations. The use of infra-red spectra for the elucidation of such stereoisomerism has been particularly fruitful in steroid chemistry, although the methods of assignment have necessarily been entirely empirical.

R. N. Jones and his co-workers (Jones *et al.*, 1951, 1953; Cole *et al.*, 1952) have noted that the conformation of the C—O bond in 3-hydroxy and 3-acetoxy steroids, as deduced from chemical evidence, may be correlated with the frequency of the C—O stretching vibration and the complexity of the acetate band near 1240 cm^{-1}. These investigations have been extended by others, with the results summarized in TABLE 16 (*cf* Fürst *et al.*, 1952; Rosenkrantz and Zablow, 1953).

TABLE 16. HYDROXYL AND ACETOXYL ABSORPTION BY AXIAL AND EQUATORIAL SUBSTITUENTS

Compound type	A/B ring fusion	Conformation of C—O	ν(C—O) cm^{-1}	Acetate band-type (1230 cm^{-1})
Cholestan { -2α-ol	trans	Equatorial	1030	Simple
-2β-ol		Axial	1010	Complex
-3α-ol		Axial	1000	Complex
-3β-ol		Equatorial	1040	Simple
-4α-ol		Equatorial	1040	Complex
-4β-ol		Axial	1000	Complex
Cholest-5-en-3β-ol	—	Equatorial	1050	Simple
Coprostan-3α-ol	cis	Equatorial	1040	Simple
Coprostan-3β-ol	cis	Axial	1030	Complex

It will be noted that equatorial hydroxyl groups give rise to bands near 1040 cm^{-1} and that equatorial acetoxyl substituents give rise to single bands in the 1240 cm^{-1} region, whereas for axial hydroxyl groups the C—O frequencies are near 1000 cm^{-1} and the acetate bands are complex. (Exceptions to this general rule are provided, however, by the 3-hydroxy-5β-steroids which show little difference in C—O frequencies for the two conformations (Cole *et al.*, 1952), and by 4α-acetoxycholestane (Fürst *et al.*, 1952) and a few other acetates which also show complex rather than single-band absorption near 1240 cm^{-1}.) The difference in the frequencies due to the two types of hydroxyl substituents may be ascribed to a difference in the restoring forces exerted by the ring on the C—O stretching vibrations (Cole *et al.*, 1952). Contrary to some suggestions (see also Rosenkrantz *et al.*, 1952), neither the C—O frequencies nor the structure of the 1240 cm^{-1} acetate band can be correlated with the configuration of the hydrogen atom at the A/B ring-junction (Cole, 1952) but the multiplicity in the acetate band may be due to the presence of labile rotational isomers of slightly differing energy, since free rotation is more likely for equatorial than for axial acetoxyl groups, independently of their position in the ring (Jones *et al.*, 1951).

Cole (1952) has used the above correlations to show that lumistan-3β-ol (FIGURE 12), which shows a strong band due to C—O stretching at 1010 cm^{-1} and the acetate of which exhibits complex absorption near 1240 cm^{-1}, has an axial hydroxyl group. The epimer, lumistan-3α-ol, shows a C—O stretching frequency at 1034 cm^{-1} and possesses an equatorial hydroxyl group as expected from the method of preparation.

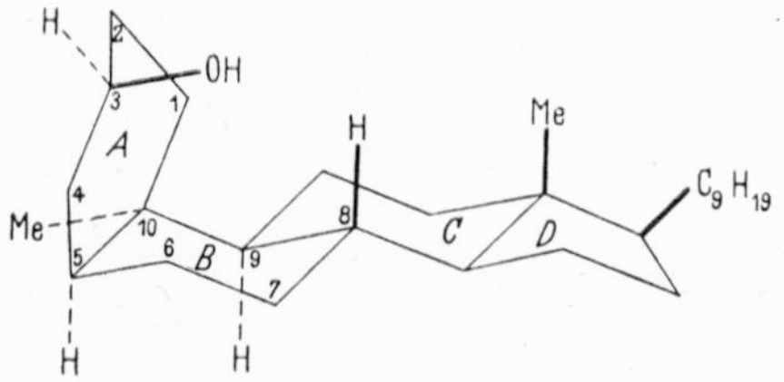

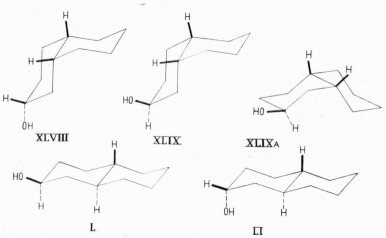

FIGURE 12.   Lumistan-3β-ol

The same empirical rules have also been shown to apply to bicyclic systems.   The four isomeric 2-decalols (XLVIII, m.p. 105°; XLIX, m.p. 18°; L, m.p. 75°; and LI, m.p. 53°), have, according to chemical evidence, the structures shown below (Dauben and Hoerger, 1951). Dauben, Hoerger and Freeman (1952) have compared the infra-red spectra of the decalols and their acetates with the data obtained for analogous steroids.   The acetates of XLVIII and L show one band

FIGURE 13.   Stereochemistry of the isomeric 2-decalols

near 1240 cm^{-1} (although the acetate of L shows two bands under high resolution), as expected for equatorial substituents, while the acetates of XLIX and LI exhibit complex bands in this region, in agreement with the axial conformation.   The differences in the spectra of the alcohols themselves are not as clearly defined, more complex absorption being found in the region 1050–1000 cm^{-1} than in corresponding hydroxysteroids, but they, nevertheless, support the assigned structures.   Consideration of the correlations established for steroids

(TABLE 16) indicates that the C—O frequencies of structures XLVIII, XLIX and L should be rather similar and located between 1040 and 1030 cm^{-1}, but that the C—O frequency in structure LI may be expected to be near 1000 cm^{-1}. Mills (1953) has pointed out that *any* monosubstituted *cis*-decalin derivative can exist with its substituent equatorial, on account of the flexibility of the *cis*-decalin system (*cf* p. 41); the 2-decalol of m.p. 18° may therefore exist as a mixture of the conformations XLIX and XLIXA.

Similar empirical methods have been developed for steroids containing other types of functional groups. Jones and his co-workers have investigated the infra-red spectra of a large number of steroids containing carbonyl functions, and have shown that not only the type of carbonyl group (ester, ketone, *etc*), but also its position in the molecule, can be distinguished by means of the C=O stretching frequency. The bromination of ketosteroids is a reaction frequently used in steroid chemistry but the position of substitution and extent of reaction are not always evident. Jones, Humphries and Dobriner (1950) suggested that bromination α- to the carbonyl group results in an increase in the C=O frequency and also distinguished between 2:2- and 2:4- dibromo-3-oxosteroids in this way. Subsequent work has shown, however, that α-bromination in 3-, 7-, 11-, and 12-oxosteroids does not invariably result in an appreciable C=O frequency shift. Data for an epimeric pair of 11-bromo-12-ketones, in which the configurations of the bromine atoms are known from chemical evidence, indicate that a shift of about 20 cm^{-1} occurs only when the C$_\alpha$—Br and C=O groups are roughly co-planar, that is when the bromine is equatorial in the chair or axial in the boat form of the *cyclo*hexanone ring (R. N. Jones *et al.*, 1952; R. N. Jones, 1953). Jones has suggested that in such planar conformations the single-bond character of the carbonyl group will be decreased by the field effect of the C—Br bond, and that this field effect will be negligible in the non-planar conformations. The assumption that the steroid ring A maintains its chair conformation on bromination, has been criticized on the grounds that ring A is not rigid and may well take up the boat conformation if there is appreciable steric interaction between the bromine atom and the methyl group at C-10 in the chair form. The conclusion, based on an assumed chair conformation for the *cyclo*hexanone ring, that the C—Br bonds in 2-bromocholestan-3-one and 4-bromocoprostan-3-one are equatorial is, however, in agreement with the chemical evidence which indicates α- and β-configurations, respectively, for the bromine substituent in these two compounds (Jones, 1953; Fieser *et al.*, 1953; Corey, 1953c, 1954).

It has recently been shown that equatorial and axial bromine substituents next to a carbonyl group can also be distinguished by their effect on the low-intensity ultra-violet absorption band associated with the keto group (Cookson, 1954; *cf* Barr *et al.*, 1938).

The chair form has been assumed to be the stable conformation of simple α-brominated *cyclo*hexanones and Corey (1953a) has deduced that the C—Br bond in 2-bromo*cyclo*hexanone is axial since the C=O frequency in this compound is only 4 cm^{-1} greater than in *cyclo*-hexanone itself (1712 cm^{-1}). In 2-bromo-4:4-dimethyl*cyclo*hexanone the C=O frequency shows a shift of 16 cm^{-1}, suggesting that the bromine is equatorial so that steric interaction with the methyl groups is a minimum. A shift of similar magnitude (22 cm^{-1}) occurs in 7-bromo*spiro*-(4:5)decan-6-one, but a weak band at 1701 cm^{-1} may be due to the axial bromide.

Infra-red spectroscopic studies have also led to the elucidation of the stereochemistry of dibromo*cyclo*hexanones (Corey, 1953b). Three solid isomers, all containing the bromine substituents adjacent to the carbonyl group, are known. One of these isomers, of m.p. 49°, which shows a carbonyl stretching frequency at 1727 cm^{-1}, is known from chemical evidence to be 2:2-dibromo*cyclo*hexanone, but the structures of the other two remained uncertain, despite extensive investigations by Wallach. Corey found that one of these isomers of m.p. 110°, has a carbonyl band at 1750 cm^{-1}; the shift of 38 cm^{-1} with respect to the carbonyl band of *cyclo*hexanone corresponds to the presence of two equatorial substituents and indicates that this isomer is *cis*-2:6-dibromo*cyclo*hexanone. The third isomer, of m.p. 36°, must be *trans*-2:6-dibromo*cyclo*hexanone and has a carbonyl frequency of 1732 cm^{-1}, in agreement with the presence of one equatorial and one axial substituent.

Frequency differences similar to those found for alicyclic α-brom-ketones have been observed with epimeric alkylated ketones, but the

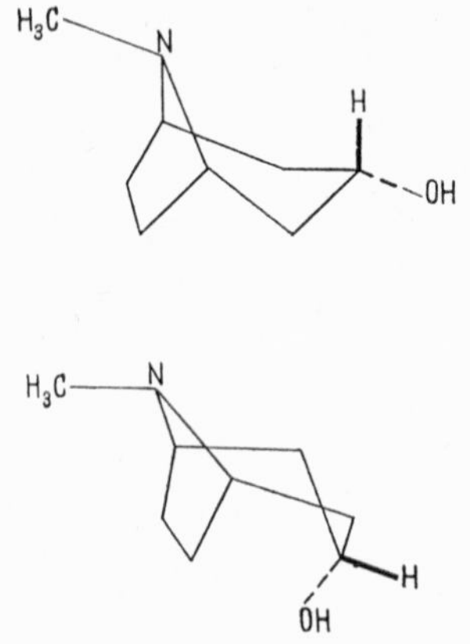

Tropine
LII

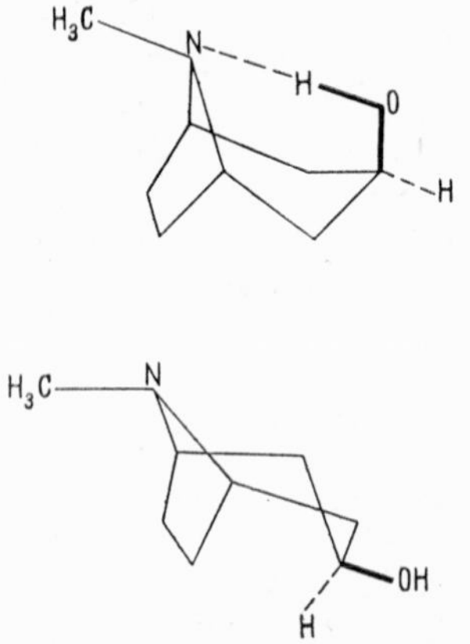

Pseudotropine
LIII

data at present available are insufficient for any safe generalizations to be made (Lukes *et al.*, 1953).

Pseudotropine—The use of hydrogen-bonding in determining the conformation of alicyclic ring compounds (Kuhn, 1952) has been noted previously (see p. 166). An important application of this method has been the confirmation of the structures assigned to tropine and pseudotropine from chemical evidence; intramolecular hydrogen-bonding is detectable in pseudotropine (LIII) but not in tropine (LII), so that the former must have the *cis*-structure (Zenitz *et al.*, 1952; for further discussion of these compounds see p. 81).

REFERENCES

Adams, R. and Finger, G. C. (1939) *J. Amer. chem. Soc.* **61,** 2828
— and Yuan, H. C. (1933) *Chem. Rev.* **12,** 261
Allan, J. L. H. and Whiting, M. C. (1953) *J. chem. Soc.* 3314
Anderson, D., Le Fèvre, R. J. W. and Savage, J. (1947) *ibid* 445
Anderson, J. A. and Seyfried, W. D. (1948) *Analyt. Chem.* **20,** 998
Arnold, R. T., Webers, V. J. and Dodson, R. M. (1952) *J. Amer. chem. Soc.* **74,** 368
Aston, J. G., Szasz, G., Wooley, H. W. and Brickwedde, F. G. (1946) *J. chem. Phys.* **14,** 67
Badger, G. M., Campbell, J. E., Cook, J. W., Raphael, R. A. and Scott, A. I. (1950) *J. chem. Soc.* 2326
Badger, R. M. and Zumwalt, L. R. (1938) *J. chem. Phys.* **6,** 711
Bailey, W. J. and Golden, H. R. (1953) *J. Amer. chem. Soc.* **75,** 4780
Barnard, D., Bateman, L., Harding, A. J., Koch, H. P., Sheppard, N. and Sutherland, G. B. B. M. (1950) *J. chem. Soc.* 915
Barnes, R. B., Liddel, U. and Williams, V. Z. (1943) *Industr. Engng. Chem. (Anal.)* **15,** 659
Barr, T., Heilbron, I. M., Jones, E. R. H. and Spring, F. S. (1938) *J. chem. Soc.* 334
Barton, D. H. R. (1953) *ibid* 1027
— and Brooks, C. J. W. (1951) *ibid* 257
Bastiansen, O. (1949) *Acta chem. Scand.* **3,** 408
Beale, R. N. and Roe, E. M. F. (1952) *J. Amer. chem. Soc.* **74,** 2302 ; (1953) *J. chem. Soc.* 2755
Beaven, G. H., Hall, D. M., Lesslie, M. S. and Turner, E. E. (1952) *ibid* 854
Beeby, M. H., Mann, F. G. and Turner, E. E. (1950) *ibid* 1923
Bentley, J. B., Everard, K. B., Marsden, R. J. B. and Sutton, L. E. (1949) *ibid* 2957
Bentley, K. W. and Robinson, R. (1952) *ibid* 947
Bergmann, E. D. and Pelchowicz, Z. (1953) *J. Amer. chem. Soc.* **75,** 2663
Bernstein, H. J. and Ramsay, D. A. (1949) *J. chem. Phys.* **17,** 556
Blomquist, A. T., Burge, R. E. and Sucsy, A. C. (1952) *J. Amer. chem Soc.* **74,** 3636
— Liu, L. H. and Bohrer, J. C. (1952) *ibid* **74,** 3643
Bohr, N. (1913) *Phil. Mag.* **26,** 476, 857
Booker, H., Evans, L. K. and Gillam, A. E. (1940) *J. chem. Soc.* 1453
Brackman, D. S. and Plesch, P. H. (1952) *ibid* 2188
Bradacs, K. and Kahovec, L. (1940) *Z. phys. Chem.* **B48,** 635
Braude, E. A. (1945) *Annu. Rep. Progr. Chem.* **42,** 105; (1949) *J. chem. Soc.* 1902; (1950) *ibid* 379; (1951) *Chem. & Ind.* 1002
— Bruun, T., Weedon, B. C. L. and Woods, R. J. (1952) *J. chem. Soc.* 1419
— and Coles, J. A. (1951) *ibid* 2085; (1952) *ibid* 1425
— and Evans, E. A. (1954) *ibid* 607

Braude, E. A., Fawcett, J. S. and Webb, L. A. A. (1954) *ibid* 1049
— and Jones, E. R. H. (1945) *J. chem. Soc.* 498; (1950) *J. Amer. chem. Soc.* **72,** 1041
— — Koch, H. P., Richardson, R. W., Sondheimer, F. and Toogood, J. B. (1949) *J. chem. Soc.* 1890
— — and Stern, E. S. (1947) *ibid* 1087
— Sondheimer, F. and Forbes, W. F. (1954) *Nature, Lond.* **173,** 117
— and Timmons, C. J. (1950) *J. chem. Soc.* 2000
Brockmann, H. and Randebrock, R. (1951) *Chem. Ber.* **84,** 533
— and Dorlars, A. (1952) *ibid* **85,** 1168
Brooker, L. G. S., White, F. L., Heseltine, D. W., Keyes, G. H., Dent, S. G. and van Lare, E. J. (1953) *J. photogr. Sci.* **1,** 173
— — Sprague, R. H., Dent, S. G. and van Zandt, G. (1947) *Chem. Rev.* **41,** 325
Brunings, K. J. and Corwin, A. H. (1942) *J. Amer. chem. Soc.* **64,** 593
Burawoy, A. (1939) *J. chem. Soc.* 1177
— and Chamberlain, J. T. (1952) *ibid* 2310
Calvin, M. (1939) *J. org. Chem.* **4,** 256
Celmer, W. D. and Solomons, I. A. (1953) *J. Amer. chem. Soc.* **75,** 3430
Cole, A. R. H. (1952) *J. chem. Soc.* 4969
— Jones, R. N. and Dobriner, K. (1952) *J. Amer. chem. Soc.* **74,** 5571
Cookson, G. H. and Mann, F. G. (1949) *J. chem. Soc.* 2888
Cookson, R. C. (1954) *ibid* 282
Cope, A. C. and Estes, L. L. (1950) *J. Amer. chem. Soc.* **72,** 1128
— Pike, R. A. and Spencer, C. F. (1953) *ibid* **75,** 3212
Corey, E. J. (1953a, b, c) *ibid* **75,** 2301, 3297, 4832; (1954) *ibid* **76,** 175
Cram, D. J. (1952) *ibid* **74,** 2137
Crombie, L. (1952) *J. chem. Soc.* 2997, 4338; (1952) *Quart. Rev. chem. Soc., Lond.* **6,** 101
Dale, J. and Zechmeister, L. (1953) *J. Amer. chem. Soc.* **75,** 2379
Dauben, W. G. and Hoerger, E. (1951) *ibid* **73,** 1504
— — and Freeman, N. K. (1952) *ibid* **74,** 5206
Dhar, J. (1932) *Indian J. Phys.* **7,** 43
Donaldson, D. M. and Robertson, J. M. (1953) *J. chem. Soc.* 17
Dreiding, A. S. and Pratt, R. J. (1954) *J. Amer. chem. Soc.* **76,** 1902
Eccleston, B. H., Coleman, H. J. and Adams, N. G. (1950) *ibid* **72,** 3866
Evans, A. G. (1946) *Trans. Faraday Soc.* **42,** 719
Evans, L. K. and Gillam, A. E. (1941) *J. chem. Soc.* **815;** (1943) *ibid* 565
Farrar, K. R., Hamlet, J. C., Henbest, H. B. and Jones, E. R. H. (1952) *ibid* 2657
Fieser, L. F. and Dominguez, X. A. (1953) *J. Amer. chem. Soc.* **75,** 1704
— and Huang, W.-Y. (1953) *ibid* **75,** 4837
Freeman, N. K. (1953) *ibid* **75,** 1859
French, H. S. and Wiley, L. (1949) *ibid* **71,** 3702
Friedel, R. A., Orchin, M. and Reggel, L. (1948) *ibid* **70,** 199
Fürst, A., Kuhn, H. H., Scotoni, R. and Günthard, H. H. (1952) *Helv. chim. acta* **35,** 951
Garbers, C. F., Eugster, C. H. and Karrer, P. (1952) *ibid* **35,** 1850; Eugster, C. H., Garbers, C. F. and Karrer, P. (1953) *ibid* **36,** 1378
Gerding, H., Smit, E. and Westrik, R. (1942) *Rec. Trav. chim. Pays-Bas* **61,** 561
Gerhard, S. L. and Dennison, D. M. (1933) *Phys. Rev.* **43,** 197
Gillam, A. E. and El Ridi, M. S. (1936) *Biochem. J.* **30,** 1735
Gordy, W., Smith, W. V. and Trambarulo, R. F. (1953) *Microwave Spectroscopy* New York, Wiley
Gray, H. F., Rasmussen, R. S. and Tunnicliff, D. D. (1947) *J. Amer. chem. Soc.* **69,** 1630

Grovenstein, E. and Lee, D. E. (1953) *ibid* **75**, 2639
Grummitt, O. and Christoph, F. J. (1951) *ibid* **73**, 3479
Guy, J. (1949) *J. Chim. phys.* **46**, 469
Hall, R. H., Philpotts, A. R., Stern, E. S. and Thain, W. (1951) *J. chem. Soc.* 3341
Hampson, G. C. and Robertson, J. M. (1941) *ibid* **409**
Hantzsch, A. (1910) *Ber. dtsch. chem. Ges.* **43**, 1651
Hassel, O. (1943) *Tidsskr. Kemi Bergv.* **3**, 32
Haszeldine, R. N. (1951) *Nature, Lond.* **168**, 1028; (1952) *J. chem. Soc.* 2504
Hatch, L. F. and Nesbitt, S. S. (1950) *J. Amer. chem. Soc.* **72**, 727; *cf* Mislow, K.
  and Hellman, H. M. (1951) *ibid* **73**, 244
— and Harwell, K. E. (1953) *ibid* **75**, 6002
Henbest, H. B. and Woods, G. (1952) *J. chem. Soc.* 1150
Hendricks, S. B., Wulf, O. R., Hilbert, G. E. and Liddel, U. (1936) *J. Amer. chem.
  Soc.* **58**, 1991
Herzberg, G. (1950) *Molecular Spectra and Molecular Structure* New York, van
  Nostrand
Hill, T. L. (1948) *J. chem. Phys.* **16**, 399
Hirshberg, Y. (1948) *Trans. Faraday Soc.* **44**, 285
Hodgson, H. (1948) *J. chem. Soc.* 1097
Inhoffen, H. H., Bohlmann, F., Bartram, K., Rummert, G. and Pommer, H. (1950)
  Liebigs Ann. **570**, 54; (1951) *ibid* **571**, 75
— Isler, O., von der Bey, G., Raspé, G., Zeller, P. and Ahrens, R. (1953) *ibid*
  580, 7
Jackson, J. E., Paschke, R. F., Tolberg, W. E., Boyd, H. M. and Wheeler, D. H.
  (1952) *J. Amer. Oil Chem. Soc.* **29**, 229
Jones, R. N. (1941) *J. Amer. chem. Soc.* **63**, 1658; (1943) *ibid* **65**, 1818; (1945) *ibid*
  67, 2127; (1947) *Chem. Rev.* **41**, 353; (1950) *J. Amer. chem. Soc.* **72**, 5322;
  (1953) *ibid* **75**, 4839
— Humphries, P., and Dobriner, K. (1950) *J. Amer. chem. Soc.* **72**, 956; (1951)
  ibid **73**, 3215 (with Herling, F.)
— Katzenellenbogen, E. and Dobriner, K. (1953) *ibid* **75**, 158
— Ramsay, D. A., Herling, F. and Drobriner, K. (1952) *ibid* **74**, 2828
Karle, I. L. and Brockway, L. O. (1944) *ibid* **66**, 1974
Karrer, P. and Jucker, E. (1950) *Carotenoids*, translated by E. A. Braude,
  Amsterdam, Elsevier
King, S. M., Bauer, C. R. and Lutz, R. E. (1951) *J. Amer. chem. Soc.* **73**, 2253
Kiprianov, A. I. and Ushenko, I. K. (1950) *J. gen. Chem. Moscow* **20**, 134, 514
— and Zhmurova, I. N. (1952) *Doklady Akad. Nauk SSSR* **85**, 789
Kistiakowsky, G. B. (1936) Private communication quoted by Pickett, L. W.,
  Walter, G. F. and France, H. (1936) *J. Amer. chem. Soc.* **58**, 2296
Klevens, H. B. and Platt, J. R. (1949) *ibid* **71**, 1714
Koch, H. P. (1951) *J. chem. Soc.* 512
Koechlin, B. A., Kritchevsky, T. H. and Gallagher, T. F. (1950) *J. biol. Chem.*
  184, 393
Köster, H. (1947) *Chem. Ber.* **80**, 248
Kohlrausch, K. W. and Wittek, H. (1941) *Z. phys. Chem.* **B48**, 177
Kozima, K. and Yoshino, T. (1953) *J. Amer. chem. Soc.* **75**, 166
Kronig, R. de L. (1935) *The Optical Basis of the Theory of Valence*, Cambridge University
  Press
Krumholz, P. (1951) *J. Amer. chem. Soc.* **73**, 3487
Kuhn, L. P. (1952) *ibid* **74**, 2492
— Lutz, R. E. and Bauer, C. R. (1950) *ibid* **72**, 5058
Langseth, A. and Bak, B. (1940) *J. chem. Phys.* **8**, 403
Larnaudie, M. (1952) *C.R. Acad. Sci., Paris* **235**, 154; (1953) *ibid* **236**, 909

Leonard, N. J. and Blout, E. R. (1950) *J. Amer. chem. Soc.* **72,** 484
— and Mader, P. M. (1950) *ibid* **72,** 5388; Leonard, N. J. and Robinson, G. C. (1953) *ibid* **75,** 2714
Le Fèvre, R. J. W., O'Dwyer, M. F., and Werner, R. L. (1953) *Chem. & Ind.* 378
— and Vine, H. (1938) *J. chem. Soc.* 1878
Lewis, G. N. and Calvin, M. (1939) *Chem. Rev.* **25,** 273
— Magel, T. T. and Lipkin, D. (1940) *J. Amer. chem. Soc.* **62,** 2973
Lord, R. C. and Merrifield, R. E. (1953) *J. chem. Phys.* **21,** 166
Lukes, R. M., Poos, G. I., Beyler, R. E., Johns, W. F. and Sarrett, L. H. (1953) *ibid* **75,** 1707
Lunt, J. C. and Sondheimer, F. (1950) *J. chem. Soc.* 2957
Lusskin, R. M. and Winston, L. (1949) *J. Amer. chem. Soc.* **71,** 2412
MacGillavry, C. H., Kreuger, A. and Eichhorn, E. L. (1951) *Proc. Acad. Sci. Amst.* **B54,** 449
Mackle, H. and Sutton, L. E. (1951) *Trans. Faraday Soc.* **47,** 691
Mills, J. A. (1953) *J. chem. Soc.* 260
Milone, M. and Borello, E. (1953) *Gazz. chim. ital.* **83,** 153
Mixer, R. Y., Heck, R. F., Winstein, S. and Young, W. G. (1953) *J. Amer. chem. Soc.* **75,** 4094
Myers, G. S. (1951) *ibid* **73,** 2100
Newman, M. S. and Deno, N. C. (1951) *ibid* **73,** 3644
— and Wolf, M. (1952) *ibid* **74,** 3225
Oroshnik, W., Karmas, G. and Mebane, A. D. (1952) *ibid* **74,** 295
O'Shaughnessy, M. T. and Rodebush, W. H. (1940) *ibid* **62,** 2906
Parr, R. G. and Mulliken, R. A. (1950) *J. chem. Phys.* **18,** 1338
Paschke, R. F., Tolberg, W. E. and Wheeler, D. H. (1953) *J. Amer. Oil Chem. Soc.* **30,** 97
Pauling, L. (1939) *Fortschr. Chem. org. Naturst.* **3,** 203; (1949) *Helv. chim. acta* **32,** 2241
Person, W. B., Pimentel, G. C. and Pitzer, K. S. (1952) *J. Amer. chem. Soc.* **74,** 3437
Pesch, E. and Friess, S. L. (1950) *ibid* **72,** 5756
Phillips, A. P. and Graham, P. L. (1952) *ibid* **74,** 1552
Philpotts, A. R. and Thain, W. (1950) *Nature, Lond.* **166,** 1028
Pickett, L. W., Walter, G. F. and France, H. (1936) *J. Amer. chem. Soc.* **58,** 2296
Prelog, V., Ruzicka, L., Barman, P. and Frenkiel, L. (1948) *Helv. chim. acta* **31,** 92; Prelog, V., Barman, P. and Zimmermann, M. (1949) *ibid* **32,** 1284
Privett, O. S., Lundberg, W. O., Khan, N. A., Tolberg, W. E. and Wheeler, D. H. (1953) *J. Amer. Oil Chem. Soc.* **30,** 61
Pullman, A., and Berthier, G. (1950) *Bull. Soc. chim. Fr.* **16,** 81; (1951) *C.R. Acad. Sci., Paris* **233,** 748
Ramart-Lucas, P. and Hoch, J. (1952) *Bull. Soc. chim. Fr.* 220
Ramsay, D. A. and Sutherland, G. B. B. M. (1947) *Proc. roy. Soc.* **A190,** 245
Rasmussen, R. S. (1943) *J. chem. Phys.* **11,** 249; (1948) *Fortschr. Chem. org. Naturst.* **5,** 331
Remington, W. R. (1945) *J. Amer. chem. Soc.* **67,** 1838
Riemschneider, R. (1953) *Gazz. chim. ital.* **83,** 152
Rigby, W. (1949) *J. chem. Soc.* 1586
Robinson, R. (1947) *Nature, Lond.* **160,** 815; *Proc. roy. Soc.* **B135,** 14
Rosenkrantz, H., Milhorat, A. T. and Farber, M. (1952) *J. biol. Chem.* **195,** 509
— and Zablow, L. (1953) *J. Amer. chem. Soc.* **75,** 903
Saunders, R. A. and Smith, D. C. (1949) *J. appl. Phys.* **20,** 953
Schomaker, V. and Pauling, L. (1939) *J. Amer. chem. Soc.* **61,** 1769
Searles, S., Tamres, M. and Barrow, G. M. (1953) *ibid* **75,** 71
Sheppard, N. and Simpson, D. M. (1952) *Quart. Rev. chem. Soc., Lond.* **6,** 1
Sinclair, R. G., McKay, A. F., Myers, G. S. and Jones, R. N. (1952) *J. Amer. chem. Soc.* **74,** 2578

Sondheimer, F. (1952) *J. Amer. chem. Soc.* **74,** 4040
Strandberg, M. W. P. (1953) *Microwave Spectroscopy,* London, Methuen
Sugden, T. M. and Walsh, A. D. (1945) *Trans. Faraday Soc.* **41,** 76
Sutherland, G. B. B. M. and Vallance Jones, A. (1950) *Disc. Faraday Soc.* **9,** 281
Szasz, G. J. and Sheppard, N. (1953) *Trans. Faraday Soc.* **49,** 358
Tarbell, D. S. and McCall, M. A. (1952) *J. Amer. chem. Soc.* **74,** 48
Tetlow, K. S. (1950) *Research, Lond.* **3,** 187
Thompson, H. W., Vago, E. E., Corfield, M. C. and Orr, S. F. D. (1950) *J. chem. Soc.* 214
Tulinskie, A., DiGiacomo, A. and Smyth, C. P. (1953) *J. Amer. chem. Soc.* **75,** 3552
Turner, R. B. and Voitle, D. M. (1951) *ibid* **73,** 1403
Wheland, G. W. (1944) *The Theory of Resonance,* New York, Wiley
Williamson, B. and Rodebush, W. H. (1941) *J. Amer. chem. Soc.* **63,** 3018
Wilson, E. B. (1951) *Annu. Rev. phys. Chem.* **2,** 151; (1952) *Ann. N.Y. Acad. Sci.* **55,** 943
Wolfe, W. C., Doukas, H. M. and Ard, J. S. (1954) *J. Amer. chem. Soc.* **76,** 627
Woodward, R. B. (1942) *J. Amer. chem. Soc.* **64,** 72
Zbinden, R. (1953) *Helv. phys. Acta* **26,** 129
Zechmeister, L. (1944) *Chem. Rev.* **34,** 267
— LeRosen, A. L., Schroeder, W. A., Polgar, A. and Pauling, L. (1943) *J. Amer. chem. Soc.* **65,** 1940
— and Wallcave, L. (1953) *ibid* **75,** 5342
Zenitz, B. L., Martini, C. M., Prizna, M. and Nachod, F. C. (1952) *ibid* **74,** 5564

COLLECTED REFERENCES

A. *Wave-mechanical Treatments of Unsaturation Electrons*
(*Simpler Methods*)

Lewis, G. N. and Calvin, M. (1939) *Chem. Rev.* **25,** 273
Mulliken, R. S. (1939) *J. chem. Phys.* **7,** 14, 20, 121, 339, 364, 570; (1942) *Rev. mod. Phys.* **14,** 265
Bayliss, N. S. (1948) *J. chem. Phys.* **16,** 287; (1949) *ibid* **17,** 1353; (1952) *Quart. Rev. chem. Soc., Lond.* **4,** 319

B. *Wave-mechanical Treatments of Unsaturation Electrons*
(*More Complex Methods*)

Kuhn, W. (1948) *Helv. chim. acta* **31,** 1780
Kuhn, H. (1949) *J. chem. Phys.* **17,** 1198; (1951) *Helv. chim. acta* **34,** 1308
Dewar, M. J. S. (1952) *J. chem. Soc.* 3532, 3544

C. *Diene and Triene-carboxylic Acids*

Elvidge, J. A., Linstead, R. P., Sims, P. and Orkin, B. A. (1950) *J. chem. Soc.* 2235
— — — (1951) *ibid* 3386; (1953) *ibid* 1793
— — and Smith, J. F. (1952) *ibid* 1026; (1953) *ibid* 708
Eisner, U., Elvidge, J. A. and Linstead, R. P. (1953) *ibid* 1372
Mildner, P. and Weedon, B. C. L. (1953) *ibid* 3294 (trienes)

D. *Benzene Derivatives with Unsaturated Side-chains*

Rodebush, W. H. and Feldmann, I. (1946) *J. Amer. chem. Soc.* **68,** 896; Murray, M. J. and Gallaway, W. S. (1948) *ibid* **70,** 3867; Beale, R. N. and Roe, E. M. F. (1952) *ibid* **74,** 2302 (styrenes)
Ross, S. D. (1948) *J. Amer. chem. Soc.* **70,** 4039; Fehnel, E. A. (1950) *ibid* **72,** 1404; Moser, C. and Kohlenberg, A. I. (1951) *J. chem. Soc.* 804 (benzoic acids and esters)
Brown, W. G. and Reagan, H. (1947) *J. Amer. chem. Soc.* **69,** 1032; Ungnade, H. (1954) *ibid* **76,** 1601 (nitro compounds)
Blumberger, J. S. P. (1944) *Rec. Trav. chim. Pays-Bas* **63,** 127; Brode, W. R. and Morris, R. J. (1948) *J. org. Chem.* **13,** 200 (azo-dyes)

E.   Infra-red Spectra of cis- and trans-*Ethylenes*

Crombie, L. and Harper, S. H. (1950) *J. chem. Soc.* 873, 1707, 1714; Sondheimer, F.
  (1950) *ibid* 877 (Lex-3-en-1-ol)
— — (1952) *ibid* 869 (jasmone)
— — Stedman, R. E. and Thompson, D. (1951) *ibid* 2445 (cinerolone)
Baer, E. and Fischer, H. O. (1947) *J. biol. Chem.* 170, 337 (selachyl alcohol)
McCutcheon, J. W., Crawford, M. F. and Welsh, H. L. (1941) *Oil & Soap* 18, 9;
  Myers, G. S. (1951) *J. Amer. chem. Soc.* 73, 2100; Sinclair, R. G., McKay, A. F.,
  Myers, G. S. and Jones, R. N. (1952) *ibid* 74, 2578 (oleic and linoleic acids and
  esters)
Jones, R. N. (1950) *J. Amer. chem. Soc.* 72, 5322; Turnbull, J. H., Whiffen, D. H.
  and Wilson, W. (1950) *Chem. & Ind.* 626 (ergost-22-ene derivatives)
Rao, P. C. and Daubert, B. F. (1948) *J. Amer. chem. Soc.* 70, 1102 (vaccenic acid)
Lemon, H. W. and Cross, C. K. (1949) *Canad. J. Res.* B27, 610; Shreve, O. D.,
  Heether, M. R., Knight, H. B. and Swern, D. (1950) *Anal. Chem.* 22, 1498 (oleic
  and linoleic acids and esters)
Mislow, K. (1952) *J. Amer. chem. Soc.* 74, 5155 (sphingolipids)

F.   Infra-red Spectra of Substituted Ethylenes

Emschwiller, G. and Lecomte, J. (1937) *J. Phys. Radium* 8, 130
Ta, Y. (1938) *C.R. Acad. Sci., Paris* 207, 326
Bernstein, H. J. and Ramsay, D. A. (1949) *J. chem. Phys.* 17, 556 (1:2-di-
  chloroethylene)
— and Powling, J. (1951) *J. Amer. chem. Soc.* 73, 1843 (1:2-dichloro-propene)
Hatch, L. F. and D'Amico, J. J. (1951) *ibid* 73, 4393 (2:3-dichlorobut-2-ene)
— — and Ruhnke, E. V. (1952) *ibid* 74, 123 (trisubstituted propenes)

5

THE CORRELATION OF CONFIGURATIONS

J. A. Mills and W. Klyne

KNOWLEDGE of configurational relations between different types of optically active compounds is important for practical as well as theoretical reasons.   It is necessary in many branches of biochemistry, *e.g.* in studies on metabolism and on the action of drugs, and in formulating theories of biogenesis.   Reaction mechanisms may often be studied more easily with the aid of optically active reagents, and extensive correlations are needed to check mathematical treatments of the origin of optical rotatory power.

It seems surprising in view of the importance of stereochemical factors in biological processes that more attention has not been paid to correlation problems in the past.   It is perhaps significant that the Biochemical Society devoted its first symposium (1948) to the ' Relation of optical form to biological activity in the amino-acid series '.   Yet the definitive correlation of the α-amino-acids with the α-hydroxyacids (and therefore the carbohydrates) dates only from 1950 and the correlation of the steroids with glyceraldehyde has just been achieved this year (1953).   It is of little more than academic interest to the structural organic chemist whether the conventions used for representing the formulae of, say, testosterone and L-alanine agree or not; but it will be quite impossible for a biochemist to give an adequate account of the interaction between steroid hormones and proteins until the stereochemical relations between them are known.   The determination of the structure of an asymmetrical natural product should not be considered as complete until the stereochemistry of the compound has been correlated with that of a standard substance.

Optically active glyceraldehyde is the standard substance to which all other optically active compounds are related if methods are available.   The developments that led to the adoption of the arbitrarily chosen configuration (I) for (+)-glyceraldehyde as the practical standard for carbohydrates have been discussed in many text-books, and a clear account is given by Hudson (1948).   The present review deals mainly with the correlation of other groups of compounds with glyceraldehyde.   Until recently, a second standard configuration (II) for natural serine was needed as the reference for α-amino-acids, but, as will be explained, the standards I and II are now known to be equivalent.

Configurations will be given relative to the conventional standard I, and if we say that X has been correlated with glyceraldehyde we mean that we know which of the two possible molecular models represents a particular enantiomorph of X when I is chosen as the representation of (+)-glyceraldehyde. Such a correlation is quite independent of the absolute correctness of the standard configuration I, and of systems of nomenclature used to describe the configurations.

It is now generally accepted that, thanks to a fortunate chance on Fischer's part, I represents the true absolute configuration of (+)-glyceraldehyde. This follows from the ingenious applications of x-ray crystallography to sodium rubidium tartrate by Bijvoet, Peerdeman and van Bommel (1951). The absolute configuration of a substance is therefore known if it has been correlated with glyceraldehyde.

Several attempts have been made to calculate absolute configurations mathematically. Some recent calculations agree with Bijvoet's result, but others are contradictory or for substances that cannot as yet be correlated with glyceraldehyde. The situation has been reviewed by Kuhn (1952), and also discussed by Wheland (1949b).

In the established correlations, at least one asymmetric carbon atom in an asymmetric molecule has been compared in some way with the asymmetric atom of (+)-glyceraldehyde, but this need not be so : absolute configurations for compounds not otherwise correlated with glyceraldehyde may in future be determined by x-ray crystallography, or by mathematical calculations.

It is impossible here to list all known configurational correlations, and only representative examples of each of the important methods will be given, chosen as far as possible to include a few key compounds in each class, and from sources that refer extensively to the details of earlier work. References to many other correlations are listed at the end of the chapter under appropriate headings (p. 219). An excellent review by Freudenberg (1933a) summarizes the position at that date, and many of the extensive and important correlations achieved by Levene and his colleagues have been discussed by Levene and Rothen (1936, 1938). Wheland (1949a) has discussed certain aspects of configurational correlations.

The correlations between the principal classes of compounds considered in this chapter are summarized in FIGURE 1.

Correlation of configuration at different centres in the same molecule will not generally be considered here. For compounds containing several asymmetric centres, it has been usual for the stereochemistry of the centres relative to each other to be established, followed by a correlation of one of the centres with glyceraldehyde. The correlation is greatly strengthened if two or more centres are independently related to glyceraldehyde.

At present, compounds optically active through molecular dissymmetry not consequent on the presence of individual asymmetric carbon atoms (allenes, spirans, hindered diphenyls, *etc*), and compounds containing asymmetric atoms other than carbon, have not been correlated with glyceraldehyde. The need for correlations of this type is shown by the recent discoveries of the natural occurrence of an optically active sulphoxide, sulphoraphen (Schmid and Karrer, 1948), and an optically active allene, mycomycin (Celmer and Solomons, 1953).

Illustrations and Nomenclature

Molecular configurations should ideally be compared by examination of suitably constructed three-dimensional models, but in practice unambiguous plane-projection diagrams are usually sufficient. Projection formulae for acyclic compounds are drawn according to the Fischer convention (see Hudson, 1948). Asymmetric centres are projected independently, if there are several: at each, the two bonds forming part of the main chain of atoms are considered to lie below the plane of the page, and the attached groups to project towards the observer, as in the Fischer projection (IB) of (I). For compounds with one asymmetric centre, the use of heavy and dotted lines, as in (IA), avoids ambiguity. Cyclic compounds are usually projected with the rings in the plane of the paper and the relative positions of attached groups shown by heavy and dotted lines for groups above and below the plane of the rings.

A comprehensive system of nomenclature for optically active compounds is desirable, although not essential, when configurational relationships are discussed, and several attempts have been made to derive a configurational nomenclature that would embrace all classes of optically active compounds. Carbohydrates and related substances are conventionally classed as D_g or L_g (small capitals) according to the relationship of their highest-numbered asymmetric carbon atom to that of D-glyceraldehyde (I). Amino-acids and related substances are called D_s and L_s depending on the relationship of their α-carbon atom to that of serine (II). The subscripts ' g ' and ' s ' can often be omitted when no danger of confusion arises (see *J. chem. Soc.* (1952) 5108; *Biochem. J.* (1948) **42**, 1; (1952) **52**, 1).

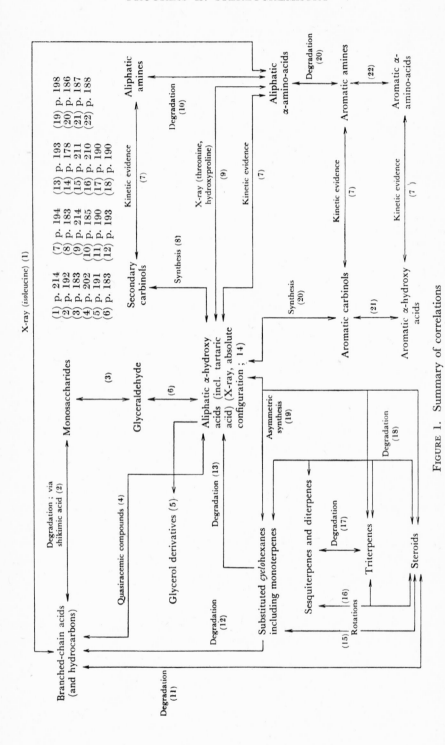

FIGURE 1. Summary of correlations

These conventions cannot however be extended to branched-chain compounds, and may lead to difficulty when applied to substances quite closely related to the sugars (Buchanan, 1951; Cahn and Ingold, 1951; Crombie and Harper, 1950a; Wheland, 1949a).

Cahn and Ingold (1951) developed a logical and comprehensive configurational nomenclature based on the spatial arrangement of substituent groups round individual asymmetric atoms in three-dimensional models, a priority of groups being determined by a 'Sequence Rule' which took into account the atomic number and mode of linkage of all atoms. This procedure is, however, not easily applied to complex molecules except after much practice, and the derived notation may not reflect structural similarities between closely related compounds, especially cyclic ones.

A procedure, which in the opinion of the present authors is somewhat easier to apply, describes the conventional projection formula, the configuration at each asymmetric atom being denoted by the use of one or other of a suitable pair of symbols. We propose to use italic capitals D and L (cf Linstead, Lunt and Weedon, 1950) to avoid confusion with the small capitals D and L of carbohydrates and amino-acids while emphasizing the close relationship of the new symbols to the older ones. One such procedure has been developed for aliphatic compounds by Ställberg-Stenhagen (1949) and Linstead et al (1950), and extended to cover more complex structures by Ställberg-Stenhagen (1950) and particularly by Klyne (1951b). Mills (unpublished) has shown that such a procedure may be developed to cover practically all classes and complexities of molecules containing asymmetric quadricovalent atoms.

The procedure suggested by Klyne will be used for convenience here. Acyclic compounds are drawn as a Fischer projection with the principal numbered chain vertical and numbered from the top. Any substituent at an asymmetric atom is given the designation L (in addition to the symbol denoting the point of attachment) if it lies on the left-hand side of the vertical chain, and the designation D (plus symbol for position) if it lies on the right-hand side.

The systematic name for I would be αD:β-dihydroxypropion-aldehyde or $2D$:3-dihydroxypropanal, and for II, αL-amino-β-hydroxypropionic acid; the more customary names such as D-glycer-aldehyde and L-serine will undoubtedly be used generally for well-known compounds. Other examples of the proposed nomenclature are βD-methyladipic acid (LV), butan-$2D$-ol (XV), and $2L$-methyl-butanol (XLIX). For the procedure to be followed with cyclic compounds, see Klyne (1951b).

METHODS AVAILABLE FOR THE ESTABLISHMENT OF CONFIGURATION

The configurations of two compounds may be correlated by purely chemical methods, such as degradation or synthesis that does not involve an asymmetric centre, ring-closure between substituents in cyclic compounds, or a displacement reaction that involves an asymmetric centre but is known to be stereospecific. In other cases, a kinetic study of a displacement reaction at an asymmetric centre, or the achievement of a partial asymmetric synthesis, may provide the necessary information. Sometimes, purely physical methods may be used, as in the use of molecular rotations, the detection of ' quasi-racemic compounds ' from melting-point diagrams, and the use of x-ray or electron-diffraction procedures. Enzymic methods may be valuable for many biologically important compounds.

In general, it has been easier to achieve correlations between members of a family of compounds of one structural type (*e.g.* mono-saccharides; α-amino-acids; homologous secondary alcohols) than between compounds of similar structural type with different functional groups attached to the asymmetric centre (*e.g.* α-amino-acids and α-hydroxyacids); the most difficult correlations have been those between quite dissimilar compounds, such as secondary alcohols and branched-chain hydrocarbons.

CHEMICAL CORRELATIONS WITHOUT DISTURBANCE OF THE ASYMMETRIC CENTRE

The establishment of a direct chemical relationship between the standard substance and that to be correlated, using reactions that do not involve the asymmetric centre concerned, is decisive. This was the first method available for correlations, and Freudenberg, Levene, and other early workers in the field used it extensively and with ingenuity to establish relationships between the sugars and numerous hydroxy-acids and secondary alcohols, and between the terpenoids and other branched-chain compounds. In its simplest form the method is practically limited to correlations of asymmetric centres of the same structural type, and other approaches were necessary to provide correlations between branched-chain compounds and secondary alcohols, and thereby correlate the terpenoids with glyceraldehyde.

Secondary Alcohols and Related Compounds

Freudenberg (1914), Wohl and Momber (1917), and others (*cf* Brewster, Hughes, Ingold and Rao, 1950), established important relationships between (+)-glyceraldehyde (I), (−)-lactic acid (V), (−)-tartaric acid (VII) and (+)-malic acid (IX), the key intermediate being (+)-*iso*serine (III). Levene and his colleagues later related (−)-lactic acid (V) to (+)-butan-2-ol (XV) through(−)- and (+)-*β*-

$$
\begin{array}{ccccc}
\text{CHO} & \text{CO}_2\text{H} & \text{CO}_2\text{H} & \text{CO}_2\text{H} & \text{CO}_2\text{H} \\
| & | & | & | & | \\
\text{H—C—OH} & \text{H—C—OH} & \text{H—C—OH} & \text{H—C—OH} & \text{H—C—OH} \\
| & | & | & | & | \\
\text{CH}_2\text{OH} & \text{CH}_2\text{OH} & \text{CH}_2\text{NH}_2 & \text{CH}_2\text{Br} & \text{CH}_3
\end{array}
$$

$\xrightarrow{\text{HgO}}$ $\xleftarrow{\text{HNO}_3}$ $\xrightarrow{\text{NOBr}}$ $\xrightarrow{\text{Na/Hg}}$

(+) (−)-Glyceric acid (+)-*iso*Serine (−)-Lactic acid
 I III IV V

$\downarrow$ HCN $\uparrow$ Curtius

$$
\begin{array}{ccccc}
\text{CN} & \text{CO}_2\text{H} & \text{CO}_2\text{H} & \text{CO}_2\text{H} & \text{CO}_2\text{H} \\
| & | & | & | & | \\
\text{HO—C—H} & \text{HO—C—H} & \text{H—C—OH} & \text{H—C—OH} & \text{H—C—OH} \\
| & | & | & | & | \\
\text{H—C—OH} & \text{H—C—OH} & \text{CH}_2 & \text{CH}_2 & \text{CH}_2 \\
| & | & | & | & | \\
\text{CH}_2\text{OH} & \text{CO}_2\text{H} & \text{CO.NH}_2 & \text{CO}_2\text{Me} & \text{CO}_2\text{H}
\end{array}
$$

$\rightarrow$ $\leftarrow$ $\leftarrow$

(−)-Tartaric acid (+)-Malic acid
VI VII VIII IX

$$
\begin{array}{cccc}
\text{CH}_3 & \text{CH}_3 & \text{CH}_3 & \text{CH}_3 \\
| & | & | & | \\
\text{HO—C—H} & \text{HO—C—H} & \text{HO—C—H} & \text{HO—C—H} \\
| & | & | & | \\
\text{CO}_2\text{H} & \text{CH}_2\text{OH} & \text{CH}_2\text{Br} & \text{CH}_2\text{CO}_2\text{H}
\end{array}
$$

$\xrightarrow[\text{Blanc}]{\text{Bouveault-}}$ $\xrightarrow{\text{HBr}}$ $\xrightarrow[\text{hydrolysis}]{\text{KCN}}$

(−) (−)   (−)
V X XI XII

$$
\begin{array}{cccc}
\text{CH}_3 & \text{CH}_3 & \text{CH}_3 & \text{CH}_3 \\
| & | & | & | \\
\text{H—C—OH} & \text{H—C—OH} & \text{H—C—OH} & \text{H—C—OH} \\
| & | & | & | \\
\text{CH}_2\text{CO}_2\text{H} & \text{CH}_2\text{CH}_2\text{OH} & \text{CH}_2\text{CH}_2\text{I} & \text{CH}_2\text{CH}_3
\end{array}
$$

$\xrightarrow[\text{Blanc}]{\text{Bouveault-}}$ $\xrightarrow{\text{HI}}$ $\xrightarrow{\text{H}_2/\text{Pd}}$

(+) (+) (+) (+)-Butan-2-ol
XIII XIV XV

hydroxybutyric acids (XII and XIII, respectively), and extended their correlations to include numerous other secondary alcohols (Levene *et al*, 1925–1927).

Doering and Young (1952) suggested that a secondary alcoholic group might have participated in some of the reactions on neighbouring groups performed in certain of the above correlations, thereby making the results unreliable. In a reinvestigation of some of Levene's work, they used methyl ethers of the secondary alcoholic intermediates, because the participation of the asymmetric centre in a reaction could then be more readily detected. Their results confirmed the earlier work.

Most of the key correlations in the group including the secondary alcohols, glyceraldehyde, hydroxyacids and sugars have been determined in more than one way, and are established beyond doubt. The degradation of carbohydrates in various ways, especially with periodic acid (Jackson and Hudson, 1937; Maclay, Hann and Hudson, 1939), can provide correlations between glyceraldehyde and lactic, malic and tartaric acids, and published data seem to be in complete harmony with the above configurations. Wolfrom, Lemieux, Olin and Weisblat (1949) have checked the correlation between lactic acid and glyceraldehyde, and Wiberg (1952) the correlation between lactic acid and butan-2-ol.

The most important configurational application of the cleavage of vicinal glycol groups by periodic acid (reviewed by Jackson, 1944) is the determination of the anomeric configuration of glycosides (Jackson and Hudson, 1937). For example, if a D-ribofuranoside (XVI) gives on oxidation with periodic acid the same dialdehyde (XVII) as is obtained on oxidation of a β-D-glucopyranoside (XVIII) of established configuration, then (XVI) must also have the β-configuration.

| XVI | XVII | XVIII |

Amino-acids

The correlation of the α-amino-acids with glyceraldehyde is considered on p. 194. Many of the natural α-amino-acids have been correlated with one another and with the standard amino-acid serine (II) by chemical methods not involving the asymmetric carbon atom. The results confirm the impression gained from other studies that all natural amino-acids commonly derived from proteins belong to the L-series. Neuberger (1948) has reviewed the stereochemical correlation of α-amino-acids.

One interesting correlation achieved by Barrow and Ferguson (1935) depends on the fact that if two optically active compounds C*abcx* and C*abcy* have the groups *a*, *b*, *c* similarly disposed with respect to *x* and *y*, and a common group *c* is replaced by *y* and *x* respectively, the two products C*abxy* will be of opposite configuration. Barrow and Ferguson converted natural L-(+)-alanine (XIX) into (−)-2-amino-3-methylbutane (XXII), and natural L-(+)-valine (XXIII) into the enantiomorphous amine (XXVI), thereby providing evidence that natural alanine and valine have the same configuration. The result is correct, but the method is not entirely convincing, because the asymmetric centre could conceivably be involved in the reactions leading to replacement of a hydroxyl group by a hydrogen atom. Partial racemization was observed during the reactions.

$$
\begin{array}{cccc}
\underset{\substack{\text{(+)-Alanine}\\ \text{XIX}}}{\underset{\displaystyle \overset{|}{\text{CH}_3}}{\overset{\displaystyle \text{CO}_2\text{H}}{\text{NH}_2{-}\overset{|}{\underset{|}{\text{C}}}{-}\text{H}}}}
\xrightarrow[\text{MeMgI}]{\text{Esterify}}
\underset{\text{XX}}{\underset{\displaystyle \overset{|}{\text{CH}_3}}{\overset{\displaystyle \text{CMe}_2\text{OH}}{\text{NH}_2{-}\overset{|}{\underset{|}{\text{C}}}{-}\text{H}}}}
\xrightarrow{\text{PCl}_5}
\underset{\text{XXI}}{\underset{\displaystyle \overset{|}{\text{CH}_3}}{\overset{\displaystyle \text{CMe}_2\text{Cl}}{\text{NH}_2{-}\overset{|}{\underset{|}{\text{C}}}{-}\text{H}}}}
\xrightarrow{\text{H}_2/\text{Pt}}
\underset{\substack{(-)\\ \text{XXII}}}{\underset{\displaystyle \overset{|}{\text{CH}_3}}{\overset{\displaystyle \text{CHMe}_2}{\text{NH}_2{-}\overset{|}{\underset{|}{\text{C}}}{-}\text{H}}}}
\end{array}
$$

$$
\begin{array}{cccc}
\underset{\substack{\text{(+)-Valine}\\ \text{XXIII}}}{\underset{\displaystyle \overset{|}{\text{CHMe}_2}}{\overset{\displaystyle \text{CO}_2\text{H}}{\text{NH}_2{-}\overset{|}{\underset{|}{\text{C}}}{-}\text{H}}}}
\xrightarrow[\text{on ester}]{\text{Bouveault--Blanc}}
\underset{\text{XXIV}}{\underset{\displaystyle \overset{|}{\text{CHMe}_2}}{\overset{\displaystyle \text{CH}_2\text{OH}}{\text{NH}_2{-}\overset{|}{\underset{|}{\text{C}}}{-}\text{H}}}}
\xrightarrow{\text{HBr}}
\underset{\text{XXV}}{\underset{\displaystyle \overset{|}{\text{CHMe}_2}}{\overset{\displaystyle \text{CH}_2\text{Br}}{\text{NH}_2{-}\overset{|}{\underset{|}{\text{C}}}{-}\text{H}}}}
\xrightarrow{\text{H}_2/\text{Pt}}
\underset{\substack{(+)\\ \text{XXVI}}}{\underset{\displaystyle \overset{|}{\text{CHMe}_2}}{\overset{\displaystyle \text{CH}_3}{\text{NH}_2{-}\overset{|}{\underset{|}{\text{C}}}{-}\text{H}}}}
\end{array}
$$

Karrer and his colleagues (Karrer, Portmann and Suter, 1948; Karrer and Erhardt, 1951; Karrer and Dinkel, 1953) have used lithium aluminium hydride to reduce α-amino-acids (as esters) (XXVII) to the corresponding α-amino-alcohols (XXVIII); the ON-ditoluene-p-sulphonyl derivatives of the latter have then been reduced again with lithium aluminium hydride to give N-toluene-p-sulphonyl derivatives of amines lacking the primary hydroxyl group (XXXI). This provides a valuable means of correlating compounds of types XXVII, XXVIII and XXXI (cf also p. 188).

$$
\begin{array}{ccc}
\underset{\text{XXVII}}{\underset{\displaystyle \overset{|}{\text{R}}}{\overset{\displaystyle \text{CO}_2\text{Me}}{\text{NH}_2{-}\overset{|}{\underset{|}{\text{C}}}{-}\text{H}}}}
\xrightarrow{\text{LiAlH}_4}
\underset{\text{XXVIII}}{\underset{\displaystyle \overset{|}{\text{R}}}{\overset{\displaystyle \text{CH}_2\text{OH}}{\text{NH}_2{-}\overset{|}{\underset{|}{\text{C}}}{-}\text{H}}}}
\xrightarrow{\text{TsCl}}
\underset{\text{XXIX}}{\underset{\displaystyle \overset{|}{\text{R}}}{\overset{\displaystyle \text{CH}_2\text{OTs}}{\text{TsNH}{-}\overset{|}{\underset{|}{\text{C}}}{-}\text{H}{-}}}}
\end{array}
$$

$$
\text{LiAlH}_4
$$

$$
\begin{array}{cc}
\underset{\text{XXXI}}{\underset{\displaystyle \overset{|}{\text{R}}}{\overset{\displaystyle \text{CH}_3}{\text{NH}_2{-}\overset{|}{\underset{|}{\text{C}}}{-}\,\text{H}}}}
\xrightarrow{\text{TsCl}}
\underset{\text{XXX}}{\underset{\displaystyle \overset{|}{\text{R}}}{\overset{\displaystyle \text{CH}_3}{\text{TsNH}{-}\overset{|}{\underset{|}{\text{C}}}{-}\text{H}}}} \longleftarrow
\end{array}
$$

$$
\text{Ts} = p\text{-CH}_3 \cdot \text{C}_6\text{H}_4 \cdot \text{SO}_2
$$

Noyce and Denney (1950) have shown that asymmetric centres adjacent to a carbonyl or alkoxycarbonyl group are not affected when such a group is reduced with lithium aluminium hydride. This reagent is being used widely in work on correlations.

185

Phenyl-substituted Compounds

The correlation with glyceraldehyde of compounds carrying a phenyl group directly attached to an asymmetric atom (general type XXXIII) presents some special difficulties.

$$
\begin{array}{ccccc}
 & & & \text{synthesis} \\
\text{CO}_2\text{H} & & & & \\
| & \xleftarrow{\text{oxidation}} & \text{H—C*—X} & \xrightarrow{\text{H}_2} & \text{H—C*—X} \\
\text{H—C*—X} & & | & & | \\
| & & \text{Y} & & \text{Y} \\
\text{Y} & & & & \\
\text{XXXII} & & \text{XXXIII} & & \text{XXXIV}
\end{array}
$$

Direct chemical correlation involves *either* the breaking down of the aromatic ring, leaving only the C-1 (usually as CO_2H) attached to the asymmetric carbon atom C* (XXXII) *or* the building up of a *cyclo*hexane ring from C-1 (usually present in the starting material as carboxyl) and the preparation of the same compound (XXXIV) by catalytic reduction of (XXXIII). Examples of these two processes are (*i*) the degradation of (+)-α-phenylethylamine to D(−)-alanine (XXXIII—→XXXII; X = NH₂; Y = Me) by Leithe (1931), and (*ii*) the synthesis of (−)-*cyclo*hexylmethylcarbinol from D-(−)-lactic acid (XXXII—→XXXIV; X = OH, Y = Me) by Levene and Harris (1936).

Evidence from physical properties (optical rotations, quasi-racemic compounds) and from enzymic reactions may also be useful, but it requires interpreting with great caution.

The correlations of some of the most important types of phenyl-substituted structures are shown in formulae XXXV–XLVII. The correlation between (−)-lactic acid (V) and (−)-mandelic acid (XLIV) has been discussed by Mislow (1951) with detailed references to previous chemical work and to a variety of earlier evidence from biochemical reactions, quasi-racemic compounds and optical rotations. This correlation is supported by Prelog's work on asymmetric synthesis (1953).

The correlation between (−)-alanine (XXXV) and (−)-amino-acetic acid (XLV) via the amine (XXXIX) was carried out by Kuna, Ovakimian and Levene (1941) and by Leithe (1931, 1932). Enzymic evidence (Rudman, Meister and Greenstein, 1952) supports the allotment of configuration (XLV) to the (−)-amino-acid.

Evidence from kinetic studies (Hibbin, Hughes and Ingold, 1954)* now shows that (−)-mandelic acid (XLIV) and (−)-aminophenyl-acetic acid (XLV) are configurationally related.

* We are greatly indebted to Professor C. K. Ingold, F.R.S., for advance information about this paper.

PHENYL-SUBSTITUTED DERIVATIVES
CORRELATION WITH SIMPLE ALIPHATIC COMPOUNDS

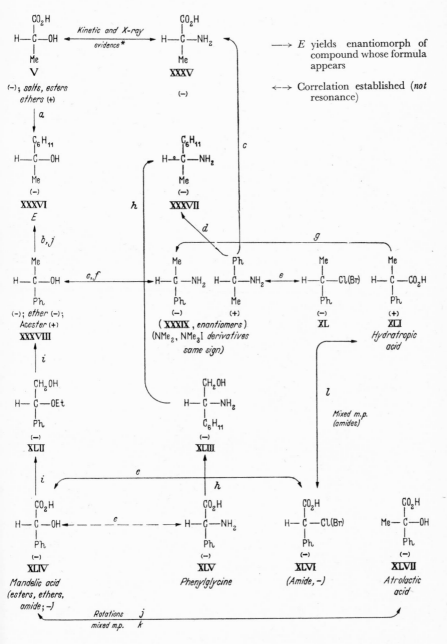

References: *See pp. 194 and 214; *a* Levene and Harris, 1936; *b* Levene and Stevens, 1930; *c* Leithe, 1931; *d* Leithe, 1932; *e* Brewster, Hughes, Ingold *et al*, 1950; *cf* Ingold, 1953 (kinetic evidence); *f* Snyder and Brewster, 1949; *g* Bernstein and Whitmore, 1939; Arcus and Kenyon, 1939; *h* Kuna *et al* 1941; *i* Mislow, 1951; *j* Freudenberg, Todd and Seidler, 1933; *k* Mislow and Heffler, 1952; *l* as *k*.

Very recently Watson and Youngson (1954) have correlated
(−)-aminophenylacetic acid with (−)-α-phenylethylamine (XXXIX)
using the lithium aluminium hydride method of Karrer (see p. 185).
This result confirms the allotment of configuration (XLV) to the
(−)-amino-acid. (We are greatly indebted to Dr. M. B. Watson,
Aberdeen, for a copy of this paper before publication.)

References to some other correlations of phenyl-substituted structures
are listed on pp. 220–21.

Branched-chain Compounds

Compounds owing their asymmetry to branching in a saturated
carbon chain may be degraded or transformed with less risk that a
correlation may be invalidated by unforeseen neighbouring-group
effects. The chief risk is that a labile asymmetric centre next to a
carboxyl or carbonyl group may, under the influence of acid or base,
suffer racemization, or transformation to a thermodynamically more
stable configuration if there are other asymmetric centres present.
Cyclic structures are especially subject to this risk.

Natural (−)-2-methylbutanol (' active amyl alcohol ') is a convenient reference standard for branched-chain structures (Crombie
and Harper, 1950a), and it is now known to have the configuration
XLIX relative to glyceraldehyde, although a proof of this is deferred to
pp. 192 and 202. The relation between XLIX, (+)-α-methylbutyric
acid (XLVIII), (+)-methylsuccinic acid (LII) and (+)-β-methyladipic
acid (LV) have been firmly established, the earlier results being due

$$
\begin{array}{cccc}
\mathrm{CO_2H} & \mathrm{CH_2OH} & \mathrm{CH_2Cl} & \mathrm{CH_2Cl} \\
| & | \quad PCl_3 & | \quad Cl_2 & | \\
\mathrm{Me-C-H} \longleftarrow & \mathrm{Me-C-H} \longrightarrow & \mathrm{Me-C-H} \xrightarrow{\text{light}} & \mathrm{Me-C-H} \\
| & | & | & | \\
\mathrm{CH_2CH_3} & \mathrm{CH_2CH_3} & \mathrm{CH_2CH_3} & \mathrm{CH_2CH_2Cl} \\
(+) & (-) & (+) & (-) \\
\text{XLVIII} & \text{XLIX} & \text{L} & \text{LI}
\end{array}
$$

$$
\begin{array}{ccccc}
\mathrm{CO_2H} & \mathrm{CH_2OH} & \mathrm{CH_2Br} & \mathrm{CH_2CO_2H} & \mathrm{CH_2Cl} \\
| & | \quad KOAc & | & | & | \\
\mathrm{H-C-Me} \leftarrow & \mathrm{H-C-Me} \leftarrow & \mathrm{H-C-Me} \leftarrow & \mathrm{H-C-Me} \longrightarrow & \mathrm{H-C-Me} \\
| & | & | & | & | \\
\mathrm{CH_2CO_2H} & \mathrm{CH_2CH_2OH} & \mathrm{CH_2CH_2Br} & \mathrm{CH_2CH_2CO_2H} & \mathrm{CH_2CH_2} \\
(+) & (+) & (+) & (+) & (+) \\
\text{LII} & \text{LIII} & \text{LIV} & \text{LV} & \text{LVI}
\end{array}
$$

to Marckwald (1899) and von Braun and Jostes (1926), among others;
the final link through the enantiomorphous dichloro-compounds LI
and LVI was provided by Brown, Kharasch and Chao (1940).

Monoterpenes

Methylsuccinic and β-methyladipic acids result from the degradation of several terpenes, and a study of these degradations and other

reactions (for details of terpene chemistry, see Simonsen and Owen, 1947, 1949), established correlations of all monoterpenoids (except the thujane group) with simpler branched-chain compounds, and ultimately with glyceraldehyde. Hückel (1941, 1948) provided the final links between the different classes of monoterpenoids. Birch (1950) has compiled a list of representative monoterpenoids correlated with glyceraldehyde; some typical examples are shown in formulae LVII–LXIII.

(+)-Citronellal	(+)-Limonene	(−)-Menthol	(−)-Car-3-ene
LVII	LVIII	LIX	LX

(+)-α-Pinene	(+)-Camphor	(+)-Fenchone
LXI	LXII	LXIII

Current interest in branched-chain fatty acids (see *e.g.* Weitkamp, 1945; Truter, 1951; Hansen, Shorland and Cooke, 1952) has prompted the synthesis of many members with methyl groups in various positions, from starting materials of known configuration (Velick and English, 1945; Ställberg-Stenhagen, 1946–1951; Crombie and Harper, 1950 a, b; Linstead, Lunt and Weedon, 1950, 1951). Configurations are now known for the representative α-methyl-acids (LXIV; $n = 1, 2, 7, 13$), β-methyl-acids (LXV; $n = 1, 2, 3, 14, 18, 19, 20$), *anteiso*-acids (LXVI; $n = 0, 1, 4, 12, 19$), and several members of other series. The syntheses show that all natural *anteiso*-acids have *L*-methyl groups (LXVI), and are therefore configuratively related at the methyl group to natural *iso*leucine (LXIX), which has been related to (−)-2-methylbutanol by degradation and synthesis (Ehrlich, 1907; *cf* Fones, 1954).

The work on fatty acids also established the configurations of some higher paraffin hydrocarbons, *e.g.* (+)-3*D*-methyloctane (LXVII) (Crombie and Harper, 1950) and (−)-4*L*-methyltritriacontane (LXVIII) (Ställberg-Stenhagen and Stenhagen, 1950).

Steroids

A direct chemical correlation of the steroids with acyclic compounds has recently been achieved independently in two laboratories in the following way (Cornforth, Youhotsky and Popják, 1954; Riniker, Arigoni and Jeger, 1954). Ring *D* of cholest-14-en-3β-ol was opened by treatment with ozone, and pyrolysis of the product yielded the side chain (*plus* C-15—C-17) as 4:8-dimethylnon-2-en-1-al ($OCH \cdot CH:CH \cdot CHMe \cdot [CH_2]_3 \cdot CHMe_2$). This compound was shown to be the same enantiomorph as that corresponding to (+)-citronellal (LVII). The stereochemistry of C-20 in cholestane is therefore as in (CIX, $X = H$, $X' = C_6H_{13}$) (p. 200). This result confirms the conclusions drawn from optical rotations and asymmetric synthesis (pp. 211 and 199). The correlation of calciferol methyl ether with β-methoxy-adipic acid by Lardon and Reichstein (1949), which had appeared to indicate that the steroid and glyceraldehyde conventions did not agree, must have involved an unexpected inversion at some stage.

Diterpenoids and Triterpenoids

Chemical correlations between diterpenoids and triterpenoids have been reviewed by Barton (1949), Jeger (1950) and Ruzicka (1953). The following notes cover some recent developments.

Some important correlations have been achieved by Riniker, Kalvoda, Arigoni, Fürst, Jeger, Gold and Woodward (1954) using the (−)-9-methyl-*trans*-Δ^{1,6}-3-hexalone of the Harvard steroid synthesis. This (−)-ketone, which corresponds to the natural steroids, has been transformed into (+)-9-methyl-*trans*-3-decalone and the (−)-*trans* isomers of 1-methyl-*cyclo*hexane-1:2-diacetic acid and 1-carboxy-1-methyl-*cyclo*hexane-2-acetic acid; the enantiomers of the first two of these compounds were obtained from the sesquiterpene eudesmol (*cf* also Heusser, Beriger, Anliker, Jeger and Ruzicka, 1953).

Kyburz, Riniker, Schenk, Heusser and Jeger (1953) have correlated the tetracyclic triterpenoid lanosterol with the diterpenoid manoöl by converting both natural compounds into the same (+)-4:4:9-tri-methyl-*trans*-decalin-8-carboxylic acid.

Unsymmetrical Derivatives of Glycerol

Many biologically important derivatives of glycerol (itself symmetrical, LXX) are unsymmetrical and occur naturally in optically active forms. The stereochemical correlations of these derivatives, including

unsymmetrical glycerides, phosphatidic acids, lecithins and kephalins
are due largely to H. O. L. Fischer, Baer and their colleagues (Baer
and Fischer, 1939; Sowden and Fischer, 1941; Fischer and Baer,
1941; reviews: Baer and Kates, 1948, 1950; Baer, 1951; Baer,
Maurukas and Russell, 1951; *cf* Hanahan and Jayko, 1952). They
are summarized in formulae LXX–LXXVII. Baer and Kates (1950)

UNSYMMETRICAL DERIVATIVES OF GLYCEROL

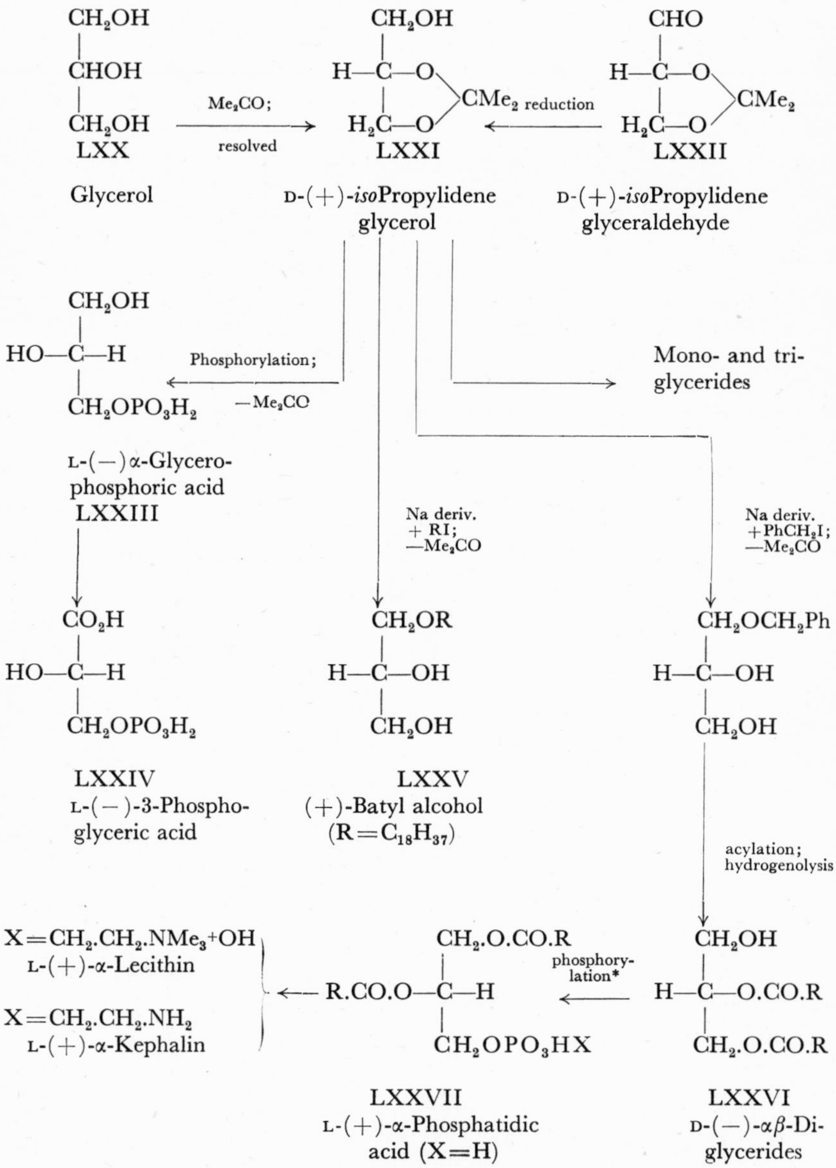

CH_2OH
$CHOH$
CH_2OH
LXX
$\xrightarrow[\text{resolved}]{\text{Me}_2CO;}$

CH_2OH
$H-C-O$
H_2C-O $\rangle CMe_2$
LXXI
$\xleftarrow{\text{reduction}}$

CHO
$H-C-O$
H_2C-O $\rangle CMe_2$
LXXII

Glycerol   D-(+)-*iso*Propylidene   D-(+)-*iso*Propylidene
                glycerol   glyceraldehyde

CH_2OH
$HO-C-H$
$CH_2OPO_3H_2$
$\xleftarrow[-\text{Me}_2CO]{\text{Phosphorylation;}}$

Mono- and tri-
glycerides

L-(−)α-Glycero-
phosphoric acid
LXXIII

Na deriv.
+ RI;
−Me₂CO

Na deriv.
+PhCH₂I;
−Me₂CO

CO_2H
$HO-C-H$
$CH_2OPO_3H_2$

CH_2OR
$H-C-OH$
CH_2OH

CH_2OCH_2Ph
$H-C-OH$
CH_2OH

LXXIV   LXXV
L-(−)-3-Phospho-   (+)-Batyl alcohol
glyceric acid $(R=C_{18}H_{37})$

acylation;
hydrogenolysis

$X=CH_2.CH_2.NMe_3^+OH$
L-(+)-α-Lecithin

$X=CH_2.CH_2.NH_2$
L-(+)-α-Kephalin

$CH_2.O.CO.R$
$\xleftarrow{} R.CO.O-C-H$
CH_2OPO_3HX

phosphory-
lation*

CH_2OH
$H-C-O.CO.R$
$CH_2.O.CO.R$

LXXVII   LXXVI
L-(+)-α-Phosphatidic   D-(−)-αβ-Di-
acid (X=H)   glycerides

*With phenylphosphorylchlorides, followed by hydrogenolysis of phenyl groups.

and Baer and Stancer (1953) have pointed out that the natural (+)-lecithins have a formal relationship to the L-α-glycerophosphoric acid of glycolysis (LXXIII).

Correlations Involving Ring-closures in Cyclic Compounds

Establishment of a bridge by ring-closure between suitable non-adjacent substituents in cyclic compounds is usually easy if the substituents are in the *cis*-relationship, but is impossible for non-adjacent groups in *trans*-relationship in the ordinary rings. This fact may sometimes be used to effect configurational correlations not readily achieved by other means.

Freudenberg has pointed out that it is possible in principle to achieve by direct chemical methods a correlation between secondary alcohols and branched-chain compounds. It is necessary to determine the relationship between two asymmetric centres in a suitable cyclic structure, then relate one centre to secondary alcohols and the other to branched-chain compounds.

A study of dihydroshikimic acid has at last solved this problem in fact (Freudenberg *et al*, 1940, 1952, 1953). Natural shikimic acid has been shown to have the configuration LXXVIII relative to glyceraldehyde (Dangschat and Fischer, 1950, and references cited there).

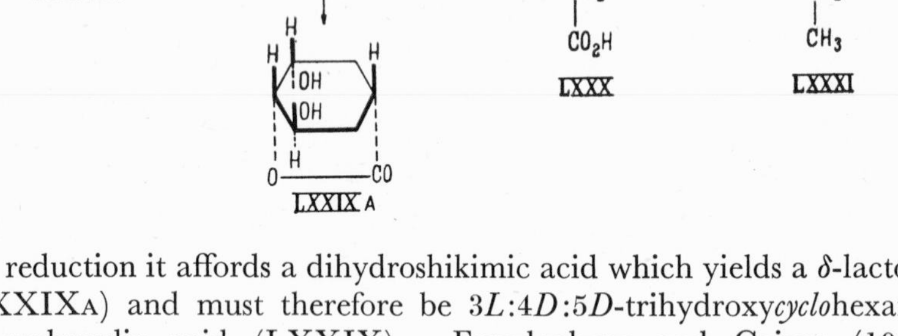

H
H OH
OH CO₂H
HO
H
Shikimic acid
LXXVIII

→

H
H 5 OH
OH
HO 3 CO₂H
H
LXXIX

↓

H
H OH
OH
H
O———CO
LXXIX A

→

CO₂H
CH₂
H—C—CO₂H
CH₂
CH₂
CO₂H
LXXX

→

CH₃
CH₂
H—C—Me
CH₂
CH₂
CH₃
LXXXI

On reduction it affords a dihydroshikimic acid which yields a δ-lactone (LXXIXA) and must therefore be 3*L*:4*D*:5*D*-trihydroxy*cyclo*hexane-1*D*-carboxylic acid (LXXIX). Freudenberg and Geiger (1952) prepared from this 3-*O*-acetyldihydroshikimic acid by way of 4:5-*O*-*iso*propylidenedihydroshikimic acid, cleaved the acetate with periodic acid, oxidized the dialdehyde to the corresponding acid, and removed the hydroxyl group arising from C-3 in LXXIX. They thereby obtained (+)-butane-1:2:4-tricarboxylic acid of high optical purity; the acid therefore has the configuration LXXX relative to glyceraldehyde. Freudenberg and Hohmann (1953) have reported

192

the reduction of this tricarboxylic acid to the corresponding triol and the further reduction of this via the tribromo compound to $(+)$-$3D$-methylhexane (LXXXI).

Noyce and Denney (1954) have reported details of another correlation between branched-chain compounds and secondary alcohols based on the same principle : $(-)$-cis-3-hydroxy*cyclo*hexanecarboxylic acid (LXXXIII) was degraded on the one hand to $(+)$-3-methyl*cyclo*hexanone (LXXXIV), already correlated with the monoterpenoids

LXXXII	LXXXIII	LXXXIV	$(-)$-Inositol LXXXV

(Hückel, 1941, 1948); on the other hand the ring of LXXXIII was opened to give $(-)$-2L-methoxyhexane-1:6-dioic acid (LXXXII; L-α-methoxyadipic acid)*.

Posternak (1936) correlated $(-)$-inositol (LXXXV) with glyceraldehyde by partial oxidation and identification of the open-chain carbohydrates produced. These results have recently been confirmed by Angyal, Macdonald and Matheson (1953).

An elegant example of the use of ring-closures is provided by Clark, Todd and Zussman (1951), who found that treatment of 5′-O-toluene-*p*-sulphonyl-2′:3′-O-*iso*propylideneadenosine (LXXXVI) with sodium

LXXXVI	LXXXVII

iodide afforded the iodide of a quaternary base (LXXXVII), the structure of this base being assigned on the basis of chemical and x-ray evidence. The occurrence of this ring-closure shows that adenosine must be 9-β-D-ribofuranosyladenine, not the α-isomer.

* LXXXII has since been correlated with glyceraldehyde by Noyce, D. S. and Canfield, J. H. (1954) *J. Amer. chem. Soc.* **76**, 3630.

The existence of the furanose ring-structure had previously been established by synthesis, and the β-configuration tentatively assigned on the basis of periodic acid cleavage of adenosine and synthetic D-glucopyranosyl-adenine (Davoll, Lythgoe and Todd, 1946, 1948).

A closely similar cyclization of 5'-O-toluene-p-sulphonyl-2':3'-O-iso-propylidenecytidine was achieved (Clark, Todd and Zussman, 1951), and together with known interconversion reactions these results directly confirm the β-configuration for most of the natural purine and pyrimidine nucleosides.

DISPLACEMENT REACTIONS INVOLVING ASYMMETRIC CENTRES

Reactions under Kinetic Control

Extensive researches by Hughes, Ingold and their collaborators have shown that a bimolecular displacement reaction (S_N2) involves as a necessary consequence a complete inversion of configuration at the carbon atom concerned, if this is asymmetric. (For a review, see Ingold, 1953; de la Mare this volume, Chapter 3.) Brewster, Hughes, Ingold and Rao (1950) used this fact to establish from their experimental results a decisive correlation of serine with glyceraldehyde.

The key reactions were those of $(+)$-α-bromopropionic acid (LXXXIX) with sodium hydroxide and with sodium azide, affording

$(+)$- lactic acid (LXXXVIII) and α-azidopropionic acid (LXXXIXA) respectively. Both reactions were performed under kinetic control, and were found to be true S_N2 reactions, therefore each involved an inversion of configuration. The azidopropionic acid was reduced catalytically to $(+)$-alanine (XC), a reaction not likely to disturb the configuration. Since lactic acid had already been correlated with glyceraldehyde (p. 183), and alanine with serine, by classical methods, the kinetically controlled reactions provided a direct link between the standard configuration (I) for $(+)$-glyceraldehyde and the standard configuration II for natural $(-)$-serine; the two standards are equivalent, and the previously determined configurations of amino-acids relative to serine are also the configurations relative to glyceraldehyde.

Brewster, Hiron, Hughes, Ingold and Rao (1950) have further used configurational relationships determined under kinetic control to establish correlations between a number of alcohols, ethers, halides and

Table 1. Signs of Rotation of Configuratively Related Alcohols, Ethers, Halides and Amines (Based on Ingold, 1953, p. 386)

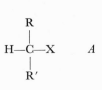

All signs are for compounds of the general formula A correctly correlated with glyceraldehyde. The correlations *within* each line of the table have been obtained by kinetic or related methods (Ingold, 1953) except those in parentheses which are by other reliable methods. The correlations *between* lines are by other methods; for references see last column.

R	R'	X=				References
		OH	OMe,OEt	Cl,Br,I	NH_2	
Me	Et	+	(+)	+	+ a	5
Me	$\begin{cases} n\text{-}C_3H_7 b \\ \text{to } n\text{-}C_7H_{15} \end{cases}$	+	+	+	+ a	4
CO_2H	Me	− c	+	+	−	p. 183
CH_2CO_2H	Me	−		−	(−)	2; p. 183
CO_2H	$CH_2 \cdot CO_2H$	+		+	+ e	p. 183
Me	C_6H_5	−	−	−	− a	p. 187
CO_2H	C_6H_5	−	(−)	−	− d	3; p. 187
CO_2H	$CH_2C_6H_5$	+		+	+	1
CH_2CO_2H	C_6H_5	+		+		

Notes: a Rotations refer to pure liquid amines; b Various members studied; for details, see Ingold, 1953 c Salts are (+); d Kinetic evidence now agrees with other evidence (Hibbin, Hughes and Ingold, 1954); this corrects previous kinetic evidence (Ingold, 1953); e Cation (−)in aqueous HCl.

References 1. Goldschmidt and Freyss, 1933; 2. Balenović, Cerar and Fuks, 1952; 3. McKenzie, 1899; 4. Freudenberg, 1933a, p. 696; 5. Tarbell and Paulson 1942.

amines; some of the results are shown in Table 1 (*cf* Ingold, 1953). They also showed that the deamination reaction, when applied to saturated acyclic amines, has the characteristics of a typical S_N1 reaction, proceeding with racemization together with an excess of inversion.

$$R \cdot NH_2 + HNO_2 \xrightarrow[H_2O]{H^+} R \cdot OH; \qquad R \cdot NH_2 + HNO_2 \xrightarrow[EtOH]{H^+} R \cdot OEt;$$

$$R \cdot NH_2 + NOCl \xrightarrow{HCl} R \cdot Cl$$

The same is true of the deamination of α-amino-esters, but the deamination of free α-amino-acids occurs with retention of configuration, because of the participation of the carboxylate anion in the displacement reaction.

For cyclic structures, the deamination reaction as a tool for correlation must be used with even greater care. (See Chapter 2, p. 66.)

Stereospecific Displacement Reactions

Several intramolecular displacement reactions are known to proceed with practically complete retention of configuration when they occur at an asymmetric centre. They include the Hofmann, Curtius, Schmidt and Lossen procedures for degrading carboxylic acid to amines,

$$
\underset{\underset{R'}{|}}{\overset{\overset{R}{|}}{H-C-CO_2H}} \longrightarrow \underset{\underset{R'}{|}}{\overset{\overset{R}{|}}{H-C-NH_2}} ,
$$

the Wolff rearrangement of diazoketones used in the Arndt-Eistert procedure for chain-lengthening,

$$
\underset{\underset{R'}{|}}{\overset{\overset{R}{|}}{H-C-CO\cdot Cl}} \xrightarrow{CH_2N_2} \underset{\underset{R'}{|}}{\overset{\overset{R}{|}}{H-C-CO\cdot CHN_2}} \xrightarrow{Ag_2O} \underset{\underset{R'}{|}}{\overset{\overset{R}{|}}{H-C-CH_2\cdot CO_2H}}
$$

and the migration of asymmetric groups during Beckmann rearrangements. The literature on these reactions has been reviewed by Wheland (1949), Alexander (1951), and Ingold (1953). Examples are the degradation of $(+)$-α-phenylpropionic acid to $(-)$-α-phenylethylamine (XLI⟶XXXIX, p. 187; Bernstein and Whitmore, 1939; Arcus and Kenyon, 1939), and the synthesis of $(+)$-β-aminobutyric acid (XCI) from L-$(+)$-alanine (XC) (Arndt–Eistert reaction, Balenović *et al*, 1952).

$$
\text{XCI} \qquad
\begin{array}{c}
CO_2H \\
| \\
CH_2 \\
| \\
H_2N-C-H \\
| \\
CH_3
\end{array}
$$

The cleavage of alkyl ketones by per-acids is also an intramolecular reaction proceeding with retention of configuration (Turner, 1950; Mislow and Brenner, 1953; Doering and Dorfman, 1953).

$$
\underset{\underset{R'}{\vdots}}{\overset{\overset{R}{\vdots}}{H-C-CO\cdot Me}} \xrightarrow{Ph\cdot CO_3H} \underset{\underset{R'}{\vdots}}{\overset{\overset{R}{\vdots}}{H-C-O\cdot CO\cdot Me}}
$$

These reactions are potentially very valuable for correlations of branched-chain structures with asymmetric alcohols or amines, but they have so far been used for establishing relationships within molecules rather than for correlations with glyceraldehyde. Gallagher and Kritchevsky (1950) and Klyne (1951a) used the per-acid cleavage

196

method to establish orientations of hydroxyl groups in steroids at C-17 and C-20, respectively. A very interesting application would be the correlation of α-methylbutyric acid (XLVIII) with butan-2-ol and 2-butylamine, but this does not seem to have been attempted. Some recent work on displacement reactions has been summarized by Kenyon (1951). Earlier work by Kenyon's school is outlined by Shriner, Adams and Marvel (1943).

Other Displacement Reactions

Several workers have synthesized optically active branched-chain compounds from straight-chain precursors by reactions involving the displacement by another anion of an anion attached to an asymmetric centre. The reactions have not been examined kinetically, but Walden inversions may reasonably be expected in such cases. With this assumption (the likely points of inversion being shown below), the results provide a consistent set of correlations, each suggesting that XLIX is the correct representation of $(-)$-2-methylbutanol on the glyceraldehyde convention. The configurations for the starting materials, relative to glyceraldehyde, are well known, and the branched-chain products have all been correlated with 2-methylbutanol by unequivocal methods.

Levene and Marker (1931) prepared several branched-chain acids by the malonic ester synthesis; *e.g.* $(-)$-3-methylpentanoic acid XCIV from $(+)$-2-butyl bromide XCII. Racemization sometimes occurred during the malonic ester synthesis, but the correlations from the successful experiments are consistent.

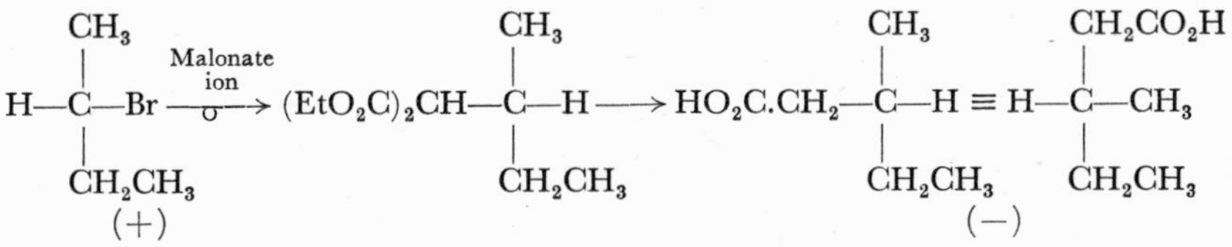

$$
\begin{array}{cccc}
\mathrm{CH_3} & \mathrm{CH_3} & \mathrm{CH_3} & \mathrm{CH_2CO_2H} \\
| & | & | & | \\
\mathrm{H{-}C{-}Br} \xrightarrow[\text{o}]{\text{Malonate ion}} (\mathrm{EtO_2C})_2\mathrm{CH{-}C{-}H} \longrightarrow \mathrm{HO_2C.CH_2{-}C{-}H} \equiv \mathrm{H{-}C{-}CH_3} \\
| & | & | & | \\
\mathrm{CH_2CH_3} & \mathrm{CH_2CH_3} & \mathrm{CH_2CH_3} & \mathrm{CH_2CH_3} \\
(+) & & (-) & \\
\text{XCII} & \text{XCIII} & \text{XCIV} &
\end{array}
$$

$$
\begin{array}{cccc}
\mathrm{CH_3} & \mathrm{CH_3} & \mathrm{CH_3} & \mathrm{CO_2H} \\
| & | & | & | \\
\mathrm{H{-}C{-}OTs} \xrightarrow[\text{o}]{\mathrm{CN^-}} \mathrm{CN{-}C{-}H} \longrightarrow \mathrm{HO_2C{-}C{-}H} \equiv \mathrm{H{-}C{-}CH_3} \\
| & | & | & | \\
\mathrm{CH_2CH_3} & \mathrm{CH_2CH_3} & \mathrm{CH_2CH_3} & \mathrm{CH_2CH_3} \\
(+) & (-) & (-) & \\
\text{XCV} & \text{XCVI} & \text{XCVII} &
\end{array}
$$

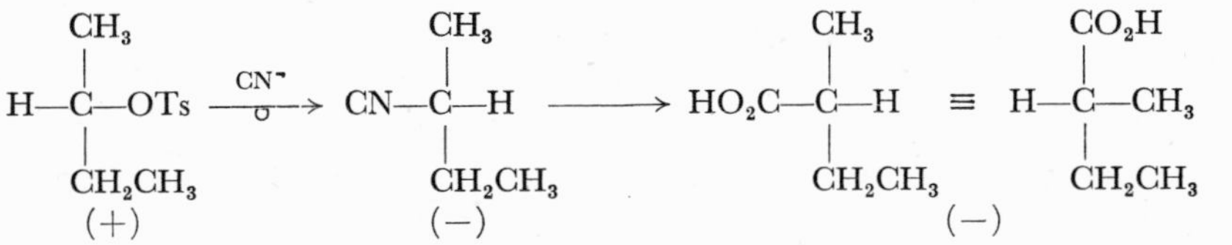

Kenyon, Phillips and Pittman (1935) treated $(+)$-2-butyl toluene-*p*-sulphonate (XCV) with potassium cyanide and obtained a nitrile (XCVI) that afforded $(-)$-2-methylbutyric acid (XCVII) on hydrolysis; *cf* formula XLVIII for $(+)$-2-methylbutyric acid.

From the reaction of (−)-2-octyl bromide (XCVIII) with sodium allyl, Letsinger and Traynham (1950) obtained (−)-4-methyldec-l-ene (XCIX), which was degraded to (−)-3-methylnonane (C). The latter was related to 2-methylbutanol by synthesis. The reaction with sodium allyl involved only slight racemization. Ulrich, Gentes, Lane and Wallis (1950) have described analogous reactions that provided correlations consistent with this.

$$
\begin{array}{cccc}
 & & & \text{CH}_3 \\
\text{CH}_3 & & \text{CH}_3 & \text{CH}_3 & | \\
| & \overbrace{\text{CH}_2\!=\!\text{CH}\!=\!\text{CH}_2} & | & | & \text{CH}_2 \\
\text{Br—C—H} & \xrightarrow{\hspace{0.5cm}\sigma\hspace{0.5cm}} & \text{H—C—CH}_2\cdot\text{CH:CH}_2 & \text{H—C—CH}_2\text{CH}_3 & | \\
| & & | & | & \equiv \text{CH}_3\text{—C—H} \\
(\text{CH}_2)_5 & & (\text{CH}_2)_5 & \longrightarrow \quad (\text{CH}_2)_5 & | \\
| & & | & | & (\text{CH}_2)_5 \\
\text{CH}_3 & & \text{CH}_3 & \text{CH}_3 & | \\
& & & & \text{CH}_3 \\
(-) & & (-) & (-) \\
\text{XCVIII} & & \text{XCIX} & \text{C}
\end{array}
$$

These three sets of correlations between straight-chain and branched-chain compounds agree with those deduced from the study of quasi-racemic compounds (p. 201), from direct chemical methods (p. 192) and from x-ray evidence (p. 214), and the above interpretations of the mechanisms appear to be sound. However, such displacement reactions can never be as reliable a source of correlations as are reactions which have been studied kinetically.

ASYMMETRIC SYNTHESIS

Two groups of workers have recently studied the probable conformations of certain acyclic systems and the course of reactions dependent on these. They have applied these ideas to the correlation of configurations.

Prelog and his colleagues (Prelog, 1953) have considered the stereochemical course of reactions between α-ketoesters (CII) of asymmetric alcohols (CI) and Grignard reagents previously studied intensively by McKenzie. They found that one of the two diastereoisomers (CIII) predominated and that the stereochemistry of this predominant isomer at C* could be correlated with that of the carbinol atom of the alcohol. The letters L, M and S in formulae refer to large, medium and small substituents attached to the carbinol carbon atom of CI.

$$
\begin{array}{ccc}
\text{HO·C}SML & \longrightarrow & \text{R·*CO·CO·O·C}SML \\
\text{CI} & & \text{CII} \quad \downarrow \\
& & \qquad\qquad \downarrow \text{R'MgX} \\
\text{RR'*C(OH)·CO}_2\text{H} & \longleftarrow & \text{RR'*C(OH)·CO·O·C}SML \\
\text{CIV} & & \text{CIII}
\end{array}
$$

The hypothesis which they proposed was that the Grignard reagent R′MgX would attack C* preferentially from the side on which the smallest substituent S lies. This requires a consideration of the possible conformations of the group CSML. In the case where $S = H$ and $L \gg M$ the determining factor is the reaction of the Grignard reagent with that conformation where S (H) is in the plane of the ester grouping and M and L in front and behind respectively. The preferential attack will be as shown in CVA or CVB from the side of the smaller alkyl group M :

CVA   CVB

The results may be summarized as follows: the alcohols as phenyl-glyoxylic esters (R = Ph) are treated with methyl magnesium iodide (R′ = Me) giving esters of atrolactic acids which are then hydrolysed.

Thirty-seven reactions of this type (studied chiefly by McKenzie and co-workers) were tabulated by Prelog. All but five of these supported the rule proposed above. Three of the exceptions were examined experimentally by Prelog, who found that the apparent exceptions were due to incomplete hydrolysis of the atrolactic esters. Complete hydrolysis gave acids of the sign predicted by the rule.

In dealing with cyclic compounds of the type CVI, the degree of substitution of the ring-members adjacent to the asymmetric centre is considered in deciding which is the ' larger ' substituent for the purposes of the rule.

Thus, if X is a methylene group and Y a tertiary or quaternary carbon atom (often a ring-junction), then Y counts as the larger substituent. Prelog has used hydroxyl groups at C-3 in the triterpenoids (CVII) and at C-7 and C-17 in the steroids (CVIII) for correlations. C-3 in

199

the steroids was found unsuitable since it is flanked by two methylene groups and the synthetic reaction is hardly asymmetric. Prelog and Tsatsas (1953) have applied these ideas to hydroxyl groups at C-20 in the steroids. Their results confirm the previous allotment of configurations at C-20 (see CIX) by Fieser and Fieser (1949) (see also Klyne, 1951a).

CVI   CVII   CVIII   CIX

Cram and his colleagues considered similar reactions in which the reacting carbonyl group is directly adjacent to the asymmetric carbon atom (Cram and Abd Elhafez, 1952, and five following papers). They have proposed the following rule of steric control of asymmetric induction in the syntheses of acyclic systems. ' In [non-catalytic] reactions of the following type, that diastereomer will predominate which would be formed by the approach of the entering group [R'] from the *least hindered side* of the double bond when the rotational conformation of the C—C bond is such that the double bond is flanked by the two least bulky groups [M and S] attached to the adjacent asymmetric centre [C*].'

CX   CXI

The evidence on which this rule is based is taken from thirty-five reactions (twenty-seven from previous work and eight from Cram's own work). In all cases the isomer which would be predicted by the rule predominated in the product; the configurations of these isomers had been established by independent methods. The reactions included those of ketones and aldehydes with Grignard reagents; reduction of ketones with lithium aluminium hydride, sodium and alcohol, sodium amalgam and water, and aluminium *iso*propoxide (Meerwein–Ponndorf); reduction of oximes to amines with sodium amalgam. Cram points out that the reaction is kinetically controlled in all cases except the Meerwein-Ponndorf reaction. This last-mentioned reaction is reversible, and if it were run for a very long time the products would be thermodynamically controlled. However, the reaction is not usually run long enough to permit the establishment of an equilibrium. Cram indicates that the reasons for the rule may be quite different in different cases and briefly discusses some examples.

The authors then give representative illustrations of a series of fifty reactions in the literature where the configurations of the products were previously unknown and can be deduced from the rule. One difficulty which may arise in applying the rules of Prelog and of Cram lies in deciding what is the order of effective bulk of the three groups (*L, M* and *S*) attached to the asymmetric carbon atom.

Both rules of asymmetric synthesis will be of great value in correlation problems, particularly that of Prelog, since his method can be applied in principle to almost any carbinol.

Other workers have discussed the use of asymmetric synthesis in individual reactions to achieve correlations, *e.g.* Curtin, Harris and Meislich (1952), Grignard reaction of benzoin; Mosher and La Combe (1950), reduction by Grignard reagent, correlating (+)-pinacolyl alcohol (CXII) with (−)-2-methylbutanol; Doering and Young, (1950, 1952) and Jackman, Mills and Shannon (1950), Meerwein-Ponndorf reductions.

$$
\begin{array}{c}
CH_3 \\
| \\
H\!\!-\!\!C\!\!-\!\!OH \\
| \\
CMe_3
\end{array}
$$

CXII

CORRELATIONS FROM THE STUDY OF QUASI-RACEMIC COMPOUNDS

The principles underlying the formation of ' quasi-racemic compounds ' (formerly but wrongly called ' active racemates ') have been recognized for a considerable time, but the method has only recently yielded results of outstanding importance for configurational correlations. These developments are due largely to Fredga, who has reviewed much of his own and the earlier work [Fredga (1944); see also Lettré (1943).]

Quasi-racemic compounds are equimolecular compounds formed between two optically active compounds of very similar structure but of ' opposite ' configuration, such as CXIV and CXV. The name indicates their close relationship to true racemic compounds formed from equimolecular mixtures of true enantiomorphs, such as CXIII and CXIV, and in each case the formation of the equimolecular compound is detected by the study of melting-point curves of mixtures of the components. A quasi-racemic compound usually will be optically active, unless the two components have identical molecular rotations under the conditions used for the measurements.

The curves of FIGURE 2 show the three types of behaviour found on constructing melting-point curves for mixtures of true enantiomorphs.

The components may form a series of solid solutions (a) or give a simple eutectic (b), or in some cases may afford a true racemic compound, detected by the presence of two eutectics and a symmetrical maximum at equimolecular concentrations (c).

Melting-point curves for pairs of structurally similar optically active compounds C$abcx$ and C$abcy$ will also fall into three classes that correspond to the classes of FIGURE 2, but the curves will in general be unsymmetrical (FIGURE 3). Solid solutions may be formed (d), or a simple eutectic (e), or occasionally there may be evidence for the presence of an equimolecular compound (f); the last is a quasi-racemic compound.

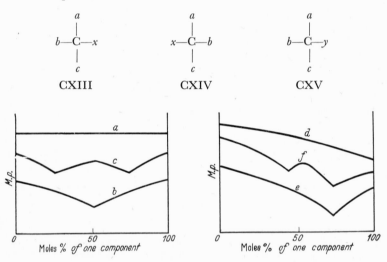

CXIII CXIV CXV

FIGURE 2. Melting-point curves for true enantiomorphs CXIII and CXIV

FIGURE 3. Melting-point curves for ' quasi-'enantiomorphs CXIV and CXV

So far as is known, curves of type (f) have been observed (during the comparison of substances containing one asymmetric centre) only when the substances compared have been of closely similar structure and of opposite configuration. Curves of types d and e are observed with components of like configuration, and may be observed with substances of opposite configuration; like the formation of true racemic compounds from enantiomorphs, the formation of quasi-racemic compounds is not of general occurrence.

Fredga's most important result was the correlation of methyl-succinic acid with malic acid. It was known that ($+$)-malic acid (IX) afforded a xanthate ester (CXVI) by methods not likely to cause configurational changes ,and that an isomeric xanthate ester (CXVII) could be hydrolysed to ($-$)-thiolsuccinic acid (CXVIII), also by methods not likely to invert the configuration. The two xanthates

CXVI and CXVII afforded a quasi-racemic compound, therefore they are of opposite configuration, and likewise $(+)$-malic acid and $(-)$-thiolsuccinic acid are of opposite configuration (Fredga, 1941). $(-)$-Thiolsuccinic acid afforded a quasi-racemic compound with $(+)$-methylsuccinic acid, therefore the two compounds are of opposite configuration, and consequently $(+)$-methylsuccinic acid is of the same configuration as $(+)$-malic acid, and is to be represented by LII on the glyceraldehyde convention (Fredga, 1942). If one component of each pair was replaced by its enantiomorph, quasi-racemic compounds were not detected.

$$
\begin{array}{ccc}
CO_2H & & CO_2H \\
| & & | \\
H-C-OH & \longrightarrow & H-C-O\cdot CS\cdot SEt \\
| & & | \\
CH_2CO_2H & & CH_2CO_2H \\
(+) & & (-) \\
IX & & CXVI
\end{array}
$$

$$
\begin{array}{ccccc}
CO_2H & & CO_2H & & CO_2H \\
| & & | & & | \\
EtO\cdot CS\cdot S-C-H & \longrightarrow & HS-C-H & \longleftarrow & H-C-CH_3 \\
| & & | & & | \\
CH_2CO_2H & & CH_2CO_2H & & CH_2CO_2H \\
(-) & & (-) & & (+) \\
CXVII & & CXVIII & & LII
\end{array}
$$

These results provided the most decisive evidence for the correctness of the correlations between branched-chain compounds and glyceraldehyde discussed above until direct chemical correlations were achieved recently by Noyce and Denney (1954) and by Freudenberg and Hohmann (1953) (see also p. 192). Supporting evidence was available from other sources (pp. 197 and 211), and from the study of further quasi-racemic compounds: the results (Fredga and Sahlberg, 1944; Fredga and Leskinen, 1944; Fredga, 1947; Fredga and Miettinen, 1947) are consistent with the above correlation of methylsuccinic acid, and with views about interrelations between monocyclic and bicyclic terpenes deduced by other methods. One interesting result is that all monosubstituted $(+)$-alkylsuccinic acids examined have the D-configuration.

Fredga (1944, and later papers) has also used the formation of quasi-racemic compounds to correlate various amino-, hydroxy- and thiol-acids.

The definite formation of a quasi-racemic compound may be taken as evidence of opposite configurations in the components, provided the substituents are fairly similar in size and shape, but several confirmatory correlations are obviously desirable in each case. The significant results reported so far seem all to be for acyclic compounds containing only one asymmetric centre. However, Lettré (1932) has described some very interesting results with steroids; his data have not been analysed in detail in recent years, but in several cases it appears that equimolecular compounds were formed between substances having opposite configurations at *two* asymmetric centres.

CORRELATIONS FROM THE STUDY OF OPTICAL ROTATIONS

Principles

Correlations deduced solely from optical rotation data cannot in many cases be accepted as decisive, but the optical method often provides an easy, and sometimes the only available, way of achieving a correlation. The method can yield valuable information when used with care and a proper understanding of its limitations. For a fuller review, see Klyne (1954).

Molecular rotations, not specific rotations, are used. They must be observed for the same wavelength of light, be free of any serious deviations due to solvent, concentration or temperature effects, and be of the appropriate order of accuracy. Apart from these practical precautions, the important requirement for sound correlations is the choice of an adequate number of true analogies. Comparisons at several wavelengths, or the construction of a rotatory dispersion curve, may be of value.

The choice of analogies is particularly important. Compounds compared should be as closely similar as possible; it is not permissible to compare tertiary alcohols with secondary alcohols, or acyclic compounds with cyclic compounds. The Rule of Optical Superposition (van't Hoff, 1894; Guye and Gautier, 1894) hardly ever holds in its original quantitative form; the total molecular rotation is not the sum of independent, additive contributions from the individual asymmetric centres, the contribution from any single centre being influenced in a complex way through the *vicinal action* of other asymmetric centres and structural features such as unsaturation and chain-branching. A small alteration in the structure of a complex molecule may alter the contributions from several centres. Whether significant vicinal action is likely, and its probable magnitude, can only be assessed by the careful study of related compounds (see *e.g.* Rupe and Häfliger, 1940, and earlier papers; Freudenberg and Kuhn, 1931; Barton and Cox, 1948).

Vicinal action between two centres usually decreases rapidly the further they are separated by saturated atoms; Tschugaeff (1898) generalized this in his Distance Rule (*Entfernungssatz*). As a consequence of this effect, the molecular rotations of higher members of homologous series containing one or two asymmetric atoms tend to reach a limiting value, or zero. Sometimes certain structural possibilities may be excluded on this basis; *e.g.* work on long-chain fatty acids (Ställberg-Stenhagen, 1947, and later papers) indicates the following limiting values: α-methyl acids, $[M]_D \sim 28°$; β-methyl acids, $\sim 13-15°$; and *anteiso*-acids, $\sim 14°$; $[M]_D$ falls to a very low value as the methyl group is moved near to the centre of a long chain.

Single Measurements

A single measurement of rotation may suffice to fix the configuration of a compound beyond reasonable doubt. This is true for some homologous series of acyclic compounds containing a single asymmetric centre carrying only *n*-alkyl groups, or a functional group and *n*-alkyl groups. All known members of the series of *D*-alkylalkanes (CXIX; $l > m > n$), alkan-*D*-ols (*D*-carbinols; CXX; $m > n$), 2*L*-methylalkanoic acids (CXXI), 3*D*-methylalkanoic acids (CXXII) (except when $n = 1$), and *L-anteiso*acids (CXXIII) are dextrorotatory for the sodium D-line, and it may safely be predicted that other members will be dextrorotatory.

The data available (*cf* TABLE 1, p. 195) suggest that secondary alcohols, halides and primary amines of the same configuration will have rotations of the same sign (*cf* the 2-butyl derivatives), but more examples are needed before this generalization can be considered as established.

CXIX	CXX	CXXI	CXXII	CXXIII
CH_3	CH_3	CO_2H	CO_2H	CO_2H
$(CH_2)_m$	$(CH_2)_n$	CH_3-C-H	CH_2	$(CH_2)_n$
$H-C-(CH_2)_nCH_3$	$H-C-OH$	$(CH_2)_n$	$H-C-CH_3$	CH_3-C-H
$(CH_2)_l$	$(CH_2)_m$	CH_3	$(CH_2)_n$	CH_2
CH_3	CH_3		CH_3	CH_3

Optical data for monocyclic terpenes show some interesting regularities (Mills, 1952) ; *e.g.* known compounds represented by the structure and configuration (CXXIV) in which R and R' are suitable combinations of the groups Me, $CHMe_2$, $CMe:CH_2$, CH_2OH, CMe_2OH, CH_2OAcyl and CMe_2OAcyl, all have molecular rotations within the range $+ 130°$ to $+ 170°$. This fact was used to assign configurations to two monocyclic sesquiterpenes.

Marker (1936) used the extensive evidence available from the work of Levene, Freudenberg, von Braun and others to compile a table of twenty nine substituent groups, assigning an order of precedence to the groups from which could be deduced the sign of rotation of a tri-substituted methane containing any three of the groups. For many simple compounds, including the homologous series above, the predictions are correct, but Marker's rules should be used with reserve, because they were drawn up before configurations of branched-chain compounds were established with precision, and may need revision.

An attempt by Stokes and Bergmann (1952) to apply Marker's rules to cyclic compounds has proved to be invalid (Mills, 1953), but modified rules relating configuration to rotation for cyclic alcohols have been worked out (Klyne and Stokes, 1954).

CXXIV	CXXV	CXXVI

Rotational Shifts

The Displacement Rule (Rule of Shift; *Verschiebungssatz*) formulated by Freudenberg (1933b) is more generally useful than the rules based on measurement of single rotations, and may be used to correlate compounds belonging to different classes. This rule, essentially similar to an earlier suggestion by Clough (1918), states that if two similarly constituted asymmetric molecules are chemically altered in the same way the change in molecular rotation will be in the same direction in each case (and usually of the same order of magnitude). The essential requirement is similarity of structure; neglect of this factor renders some earlier applications unsatisfactory. If possible, the shifts observed should be large, and an extended series of comparisons is desirable.

Stevens (1933) and Stevens, Higbee and Armstrong (1938) used the displacement rule to assign configurations to (+)-pinacolyl alcohol (CXXV) and (−)-*tert*-butyl *n*-propyl carbinol (CXXVI). The evidence is not entirely convincing, but the configuration for pinacolyl alcohol agrees with that deduced by Mosher and La Combe (1950) from a study of the abnormal Grignard reaction (p. 201).

α-Substituted Acids

Neuberger (1948) has reviewed the extensive optical studies carried out in attempts to correlate α-amino-acids with each other and with α-hydroxyacids. Before the formal enunciation of the Displacement Rule, Freudenberg and Rhino (1924) had examined the rotational data for derivatives of natural (+)-alanine and of L-(+)-lactic acid, and had concluded that the two substances were configuratively related. Part of their evidence is collected in TABLE 2; for simplicity, figures are given for (+)- lactic acid, although the authors actually worked with (−)-lactic acid. To increase the probability that the observed rotational shifts were truly comparable, derivatives of the two acids were used with both functional groups substituted. The general trend in both series was similar for several wavelengths of light, but the data are not convincing in all details.

TABLE 2.   CORRELATION OF L-(+)-ALANINE AND L-(+)-LACTIC ACID

Comparison of compounds of the types $CH_3 \cdot CH(OR) \cdot COR'$ and $CH_3CH(NHR) \cdot COR'$ (Freudenberg et al, 1924, 1935).

All values are $[M]_{5780}$. Dash in solvent column indicates pure liquid.

Δ values are with reference to the first compound listed in each group.

R (Substituent on OH or NH₂)	R' (Substituent on carboxyl group)	Lactic acid series			Alanine series		
		M	solvent	Δ	M	solvent	Δ
(Δ Values with reference to compound *)							
CH_3CO	OEt *	−72	—	—	−74	—	—
$C_6H_{11}CO$	OEt	−43	—	+29	−86	EtOH	−12
C_6H_5CO	OMe	+36	—	+107	−3	Py	+71
C_6H_5CO	OEt	+16	$C_2H_2Cl_4$	+88	+39	$C_2H_2Cl_4$	+113
C_6H_5CO	NH₂	+120	$H \cdot CO_2H$	+192	+85	$H \cdot CO_2H$	+159
$p\text{-}C_7H_7.SO_2$ {	OEt	−109	—	−37	−78	EtOH	−4
	NH₂	− 87	Py	−15	−44	Py	+30
(Δ Values with reference to compound **)							
EtO_2C {	NHC_6H_5 **	−117	EtOH	—	−133	EtOH	—
	OC_6H_5	−84	—	+33	−57	EtOH	+76
	OEt	−78	—	+39	−8	—	+125
	NMe₂	−11	—	+106	−26	EtOH	+107
(Δ Values with reference to compound ***)							
$Et \cdot SO_2$ {	NHC_6H_5 ***	−181	EtOH	—	−159	EtOH	—
	OC_6H_5	−119	—	+62	−122	EtOH	+37
	OEt	−93	—	+88	−53	—	+106
	NMe₂	−5	—	+176	−61	EtOH	+98

Freudenberg, Kuhn and Bumann (1930) obtained more consistent rotational shifts when comparing derivatives of α-chloro-, α-bromo-, α-iodo- and α-azido-propionic acid, presumably because the azido-group is more nearly comparable to a halogen atom than a modified amino-group is to a modified hydroxyl group.

Other rotational shifts studied during attempts to correlate all natural amino-acids with serine include those caused by conversion of α-amino-acids to hydantoins, by alteration of pH of solutions, and by formation of copper complexes; the last two methods included studies of rotatory dispersion. The details of these investigations are given by Neuberger (1948).

None of these earlier studies of rotational shifts could be regarded as proving a definite correlation between α-amino-acids and glyceraldehyde, but they did strongly suggest that natural α-amino-acids possess the L-configuration, and this has been confirmed by the kinetic studies of Hughes, Ingold and co-workers (p. 194), by arguments based on the configuration and reactions of D_g-glucosamine (Wolfrom, Lemieux and Olin, 1949) and by x-ray evidence (p. 214).

Carbohydrates

The optical method has been particularly successful in the study of carbohydrates. Hudson's early discovery that the rule of optical superposition holds quite accurately for many anomeric O-glycosides, generalized in his Rules of Isorotation (Hudson, 1909), led to other generalizations such as the Amide Rule, Phenylhydrazide Rule and Lactone Rule. Discussions of these, and the part they have played in the development of carbohydrate chemistry, will be found in text-books (*e.g.* Pigman and Goepp, 1948) and in Hudson's collected papers (1946). The latest of such generalizations about carbohydrate configurations is the Benziminazole Rule reviewed by Richtmyer (1951).

Apart from the Rules of Isorotation, and a recent extension of the Lactone Rule (Hudson, 1939), the above generalizations are qualitative, and relate configuration to the sign of rotation of a derivative of an aldonic acid, rather than to the rotational shift occurring during formation of the derivative. It might be profitable to reassess the data taking into account the magnitudes of the rotational shifts involved.

Reliable chemical methods are now available for determining configurations at most asymmetric centres in sugars, but the optical methods are still of value, particularly for assignment of configurations to O-glycosides. For aldopyranosides, the molecular rotation of an α-D-glycoside (CXXVII) is usually $350°$ to $400°$ more positive than that of the β-D-anomer (CXXVIII), and if both forms are available the optical method will normally be decisive. Even if only one form is available, the optical method may give a decisive result if supplemented by other methods, such as cleavage by periodic acid (p. 184). Klyne (1950) has used optical rotations to assign configurations to many naturally-occurring steroid glycosides.

CXXVII CXXVIII

These earlier studies of molecular rotation data for sugars and amino-acids were important in emphasizing the need for sufficient true analogies in the comparisons, and in drawing attention to departures from the quantitative rules of optical superposition. For example, changes in the rotation of α-halogeno-acids and α-amino-acids during salt formation with alkali led Clough (1918) and Levene, Mori and Mikeska (1927) to deduce correlations between the two classes that are now known to be incorrect; the comparisons were invalidated by the fact that the α-amino-acids can in certain pH ranges exist as zwitterions, whereas α-halogeno-acids cannot.

Steroids and Terpenoids

Optical rotations have been widely employed for assignment of configurations within the steroid field, particularly by Barton and his colleagues, using a form of the Rule of Shift termed the Method of Molecular Rotation Differences (Barton and Jones, 1944; Barton, 1945 and many subsequent papers; *cf* Callow and Young, 1936; Bernstein, Wallis *et al*, 1941, 1942, 1946; Fieser and Fieser, 1949). The striking success of these studies firmly established the optical method as a tool in configurational correlations.

The rotational shifts caused by the introduction of hydroxyl groups, carbonyl groups or unsaturation into the steroid nucleus, or by alteration of substituents (*e.g.* hydroxyl $\rightarrow$ acetate or benzoate; hydroxyl $\rightarrow$ carbonyl) are highly characteristic for the different nuclear positions and orientations of substituents. Barton and Klyne (1948) have compiled a list of typical steroid molecular rotation increments, with examples of the use of the data to check or supplement chemical evidence.

The success of the optical method in the steroid field is due largely to the flat, relatively rigid framework of the molecules, which holds the asymmetric centres a fixed distance apart, and makes possible the calculation of probable magnitudes of vicinal action for various structural units, and the distances over which vicinal action may operate (Barton and Cox, 1948). The shifts associated with many of the important structural and configurational changes in the steroid nucleus are large, adding to the reliability of the method.

Recently, attempts have been made to extend the methods used in the steroid field to the similar polycyclic systems found in diterpenoids and triterpenoids and to seek rotational relationships between steroids and simpler compounds that might link the steroids with glyceraldehyde.

In a fully documented paper, Klyne (1952b) presented a large body of evidence indicating that, in terms of the conventional steroid projection formula CXXIX, the projection CXXX represents the natural form of a typical pentacyclic triterpenoid (oleanan-3β-ol; new numbering) and not its enantiomorph. The diagrams emphasize the striking similarity of triterpenoids to steroids in structure and stereochemistry (*cf* Halsall, Jones and Meakins, 1952).

The correlation of the two classes was carried out by establishing for steroids certain principles about the rotational contributions of individual rings (rather than isolated asymmetric centres) and the effect of substituents on the rotational contribution of the rings, and

209

then tracing a parallel behaviour in individual rings of typical triterpenoids.

The following are some of the important principles established:

(*1*) The contribution of a terminal ring, *i.e.* A or D in CXXIX, A or E in CXXX, is, to a first approximation, independent of the nature of the rest of the molecule, provided the adjacent ring is a saturated unsubstituted *cyclo*hexane ring.

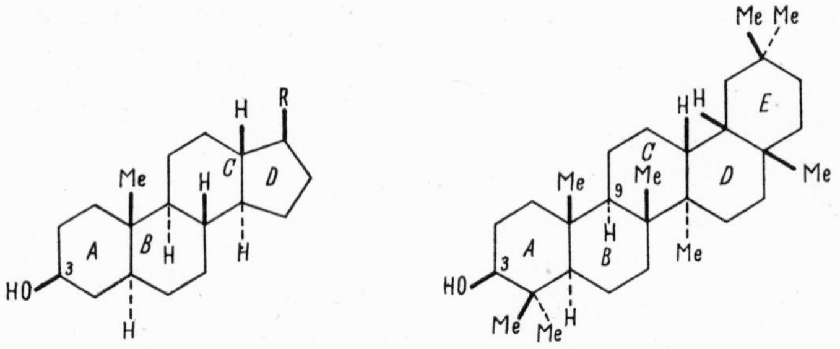

CXXIX   CXXX

(*2*) Terminal rings in suitably modified steroids are often of recognizably enantiomeric types, *e.g.* ring D of the androstan-16-one CXXXI and ring A of the A-nor-steroid 2-ketone CXXXII. An operation carried out on two rings of enantiomeric types produces molecular rotational shifts (Δ values) of opposite sign and roughly of the same magnitude, whereas operations on rings of the same type produce shifts of the same sign. The *trans-β*-indanone structures shown are outstanding examples of this: the Δ-value of the 16-keto-group ($[M]_D$16-ketone—$[M]_D$16-CH_2-compound) in CXXXI is $-460°$ to $-520°$, whereas the Δ value of the 2-keto-group in an A-nor-steroid CXXXII is $+350°$ to $+460°$.

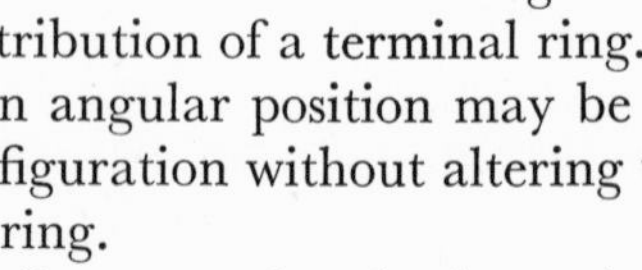

CXXXI   CXXXII

(*3*) The presence or absence of non-angular methyl groups has little effect on the contribution of a terminal ring. It is also likely that a hydrogen atom at an angular position may be replaced by a methyl group of the same configuration without altering the sign of the contribution of the terminal ring.

The contributions of structural units in typical triterpenoids were then compared with corresponding contributions in steroids. The rotational behaviour of ring A of triterpenoids is clearly comparable with, and not enantiomeric to, that of ring A of steroids, although the former carries the *gem*-dimethyl group. With few exceptions, data for the intermediate rings were also consistent with the formulation CXXX for compounds of the oleanane group. Chemical studies (*cf* Barton and Holness, 1952) had reduced the number of possible configurations for oleanane to four, *viz* two pairs of enantiomorphs (CXXX, its 9β-epimer, and their mirror-images). The rotational evidence indicated clearly that CXXX was correct; fortunately this was confirmed shortly afterwards by x-ray methods (Abd El Rehim and Carlisle, 1954).

Rotations have also been used to correlate several classes of diterpenoids and sesquiterpenoids with steroids (Klyne, 1953a; *cf* Zeiss and Martin, 1953).

Recently, attempts have been made to correlate steroids with monocyclic terpenoids, based on examinations of the rotational changes attendant on epimerization at individual asymmetric centres. The most satisfactory evidence relates to allylic alcohols. Mills (1952) showed that, in epimeric pairs of allylic terpene alcohols already correlated with glyceraldehyde by the work of Fredga (p. 202), an alcohol containing the structural unit CXXXIII always has a molecular rotation more positive (by about 200° to 300°) than that of its epimer

CXXXIII   CXXXIV

containing the enantiomeric unit (CXXXIV), irrespective of the position of alkyl substituents. Esterification greatly enhances the difference between epimers. Epimeric allylic steroid alcohols also show similar large differences in molecular rotation, enhanced by esterification, and it was found that the rotational differences for known pairs of epimers conform to a regular pattern, the sign of the difference for an α, β pair of allylic epimers being determined by the enantiomeric nature of the *cyclo*hexenol units contained in them, irrespective of the position of the unit in the steroid skeleton. Klyne (1952a) and Stokes and Bergmann (1952) had also discussed allylic steroid alcohols. Comparison of the rotational shifts in the allylic steroids and in the terpene alcohols indicated that the conventional projection (CXXIX) correctly represents natural steroids relative to glyceraldehyde. For example, cholest-4-en-3α-ol (CXXXV), ($[M]_D + 467°$) which contains the unit CXXXIII, is more dextrorotatory than its β-epimer (CXXXVI; + 170°) which contains the unit CXXXIV.

Mills (1953) has also traced relationships between rotational shifts caused by epimerization of hydroxyl groups in saturated steroid alcohols and in monocyclic terpene alcohols that have a formal resemblance to individual rings of steroids. The results indicated that the steroid and glyceraldehyde conventions are in agreement.

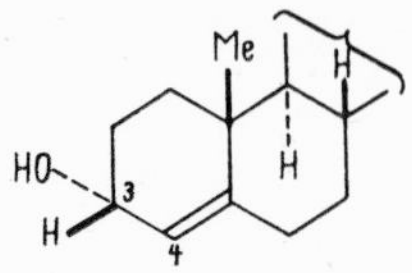

CXXXV 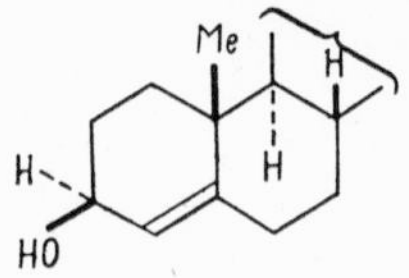   CXXXVI

The configurations for steroids deduced from these optical comparisons agree with those deduced by Dauben, Dickel, Jeger and Prelog (1953) from studies of asymmetric syntheses. They have just been confirmed by the evidence from the degradations discussed on p. 190.

Stokes and Bergmann (1951, 1952) discussed the rotational shifts characteristic of individual asymmetric centres in steroids, and also drew comparisons between steroids and simpler cyclic molecules. Their data cannot be used directly to correlate steroids with glyceraldehyde, because Marker's Rule (p. 205) cannot be applied to cyclic structures (Mills, 1953), but Klyne and Stokes (1954) have shown that suitable rules may be developed to classify the rotational behaviour of hydroxyl groups adjacent to asymmetric centres in rings.

Barnes, Barton, Fawcett and Thomas (1953) have used the generalized method of molecular rotations to show that C-20 in the lanostane series has the same configuration as C-20 in the cholestane series. Many optical correlations between centres of asymmetry in the steroid side chain and simple aliphatic compounds are discussed by Klyne and Stokes (1954).

Klyne (1953b) has used these rules to correlate the yohimbine alkaloids (CXXXVII) with the steroids and thence with glyceraldehyde (cf Stork and Hill, 1954; van Tamelen and Shamma, 1954).

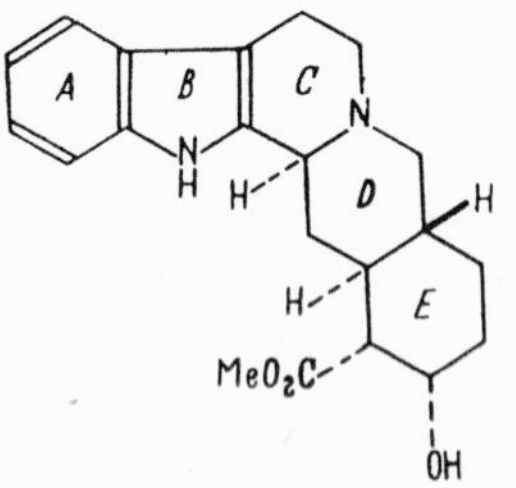

Yohimbine
CXXXVII

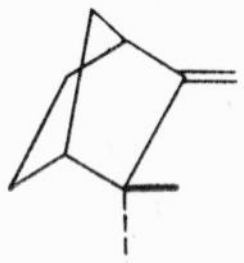

CXXXVIII 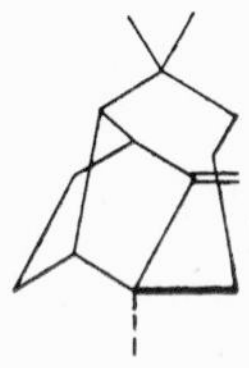   CXXXIX

A further example of the method of generalized molecular rotation differences is provided by Ourisson (1953) who has correlated the sesquiterpenoid longifolene (CXXXIX) with camphene (CXXXVIII).

ENZYMIC EVIDENCE

Stereochemical correlations based on the specificity of enzyme action (*cf* Chapter 8) have been of particular value in studies on α-amino-acids and α-hydroxy acids. Greenstein and his colleagues have isolated a number of synthetic aliphatic L-amino-acids by preferential hydrolysis of the racemic *N*-acyl derivatives (Birnbaum, Levintow, Kingsley and Greenstein, 1952, and previous references there). More recent papers extend this work to phenylglycine (Rudman, Meister and Greenstein, 1952), $\alpha\beta$-diaminopropionic acid (Birnbaum, Koegel, *et al*, 1952) and *iso*valine (CXL, Baker *et al*, 1952).

The last-named compound contains a tertiary carbon atom (C-2). The 2*L*-amino enantiomer is dextrorotatory (in water), and Neuberger (1948) comments on the fact that this acid shows an abnormal rotational change on the formation of the cation. A useful review of enzymic resolution methods for amino-acids is given by Berg (1953).

Baker and Meister (1951) used the nitrous acid reaction to prepare from the amino-acids a series of optically active α-hydroxyacids. Configurations were allotted on the assumption (Brewster *et al*, 1950) that replacement of the amino by the hydroxyl group occurred without inversion.

Bergmann, Zervas, Rinke and Schleich (1934) used enzymic evidence to correlate the configuration at C-2 in D_g-glucosaminic acid (CXLI) with that of the α-carbon atom of alanine. Peptides in which the amino group of glucosaminic acid was combined with natural amino-acids could not be split by an intestinal dipeptidase which is specific for peptides of L-amino-acids (CXLII). The enzyme could, however, split peptides formed similarly from the 2-epimer of glucosaminic acid.

Dalgliesh (1953) has used enzymic evidence in discussing the configuration of adrenaline (epinephrine) and noradrenaline (arterenol). The $(-)$-isomers are (CXLIII; R = Me and H respectively; Ar = 3 : 4-$C_6H_3(OH)_2$). Decarboxylation of one enantiomorph of

213

erythro-dihydroxyphenylserine (CXLIV) with an L-amino-acid decarboxylase gave (CXLIII, R = H).

$$\underset{\text{CXLIII}}{\overset{\displaystyle \begin{array}{c} CH_2 \cdot NHR \\ | \\ HO—C—H \\ | \\ Ar \end{array}}{}} \xleftarrow{\text{L-decarboxylase}} \underset{\text{CXLIV}}{\overset{\displaystyle \begin{array}{c} CO_2H \\ | \\ NH_2—C—H \\ | \\ HO—C—H \\ | \\ Ar \end{array}}{}}$$

The use of enzymic evidence to determine the type of linkage (α or β) between monosaccharide units in an oligosaccharide or polysaccharide is well known. Confirmation may often be available from optical rotations.

Further examples of enzymic methods may be found in the appropriate chapters of Sumner and Myrbäck's *The Enzymes* (1950-1952).

X-RAY EVIDENCE

X-ray examination of crystals will not give evidence of absolute configurations except by the special methods employed by Bijvoet *et al* (1951). It can however give correlations between one asymmetric centre and another in the same compound which are beyond question. An important recent example is work on L_s-threonine (CXLV) (Shoemaker *et al*, 1950) and L_s-hydroxyproline (CXLVI; Zussman, 1951) which provides a link between the glyceraldehyde series and the amino-acid series.

CXLV   CXLVI   CXLVII

The correlation of branched-chain aliphatic compounds with unbranched compounds, discussed on pp. 192 and 203, has recently been confirmed by x-ray crystallography (Trommel, 1954)*. Examination of *iso*leucine hydrochloride proved that the *erythro* relationship between the two centres of asymmetry shown in LXIX is correct.

The detailed work of Dr. Dorothy Crowfoot-Hodgkin and her colleagues on steroids (Carlisle and Crowfoot, 1945; Crowfoot and

* We are greatly indebted to Professor J. M. Bijvoet (Utrecht) for his kind permission to quote these results, which were disclosed at a lecture given at University College, London, in March 1954.

Dunitz, 1948; Hodgkin and Sayre, 1952) has provided absolutely reliable evidence for the relative configuration of all the ring-junctions in the steroids. Abd El Rehim and Carlisle (1954) and Curtis, Fridrichsons and Mathieson (1952) have similarly settled certain doubtful points in the stereochemistry of the pentacyclic and tetra-cyclic triterpenoids respectively.

Another important illustration of the use of x-ray evidence is provided by the work of Crowfoot, Bunn, Rogers-Low and Turner-Jones (1949) on penicillin (CXLVII). Knowledge of the configuration relative to serine of the $\beta\beta$-dimethylcysteine residue, which is D_s, permits the allotment of configuration at the ' aldehyde ' C atom marked*, of the aminomalonic semi-aldehyde unit, which would be extremely difficult to settle in any other way.

Penicillin provides a good example to show that configurational correlations have in some cases definite biogenetic significance. The alanine derived from the semi-aldehyde unit of penicillin is the L_s-isomer. Arnstein and Grant (1954) have shown by isotope studies that L_s-cystine is incorporated into penicillin by *Penicillium chrysogenum* to about five times the extent that the D_s-isomer is incorporated, which suggests that a stereochemically specific reaction is involved in the synthesis.

Conclusion

It is hoped that this chapter has demonstrated what an important and fascinating field is open in the study of stereochemical correlations. The data for many correlations undoubtedly lie in the literature, so far unheeded. Among the groups of biologically important compounds which remain to be correlated with glyceraldehyde are many alkaloids, the flavans (catechin and similar C-6—C-3—C-6 structures) lignans, vitamin E, biotin, *etc.*

REFERENCES

Abd El Rehim, A. M. and Carlisle, C. H. (1954) *Chem & Ind.* 279
Alexander, E. R. (1951) *Principles of Ionic Organic Reactions*, chap. 3, New York, Wiley
Angyal, S. J., Macdonald, C. G. and Matheson, N. K. (1953) *J. chem. Soc.* 3321
Arcus, C. L. and Kenyon, J. (1939) *ibid* 916
Arnstein, H. R. V. and Grant, P. T. (1954) *Biochem. J.* **57**, 353
Baer, E. (1951) *J. biol. Chem.* **189**, 235
— and Fischer, H. O. L. (1939) *J. Amer. chem. Soc.* **61**, 761
— and Kates, M. (1948) *ibid* **70**, 1395; (1950) *ibid* **72**, 942
— Maurukas, J. and Russell, M. (1951) *Science,* **113**, 12
— and Stancer, H. C. (1953) *J. Amer. chem. Soc.* **75**, 4510
Baker, C. G., Fu, S. C. J., Birnbaum, S. M., Sober, H. A. and Greenstein, J. P. (1952) *ibid* **74**, 4701
— and Meister, A. (1951) *ibid* **73**, 1336.
Balenović, K., Cerar, D. and Fuks, Z. (1952) *J. chem. Soc.* 3316
Barnes, C. S., Barton, D. H. R., Fawcett, J. S. and Thomas, B. R. (1953) *ibid* 576
Barrow, F. and Ferguson, G. W. (1935) *ibid* 410

Barton, D. H. R. (1945) *ibid* 813; (1949) *Quart. Rev. chem. Soc.*, *Lond.* **3,** 36; (1953) *J. chem. Soc.* 1027
— and Cox, J. D. (1948) *J. chem. Soc.* 783
— and Holness, N. J. (1952) *ibid* 78
— and Jones, E. R. H. (1944) *ibid* 659
— and Klyne, W. (1948) *Chem. & Ind.* 755
Berg, C. P. (1953) *Physiol. Rev.* **33,** 145
Bergmann, M., Zervas, L., Rinke, H. and Schleich, H. (1934) *Hoppe-Seyl. Z.* **224,** 33
Bergström, S., Lardon, A. and Reichstein, T. (1949) *Helv. chim. acta,* **32,** 1617, 2003
Bernstein, H. I. and Whitmore, F. C. (1939) *J. Amer. chem. Soc.* **61,** 1324
Bernstein, S., Kauzmann, W. J. and Wallis, E. S. (1941) *J. org. Chem.* **6,** 319
— Hicks, E. M., Clark, D. M. and Wallis, E. S. (1946) *ibid* **11,** 646
— Wilson, E. J. and Wallis, E. S. (1942) *ibid* **7,** 103
Bijvoet, J. M., Peerdeman, A. F. and van Bommel, A. J. (1951) *Nature, Lond.* **168,** 271
Birch, A. J. (1950) *Annu. Rep. Progr. Chem.* **47,** 191
Birnbaum S. M., Koegel, R. J., Fu, S. C. J. and Greenstein, J. P. (1952) *J. biol. Chem.* **198,** 335
— Levintow, L., Kingsley, R. B. and Greenstein, J. P. (1952) *ibid* **194,** 455
Brewster, P., Hiron, F., Hughes, E. D., Ingold, C. K. and Rao, P. A. D. S. (1950) *Nature, Lond.* **166,** 179
— Hughes, E. D., Ingold, C. K. and Rao, P. A. D. S. (1950) *ibid* **166,** 178
Brown, H. C., Kharasch, M. S. and Chao, T. H. (1940) *J. Amer. chem. Soc.* **62,** 3435
Buchanan, C. (1951) *Nature, Lond.* **167,** 689
Cahn, R. S. and Ingold, C. K. (1951) *J. chem. Soc.* 612
Callow, R. K., and Young, F. G. (1936) *Proc. roy. Soc. A* **157,** 194
Carlisle, C. H. and Crowfoot, D. (1945) *ibid* **184,** 64
Celmer, W. D. and Solomons, I. A. (1953) *J. Amer. chem. Soc.* **75,** 1372
Clark, V. M., Todd, A. R. and Zussman, J. (1951) *J. chem. Soc.* 2952
Clough, G. W. (1918) *ibid* **113,** 526
Cornforth, J. W., Youhotsky, I. and Popják, G. (1954) *Nature, Lond.* **173,** 536
Cowdrey, W. A., Hughes, E. D. and Ingold, C. K. (1937) *J. chem. Soc.* 1243
— — — Masterman, S. and Scott, A. D. (1937) *ibid* 1252
Cram D. J. and Abd Elhafez, F. A. (1952) *J. Amer. chem. Soc.* **74,** 5828 *cf* (1953) *ibid* **75,** 6005
Crombie, L. and Harper, S. H. (1950a) *J. chem. Soc.* 2685; (1950b) *Chem. & Ind.* 757
Crowfoot, D., Bunn, C. W., Rogers-Low, B. W. and Turner-Jones, A. (1949) in *The Chemistry of Penicillin* ed. by H. T. Clark, J. R. Johnson and R. Robinson., Chap. 11, Princeton, N.J., University Press.
— and Dunitz, J. D. (1948) *Nature, Lond.* **162,** 608
Curtin, D. Y., Harris, E. E. and Meislich, E. K. (1952) *J. Amer. chem. Soc.* **74,** 2901
Curtis, R. G., Fridrichsons, J. and Mathieson, A. McL. (1952) *Nature, Lond.* **170,** 321
Dalgliesh, C. E. (1953) *J. chem. Soc.* 3323
Dangschat, G. and Fischer, H. O. L. (1950) *Biochim. biophys. acta* **4,** 199
Dauben, W. G., Dickel, D. F., Jeger, O. and Prelog, V. (1953) *Helv. chim. acta* **36,** 325
Davoll, J., Lythgoe, B. and Todd, A. R. (1946) *J. chem. Soc.* 833; (1948) *ibid* 967
Doering, W. von E. and Dorfman, E. (1953) *J. Amer. chem. Soc.* **75,** 5595
— and Young, R. W. (1950) *ibid* **72,** 631; (1952) *ibid* **74,** 2997
Ehrlich, F. (1907) *Ber. dtsch. chem. Ges.* **40,** 2538
Fieser, L. F. and Fieser, M. (1949) *Natural Products Related to Phenanthrene,* 3rd ed., New York, Reinhold

THE CORRELATION OF CONFIGURATIONS

Fischer, H. O. L. and Baer, E. (1941) *Chem. Rev.* **29,** 287
Fones, W. S. (1954) *J. Amer. chem. Soc.* **76,** 1337
Fredga, A. (1941) *Ark. Kemi Min. Geol.* **14B,** No. 27; (1942) *ibid* **15B,** No. 23; (1944) *The Svedberg Anniversary Volume* p. 261. Stockholm; Almqvist and Wiksells; (1947) *Ark. Kemi Min. Geol.* **24A,** No. 32
— and Leskinen, E. (1944) *ibid* **19B,** No. 1
— and Miettinen, J. K. (1947) *Acta chem. scand.* **1,** 371
— and Sahlberg, U. (1944) *Ark. Kemi Min. Geol.* **18A,** No. 16
Freudenberg, K. (1914) *Ber. dtsch. chem. Ges.* **47,** 2027; (1933a) *Stereochemie*, pt. 2, pp. 662-730, Leipzig and Vienna, Deuticke ; (1933b) *Ber. dtsch. chem. Ges.* **66,** 177
— Brauns, F. and Siegel, H. (1923) *Ber. dtsch. chem. Ges.* **56,** 193
— and Geiger, J. (1952) *Liebigs Ann.* **575,** 145
— and Hohmann, W. (1953) *ibid* **584,** 54
— and Kuhn, W. (1931) *Ber. dtsch. chem. Ges.* **64,** 703
— — and Bumann, I. (1930) *ibid* **63,** 2380
— and Markert, L. (1925) *ibid* **58,** 1753
— Meisenheimer, H., Lane, J. T. and Plankenhorn, E. (1940) *Liebigs Ann.* **543,** 162
— and Meister, M. (1935) *ibid* **518,** 86
— and Rhino, F. (1924) *Ber. dtsch. chem. Ges.* **57,** 1547
— Todd, J. and Seidler, R. (1933) *Liebigs Ann.* **501,** 199
Gallagher, T. F. and Kritchevsky, T. H. (1950) *J. Amer. chem. Soc.* **72,** 882
Goldschmidt, S. and Freyss, G. (1933) *Ber. dtsch. chem. Ges.* **66,** 784
Guye, P. A. and Gautier, M. (1894) *C.R. Acad. Sci., Paris* **119,** 740, 953
Halsall, T. G., Jones, E. R. H. and Meakins, G. D. (1952) *J. chem. Soc.* 2862
Hanahan, D. J. and Jayko, M. E. (1952) *J. Amer. chem. Soc.* **74,** 5070
Hansen, R. P., Shorland, F. B. and Cooke, N. J. (1952) *Biochem. J.* **52,** 203
Heusser, H., Beriger, E., Anliker, R., Jeger, O. and Ruzicka, L. (1953) *Helv. chim. acta* **36,** 1918
Hibbin, B. C., Hughes, E. D. and Ingold, C. K. (1954) *Chem. & Ind.* 933
Hodgkin, D. C. and Sayre, D. (1952) *J. chem. Soc.* 4561
Hückel, W. (1941) *J. prakt. Chem.* **157,** 225; (1948) *FIAT Review, Theoretical Organic Chemistry* pt. 1, p. 58.
Hudson, C. S. (1909) *J. Amer. chem. Soc.* **31,** 66; (1939) *ibid* **61,** 1525; (1946) *Collected Papers* New York, Academic Press; (1948) *Advanc. Carbohyd. Chem.* **3,** 1
Ingold, C. K. (1953) *Structure and Mechanism in Organic Chemistry*, p. 368, London, Bell
Jackman, L. M., Mills, J. A. and Shannon, J. S. (1950) *J. Amer. chem. Soc.* **72,** 4814
Jackson, E. L. (1944) *Org. React.* **2,** 341
— and Hudson, C. S. (1937) *J. Amer. chem. Soc.* **59,** 994
Jeger, O. (1950) *Fortschr. Chem. org. Naturst.* **7,** 1
Karrer, P. and Dinkel, P. (1953) *Helv. chim. acta* **36,** 122
— and Erhardt, K. (1951) *ibid* **34,** 2202
— Portmann, P. and Suter, M. (1948) *ibid* **31,** 1617
Kenyon, J. (1951) *Bull. Soc. chim. Fr.*, **C,**64
— Phillips, H. and Pittman, V. P. (1935) *J. chem. Soc.* 1072
Klyne, W. (1950) *Biochem. J.* **47,** xli; (1951a) *Chem. & Ind.* 426; (1951b) *ibid* 1022; (1952a) *Helv. chim. acta* **35,** 1224; (1952b) *J. chem. Soc.* 2916; (1953a) *ibid* 3072; (1953b) *Chem. & Ind.* 1032; (1954) in *The Structures of Organic Compounds*, ed. E. A. Braude, and F. C. Nachod, New York, Academic Press (in press)
— and Stokes, W. M. *J. chem. Soc.* 1979; *cf* (1953) *Biochem. J.* **55,** xxviii
Kuhn, W. (1952) *Z. Elektrochem.* **56,** 506
Kuna, M., Ovakimian, G. and Levene, P. A. (1941) *J. biol. Chem.* **137,** 337
Kyburz, E., Riniker, B., Schenk, H. R., Heusser, H. and Jeger, O. (1953) *Helv. chim. acta* **36,** 1891

217

Lardon, A. and Reichstein, T. (1947) *ibid* **32**, 2003
Leithe, W. (1931) *Ber. dtsch. chem. Ges.* **64**, 2827; (1932a, b) *ibid* **65**, 660, 927
Letsinger, R. L. and Traynham, J. G. (1950) *J. Amer. chem. Soc.* **72**, 849
Lettré, H. (1932) *Liebigs Ann.* **495**, 41; (1943) *Ergebn. Enzymforsch.* **9**, 1
Levene, P. A. and Haller, H. L. (1925) *J. biol. Chem.* **65**, 49; (1926) *ibid* **67**, 329; **69**, 165
— and Harris, S. A. (1936) *ibid* **113**, 55
— and Marker, R. E. (1931) *J. biol. Chem.* **91**, 77, 405, 687; **93**, 749
— Mori, T. and Mikeska, L. A. (1927) *ibid* **75**, 337
— and Rothen, A. (1936) *J. org. Chem.* **1**, 76; (1938) *Organic Chemistry*, chap. 21, ed. H. Gilman, 1st ed. New York, Wiley
— and Stevens, P. G. (1930) *J. biol. Chem.* **87**, 375; **89**, 471
— and Walti, A. (1926) *ibid* **68**, 415
— — and Haller, H. L. (1927) *ibid* **71**, 465
Linstead, R. P., Lunt, J. C. and Weedon, B. C. L. (1950) *J. chem. Soc.* 3333; (1951) *ibid* 1130
McKenzie, A. (1899) *ibid* **75**, 761
Maclay, W. D., Hann, R. M. and Hudson, C. S. (1939) *J. Amer. chem. Soc.* **61**, 1660
Marckwald, W. (1899) *Ber. dtsch. chem. Ges.* **32**, 1089
Marker, R. E. (1936) *J. Amer. chem. Soc.* **58**, 976
Mills, J. A. (1952) *J. chem. Soc.* 4976; (1953) *Chem. & Ind.* 218
Mislow, K. (1951) *J. Amer. chem. Soc.* **73**, 3954
— and Brenner, J. (1953) *ibid* **75**, 2318
— and Heffler, M. (1952) *ibid* **74**, 3668
Mosher, H. S. and La Combe, E. (1950) *J. Amer. chem. Soc.* **72**, 3994
Neuberger, A. (1948) *Advanc. Protein Chem.* **4**, 297
Noyce, D. S. and Denney, D. B. (1950) *J. Amer. chem. Soc.* **72**, 5743; (1954) *ibid* **76**, 768
Ourisson, G. (1953) *Chem. & Ind.* 916
Pigman, W. W. and Goepp, R. M. (1948) *Chemistry of the Carbohydrates*, New York, Academic Press
Posternak, T. (1936) *Helv. chim. acta* **19**, 1007
Prelog, V. *et al* (1953) *ibid* **36**, 308 and two succeeding papers
— and Tsatsas, G. (1953) *ibid* **36**, 1178
Richtmyer, N. K. (1951) *Advanc. Carbohyd. Chem.* **6**, 196
Riniker, B., Arigoni, D. and Jeger, O. (1954) *Helv. chim. acta* **37**, 546
— Kalvoda, J., Arigoni, D., Fürst, A., Jeger, O., Gold, A. M. and Woodward, R. B. (1954) *J. Amer. chem. Soc.* **76**, 313
Rudman, D., Meister, A. and Greenstein, J. P. (1952) *ibid* **74**, 551
Rupe, H. and Häfliger, F. (1940) *Helv. chim. acta* **23**, 53
Ruzicka, L. (1953) *Experientia*, **9**, 357
Schmid, H. and Karrer, P. (1948) *Helv. chim. acta* **31**, 1017
Shoemaker, D. P., Donohue, J., Schomaker, V. and Corey, R. B. (1950) *J. Amer. chem. Soc.* **72**, 2328
Shriner, R. L., Adams, R. and Marvel, C. S. (1943) in *Organic Chemistry* ed. H. Gilman. 2nd ed. p. 274 *et seq*, New York, Wiley
Simonsen, J. L. and Owen, L. N. (1947-1949) *The Terpenes*, 2nd ed. Vols. 1 and 2. Cambridge University Press
Snyder, H. R. and Brewster, J. H. (1949) *J. Amer. chem. Soc.* **71**, 291
Sowden, J. C. and Fischer, H. O. L. (1941) *ibid* **63**, 3244
Ställberg-Stenhagen, S. (1946) *Ark. Kemi. Min. Geol.* **23A**, No. 15; (1947) *ibid* **25A**, No. 10; (1948) *ibid* **26A**, No. 1; (1949) *Ark. Kemi.* **1**, 187; (1950) *ibid.* **2**, 95, 431; (1951) *ibid* **3**, 117
— and Stenhagen, E. (1947) *ibid* **24B**, No. 9; (1950) *J. biol. Chem.* **183**, 223

Stevens, P. G. (1933) *J. Amer. chem. Soc.* **55**, 4237
— Higbee, W. E. and Armstrong, R. T. (1938) *ibid* **60**, 2658
Stokes, W. M. and Bergmann, W. (1951) *J. org. Chem.* **16**, 1817; (1952) *ibid* **17**, 1194
Stork, G. and Hill, R. K. (1954) *J. Amer. chem. Soc.* **76**, 949
Sumner, J. B. and Myrbäck, K. (1950-52). *The Enzymes* Two vols, in four parts, New York, Academic Press
Tarbell, D. S., and Paulson, M. C. (1942) *J. Amer. chem. Soc.* **64**, 2842
Trommel, J. (1954) *Proc. Acad. Sci. Amst.* B **57**, 364
Truter, E. V. (1951) *Quart. Rev. chem. Soc.*, *Lond.* **5**, 390
Tschugaeff, L. (1898) *Ber. dtsch. chem. Ges.* **31**, 360
Turner, R. B. (1950) *J. Amer. chem. Soc.* **72**, 878
Ulrich, S. E., Gentes, F. H., Lane, J. F. and Wallis, E. S. (1950) *ibid* **72**, 5127
van Tamelen, E. E. and Shamma, M. (1954) *ibid* **76**, 950
van't Hoff, J. H. (1894) *Die Lagerung der Atome im Raume*, p. 119, Brunswick, Vieweg
Velick, S. F. and English, J. (1945) *J. biol. Chem.* **160**, 473
von Braun, J. and Jostes, F. (1926) *Ber. dtsch. chem. Ges.* **59**, 1091, 1444
Watson, M. B. and Youngson, G. W. (1954) *J. chem. Soc.* 2145
Weitkamp, A. W. (1945) *J. Amer. chem. Soc.* **67**, 447
Wheland, G. W. (1949) *Advanced Organic Chemistry*, 2nd ed. *a* Chap. 6; *b* chap. 12, New York, Wiley
Wiberg, K. B. (1952) *J. Amer. chem. Soc.* **74**, 3891
Wohl, A. and Momber, F. (1917) *Ber. dtsch. chem. Ges.* **50**, 455
— and Schellenberg, R. (1922) *ibid* **55**, 1404
Wolfrom, M. L., Lemieux, R. U. and Olin, S. M. (1949) *J. Amer. chem. Soc.* **71**, 2870
— — — and Weisblat, D. I. (1949) *ibid* **71**, 4057
Zeiss, H. H. and Martin, W. B. (1953) *J. Amer. chem. Soc.* **75**, 5935
Zussman, J. (1951) *Acta cryst.*, *Camb.* **4**, 72

ADDITIONAL REFERENCES

The following is a selection of references (mainly recent) to other papers on correlations; particular attention has been paid to natural products. The list is far from exhaustive and in many cases reference is made only to the last one or two of a series of papers.

Aliphatic Compounds
Straight-chain: One Centre of Asymmetry
α- and β-Hydroxyacids and related compounds : Lemieux, R. U. and Giguere, J. (1951) *Canad. J. Chem.* **29**, 678. α-Hydroxyglutaric acid: Fischer, E. and Moreschi, A. (1912) *Ber. dtsch. chem. Ges.* **45**, 2447. α-Aryloxypropionic acids (plant-growth regulators): Fredga, A. and Matell, M. (1952) *Ark. Kemi* **3**, 429; **4**, 325; Wain, R. L. (1953) *Roy. Inst. Chem. Lectures*, No. 2.

Aminoacids (newer discoveries among natural products): Hausmann, W. and Craig, L. C. (1952) *J. biol. Chem.* **198**, 405; Newton, G. G. F. and Abraham, E. P. (1953) *Nature, Lond.* **172**, 395 (α-aminoadipic acid) ; Woolley, D. W., Schaffner, G. and Braun, A. C. (1952) *J. biol. Chem.* **198**, 807 (tabtoxinine; αα'-diamino-β-hydroxypimelic acid); 3 : 6-diaminohexanoic acid (from streptothricin), Carter, H. E. *et al* (1952) *J. Amer. chem. Soc.* **74**, 3704; van Tamelen, E. E. and Smissman, E. E. (1952) *ibid* **74**, 3713.

1-Aminopropan-2-ol (from cobalamin, vitamin B_{12}) Wolf, D. E., Jones, W. H. Valiant, J. and Folkers, K. (1950) *J. Amer. chem. Soc.* **72**, 2820.

Pantoic acid (2 : 4-dihydroxy-3 : 3-dimethylbutanoic acid—and lactone) Grüssner, A., Gätzi-Fichter, M. and Reichstein, T. (1940) *Helv. chim. acta* **23**, 1276.

Phosphorylated derivatives of glycerol, etc.—α-glycerophosphoric acid, Fischer, H. O. L. and Baer, E. (1939) *J. biol. Chem.* **128**, 491; 3-phosphoglyceraldehyde, Meyerhof, O. and Junowicz-Kocholaty, R. (1943) *J. biol. Chem.* **149**, 71; 2- and 3-phosphoglyceric acids, Meyerhof, O. and Kiessling, W. (1934) *Naturwissenschaften* **22**, 838; (1935) *Biochem. Z.* **276**, 239; Neuberg, C. (1943) *Arch. Biochem.* **3**, 105; diphospho-glyceric acids, Baer, E. (1950) *J. biol. Chem.* **185**, 763.

Straight-chain; Two Centres of Asymmetry
Propylene glycol and glycerol derivatives, including amino-compounds and ethylene oxides: Abderhalden, E. and Eichwald, E. (1914) *Ber. dtsch. chem. Ges.* **47**, 2880; (1915) **48**, 113, 1847; (1916) **49**, 2095; (1918) **51**, 1312; Levene, P. A. and Walti, A. (1926) *J. biol. Chem.* **68**, 422; (1927) **73**, 263.

Butanediols, diaminobutanes and similar compounds: Leroux, P. J. and Lucas, H. J. (1951) *J. Amer. chem. Soc.* **73**, 41; Lucas, H. J. and Garner, H. K. (1948) *ibid* **70**, 990; Rubin, L. J., Lardy, H. A. and Fischer, H. O. L. (1952) *ibid* **74**, 425; Dickey, F. H., Fickett, W. and Lucas, H. J. (1952) *ibid* **74**, 944; Helmkamp, G. K. and Lucas, H. J. (1952) *ibid* **74**, 951.

Threonine and related compounds: Elliott, D. F. (1948) *Nature, Lond.* **162**, 657; (1949) *J. chem. Soc.*, 589; (1950) *ibid* 62; Hamel, E. E. and Painter, E. P. (1953) *J. Amer. chem. Soc.* **75**, 1362.

meso-Tartaric acid (mono-substituted derivatives): Freudenberg, K. (1931): *S. B. heidelberg. Akad. Wiss. Abh.* 9.

Chloromalic acids, dichloro- and epoxy-succinic acids: Kuhn, R. *et al* (1925) *Ber. dtsch. chem. Ges.* **58**, 919; (1926) **59**, 2514; (1928) **61**, 481, 483.

Hydroxylysines (2: 6-diamino-5-hydroxyhexanoic acids; hydroxyl group not yet correlated): Fones, W. S. (1953) *J. Amer. chem. Soc.* **75**, 4865.

Sphingosine (2-aminooctadec-*trans*-4-ene-1 : 3-diol) Carter, H. E. and Humiston, C. G. (1951) *J. biol. Chem.* **191**, 727; Carter, H. E., Harrison, J. B. and Shapiro, D. (1953) *J. Amer. chem. Soc.* **75**, 1007, 4705; Carter, H. E. and Shapiro, D. (1953) *ibid* 5131; Grob, C. A. and Jenny, E. F. (1952, 1953) *Helv. chim. acta* **35**, 2106; *ibid* **36**, 1454, 1936; Marinetti, G. and Stotz, E. (1954) *J. Amer. chem. Soc.* **76**, 1347.

Branched-chain Compounds
Many compounds which had then been correlated with 2-methylbutanoic acid are listed by Freudenberg (1932, pp. 679-681). Fortunately the choice of alternative formulae made by Freudenberg for his reference substance is now known to be correct—and all the other formulae on these pages are therefore correct.

Hydrocarbons—Prelog, V. and Zalán, E. (1944) *Helv. chim. acta* **27**, 545; Gordon, G. S. and Burwell, R. L. (1949) *J. Amer. chem. Soc.* **71**, 2355; Heller, H. E. *ibid* (1952) **74**, 4858.

Acids—α-Methylglutaric acid: Fredga, A. (1947) *Ark. Kemi Min. Geol.* **24A**, No. 32. α-*iso*Propylglutaric acid, Fredga, A. and Miettinen, J. K. (1947) *Acta chem. scand.* **1**, 371. β-*iso*Propyladipic acid, Fredga, A. (1949) *ibid* **3**, 208. Other α-alkyl- and αα-dialkyl-succinic acids, Porath, J. (1949, 1951) *Ark. Kemi* **1**, 385, 525; **3**, 163.

*iso*Leucines (2-amino-3-methylpentanoic acids) : Greenstein, J.P., Levintow, L., Baker, C. G. and White, J. (1951) *J. biol. Chem.* **188**, 647.

*iso*Citric acid (l-Hydroxypropane-1 : 2 : 4-tricarboxylic acid): Pucher, G. W., Abrahams, M. D. and Vickery, H. B. (1948) *J. biol. Chem.* **172**, 579 (configuration at C-2 unknown).

Phenyl-substituted Aliphatic Compounds
Kenyon, J., Phillips, H. and Pittman, V. P. (1935) *J. chem. Soc.* 1072; Duveen, D. I. and Kenyon, J. (1939) *J. chem. Soc.* 1697; Arcus, C. L. and Strauss, H. E. (1952) *ibid* 2669; Eliel, E. L. (1949) *J. Amer. chem. Soc.* **71**, 3970; Eliel, E. L. and Freeman, J. P. (1952) *ibid* **74**, 923; Siegel, S. and Graefe, A. F. (1953) *ibid* **75**, 4521; Levene, P. A. and Marker, R. E. (1931) *J. biol. Chem.* **93**, 749; Levene, P. A., Marker, R. E. and Rothen, A. (1933) *ibid* **100**, 595; Bergmann, E. (1937) *Helv. chim. acta* **20**, 590; Burwell, R. L. jun., Shields, A. D. and Hart, H. (1954) *J. Amer. chem. Soc.* **76**, 908;

THE CORRELATION OF CONFIGURATIONS

Hart, H. and Eleuterio, H. S. (1954) *ibid* **76**, 516, 519
Cram, D. J. *et al J. Amer. chem. Soc.* (1949) **71**, 3883; (1952) **74**, 2137 *et seq*; 5518, 5846. These papers include many di-phenylsubstituted compounds with two centres of asymmetry.
Benzylalkylcarbinols and related compounds: Levene, P. A. and Walti, A. (1931) *J. biol. Chem.* **90**, 81; Levene, P. A. and Stevens, P. G. (1930) *ibid* **89**, 471.
Acetylphenylcarbinol: Roger, R. (1931) *Biochem. Z.* **230**, 327 ; Freudenberg, K., Schoeffel, E. and Braun, E. (1932) *J. Amer. chem. Soc.* **54**, 234. Benzoin: McKenzie, A. and Wren, H. (1908) *J. chem. Soc.* **93**, 309.
Phenylalanine and related compounds: Goldschmit, S. and Freyss, G. (1933) *Ber. dtsch. chem. Ges.* **66**, 784; Karrer and Erhardt (1951).
Ephedrine (2-*N*-methylamino-1-phenylpropan-1-ol): Freudenberg, K., Schoeffel, E. and Braun, E. (1932) (above); Freudenberg, K., Kuhn, W. and Bumann, I. (1930) *Ber. dtsch. chem. Ges.* **63**, 2380; Freudenberg, K. and Nicolai, F. (1934) *Liebigs Ann.* **510**, 223; Leithe, W. (1932) *Ber. dtsch. chem. Ges.* **65**, 660 (also acetylphenylcarbinol); Phillips, D. C. (1954) *Acta cryst., Camb.* **7**, 159
Chloramphenicol (2-Dichloroacetamido-1-*p*-nitrophenylpropane-1 : 3-diol) : Rebstock, M. C., Crooks, H. M. jun., Controulis, J. and Bartz, Q. R. (1949) *J. Amer. chem. Soc.* **71**, 2458; Fodor, G., Kiss, J. and Sallay, I. (1951) *J. chem. Soc.* 1858; Dunitz, J. D. (1952) *J. Amer. chem. Soc.* **74**, 995.

Alicyclic Compounds

cyclo*Propane derivatives*—Crombie, L. and Harper, S. H. (1954) *J. chem. Soc.* 470
cyclo*Hexane derivatives*—Methyl*cyclo*hexanols: Gough, G. A. C., Hunter, H. and Kenyon, J. (1926) *J. chem. Soc.* 2052; Macbeth, A. K. and Mills, J. A. (1947) *ibid* 205.
Terpenes: McNiven, N. L. and Read, J. (1952) *J. chem. Soc.* 153 and earlier references there.
Quinic acid (1 : 3 : 4 : 5-tetrahydroxy*cyclo*hexanecarboxylic acid); shikimic acid (3 : 4 : 5-trihydroxy*cyclo*hex-1-enecarboxylic acid) and related compounds: Fischer, H. O. L. and Dangschat, G. (1932) *Ber. dtsch. chem. Ges.* **65**, 1009; (1935, 1937) *Helv. chim. acta* **18**, 1206; **20**, 705; Salamon, I. I. and Davis, B. D. (1953) *J. Amer. chem. Soc.* **75**, 5567.

Heterocyclic Compounds

O-Heterocyclic
Oxirans (ethylene oxides): see propylene glycol and glycerol derivatives, butanediols, and epoxysuccinic acids (above).
Streptose: Kuehl, F. A. jun., Bishop, M. N., Flynn, E. H. and Folkers, K. (1948) *J. Amer. chem. Soc.*, **70**, 2613; Wolfrom, M. L. and De Walt, C. W., *ibid* **70**, 3148.
N-Heterocyclic
Three-membered rings—Aziridines (ethyleneimines) as for diaminobutanes (above).
Five-membered rings: Proline (pyrrolidine-2-carboxylic acid) and other 2-substituted pyrrolidines: Karrer, P. and Widmer, R. (1925) *Helv. chim. acta* **8**, 364. 2-Methylpyrrolidine: Karrer and Erhardt (1951).
Hydroxyprolines (4-hydroxypyrrolidine-2-carboxylic acids): Neuberger, A. (1945) *J. chem. Soc.* 429; Robinson, D. S. and Greenstein, J. P. (1952) *J. biol. Chem.* **195**, 383.
Six-membered rings—Pipecolinic acid (piperidine-2-carboxylic acid), coniine (2-propylpiperidine) and related compounds: Leithe, W. (1932) *Ber. dtsch. chem. Ges.* **65**, 660, 927; Löffler, K. and Friedrich, G. (1909) *ibid* **42**, 107. Baikiain (1:2:3:6-tetrahydropyridine-2-carboxylic acid), King, F. E., King, T. J. and Warwick, A. J. (1950) *J. chem. Soc.* 3590.

221

More complex compounds—Octahydropyrrocoline: Leonard, N. J. and Middleton, W. J. (1952) *J. Amer. chem. Soc.* **74,** 5776. Lupinine: Cookson, R. C. (1953) *Chem. & Ind.* 337.
Benzyl*iso*quinoline alkaloids : Leithe, W. (1930) *Ber. dtsch. chem. Ges.* **63,** 1498; (1931) *ibid* **64,** 2827. Cinchona alkaloids: Emde, H. (1932) *Helv. chim. acta* **15,** 557; Prelog, V. and Zalán, E. (1944) *ibid* **27,** 535; Prelog, V. and Häfliger, O. (1950) *ibid* **33,** 2021. Morphine: Bick, I. R. C. (1952) *Nature, Lond.* **169,** 755.

O : N-Heterocyclic
Oxazolines, see references on threonine above.

6

THE STEREOCHEMISTRY OF THE HYDROGEN BOND

L. Hunter

THE loose and rather weak attachment by which hydrogen may link two other atoms together, known as the hydrogen bond or bridge (Ger., Wasserstoffbrücke; Fr., liaison hydrogène; Sp., hidrogéno puente) can play an important and sometimes a dominant part in the stereochemical arrangement of molecules. The instability of this bond, especially towards thermal agitation and solution effects, renders it most effective, as a stereochemical influence, in solids (crystals, macromolecules, fibres), and progressively less effective in liquids, solutions and vapours.

The following is a brief summary of the part played by the hydrogen bond as a stereochemical factor.

1 In solids

Influences molecular or ionic packing within the crystal.

Underlies selective union in certain molecular (clathrate) compounds.

By providing intra- and inter-linkages in main polypeptide chains influences (and may decide) configuration of proteins.

2 In liquids and solutions

Causes intramolecular (chelate) ring formation.

Causes some surface active effects, and certain chromatographic adsorption effects.

Underlies liquid crystal formation in certain compounds.

Causes transient intermolecular coordination (*e.g.* molecular association, solute–solvent interactions) with no permanent stereochemical implications.

3 In vapours

Only the strongest hydrogen bonds survive in vapours, *e.g.* O—H—O in some dimeric fatty acids, F—H—F in hydrofluoric acid.

In spite of the marked differences in the contribution of the hydrogen bond to structure evident in 1, 2 and 3, there is not necessarily a complete change of structure at the transition points (m.p. and b.p.) of a compound; the hydrogen-bond structure will be maintained, with varying degrees of persistence and no very sharp demarcation, throughout the changes of state. No better example of this can be chosen than water, the structure of which in ice exemplifies a maximum display of hydrogen bonds, reflected in its particularly open structure. On melting, the open structure of ice partially collapses owing to the destruction of a proportion of hydrogen bonds, and some molecules achieve close packing, although the ice-structure persists within limited boundaries in the liquid. Sufficient close packing is achieved on melting, however, to produce a liquid of considerably higher density. On raising the temperature above the melting point two competing effects are operative which come into equilibrium at 4°C, the point of maximum density of water. Between 0° and 4°, increasing density is caused by further disruption of hydrogen bonds and the attainment of a higher degree of close packing; but above 4° this effect is outweighed by the normal expansion due to rise of temperature. Nevertheless, hydrogen-bond association persists, though to a diminishing degree, even up to and beyond the boiling point.

The extent to which these and similar progressive changes of structure affect the permanent configuration of molecules forms the subject matter of the present chapter.

IS THE HYDROGEN BOND LINEAR?

Until very recent times there was no evidence to show precisely where the hydrogen atom lies in relation to the two atoms between which it forms a bridge. Diffraction methods, although they indicated accurately the distance between the two atoms (usually called the ' length ' of the hydrogen bond), gave no indication of the whereabouts of the connecting hydrogen atom. It was generally assumed, however, that the bond would tend to be as nearly rectilinear as other constraining influences will allow; *i.e.* the hydrogen will lie on a straight line joining the two bridged atoms (Sidgwick, 1933). This is supported by the many examples of mono-carboxylic acids whose crystal structures reveal rectilinear dimerization (I), and, in the case of oxalic acid (Hendricks, 1935; Cox *et al.*, 1952), infinite straight chains (β-oxalic acid, II) and parallel sheets (α-oxalic acid, III).

A study of liquid crystal formation in a series of *p*-alkoxy-benzoic and -cinnamic (*trans*) acids by Bennett and Jones (1939) has also thrown light on this subject. Such molecules by themselves possess none of the attributes necessary for a display of mesomorphism (*viz* long straight chain-like structures), but pairs of molecules linked by hydrogen bonds (IV) would have the necessary structure *provided the O—H—O bonds are rectilinear*. It is significant that the methyl esters, which cannot form double molecules, show no sign of mesomorphism.

224

In face of this evidence for the rectilinear hydrogen bond it is remarkable that the limited association of oximes has been assumed to be due to dimers, depicted by Sidgwick (1934) as (V), in which the hydrogen bond must depart considerably from the rectilinear. A

I

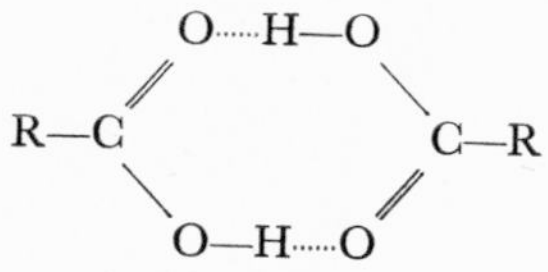

$$R-C \overset{O \cdots H-O}{\underset{O-H \cdots O}{\Big\langle}} C-R$$

II

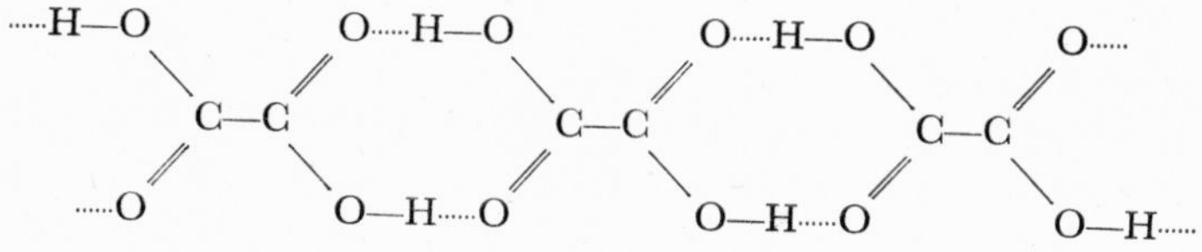

III

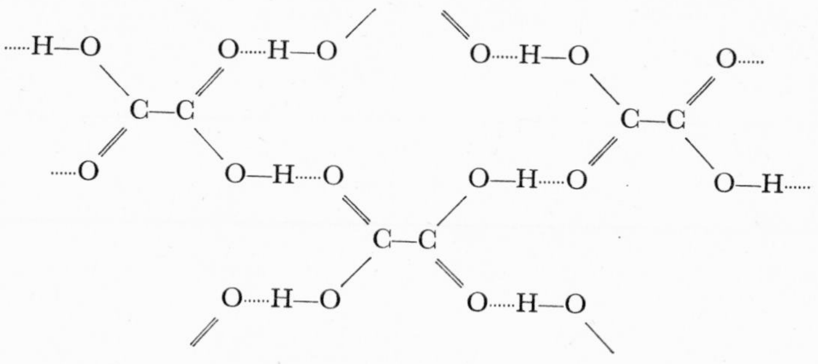

IV

$$RO-\langle \rangle -C \overset{O \cdots H-O}{\underset{O-H \cdots O}{\Big\langle}} C-\langle \rangle -OR$$

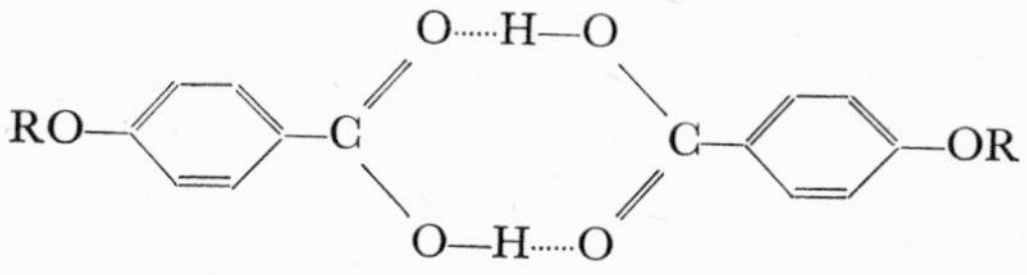

review of the cryoscopic evidence (see *e.g.* Turner, 1915) for this assumption makes it clear that as many oximes tend towards a *trimeric* state as a dimeric, and it would seem that the strainless trimer (VI) would be a much more reasonable interpretation of the facts than the traditional dimer (V). The evidence of crystal structure is conflicting on this point. Only three crystalline oximes have so far been examined: the first, acetoxime, consists of sheets of planar trimers (as in VI), the N—H—O distance being 2·78 Å (Bierlein and Lingafelter, 1951); the second, dimethylglyoxime, consists of infinite chains formed by the end-to-end linking of molecules by their oxime groups, which unite in a dimerized ring (as in V) with N—H—O distance of 2·83 Å (Merritt and Lauterman, 1952). Preliminary study of a third oxime, *syn-p*-chlorobenzaldoxime, indicates dimerization as in (V) (Jerslev, 1950).

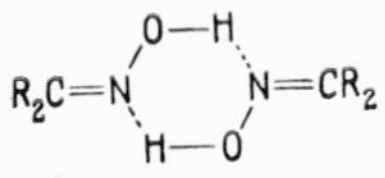

| V | VI | VII |

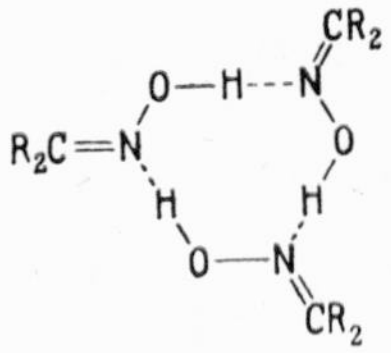

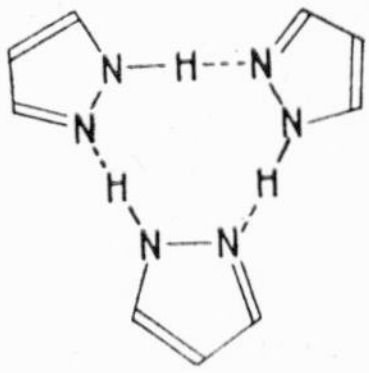

Similar objections can be raised to the dimeric formulation of pyrazoles, which can be more appropriately represented as a strainless trimer (VII) (Hayes and Hunter, 1941). Solution of these problems must await further crystal structure determinations.

Certain small molecules can show such a multiplicity of hydrogen bonding that chelate rings are formed containing two hydrogen bonds, which may well, under such constraint, depart from linearity. A six-membered ring of this kind is exemplified in crystalline (tetragonal) urea, part of the crystal structure of which is shown in (VIII) (Vaughan

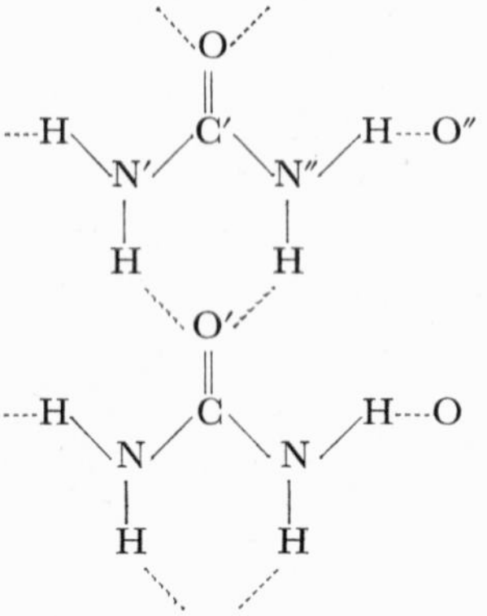

$$\angle C'N'O' = 98·5°$$
$$\angle C''N''O'' = 129°$$
$$\angle N'C'N'' = 118°$$
$$N'O' = 2·99Å$$
$$N''O'' = 3·04Å$$

VIII

and Donohue, 1952). The divergence from 120° of the two specified angles C—N⋯⋯O (98·5° and 129°) is a measure of the non-linearity of the two N—H—O bonds. It is significant that when urea forms adducts with hydrocarbons it adopts an entirely different crystalline structure, in which there is a slight shortening of the N—H—O bond lengths accompanied by a closer correspondence of the C—N⋯⋯O angles to the undistorted value of 120° (Smith, 1952). These conditions may well contribute to the stability of the urea–hydrocarbon adducts.

In cases where a bonded hydrogen atom is a member of an intra-molecular ring there may well be constraint upon the hydrogen bond resulting in a departure from its rectilinear habit, although the fact that practically all chelate rings involving hydrogen are six-membered seems to favour their representation as IX. A five-membered ring on

(A)   (B)

IX   X

similar lines (XA) would clearly be under considerable strain, and this may well be the reason why such rings, so far as they exist at all, are unstable and but weakly bonded. Whether this is due to ring strain in XA, or to the nonlinear hydrogen bond in XB, cannot yet be decided. On the other hand, seven and higher membered rings have the opportunity of assuming a puckered or multiplanar form, and this could bring the bonded atoms within suitable proximity to form a linear hydrogen bond.

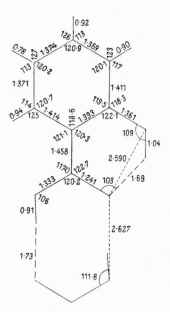

XI. Salicylic acid, showing bond lengths, bond angles, and mode of union, through carboxyl groups with second molecule (lower end).

Recent refinements in x-ray crystallographic determinations have led, in favourable circumstances, to the location of bonded hydrogen atoms in electron-density maps. In particular, a complete structural determination of crystalline salicyclic acid (Cochran, 1953) has revealed dimers in which the carboxyl hydrogen atoms are for all practical purposes collinear with the adjacent oxygens, but the hydroxyl-hydrogen atom is noticeably out of line with its neighbouring oxygen atoms (XI). In an electron-diffraction study of crystalline boric acid Cowley (1953) concluded that the hydrogen atoms are not collinear with the oxygens, but are displaced from this position as a result of attraction towards *two* oxygen neighbours.

' Bifurcated ' Hydrogen Bonds
In their investigation of the crystal structure of glycine Albrecht and Corey (1939) found each nitrogen atom to be surrounded by four oxygen atoms at distances (2·76, 2·88, 2·93, 3·05 Å) judged to be due to hydrogen bonds. This incompatibility with the zwitterion structure $^+NH_3CH_2CO_2^-$ was explained as being due to the presence of a 'shared' hydrogen bond, in which the two farthest oxygen atoms (at 2·93 and 3·05 Å) are assumed to be bonded to nitrogen through a single hydrogen atom (XII).

$$
\begin{array}{ccc}
\text{O} & \text{N} & \text{O} \\
\diagup & \diagup & \diagup \\
\text{N—H} & \text{N—H} & \text{O—H} \\
\diagdown & \diagdown & \diagdown \\
\text{O} & \text{N} & \text{O} \\
\text{XII} & \text{XIII} & \text{XIV}
\end{array}
$$

This type of bond was subsequently described as a ' bifurcated ' hydrogen bond, and has been reported in the structure of sulphamic acid (Kanda and King, 1951), dicyanodiamide (XIII) (Hughes, 1940), racemic acid hydrate (Parry, 1951) and α-iodic acid (XIV) (Rogers and Helmholz, 1941). Whatever theory is held on the nature of the hydrogen bond, bifurcation of this kind would seem to be inherently improbable, and may arise simply from the difficulty of distinguishing solely from interatomic distances between true hydrogen bonds and approaches which are merely short van der Waals' distances. Reasons have been advanced against the authenticity of bifurcated hydrogen bonds in dicyanodiamide (Donohue, 1952) and in iodic acid (Wells, 1949).

THE HYDROGEN BOND AS A DIRECTED LINK

The discovery of the hydrogen bond has released a flood of illumination upon a mass of apparently unconnected facts, and especially upon the subject of molecular association. The researches of Raoult, Beckmann, von Auwers, Turner and others at the turn of the century had shown that certain groups conferred molecular associating properties on the molecules in which they are present (see, *e.g.* Turner, 1915).

Prominent among these groups are those which are now recognized to contain a hydrogen atom in circumstances likely to give rise to a hydrogen bond. If at the same time there is present in the same group or molecule a 'negative' centre capable of accepting hydrogen, ideal conditions are created in favour of molecular association by intermolecular hydrogen bonds. Associating groups known at that time included —OH, —CONH—, —CO$_2$H, >NOH, —NH$_2$, but since then numerous others have been discovered, and it is now clear that the greatest single cause of molecular association is that due to the intermolecular sharing of a hydrogen atom.

Evidence of molecular association has for the most part been obtained from liquids and solutions, in which it must be assumed the intermolecular hydrogen bonds are constantly breaking and reforming, with no permanent stereochemical arrangement. In crystals, however, hydrogen bonds are able to form between molecules as permanent directed links which play a critical part in the mode of packing of the molecules within the crystal. These can vary widely in type from crystals composed of paired molecules (as in carboxylic acids) to the more commonly occurring infinite two- and three-dimensional molecular complexes.

Intramolecular Hydrogen Bonds (Chelate Rings)
It is the operation of the hydrogen bond *intramolecularly*, however, which leads to the most important stereochemical consequences, and it is not surprising that the original discovery and the early development of the hydrogen bond were due to observations of intramolecular group interaction. The operation of a hydrogen bond within a molecule (leading to a chelate ring) has two important consequences; firstly, molecular association is suppressed owing to the intramolecular engagement of the hydrogen atom responsible for it, and secondly, the group providing the hydrogen atom suffers a diminution of its normal chemical activity.

One of the earliest structures of this kind to be proposed (Sidgwick, 1925) was for the enolic tautomer of ethyl acetoacetate, which in spite of its definite behaviour as an alcohol possesses greater volatility, a greater solubility in hydrocarbon solvents and a lower solubility in water than the keto

$$\begin{matrix} & CH & \\ Me{\cdot}C\!\!\!\!\!\!\!\!\! & & \!\!\!\!\!\!\!\!\!C{\cdot}OEt \\ & & \\ & O{-}H{\cdots}O & \end{matrix} \qquad Me{\cdot}CO{\cdot}CH_2{\cdot}CO_2Et \qquad R{\cdot}CO{\cdot}NH{\cdot}CO{\cdot}R \qquad R{\cdot}C(OH){:}N{\cdot}CO{\cdot}R$$

XV   XVI   XVII   XVIII

tautomer (XVI). Furthermore, it is unimolecular (Auwers, 1893), and these anomalies are suitably accounted for by assigning it the structure (XV). The enolic forms of all β-diketones are represented similarly*, and where enol and keto forms of a tautomeric substance are well defined and stable crystalline solids, they frequently show striking physical differences. This may be illustrated by α-benzoyl-camphor, whose tautomeric forms are:

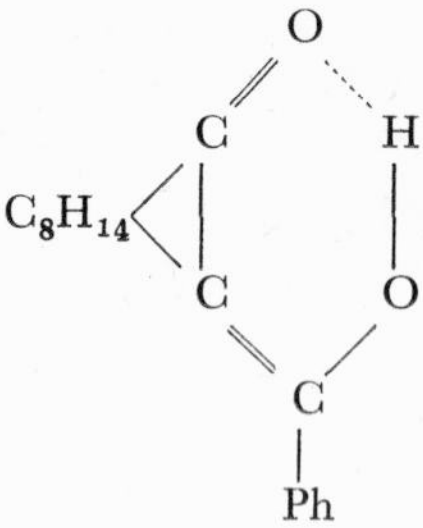

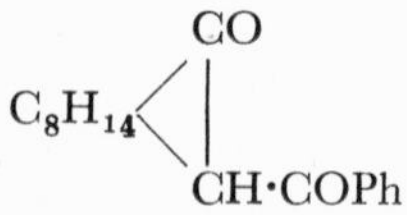

α-Benzoylcamphor

Enol form M.p. 89°; $[\alpha]_D +331°$;   *Keto form* M.p. 112°; $[\alpha]_D +152°$; solubility in benzene, 37·3 per cent   solubility in benzene, 16·9 per cent

In marked contrast is the behaviour of the diacylamides (XVII), which possess acidic character and exhibit strong molecular association, properties which are interpreted as indicating that such substances do not ' enolize ' to an imidol form (XVIII) (Hunter and Reynolds, 1950). The most fertile field of examples of chelate rings involving the hydrogen atom is to be found in aromatic compounds possessing two *ortho* substituents so constituted that one can provide and the other accept a hydrogen atom. This special kind of *ortho*-effect confers properties on such compounds not possessed by their *m*- and *p*-isomers, and it was these differences which drew attention to the need for a hydrogen-bond structure for such *ortho*-compounds (Sidgwick and Callow, 1924). Examples are the following *o*-substituted phenols

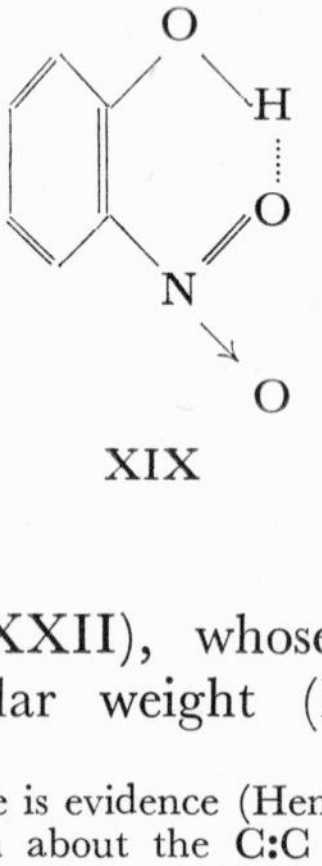

XIX 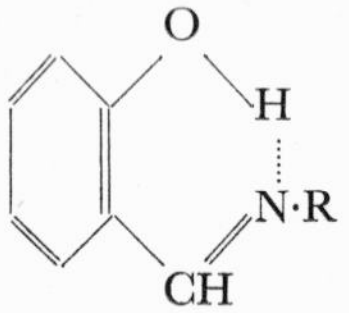   XX 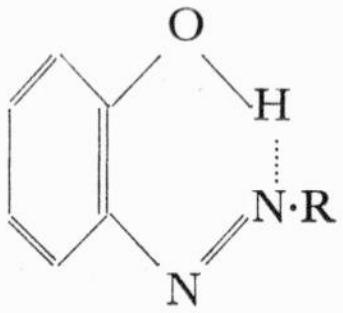   XXI 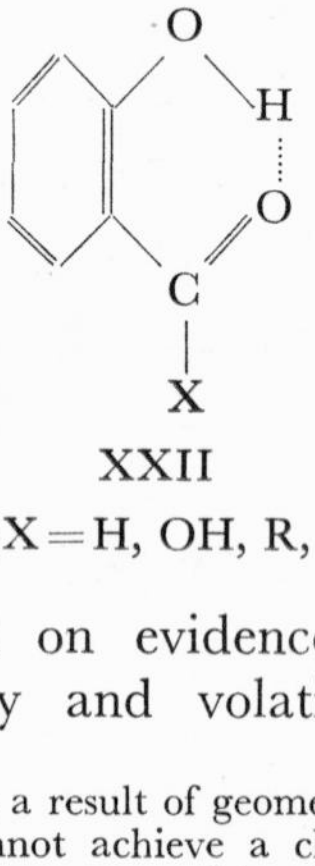   XXII

(X=H, OH, R, OR)

(XIX-XXII), whose chelate formulae are based on evidence of molecular weight (lack of association), solubility and volatility,

* There is evidence (Henecka, 1948) pointing to the existence, as a result of geometrical isomerism about the C:C double bond, of *trans*-enols, which cannot achieve a chelate structure. They readily revert owing to tautomeric change to the more stable *cis*-enol forms (as XV).

infra-red spectroscopy, and general suppression of phenolic character. The effect is not confined to phenols, and the following imino-compounds (XXIII-XXVI) have been similarly represented.

XXIII   XXIV   XXV   XXVI

(X can be —CO·R, —CS·R, —CO$_2$R, —CS$_2$R, —CN)

It is evident that the nature of the o-substituent in examples XIX-XXVI must be such that it possesses a hydrogen-acceptor atom (O or N) which can take up a position suitably close to the hydroxyl or imino group to allow the formation of a chelate ring. Successful chelation also implies an ability on the part of the atoms participating in the chelate ring to take up positions co-planar with the benzene nucleus, and this is no doubt aided by the conjugation of the two substituents with the nucleus. Two examples of unsuccessful chelation owing to the appropriate interatomic distances being too great are given in XXVII and XXVIII. o-Hydroxybenzonitrile (XXVII) is

XXVII   XXVIII

strongly associated (Auwers, 1896, 1899), possesses a wet melting point depression similar to those of its m- and p-isomers (Baker and Carruthers, 1937), and shows strong hydroxylic absorption in the infra-red (Hendricks, Wulf, Hilbert and Liddel, 1936), from which it must be concluded that the nitrogen atom does not accept hydrogen in spite of its ability to do so in favourable circumstances (Hunter and Rees, 1945). There seems little doubt that, owing to the linear disposition of the C—C≡N atoms the O—N distance in this molecule is too great (about 3·5 Å) to be bridged by hydrogen. Similarly, N-o-nitro-benzylacetamide (XXVIII) is non-chelate and consequently strongly associated, though o-nitroacetanilide (XXIII; X=COCH$_3$) is non-associated (Auwers, 1897).

Steric Interference between Vicinal Groups

The wealth of examples, such as XIX-XXVI, of *o*-disubstituted benzenes whose substituent groups coordinate by achieving a six-membered ring involving a hydrogen bond provides very strong support for the belief that an important requirement for the stability of such rings is their co-planarity with the benzene nucleus. This is confirmed by a study of the effect on chelation of the substitution of a group or groups adjacent to the potential chelate ring (Chaplin and Hunter, 1938). Thus *o*-nitroacetanilide (XXIX), by virtue of the engagement of its imino-hydrogen atom in chelate ring formation, is non-associated; but substitution of a group X in the 6-position (XXX) so interferes

CO·CH$_3$

XXIX   XXX   XXXI   XXXII

(X=Me, Br, NO$_2$; Y=Me, Br, NO$_2$, CO$_2$Et)

with the acetamido-group as to rotate it into a position transverse to the plane of the benzene nucleus, thus making its imino-hydrogen atom too remote from the nitro-group to achieve chelation. Such compounds are therefore associated. A similar effect is obtained by substituting in the 3-position (XXXI), although here it is to be expected that the new substituent orientates the nitro-group across the plane of the benzene nucleus, thus preventing chelation and increasing the tendency to molecular association. Indication of a transmission of such steric effects through *four* adjacent groups was obtained by an examination of compounds of structure (XXXII). Provided the substituent Z is sufficiently large (*e.g.* Br or Me) it can rotate its neighbouring (3-)nitro-group transverse to the plane of the benzene nucleus, thus facilitating the assumption by the 2-nitro-group of a co-planar orientation by which it can achieve chelation with the acetamido-group.

Further indications of similar effects are evident from some unpublished experiments by Dr. S. H. Harvey (University College, Leicester) on the rearrangement of *m*-substituted phenylnitramines (XXXIII). The products of this rearrangement are mainly three isomeric nitro-amines (XXXIV, XXXV and XXXVI) which on chromatographic separation are retained on the column in the order XXXVI ≫ XXXV > XXXIV. It has been established by Hoyer (1950) that among isomeric compounds that isomer which is capable of a chelate hydrogen-bond structure is the most weakly adsorbed in a chromatogram. It is inferred that the operation of hydrogen bonds between adsorbent (the author used silica gel and alumina) and adsorbate is a potent cause of chemisorption, and that intramolecular satisfaction of such bonds (as in chelation) will result in the weakening of the forces by which molecules possessing such a structure are adsorbed on the column. The above order is therefore interpreted as meaning that, whilst XXXVI is of course non-chelate, XXXIV is strongly chelate, and the intermediate position occupied by XXXV

$$NH \cdot NO_2 \qquad NH_2 \qquad NH_2 \qquad NH_2$$

XXXIII → O₂N‖ XXXIV + ‖NO₂ XXXV + XXXVI

$$(X = NO_2, F, Cl, Br, I)$$

indicates weakened chelation resulting from interference between vicinal groups. The size of the group X is sufficient to rotate the adjacent nitro-group across the plane of the benzene nucleus in XXXV so as to prevent, or at least largely to reduce, the tendency for chelate ring-formation between nitro- and amino-groups.

Other pairs of isomeric or closely related compounds which exhibit similar steric influences are collected in TABLE 1. The chelate structures shown in the first column are disturbed or even prevented by the steric interference of additional (adjacent) substituents (second column).

'HINDERED' ALCOHOLS AND PHENOLS

It has been a commonplace ever since their discovery that the isomeric aliphatic alcohols possess boiling points which markedly decrease with increasing branching (and therefore compactness) of structure (see, for example, the butyl alcohols, TABLE 2). If it is accepted that the decrease in boiling point is a result of a decrease in molecular association, it is tempting to connect this with a progressive over-shadowing of the hydroxyl group, thus hindering the approach of neighbouring molecules to form hydrogen bonds, especially as branching at the carbinol carbon atom seems to have the greatest effect. This evidence from volatility is supported by an infra-red spectroscopic study of the hexyl alcohols (Stanford and Gordy, 1940), in which it was concluded that the extent of association depends chiefly on the structural environment of the hydroxyl group rather than on the length of the carbon chain.

It must be noted, however, that a similar suppression of intermolecular hydrogen bonds could be caused as a result of decreasing acidity in this series, due to the electron-repulsive character of the methyl group; and it is now well established that increasing acidity in a hydrogen

TABLE 1. DISTURBANCES OF CHELATE STRUCTURES BY ADJACENT SUBSTITUENTS

Chelate compounds	Non-chelate compounds	Evidence for structure	References
(benzene ring) OH, NO₂	(benzene ring) OH, NO₂, NO₂	Solubility Volatility in steam	Sidgwick and Aldous (1921)
(benzene ring) OH, CO₂Et	(benzene ring) HO, OH, CO₂Et, CO₂Et	Wet m.p.	Baker and Carruthers (1937)
EtO₂C (benzene ring) OH, HO, CO₂Et	EtO₂C (benzene ring) Br, OH, HO, CO₂Et, Br	Spectroscopic	Hilbert et al. (1936)
(benzene ring) NH·CO·CH₃, CO₂Et	(benzene ring) Br, NH·CO·CH₃, Br, CO₂Et	Mol. wt. Wet m.p.	Chaplin and Hunter (1938a)
(naphthalene ring) NO₂, NH·CO·CH₃	(naphthalene ring) NH·CO·CH₃, NO₂ *	Mol. wt. Wet m.p.	Chaplin and Hunter (1938a)
	(naphthalene ring) NO₂ NO₂, NH·CO·CH₃	Mol. wt.	Chaplin and Hunter (1938b)
(anthraquinone) O, OH, NO₂, O	(anthraquinone) O, NO₂, OH, O	Differential adsorption on SiO₂-gel	Hoyer (1953)

* Interference due to peri-CH group.

atom enhances its tendency to form hydrogen bonds, and vice versa. This action will be the more effective the greater the branching of the carbon chain.

That the decrease of boiling point is not solely connected with hydrogen bonding, however, is clearly indicated by a comparison of the boiling points of the methyl ethers and of the chlorides corresponding

TABLE 2. BOILING POINTS OF BUTYL ALCOHOLS AND DERIVATIVES

	Alcohol B.p.	Methyl ether B.p.	Chloride B.p.
$CH_3CH_2CH_2CH_2OH$	117°	70°	78°
CH_3 $\diagdown$ $\quad CHCH_2OH$ $\diagup$ CH_3	108°	59°	68·5°
CH_3CH_2 $\diagdown$ $\quad CHOH$ $\diagup$ CH_3	99·5°	63°	67°
CH_3 $\vert$ $CH_3—COH$ $\vert$ CH_3	82°	55°	52°

to the butyl alcohols (TABLE 2). These compounds cannot possess a hydrogen-bond structure, but they nevertheless show a fall in boiling point (though less marked than for the alcohols) with increasing branching. We can legitimately conclude, therefore, that the decline in boiling point of the butyl alcohols shown in TABLE 2 is due to the effect of molecular structure on general intermolecular forces of which hydrogen bonding is only one aspect, and we must attribute only a partial role to the steric interference of intermolecular hydrogen bonds.

The behaviour of the so-called ' hindered ' phenols (Stillson, Sawyer and Hunt, 1945) is capable of similar explanation. These compounds are phenols substituted in one or both *ortho*-positions by large branched alkyl groups, and which suffer as a result of this considerable suppression of phenolic character, both as regards molecular association and in chemical behaviour. Infra-red spectroscopic investigations (Coggeshall, 1947) show that the substitution of large groups (*t*-butyl or *t*-amyl) has a progressively depressing effect on the molecular association of phenols only if the substituents are placed *ortho* to the hydroxyl group. An *o*-methyl substituent has a negligible effect, and the results may be summarized thus:

| Strongly associated (unhindered) | Weakly associated (partially hindered) | Non-associated (hindered) |

The authors assign a purely steric reason for the reluctance shown by hindered phenols to form intermolecular hydrogen bonds; *i.e.* the hydroxyl groups, dwarfed between large alkyl groups, are physically unable to approach sufficiently close to the hydroxyl groups of neighbouring molecules to form hydrogen bonds. But the reduced acidity of hindered phenols might well be a major contributory cause of the suppression of molecular association, and there is a great deal of evidence that such phenols lack many of the chemical properties characteristic of phenols; they give no ferric chloride colour reaction, are alkali-insoluble, and are acylated only with extreme difficulty (Stillson, Sawyer and Hunt, 1945). This reduced acidity can be a consequence of steric interference, for by preventing the hydroxyl group from achieving planarity with the benzene nucleus the large *ortho* groups deny to such phenols the possibility of resonance involving such contributions as:

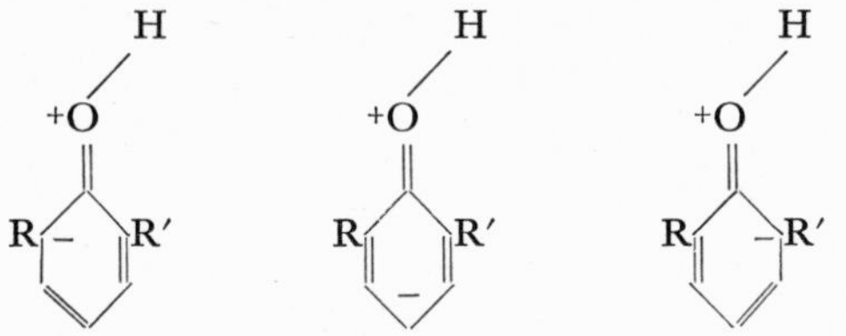

H   H   H
/   /   /
+O   +O   +O
‖   ‖   ‖
R⟨−⟩R′   R⟨ ⟩R′   R⟨ −⟩R′

Hindered phenols are therefore reduced to the status of tertiary alcohols.

Confirming the steric effect of large *ortho*-substituents in phenols, Sears and Kitchen (1949) place these observations on a quasi-quantitative basis by devising a ' hydrogen-bonding index ' for each phenol. The index depends on the shift in frequency of the infra-red absorption band of the hydroxyl group as between dilute solution, concentrated solution, and melt, and varies from 1 (unhindered) to 0 (completely hindered).

THE HYDROGEN BOND AND GEOMETRICAL ISOMERISM

There are no fixed and invariable means for determining the configuration of geometrical isomerides, and numerous pairs still remain unresolved. Occasionally, however, the physical (and even chemical) properties of a pair will present such contrasts that suspicion arises that the structural differences between them are deeper than is implied simply by a *cis-* or *trans-*disposition of groups. Such is the case when one of a pair can assume a chelate hydrogen-bond structure. Attention was first directed to this matter by Taylor and Ewbank (1926), who showed that of the two benzilmonoximes the one possessing the greater solubility in organic solvents and showing much reduced carbonyl activity is proved, by its derivation from triphenyl-*iso*-oxazole by oxidative fission (Meisenheimer, 1921), to have the configuration (*cis*) capable of chelate ring formation (XXXVII).

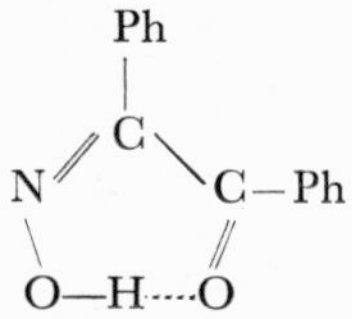

XXXVII
β-Benzilmonoxime
cis, m.p. 114°

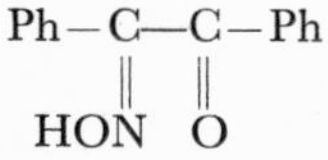

XXXVIII
α-Benzilmonoxime
trans, m.p. 138°

A somewhat later example is provided by *o*-hydroxybenzophenone oxime-acetate, the two geometrical isomers of which have been examined spectroscopically (Blatt and Russell, 1936). The lower-melting isomer, which is moderately soluble in carbon tetrachloride, shows no absorption in the infra-red region characteristic of hydroxyl, and is therefore attributed the configuration XXXIX. The higher-melting isomer, represented as XL, is scarcely soluble in carbon tetrachloride and shows strong hydroxylic absorption. This conclusion is

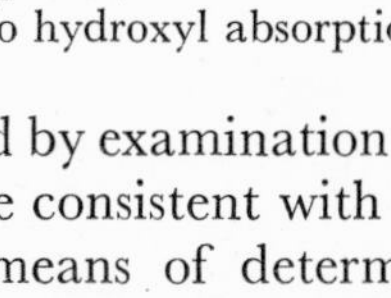

XXXIX
M.p. 95°; soluble in CCl_4.
No hydroxyl absorption

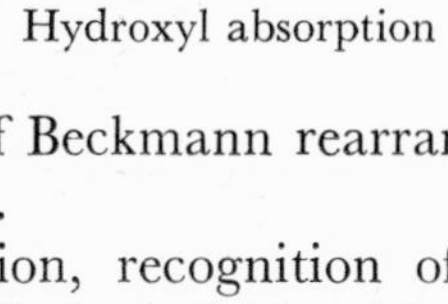

XL
M.p. 156°; insoluble in CCl_4.
Hydroxyl absorption

supported by examination of the products of Beckmann rearrangement, which are consistent with *trans* interchange.

As a means of determining configuration, recognition of chelate hydrogen-bond structures has a strictly limited field, although the literature abounds in examples to which the method could be applied. TABLE 3 contains some pairs chosen at random.

o-Hydroxyazo-compounds

The recognition of the chelate structure of *o*-hydroxyazo-compounds (XLI) provides an elegant proof of the fact, long anticipated on other grounds, that all stable azo-compounds have the *trans* configuration. It also provides the key to the unique behaviour of these compounds when compared with their *m*- and *p*-isomers, and it was their anomalous properties which led Oddo and Puxeddu (1906) to postulate a special structure for the azo derivatives of eugenol, in which the valencies of the hydrogen, oxygen and nitrogen atoms were divided as shown in

TABLE 3. USE OF CHELATE HYDROGEN-BOND STRUCTURES IN
DETERMINING CONFIGURATION

Compound	Properties	Suggested Configurations
Phenylglyoxal phenylhydrazone (Sidgwick and Ewbank, 1921)	1. α-Form, m.p. 112°, orange. Solubility in benzene, 5·8%. More soluble than β-form in all non-aqueous solvents. 2. β-Form, m.p. 145–146°, yellow. Solubility in benzene, 0·3%.	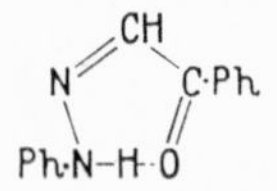 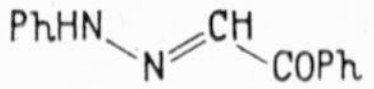 [structures]
Ethyl pyruvate phenyl-hydrazone (Simon, 1900)	1. β-Form, m.p. 31–32°. More easily soluble in organic solvents than α-form. 2. α-Form, m.p. 118°.	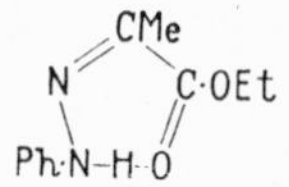 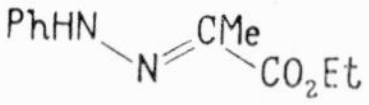 [structures]
Ethyl glyoxalate hydrazone (Staudinger, Hammet and Siegwart, 1921; cf Taylor and Ewbank, 1926)	1. Liquid form. Non-associated in benzene solution. 2. Crystalline form, m.p. 38°. Associated in benzene solution.	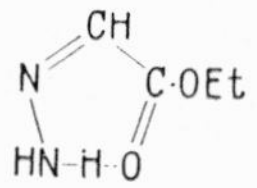 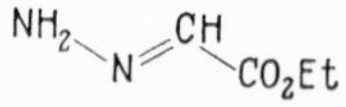 [structures]
Camphorquinone phenylhydrazone (Forster and Zimmerli, 1911)	1. β-Form, m.p. 36°. Volatile in steam. Easily soluble in organic solvents. 2. α-Form, m.p. between 183° and 190°. Not volatile in steam. Sparingly soluble in organic solvents.	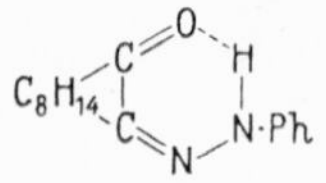 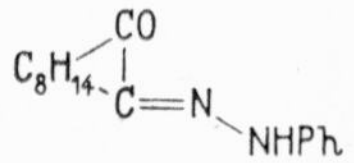 [structures]

XLII. This structure bears a close resemblance to the modern chelate formula (XLI) for such compounds, and the suggestion must rank historically as the first indication of the hydrogen bond. Justification

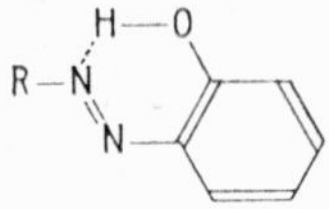

XLI 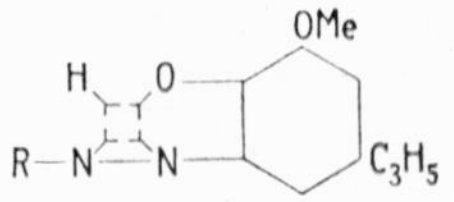   XLII

for the structure XLI now includes, in addition to the suppression of phenolic character pointed out by Oddo and Puxeddu (1906), lack of molecular association (Auwers and Orton, 1896), ability to form

238

chelate metallic derivatives (Elkins and Hunter, 1935), and spectroscopic evidence (Hendricks *et al.*, 1936). Burawoy (Burawoy *et al.*, 1952, 1953) has rejected the formulation of XLI as a resonance structure, and has claimed that such substances exist in the form of equilibria between hydroxyazo- and phenylhydrazone-tautomers, which may themselves be hydrogen-bonded by a purely electrostatic mechanism.

o-*Substituted Phenols*

In the course of an investigation of the infra-red absorption spectra of certain *o*-substituted phenols Wulf, Liddel and Hendricks (1936) observed that in addition to the characteristic peak in the neighbourhood of 7050 cm^{-1} due to the first overtone of the fundamental frequency of the hydroxyl group there is often present a second peak at a somewhat lower frequency. Such spectra have every appearance of being due to two molecular species, and the ingenious explanation advanced for this phenomenon by Pauling (1936) is based on the fact that owing to the partial double-bond character of the O-nuclear bond as a result of resonance with certain dipolar forms (see also p. 236), a somewhat transient geometrical isomerism arises. In most phenols the *cis* and *trans* forms thus set up will be equivalent as far as vibrations of the hydroxyl group are concerned; but in *o*-chlorophenol (XLIII) the forms are not equivalent, the *trans* form giving rise to the normal

trans	*cis*		
XLIII		XLIV	XLV

hydroxyl absorption, and the *cis* form, owing to weak hydrogen bonding (O—H . . . Cl), absorption at a somewhat lower frequency.

By a rough determination of the relative areas of the absorption peaks the *cis–trans* ratio is estimated (at room temperature) to be about 10/1 in *o*-chlorophenol. *o*-Bromo- and *o*-iodo-phenol behave similarly, though they show appreciably smaller proportions of the *cis* forms, and catechol and guaiacol are deduced to have structures XLIV and XLV. Support for this interpretation is forthcoming from an observation by Davies (1938) that the *cis–trans* ratio in *o*-chlorophenol is considerably reduced at a higher temperature (73°).

Furthermore, where true geometrical isomerism can arise, as in the *cis* and *trans* diols of the *cyclo*-paraffin series, there is clear evidence from infra-red absorption indicating which diol possesses bonded hydroxyl groups and which not; so that a configuration can often be unequivocally assigned from a study of absorption spectra (Kuhn, 1952).

Amides

The constraint of the —CONH— group in the *cis* form (XLVI) as a result of its participation in a cyclic system leads to the linking of molecules in pairs (XLVIII) in the crystal structure of isatin (Goldschmidt and Llewellyn, 1950), and the cryoscopic behaviour of α-piperidone in benzene solution indicates a preponderance of dimeric molecules (XLIX) in solution (Jenkins and Taylor, 1937). In a

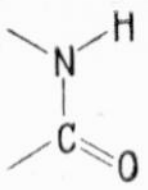

cis-form, present in cyclic amides	*trans*-form	
XLVI	XLVII	XLVIII

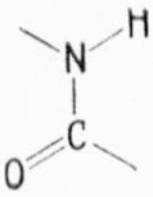

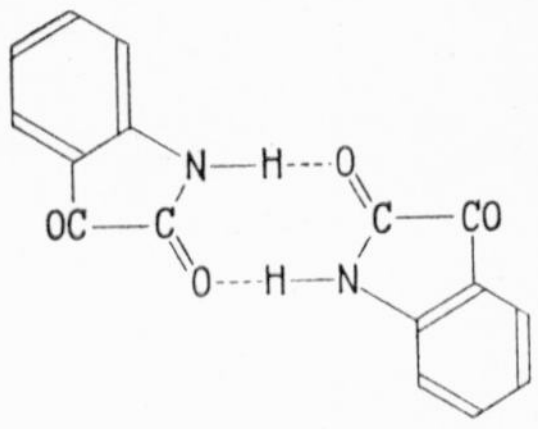

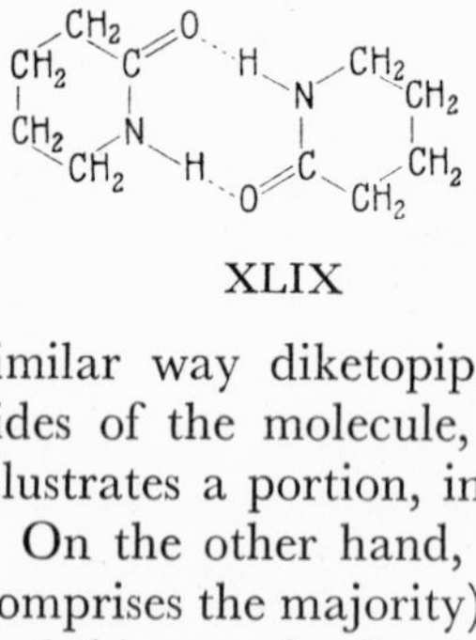

XLIX	L

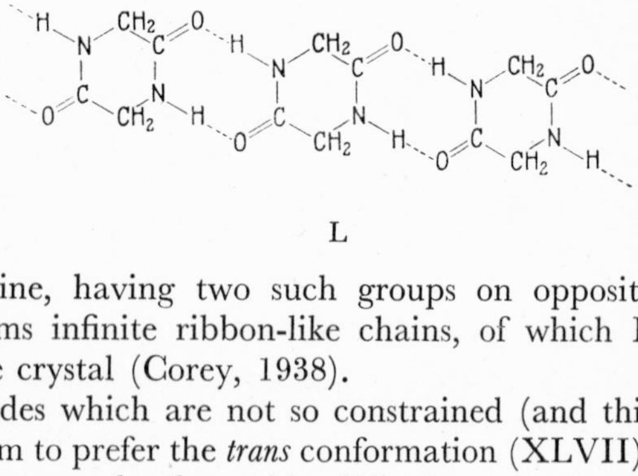

similar way diketopiperazine, having two such groups on opposite sides of the molecule, forms infinite ribbon-like chains, of which L illustrates a portion, in the crystal (Corey, 1938).

On the other hand, amides which are not so constrained (and this comprises the majority) seem to prefer the *trans* conformation (XLVII), and this must be the chief reason why the amides differ from the closely related carboxylic acids in forming chain polymers rather than dimers.

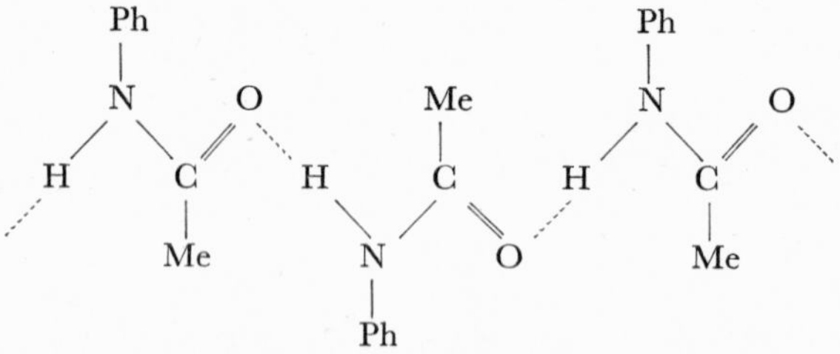

LI

This tendency has been evident from molecular weight studies (Auwers, 1893 ; Meldrum and Turner, 1908 ; Chaplin and Hunter, 1937), and is now confirmed by the crystal structure of acetanilide (LI), deduced by Brown and Corbridge from x-ray diffraction (1948).

The case of amides possessing the —$CONH_2$ group is further complicated by the fact that both hydrogen atoms can form bridges, thus creating an infinite network of molecules as in crystalline acetamide (Senti and Harker, 1940).

HYDROGEN BONDING DEDUCED FROM THE STRENGTH OF ACIDS

For a limited number of suitably substituted carboxylic acids a chelate hydrogen-bond structure may be inferred from their abnormal ionization constants. The first suggestion of this kind was due to Branch and Yabroff (1934), who accounted in this way for the abnormally high constant of salicylic acid in comparison with those of its m- and p-isomers. They pointed out that chelation within the salicyl group, for which there is a wealth of evidence from other sources, would stabilize the salicylate ion (LII), resulting in a reduced proton attraction. A similar though much enhanced effect is produced in 2:6-dihydroxybenzoic acid, the stabilized anion of which is depicted in (LIII) (Baker, 1936). It is probable that the unusually large first

LII   LIII   LIV   LV   LVI

ionization constant of phthalic acid ($K_1 = 1 \times 10^{-2.9}$) is in part due to a similar stabilization of the hydrogen phthalate ion (LIV), although this must be partly due to the acid-strengthening effect of the second carboxyl group (Hunter, 1953). The influence of these structures on the strengths of the substituted benzoic acids is seen in TABLE 4A where their ionization constants are compared with that of unsubstituted benzoic acid in the values of the ratio K(substituted acid)/K (benzoic acid). The effect of ortho-substitution is very marked, and even in N-acetylanthranilic acid, where the reduced acidity of the imino-hydrogen atom would be expected to give rise to a weaker bond (N—H⋯⋯O) as in the anion (LV), it is considerable; it is still greater in 2:6-di(acetamido)-benzoic acid (A. Datyner, personal communication).

On the other hand, the opposite effect should result from the stabilization of a carboxyl (or sulphonic acid) group as a result of fixation through a strong hydrogen bond; such an acid would resist ionization. This must in part account for the abnormal weakness of o-fluorobenzoic acid compared with its chloro-, bromo-, and iodo-analogues (TABLE 4B). That it is a stronger acid than benzoic is due to the electron-attractive character of fluorine, but that it is substantially weaker than its analogues must be largely due to the formation of the strong F—H—O bond (LVI). Similar bonds, if formed at all in o-chlorobenzoic acid, are known to be extremely weak.

TABLE 4. RELATIVE IONIZATION CONSTANTS OF SUBSTITUTED AND UNSUBSTITUTED
BENZOIC ACIDS
Values of K(substituted acid)$/K$(benzoic acid)

Position of substituent	Substituent						
	(A)			(B)			
	OH	CO₂H	NH·CO·CH₃	F	Cl	Br	I
o-	15·9	19·3*	3·93	8·61	18·2	22·3	21·9
m-	1·26	4·58*	1·42				
p-	0·44		0·86				
o-o'-di-	~800		~160				

*These ratios are for the first ionization constant (K_1).

The weakness of the α-sulpho-fatty acids (LVII), which act in regard to acidity as carboxylic rather than as sulphonic acids, has been attributed to the same cause; and methylsulphonacetic acid (LVIII), which would be expected to be a very strong acid by virtue of the strongly

CH₃·SO₂·CH₂·CO₂H

LVII   LVIII   LIX

electron-attractive sulphone group, is much weakened $(K=1 \times 10^{-2·3})$ as a result of its chelate structure (LIX) (Branch and Calvin, 1945). Similarly the second ionization constant of phthalic acid $(K_2=1 \times 10^{-5·5})$ is very small as a result of the stabilization of the hydrogen-phthalate anion (LIV), which would be expected to resist ionization (Hunter, 1953).

THE HYDROGEN BOND AS A FACTOR IN CRYSTAL STRUCTURE

The importance of the hydrogen bond as a major cause of molecular association (particularly in organic compounds) has already been stressed (p. 228). It is a natural corollary that the hydrogen bond is equally important as a factor in crystal structure, for molecular association in liquids, solutions or vapours must be pictured substantially as a survival of disordered portions of the crystalline arrangement throughout limited spaces in these states. Indeed the hydrogen bond must be regarded as the strongest of the intermolecular forces operative in crystal lattices. Support for this is provided by the fact that, with very few exceptions, the melting points of associated substances are considerably lowered by replacing the hydrogen atoms responsible for the association by alkyl, acyl, and sometimes even aryl groups, and that *o*-disubstituted aromatic derivatives capable of chelate hydrogen bond formation possess (in nearly every case) lower melting points than their *m*- and *p*-isomers.

Apart from their effect on melting point, however, intermolecular hydrogen bonds play a dominating part in deciding the mode of molecular packing in crystals, molecules tending to juxtapose themselves at the groups capable of yielding hydrogen bonds. Some examples of this effect have already been considered (*e.g.* isatin, diketopiperazine, acetanilide, carboxylic acids, acetoxime), and others are listed below. Where hydrogen donor and acceptor groups are at opposite ends of a molecule, there frequently results an end-to-end linking which is either rectilinear, or, if other factors require it, some variety of chain. Examples are:

Hydrogen cyanide (Dulmage and Lipscomb, 1951)—Infinite linear chains, C—H—N = 3·18 Å. This accounts for its molecular association, high boiling point, high dielectric constant, and probably its tautomeric behaviour.

Formic acid—Although this acid prefers dimers in the vapour phase (Pauling and Brockway, 1934), it forms infinite chains in the crystal, each molecule being linked to two neighbours by O—H—O bonds of length 2·58 Å (Holtzberg *et al.*, 1953).

p-*Nitroaniline* (Abrahams and Robertson, 1948)—End-to-end arrangement with N—H—O bonds 3·07 and 3·11 Å.

p-*Aminophenol* (Brown, 1951)—End-to-end arrangement, complicated by cross-links between chains; each molecule makes three hydrogen bonds (N—H—O) of lengths 2·83, 3·13 and 3·18 Å.

Quinol (Palin and Powell, 1947)—This compound, on the other hand, owing partly to the angular nature of the hydroxyl group, adopts an elaborate infinite three-dimensional cagework.

Flexible molecules (*e.g.* containing saturated aliphatic chains) are frequently held in some particular conformation by hydrogen bonds, good examples being the zwitterionic amino-acids and dipeptides. Another example is provided by ethylene dinitroamine (Llewellyn and Whitmore, 1948), in which each molecule is anchored in position by hydrogen bonds to four adjacent molecules. It is not clear which of the two nitro-oxygen atoms is involved in the bond, but the

243

intermolecular N—O distances are 3·01 and 3·09 Å, the molecular environment being as follows (private communication from the late Dr. F. E. Whitmore):

LX

This arrangement would account for the laminar structure of the crystal, and also for the shortening of the N—N distance (to 1·33 Å) reported by the authors, for such a hydrogen-bond structure would show mesohydric tautomerism, thus giving the N—N link a partial double-bond character ($-NHNO_2 \rightleftharpoons -N:NOOH$).

The effect of hydrogen bonds in deciding the molecular configuration adopted by certain natural macro-molecules is well illustrated by the α-helix common to many proteins, in which the spiral arrangement of the main polypeptide chains is maintained by N—H—O bonds closing 13-membered rings, produced by linking the O-atom of one CONH-group with the hydrogen atom of the third such group further along the chain (Rydon, 1951; Perutz, 1951). It is significant that *all* the CO and NH groups of the α-helical main chains are thus bonded (*cf* Ambrose, this volume, Chapter 7).

Polymorphism

If a molecule can adopt two or more modes of packing due to alternative hydrogen-bond arrangements of equal or nearly equal stability, conditions suitable for a display of polymorphism are created. Only two examples of this kind have been investigated; the first, α- and β-oxalic acids, has already been referred to (p. 224). The second example is the dimorphism of resorcinol, first reported by Lautz (1913), and shown by Robertson and Ubbelohde (1938) to be due to the alternative hydrogen-bond structures LXI and LXII.

Although these are the only examples of polymorphism yet known to be a result of different hydrogen-bond arrangements in the crystal, an inspection of the large number of organic types which exhibit polymorphism reveals that a high proportion possesses a hydrogen-bond structure (*e.g.* carboxylic acids, amides, anilides, ureas, sulphonamides, phenols and hydrazides). This prompts the speculation that a frequent cause of polymorphism among organic compounds may prove to be due to alternative modes of intermolecular hydrogen bonding in the crystalline polymorphs. Only a protracted study of crystal structure in this field can throw further light on this question, although interesting developments will undoubtedly accrue from infra-red spectroscopic comparison of polymorphic forms, differences between which, of course, disappear in solution (Ebert and Gottlieb, 1952).

<table>
<tr><td>α-resorcinol</td><td>β-resorcinol</td></tr>
<tr><td>LXI</td><td>LXII</td></tr>
</table>

Broken lines indicate hydrogen bonds linking oxygen atoms

Closely related to polymorphism of this kind is the phenomenon exhibited by many compounds which, while possessing a hydrogen-bond structure in the crystal, will yet form molecular adducts in which the compound adopts an entirely different intermolecular hydrogen-bond arrangement, in spite of the fact that the two constituents of the adduct are not chemically united (*e.g.* urea, Smith, 1952; Vaughan and Donohue, 1952).

Oxy-acids

Although the most frequently examined oxy-acids have been carboxylic acids, which adopt the dimeric structure described previously (p. 224), there is good reason to suppose that all oxy-acids possess structures in which all, or at least a high proportion, of their hydroxyl groups take part in hydrogen-bond formation. One of the earliest inorganic examples to be studied was boric acid (LXIII), the planar molecule of which is linked by hydrogen bonds into infinite parallel layers 3·18 Å apart (Zachariasen, 1934). This distance represents a van der Waals approach, and accounts for the perfect layer cleavage of crystalline boric acid. Subsequently, hydrogen-bond structures have been assigned to telluric (Gossner and Kraus, 1934; Pauling, 1935), α-iodic (Rogers and Helmholz, 1941; Wells, 1949), selenious (Wells and Bailey, 1949) and selenic (Wells and Bailey, 1951) acids.

In the two last, each SeO_3 pyramid or SeO_4 tetrahedron is linked by hydrogen bonds to four neighbours, resulting in infinite layer structures.

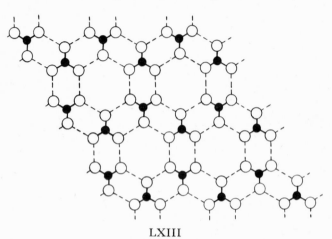

LXIII

Broken lines indicate hydrogen bonds linking oxygen atoms

Acid Salts

In view of the elaborate hydrogen bonding revealed in the crystal structures of the oxy-acids, it is not surprising that acid salts, in which only part of the acidic hydrogen of an acid has been replaced by cations, should adopt a similar arrangement. In the case of acid salts of polybasic oxy-acids the structure varies from the linking of anions by hydrogen to form an infinite chain as in sodium bicarbonate (LXIV)

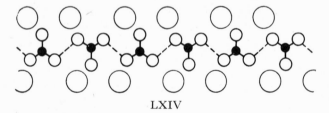

LXIV

(Zachariasen, 1933), to an infinite three-dimensional framework, as in potassium dihydrogen phosphate (LXV) (Hendricks, 1927; West, 1930), consisting of PO_4 tetrahedra in which each oxygen atom is linked through hydrogen to an oxygen of an adjacent PO_4. The cations are accommodated between the chains or in interstices of the framework.

Chemical literature abounds in examples of acid salts in which less than an integral proportion of the hydrogen in the parent acid has been replaced by cations. Examples include the acid salts of monobasic acids, and other fractionally neutralized acidic compounds such as sesquicarbonates and tetroxalates. X-ray examination has in many cases led to a simplification of their structure and is rapidly disposing

246

of the need for the old cumbersome 'molecular' formulae for such compounds. The simplest structures of this kind are the acid fluorides, which have been shown to possess the anion $[F—H—F]^-$ (Helmholz and Rogers, 1939). In KHF_2 each potassium ion is surrounded by eight equidistant fluorine atoms, which are themselves linked in pairs by hydrogen bonds. The structure of NH_4HF_2 is similar but further

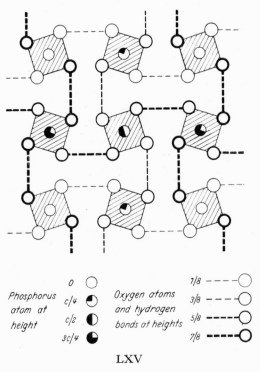

	0 ○		$7/8$ ----○	
Phosphorus	$c/4$ ◕	Oxygen atoms	$3/8$ ----○	
atom at		and hydrogen		
height	$c/2$ ◑	bonds at heights	$5/8$ -----○	
	$3c/4$ ◕		$7/8$ ━━━━○	

LXV

complicated by the hydrogen bonding of the pairs with the nitrogen atom, thus giving a continuous —N—H—F—H—F— network (Helmholz and Rogers, 1940). A recent investigation of the structure of potassium hydrogen bis-(phenylacetate) by Speakman (1949) has revealed a similar pattern, phenylacetate ions being linked in pairs by a hydrogen bond, O—H—O, of length 2·55Å; thus,

$$K^+[PhCH_2CO_2—H—O_2CCH_2Ph]^-.$$

Sodium sesquicarbonate is an example of an acid salt of a dibasic acid in which only one quarter of the acidic hydrogen remains unreplaced, $Na_3H(CO_3)_2.2H_2O$. Its structure (Brown et al., 1949) differs from that of sodium bicarbonate (Zachariasen, 1933) in having its CO_3 anions linked in pairs by hydrogen bonds, the paired anions then being linked into chains by hydrogen-bonded water molecules. This preserves the 2:1 ratio of carbonate to acidic hydrogen, and engages 6 of the 8 oxygen atoms in hydrogen bonds, although as might be expected the hydrated bonds $(O—H—O = 2\cdot72,\ 2\cdot77\ \text{Å})$ are somewhat longer than the carbonate hydrogen bonds $(O—H—O = 2\cdot53\ \text{Å})$. Other acid salts whose structures have been determined are KH_2AsO_4 (Helmholz and Levine, 1942) and $(NH_4)_2H_3IO_6$ (Helmholz, 1937).

REFERENCES

Abrahams, S. C. and Robertson, J. M. (1948) *Acta cryst., Camb.* **1,** 252
Albrecht, G. and Corey, R. B. (1939) *J. Amer. chem. Soc.* **61,** 1087
Auwers, K. von (1893a, b) *Z. phys. Chem.* **12,** 689, 693 ; (1896) *ibid* **21,** 350 ; (1897) *ibid* **23,** 449 ; (1899) *ibid* **30,** 305
— and Orton, K. J. P. (1896) *ibid* **21,** 355
Baker, W. (1936) *Nature, Lond.* **137,** 236
— and Carruthers, G. N. (1937) *J. chem. Soc.* 479
Bennett, G. M. and Jones, B. (1939) *ibid* 420
Bierlein, T. K. and Lingafelter, E. C. (1951) *Acta cryst. Camb.* **4,** 450
Blatt, A. H. and Russell, L. A. (1936) *J. Amer. chem. Soc.* **38,** 1903
Branch, G. E. K. and Calvin, M. (1945) *Theory of Organic Chemistry*, New York, Prentice-Hall, p. 230
— and Yabroff, D. L. (1934) *J. Amer. chem. Soc.* **56,** 2568
Brown, C. J. (1951) *Acta cryst., Camb.* **4,** 100
— and Corbridge, D. E. C. (1948) *Nature, Lond.* **162,** 72
— Peiser, H. S. and Turner-Jones, A. (1949) *Acta cryst., Camb.* **2,** 167
Burawoy, *et al.* (1952) *J. chem. Soc.* 4973 ; (1953) 1443
Chaplin, H. O. and Hunter, L. (1937) *ibid* 1114; (1938a, b) *ibid* 375, 1034
Cochran, W. (1953) *Acta cryst., Camb.* **6,** 260
Coggeshall, N. D. (1947) *J. Amer. chem. Soc.* **69,** 1620
Corey, R. B. (1938) *ibid* **60,** 1598
Cowley, J. M. (1953) *Acta cryst., Camb.* **6,** 516
Cox, E. G., Dougill, M. W. and Jeffrey, G. A. (1952) *J. chem. Soc.* 4854
Davies, M. M. (1938) *Trans. Faraday Soc.* **34,** 1427
Donohue, J. (1952) *J. phys. Chem.* **56,** 502
Dulmage, W. J. and Lipscomb, W. N. (1951) *Acta cryst., Camb.* **4,** 330
Ebert, A. A. and Gottlieb, H. B. (1952) *J. Amer. chem. Soc.* **74,** 2806
Elkins, M. and Hunter, L. (1935) *J. chem. Soc.* 1598
Forster, M. O. and Zimmerli, A. (1911) *ibid* 478
Goldschmidt, G. H. and Llewellyn, F. J. (1950) *Acta cryst., Camb.* **3,** 294
Gossner, B. and Kraus, O. (1934) *Z. Krystallogr.* **88,** 298
Hayes, H. T. and Hunter, L. (1941) *J. chem. Soc.* 1
Helmholz, L. (1937) *J. Amer. chem. Soc.* **59,** 2036
— and Levine, R. (1942) *ibid* **64,** 354
— and Rogers, M. T. (1939) *ibid* **61,** 2590; (1940) *ibid* **62,** 1533
Hendricks, S. B. (1927) *Amer. J. Sci.* **14,** 269; (1935) *Z. Krystallogr.* **91,** 48
— Wulf, O. R., Hilbert, G. E. and Liddel, U. (1936) *J. Amer. chem. Soc.* **58,** 1991
Henecka, H. (1948) *Chem. Ber.* **81,** 189
Hilbert, G. E., Wulf, O. R., Hendricks, S. B. and Liddel, U. (1936) *J. Amer. chem. Soc.* **58,** 548
Holtzberg, F., Post, B. and Fankuchen, I. (1953) *Acta cryst., Camb.* **6,** 127
Hoyer, H. (1950) *Z. Elektrochem.* **54,** 413; (1953) *Chem. Ber.* **86,** 1016
Hughes, E. W. (1940) *J. Amer. chem. Soc.* **62,** 1258
Hunter, L. (1953) *Chem. & Ind.* 155
— and Rees, H. A. (1945) *J. chem. Soc.* 617
— and Reynolds, N. G. (1950) *ibid* 2857

THE STEREOCHEMISTRY OF THE HYDROGEN BOND

Jenkins, G. I. and Taylor, T. W. J. (1937) *ibid* 495
Jerslev, B. (1950) *Nature, Lond.* **166,** 741
Kanda, F. A. and King, A. J. (1951) *J. Amer. chem. Soc.* **73,** 2315
Kuhn, L. P. (1952) *ibid* **74,** 2492
Lautz, H. (1913) *Z. phys. Chem.* **84,** 611
Llewellyn, F. J. and Whitmore, F. E. (1948) *J. chem. Soc.* 1316
Meisencheimer, J. (1921) *Ber. dtsch. chem. Ges.* **54,** 3206
Meldrum, A. N. and Turner, W. E. S. (1908) *J. chem. Soc.* **93,** 876; (1910) **97,** 1605, 1805
Merritt, L. L. and Lauterman, E. (1952) *Acta cryst., Camb.* **5,** 811
Oddo, G. and Puxeddu, E. (1906) *Gazz. chim. ital.* **36** [ii], 1
Palin, D. E. and Powell, H. M. (1947) *J. chem. Soc.* 208
Parry, G. S. (1951) *Acta cryst., Camb.* **4,** 131
Pauling, L. (1935) *Z. Krystallogr.* **91,** 367; (1936) *J. Amer. chem. Soc.* **58,** 94
—— and Brockway, L. O. (1934) *Proc. nat. Acad. Sci., Wash.* **20,** 336
Perutz, M. F. (1951) *Annu. Rep. Progr. Chem.* **48,** 362
Robertson, J. M. and Ubbelohde, A. R. (1938) *Proc. roy. Soc. A.* **167,** 122, 136
Rogers, M. T. and Helmholz, L. (1941) *J. Amer. chem. Soc.* **63,** 278
Rydon, H. N. (1951) *Annu. Rep. Progr. Chem.* **48,** 238 *et seq.*
Sears, W. C. and Kitchen, L. J. (1949) *J. Amer. chem. Soc.* **71,** 4110
Senti, F. and Harker, D. (1940) *ibid* **62,** 2008
Sidgwick. N. V. (1925) *J. chem. Soc.* **127,** 907; (1933) *Annu. Rep. Progr. Chem.* **30,** 114; (1934) *ibid* **31,** 41
—— and Aldous, W. M. (1921) *J. chem. Soc.* **119,** 1008
—— and Callow, R. K. (1924) *ibid* **125,** 527
—— and Ewbank, E. K. (1921) *ibid* **119,** 491
Simon, L. J. (1900) *C. R. Acad. Sci., Paris* **131,** 682
Smith, A. E. (1952) *Acta cryst., Camb.* **5,** 224
Speakman, J. C. (1949) *J. chem. Soc.* 3357
Stanford, S. C. and Gordy, W. (1940) *J. Amer. chem. Soc.* **62,** 1247
Staudinger, H., Hammet, L. and Siegwart, J. (1921) *Helv. chim. acta* **4,** 228
Stillson, G. H., Sawyer, D. W. and Hunt, C. K. (1945) *J. Amer. chem. Soc.* **67,** 303
Taylor, T. W. J. and Ewbank, E. K. (1926) *J. chem. Soc.* 2821
Turner, W. E. S. (1915) *Molecular Association*, London, Longmans Green
Vaughan, P. and Donohue, J. (1952) *Acta cryst., Camb.* **5,** 530
Wells, A. F. (1949) *ibid* **2,** 128
—— and Bailey, M. (1949) *J. chem. Soc.* 1282; (1951) *ibid* 968
West, J. (1930) *Z. Krystallogr.* **74,** 306
Wulf, O. R., Liddel, U. and Hendricks, S. B. (1936) *J. Amer. chem. Soc.* **58,** 2287
Zachariasen, W. H. (1933) *J. chem. Phys.* **1,** 634; (1934) *Z. Krystallogr.* **88,** 150

7

THE STEREOCHEMISTRY OF COMPOUNDS
OF HIGH MOLECULAR WEIGHT

E. J. Ambrose

THE science of high polymers has developed enormously in recent years and it would not be possible to cover the whole of the field in a single chapter. But the general stereochemical principles which apply to problems of high polymer structure are similar to those which apply in the case of small molecules, except that the emphasis appears to rest on some of the weaker forces of interaction which are generally neglected in materials of low molecular weight. In this chapter an attempt will be made to consider these general principles and to see how they apply in the case of those materials in which a reasonably definite structure has been deduced by physical and chemical methods.

GENERAL PRINCIPLES

The internuclear distances and bond angles for various pairs of atoms can be found from the tables provided in the Appendix. With a few exceptions the values obtained with materials of high molecular weight are very similar to those given in the Appendix, pp. 362 and 364. In the case of a simple molecule, such as ethane, the only factor affecting the stereochemistry, which is not included under internuclear distances and bond angles, is the hindered rotation about the carbon–carbon bond. This problem has been investigated by electron diffraction, Raman and infra-red spectroscopy and thermodynamic methods. For a review with references, see Ingold (1953).

It is clear that the stable conformation for the ethane molecule is of the kind shown in I, which represents an end view of the molecule looking along the carbon–carbon bond. The lower C—H bonds are arranged in mutually staggered positions with reference to the first three bonds.   There are three equivalent conformations for the molecule with an energy barrier of about $2 \cdot 9$ kcal. mole^{-1} at the intermediate non-staggered positions.

Rotation about single bonds is considered to be only of secondary importance in small molecules, but in the case of long-chain molecules it may be of primary importance in determining the molecular conformation.   In the case of many polymers the stereochemistry of the monomer units of which they are composed is well understood, but the confirmation of the entire molecule, which depends upon free rotation about valency bonds, is often extremely difficult to determine. When the groups attached to the carbon atoms are not all identical, as for example in 1 : 2-dichloroethane, a new restriction of the rotation about the carbon–carbon bond appears. This problem has been investigated by Erhardt (1932) and by Beach and Turkevich (1939) and particularly by Mizushima and his collaborators (1942–1944).

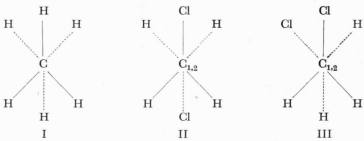

These investigators found that the *trans*-conformation II for the two halogen atoms is considerably more stable than the gauche conformation III. The relative stability of the two forms corresponds to an energy difference of about 3 kcal. $mole^{-1}$. Let us consider this result in relation to the stable conformations of a simple hydrocarbon chain IV.

In this case, if we consider the carbon–carbon bond p—q then the large halogen atoms of II and III are replaced by the main valency bonds of the chain p—r and q—s. We should therefore expect to find that the most stable conformation for the chain would be one in which the bonds pr and qs occur in *trans*-positions. This is in fact the case and corresponds to the fully extended planar zigzag form shown in IV.

$$C^{H_2} \quad C^{H_2}_r \quad {}_p C^{H_2}_{q} \quad C^{H_2}_{s'} \quad C^{H_2}$$

IV

If the polymer contains additional side groups replacing the hydrogen atoms of the methylene groups in IV, the *trans* conformation for the main chain bonds (pr, qs) may no longer be the most stable, and the structure may be one in which the side groups tend to assume a *trans* conformation about the bond pq. In this case the polymer may take up a chain conformation other than the extended form shown in IV. Bunn (1942b) has considered this problem and has defined the various conformations in the following way. The valency bond d in (V) is considered to be one of the main chain bonds of the polymer. In the extended form of chain the two adjacent valency bonds will assume the positions a and a', *i.e.* the *trans* form (VI). This conformation is defined

251

as *ada'*. There are two alternative possibilities however, *adb'* or *adc'*. The conformation *ada'* Bunn calls *A*, *adb'*, *B* and *adc'*, *C*. The conformation of successive valency bonds along the chain may be considered in this way, *e.g.* the conformation of the bond *a'* relative to the

V   VI

next carbon atom and the bond *d*. The planar zigzag carbon chain (IV) for example is represented as *AAAA*. . . . Bunn has given a valuable classification of other conformations of long chains.

In certain polymers, especially proteins, hydrogen bonds between hydrogen and oxygen or between hydrogen and nitrogen atoms play an extremely important part in determining the molecular configuration*. The occurrence of hydrogen bonds can be in part explained in terms of an attraction between the very small hydrogen proton and the lone-pair electrons of the oxygen or nitrogen atom, *e.g.* $> N—H \cdots\cdots O = C <$. This type of secondary force of cohesion was originally observed by Buswell, Deitz and Rodebush (1937). In compounds containing hydroxyl (OH) or amide (NH) groups the frequency of the infra-red absorption band associated with the vibration of the hydrogen atom is frequently lower than the value to be expected from observations on simpler molecules, but when the material is dissolved in non-polar solvents (Richards and Thompson, 1947) the frequency is restored to the higher value. For example the frequency of the O—H stretching mode, under conditions in which the groups are effectively isolated from each other, is about 3600 cm^{-1}. In the solid state it is about 3300–3400 cm^{-1}. With the N—H bond in amides, the frequency of the free bond is 3450 cm^{-1} while that of the solid is 3300 cm^{-1}. This change has been ascribed to the presence of the weak N—H $\cdots\cdots$ O=C hydrogen bonds in which the hydrogen nucleus is attracted to oxygen, so weakening the N—H valency bond and reducing the frequency of vibration. The energy associated with the NH $\cdots\cdots$ O=C bond is about 5 kcal. mole^{-1} *i.e.* slightly more than the energy associated with the barrier between various staggered conformations about valency bonds, for the case where large groups are attached to the

---

*It is appropriate to talk of different ' conformations ' of a structure when no bonds are broken in converting one into another, but to talk of ' configurations ' when the formation or breaking of any bonds, including hydrogen bonds, is or could be involved in the interconversion (*cf* Chapter 2, p. 38). This is admittedly a rather fine point of nomenclature. [*Editor*]

two adjacent carbon atoms. The stereochemistry of the hydrogen bond has been considered by Pauling, Corey and Branson (1951), by Lennard-Jones and Popple (1951) and by Robinson and Ambrose (1952). In VII the angle between the N—H bond and the vector joining the nitrogen atom to the oxygen atom(α) should not be greater than 30°. The distance between the oxygen and nitrogen atoms is $2·86 \pm 0·1$ Å. The structures are very similar in the case of the $>O \cdots\cdots H—O—$ bond.

O
˙˙˙H
α|
N

C═C

C═C

VII   VIII   IX

The introduction of unsaturated groups into a polymer chain will modify the structure in two respects. Free rotation cannot occur about the double bond, and the other valency bonds of the doubly-bound carbon atoms shown in this figure will lie in one plane. The possibility of *cis* (VIII) and *trans* (IX) forms will therefore arise. This factor enters into the problem of the structure of rubber and gutta-percha (p. 259).

In the case of polymers in the crystalline state another factor affects the conformation of the molecule. The structure will tend to arrange itself in such a form that the closest possible packing of molecules in the lattice can take place. With highly unsymmetrical molecules such packing may be achieved only by some departure from the equilibrium conformation for the chain and penetration of the van der Waals' spheres. It does not follow that such deviations will occur when the polymer is in a more dispersed condition than the solid state.

EXPERIMENTAL METHODS OF INVESTIGATING HIGH POLYMER STRUCTURE

The determination of the chemical constitution of compounds of high molecular weight is sometimes not a matter of great difficulty. This is especially true with many synthetic polymers which are built up from a series of relatively small identical units. A question may arise as to whether the units tend to polymerize in a head-to-head (X) or in a head-to-tail (XI) configuration. But the main stereochemical

X   XI

problems are usually connected with the finer details of the structure, of the kind mentioned in the previous section. For the elucidation of such structures, physical methods are required; the most effective methods have proved to be those of x-ray diffraction and spectroscopy. The x-ray method provides a detailed description of all the atomic

253

parameters in the molecule and in the crystal, where the diffraction pattern is sufficiently detailed to enable a complete analysis to be carried out. The spectroscopic method when used with polarized radiation provides information about the direction of certain valency bonds or chemical groups within the molecule and also gives an indication of the type of chemical force involved. It is in a sense complementary to the x-ray method and has proved especially useful in those cases where the diffraction pattern is too poor to enable a complete x-ray analysis to be carried out.

Long-chain polymers in which the chains all lie approximately parallel to a common axis (the fibre axis) commonly give a diffraction pattern which is known as a fibre diagram. The fibre will contain many crystallites which will have all possible orientations in the fibre apart from the fact that the chain axes all lie parallel to a common direction (FIGURE 1). The pattern obtained is therefore similar to that

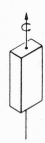

FIGURE 1. Rotation of crystal about an axis

which would be obtained in the case of a single crystal, if it were rotated about a crystallographic axis.

From an interpretation of the diffraction pattern of a fibre the so-called 'fibre repeat' is generally the first parameter to be determined. This represents the interval in ångström units at which the structure repeats itself exactly along the fibre axis, and is usually characteristic for a given polymer. From a knowledge of the fibre repeat and a consideration of the stable conformations of a polymer chain according to the methods described on p. 251, much information about the structure can often be deduced.

There are a number of compounds of high molecular weight which are not commonly obtained in the form of fibres, as for example the globular proteins, many of which can be obtained in crystalline form. These crystals do not differ, from the crystallographic point of view, from the crystals of compounds of low molecular weight (Bernal and Crowfoot, 1933). The analytical procedure will be to determine first of all the crystal symmetry, the dimensions of the unit cell and then the space group. Such an analysis has been carried out on a large number of crystalline proteins. The difficulty with globular proteins appears when an attempt is made to determine the atomic parameters within the molecule. Whereas the number of atoms in a small molecule may be only a matter of ten or twenty, there will be a thousand or more atoms in a globular protein molecule. This means that instead of finding ten or twenty terms in the Fourier series, a thousand or more will occur and for each of these terms the phase has to be determined. A Patterson synthesis can be carried out in which the phases are not required and this can provide certain valuable information (Kendrew and Perutz, 1949), but so far the determination of the complete structure has not been possible for any crystalline protein.

Infra-red spectroscopy using polarized radiation has been used for the study of high polymer and of protein structure. Infra-red absorption bands in the region from 4000–500cm^{-1} are due to molecular vibrations. The characteristic frequencies of certain normal modes of vibration of some chemical groups are, to a considerable extent, independent of the molecule to which they are attached. This is especially true for vibrations involving hydrogen atoms, in which practically all the movement in the vibration is confined to the hydrogen nuclei which are so much lighter than any of the other atoms in the molecule. It is also true for groups containing double bonds such as $>C{=}O$ groups.

FIGURE 2. Vibration of N—H bond

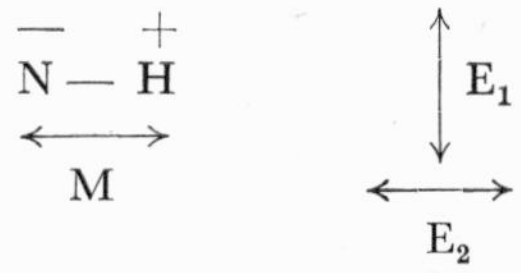

Let us consider the N—H bond shown in FIGURE 2. There is a certain mode of vibration of this group which has a characteristic frequency of 3450 cm^{-1}. In this mode of vibration the N—H bond is stretched, like a helical spring, and the magnitude of the associated electric dipole changes in the direction of M as the nuclei vibrate. If the molecule is exposed to polarized radiation then it is found that this radiation is strongly absorbed by the oscillating dipole when the electric vector of the radiation vibrates in the direction E_2. When the vector vibrates at right angles to this direction (E_1) the dipole will not absorb. (These changes in absorption are known as dichroism.)

For the determination of the direction of valency bonds in a long-chain polymer, a fibre or film is prepared with the chain axis lying approximately parallel to the fibre axis. The infra-red spectrum is then recorded with the E-vector of the radiation first parallel to the fibre axis and then perpendicular to the fibre axis. If the absorption band is more intense with the vector parallel to the fibre axis, the valency bond lies approximately parallel to this axis. If the absorption band is more intense with the vector perpendicular to the axis, the valency bonds are approximately perpendicular to the fibre axis.

In visual and ultra-violet absorption bands electronic transitions involving the whole molecule are often involved. Where aromatic or heterocyclic rings (or other conjugated groupings) occur, the absorption bands may be characteristic of these, and valuable information about the orientation of the planes of the rings or groups relative to the fibre axis can be obtained by using polarized radiation.

Another physical method which shows some promise for the study of the stereochemistry in long-chain compounds is that of optical rotatory power. In the case of compounds of low molecular weight, as **XII**, the optical rotatory power is considered to be due to the

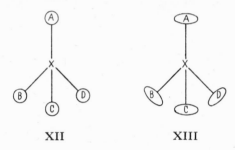

XII   XIII

presence of the asymmetric carbon atom X to which four different chemical groups or atoms are attached. If the four groups attached to the carbon atom are themselves axially symmetrical, as for example halogen and hydrogen atoms, some theories (Kirkwood, 1937; Condon, Altar and Eyring, 1937) enable calculations of optical rotatory power to be carried out with the help of the necessary atomic parameters. But if the groups attached to the carbon atoms are themselves not symmetrical (**XIII**), then we should expect according to the theory to find that the actual orientation of the groups about the valency bond attaching them to the asymmetric carbon atom must be taken into account, *i.e.* rotation about valency bonds must be considered.

This problem has been examined for long-chain polymers (Ambrose, unpublished) and it can be shown that a change in the conformation of a polymer molecule containing asymmetric carbon atoms, simply as a result of changing the positions of the groups by rotation about valency bonds, can lead to a change in the optical rotatory power of the polymer. The study of the optical rotatory power of polymers therefore provides a method of studying the important question of staggered positions about valency bonds mentioned on p. 251. The atomic parameters are not yet known which enable absolute calculations to be carried out, but certain valuable qualitative results have been obtained by Robinson and Bott (1951) and will be described in the section on polypeptides and proteins (p. 266).

Other methods which have been used for the study of long-chain polymers include birefringence (particularly streaming birefringence), viscosity, ultra-centrifuge measurements, osmotic pressure, and dielectric constant. These methods have provided valuable information about the molecular weight, shape and general electrical properties of the molecule, but do not provide solutions to the more detailed problems of stereochemistry and will not be considered in this chapter.

LONG CHAIN HYDROCARBONS

Saturated Hydrocarbons

The structure of a simple straight-chain hydrocarbon molecule ($C_{29}H_{60}$) was determined by Müller (1928). It was shown that the planar zigzag form (IV) occurs in the crystals. The repeat of pattern d

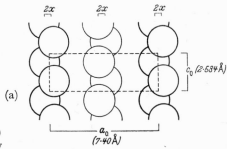

(a)

Figure 3. Polythene crystallite: (a) side view of chains; (b) end-on view of chains (Bunn, 1939)

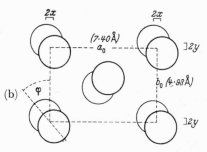

(b)

is 2·534 Å along the length of the carbon chain. This value agrees very closely with the value predicted from the bond lengths and tetrahedral angles of the carbon atoms in diamond. The hydrocarbon chains pack together in a parallel arrangement in the crystal. Similar results have been obtained with a number of other saturated hydrocarbons and the results do not appear to differ appreciably for chains containing about thirty or more carbon atoms. It might be expected therefore that a polymer built up in the form of a hydrocarbon chain would display a similar structure. This has in fact been shown to be the case for polythene. Bunn (1939) found that the repeat of pattern along the chain axis was 2·534 Å. The chains are packed within the unit cell as shown in FIGURE 3. Observations have also been carried out on this type of chain using polarized infra-red radiation (Elliott, Ambrose and Temple, 1948).

There are two characteristic molecular vibrations for the methylene ($> CH_2$) group.

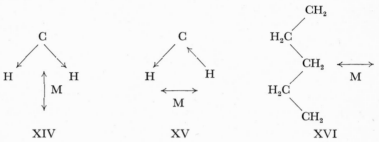

XIV   XV   XVI

In the first of these vibrations the two CH bonds stretch in phase, and the electrical dipole moment changes in the direction M (XIV). In the second mode they are out of phase, and the dipole changes as shown in XV. But in both cases the dipole lies in the plane of the paper. If therefore a polymer containing the hydrocarbon zigzag chain is examined in plane-polarized radiation the electric dipole for these vibrations should change in the direction at right angles to the polymer chain as shown in XVI.

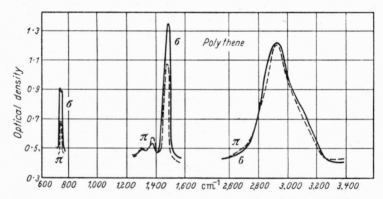

FIGURE 4. Polarized infra-red spectrum of polythene (Elliott, Ambrose and Temple, 1948): - - - - - - E-vector parallel to fibre axis; ———— E-vector perpendicular to fibre axis

In FIGURE 4 is shown the spectrum of an oriented film of polythene. The broad absorption band at about 2900 cm^{-1} is due to the vibrations shown in XIV and XV respectively. In both these cases the absorption is a maximum when the radiation is polarized so that the E-vector vibrates at right angles to the axes of the chains as would be expected from XVI. If the orientation of the polymer chains were perfect we should expect to find that no absorption at all would occur with the vector parallel to the chain axis. In certain simple crystals the changes in absorption for different positions of the polarizer

258

are very marked. With polymers it is difficult to obtain a specimen in which the chains lie strictly parallel to each other; only partial orientation (and less dichroism) is obtained.

The results obtained with polarized radiation are in general agreement with the established structure for the extended zigzag chain. This extended form of chain is also to be expected from a consideration of the stable positions for staggered valency-bonds as described on p. 251.

Unsaturated Hydrocarbons

Let us now consider the case where unsaturated bonds occur in the main chain. As mentioned previously, the ethylenic group $\left(\begin{array}{c}\diagdown\\/\end{array}C:C\begin{array}{c}\diagup\\\diagdown\end{array}\right)$ tends to assume a planar form, and this fact formed the basis for an interesting suggestion by Meyer and Mark (1928) that the difference between gutta-percha and rubber might be due to a difference between *cis-* and *trans-* configurations about the ethylenic bond for the chain. Both these polymers are built up from the same monomer, isoprene $(—CH_2—C(CH_3)=CH—CH_2—)_n$. Meyer and Mark suggested that in gutta-percha the *trans* form (IX) for the chain bonds occurs whereas in rubber the *cis* form (VIII) is present.

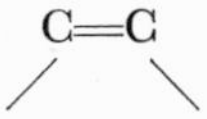

$$C=C$$
$$\diagup \qquad \diagdown$$

VIII

$$\diagdown$$
$$C=C$$
$$\diagdown$$

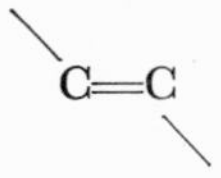

IX

The repeat of pattern along the fibre axis of β-gutta-percha is 4·7 Å. If an extended chain were present in this compound a repeat of pattern of 5·05 Å would be expected. Bunn (1942a) determined the crystal structure for this compound and found that the chain is not fully extended but includes clockwise and anti-clockwise rotations as shown (FIGURE 5). In this way the isoprene units are kept parallel and crystallographically equivalent, but the identity period along the chain is reduced to 4·7Å.

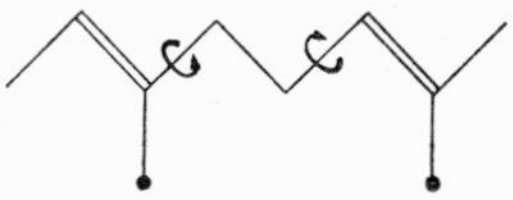

FIGURE 5. Chain of β-gutta-percha

Katz (1925) was able to show that stretched rubber is crystalline and various investigators have examined this material (*e.g.* Mark and von Susich, 1928). The unit cell was determined by Lotmar and Meyer (1936). Bunn has carried out a more complete structure determination. The structure is shown in FIGURE 6. In this case the pattern repeats after two isoprene units instead of one, as in β-gutta-percha, and the two units do not have identical configurations. The chain bonds assume a *cis* configuration about the double bond as originally suggested by Meyer and Mark (1928). But it is significant that the group

is not strictly planar, a rotation of one of the single bonds away from the plane takes place to the extent of $35°$. There is in fact also some distortion $(20°)$ in the case of β-gutta-percha.

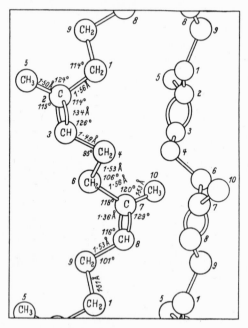

FIGURE 6.   Crystal structure of rubber (Bunn, 1942a) (chain seen from two different viewpoints)

The rubber molecule has an extremely awkward shape for packing in a crystal lattice and Bunn (1942a) considered that this is one of the reasons why the molecule deviates from an ideal configuration. The molecule endeavours to satisfy the conditions for staggered conformations as far as possible, but here again there are some deviations. Bunn considered that the energy barriers between the various conformations are less, where a double bond occurs; free rotation about the bonds marked *a* and *b* occurs quite readily. It is significant that the phenomenon of rubber-like elasticity, which is a manifestation of a high degree of flexibility in the molecule, occurs in polymers containing double bonds within the chain.

The Effect of Introducing Polar Groups into the Hydrocarbon Chain
Polar groups introduced into a hydrocarbon chain will produce
certain modifications to the structure. The amide group has been
introduced, for example, into the Nylon type of compound. A very
careful study of the amide group has been made by Corey (1938) and
Pauling, Corey and Branson (1951) using x-ray diffraction methods.
The latest data for the bond angles and interatomic distances, as

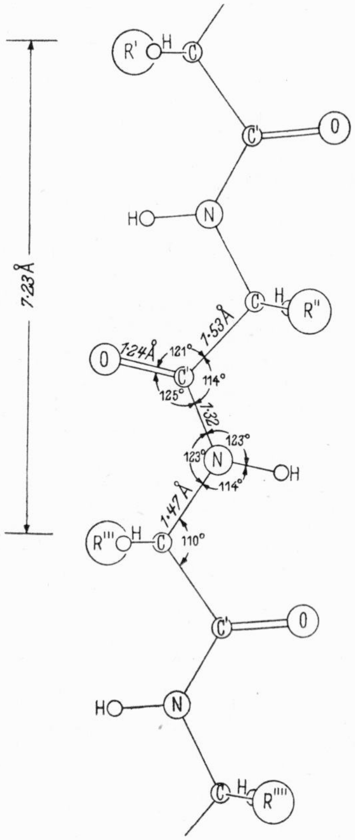

FIGURE 7. Amide linkage (Corey and Pauling, 1953)

determined for a number of compounds, are shown in FIGURE 7 (Corey
and Pauling, 1953).

It is clear that the C—N bond distance is short as compared with
a normal single bond distance of 1·5 Å. This result strongly suggests
some double bond character in this linkage. If this be the case the
—NH·CO— group is planar, with all the valency bonds, shown
in the diagram, lying in the plane of the paper. If such a group
is introduced into a hydrocarbon chain it will clearly lead to a considerable restriction in the number of possible conformations, as occurs
with the ethylenic linkage. The crystal structure of Nylon 66 has been

determined by Bunn and Garner (1947). The chains are no longer arranged, as in polythene (FIGURE 3), in almost mutually perpendicular pairs when an end-on view of the chain is obtained but the beginning of a layer type of structure can be seen. This effect is due to another restriction upon the mobility of the chain, produced by introducing polar groups. The forces of interaction between the chains will no longer be due only to van der Waals' forces, but also to hydrogen bonds between N·H and C:O groups.

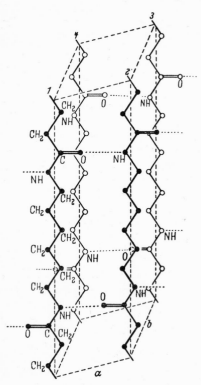

FIGURE 8. Nylon structure (Bunn and Garner, 1947)

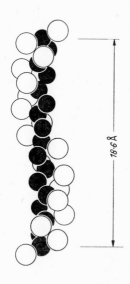

FIGURE 9. Poly*iso*butane chain (white circles represent methyl groups; black circles represent carbon atoms of chain) (Fuller, Frosch and Pape, 1940)

Any stable configuration for the molecule will be one in which all or at least a high proportion of these bonds are satisfied. This condition is fulfilled in the layer-like structure for Nylon 66 as shown in FIGURE 8.

The Nylon structure has also been examined by Elliott, Ambrose and Temple (1948) using polarized infra-red radiation. As already mentioned the N·H bond has a stretching mode of vibration with a frequency, when hydrogen-bonded to C:O, of 3300 cm^{-1}. This band shows a maximum of absorption when the E-vector of radiation vibrates at right angles to the chain axis. The C:O bond of the amide group —NH·CO— has a stretching mode with a frequency of 1650 cm^{-1}. This band also shows maximum absorption with the E-vector perpendicular to the chain axis. These results agree with a structure in which the parallel chains are held together by N—H····O=C hydrogen bonds, which lie perpendicular to the chain axis. Ambrose, Elliott and Temple (1949) have also studied the infra-red dichroism of rolled ' Nylon films '. With rolled films the sheets of hydrogen-bonded chains shown in FIGURE 8 may tend to lie parallel to the surface of the film and the N—H and C=O groups tend to lie parallel to this surface. Infra-red studies have indicated that this is the case.

The amide group is the most interesting polar group in view of its occurrence in proteins, but polymers containing ester linkages—CO·O—, sulphur bonds (—S—) and numerous other links are also known. Most of these groups produce some degree of interaction between the chains as a result of their attraction for other groups in the molecule.

The Effect of Side Chains upon the Stable Configuration of a Polymer Chain
It was mentioned in the introduction that a departure from the extended form of chain might be expected to occur if a side chain was present of size comparable to that of the main chain. In this case it would not always be possible to say which pair of groups should be arranged in a *trans* conformation in relation to a given valency bond. This effect has already been encountered in the structures of β-guttapercha and rubber, where the methyl groups affect the conformation of the main chain. Poly*iso*butane $(--CH_2 \cdot CMe_2—)_n$ also shows an effect due to the presence of the large number of methyl groups attached to the chain. The structure of this material has been examined by Fuller, Frosch and Pape (1940). In the stretched condition the polymer is highly crystalline. It is found to possess a spiral structure as shown in FIGURE 9. This form appears to be due to the need for accommodating the bulky methyl groups in such close proximity. In fact some penetration of the accepted van der Waals' spheres must take place for all conformations of the molecule. Yet, poly*iso*butane is a rubber-like material and has a highly flexible chain. This condition appears to arise, as in natural rubber, from the fact that the various distortions from normal stable forms produce a nice balance, in which no single conformation is markedly more stable than any other.

THE STRUCTURE OF PROTEINS

The properties of protein molecules are decided in part by the general properties of a long-chain polymer, in part by the polar amide group and in part by the properties of the side chains. The first definite information about the configuration of any protein chain was obtained by Meyer and Mark (1928b) who were led to suggest, as a result of x-ray diffraction studies, that the silk molecules consisted of long chains arranged somewhat like those of the hydrocarbons. Since that time the information has been extended by many workers but perhaps the most notable contribution is due to Astbury and Street (1931) and Astbury and Woods (1933) who studied the properties of wool keratin by x-ray methods: a valuable review has been given by Low (1953). For the purposes of the present discussion it would however be more convenient to approach the problem first by a consideration of simple polypeptides.

Astbury, Dalgleish, Darmon and Sutherland (1948) first investigated some simple polypeptides using x-ray diffraction methods. Thin films of the materials in unoriented form were prepared by evaporation from solvents. It was found that polyglycine $(\cdot NH \cdot CH_2 \cdot CO)_n$ gave diffraction rings somewhat similar to those observed in Nylon 66 and in silk, suggesting the presence of a ' grid ' type of structure like that of Nylon. On the other hand, the polypeptides containing longer side chains (polyleucine, poly-phenylalanine etc), did in many cases give diffraction rings somewhat similar to those observed in α-keratin. Astbury was not convinced, however, that there was a true correspondence. The infra-red data showed that absorption bands characteristic of the peptide linkage $(\cdot NH \cdot CO \cdot)$ were present, and that the bands due to the side chain portion of the skeleton were similar to those observed in the amino-acids. It was suggested that these absorption bands might provide a method of analysis for deciding the amino-acid composition of protein molecules.

It was found by Ambrose and Hanby (1949) that polypeptides of high molecular weight could be prepared and that these materials could be produced with a preferred direction of molecular orientation. When these films were examined in polarized radiation it was found that, unlike oriented films of Nylon, the absorption bands due to the N·H and C:O stretching modes of the peptide bond showed a maximum absorption with the E-vector parallel to the chain axis. (With Nylon

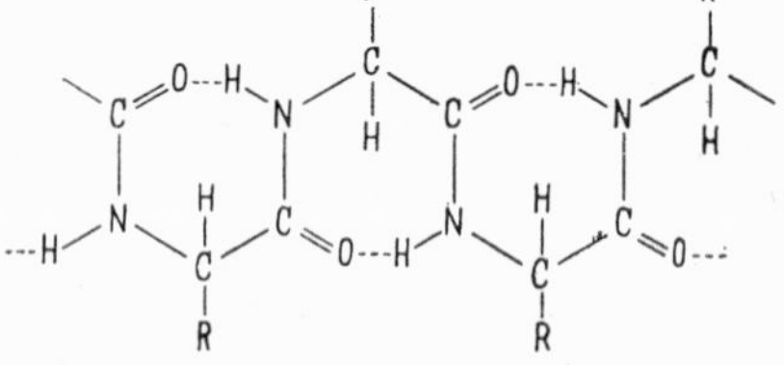

FIGURE 10. Seven-membered ring fold

the absorption is a maximum with the vector perpendicular to the chain axis.) This result suggested that a new configuration for the polypeptide chain was present in this case, the hydrogen bonds between N·H and C:O groups of the peptide being formed along the chain axis instead of perpendicular to it. A tentative configuration which was compatible with this structure was suggested. It involved seven-membered rings and was a modification of a configuration suggested by Huggins (1943) on theoretical grounds. In the structure shown in FIGURE 10, the side chains tend to lie in the same plane as the rings. This configuration appears to be preferred to the configuration shown by Huggins in which the side chains are perpendicular to the rings, because it is more in accord with the factors affecting the stability of polymer chains mentioned in the introduction. The infra-red data themselves do not give any information on this point but merely refer to the hydrogen-bonded structure of the peptide link.

In addition to the infra-red data on synthetic polypeptides, x-ray diffraction data were also obtained (Bamford, Hanby and Happey, 1949a). The fibre diagram for films prepared from *m*-cresol was similar to the diagrams which are obtained with α-keratin. But it was also found that in the case of films prepared from formic acid the pattern was similar to the silk and β-keratin diagrams. Ambrose and Elliott (1951a) carried out an investigation of the infra-red dichroism of films of synthetic polypeptides prepared from various solvents. It was found that in the case of polypeptides which were soluble in the less polar solvents (*e.g.* poly-γ-benzyl-L-glutamate) the dichroism corresponded to the folded form and was extremely high (FIGURE 11). In the case of films prepared from formic acid dichroism similar to that obtained with Nylon was observed. It became clear therefore that films prepared from non-polar solvents were indeed folded structures. The folding properties were a characteristic of the main polypeptide chain and were only dependent upon the side chains in a secondary sense. The various polypeptides with a number of different non-polar side chains showed the ability to exist both in a folded and an extended chain configuration. The effect of side chains appeared to lie mainly in their bulk, those polypeptides with small side chains tending to be stable in the extended form, whilst those with large side chains tended to be stable in the folded form (Bamford, Hanby and Happey, 1951b). This again would be in accord with the fundamental considerations for stable configurations, because the relative bulk of the main chain and of the side chain in the vicinity of the asymmetric carbon atom will decide which component must be considered as a large group when deciding the staggered positions about valency bonds.

Further evidence about the factors affecting the stability of the polypeptide chain was obtained by studying the infra-red spectra of synthetic polypeptides in solution (Ambrose and Elliott, 1951a). It was found that the spectra of synthetic polypeptides in a completely non-polar solvent (carbon tetrachloride) indicated that even when the molecules were effectively isolated from each other in dilute solution the $N\!-\!H\cdots O\!=\!C$ hydrogen bonds were still formed, *i.e.* by internal ring formation within the isolated chains. Some polypeptides in the folded form were readily soluble in non-polar solvents such as benzene whereas the same polymers, when transformed into the extended form, were completely insoluble (Bamford, Hanby and Happey, 1949b).

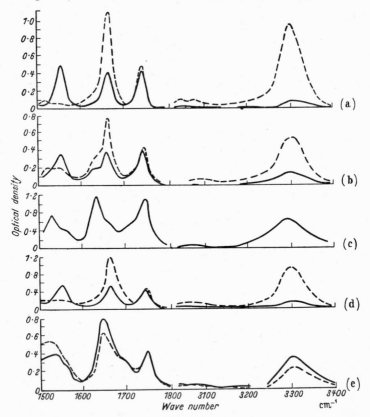

FIGURE 11. Polarized infra-red spectra of polypeptides (Ambrose and Elliott, 1951a)

- - - - - - E-vector parallel to chain axis

————— E-vector perpendicular to chain axis

(a) Poly-γ-benzyl L-glutamate, cast from chloroform (folded form)

(b) Poly-γ-methyl L-glutamate, cast from m-cresol (folded form)

(c) Poly-γ-methyl L-glutamate, cast from formic acid (extended form, unoriented)

(d) Poly-γ-methyl L-glutamate-DL-phenylalanine, 1:1, cast from m-cresol (folded form)

(e) Poly-γ-methyl L-glutamate-DL-phenylalanine, 1:1, cast from formic acid (extended form)

The optical rotatory power of the folded and extended forms of polypeptide chains has been examined by Robinson and Bott (1952) who found that the rotation changes sign as the chain configuration is altered from the folded to the extended form. The hydrogen-bonding conditions are similar in the two chains, and it appears that the alteration in optical rotatory power is due to the change in configuration about the valency bonds shown in XVII as might be expected according to the theory described on p. 256.

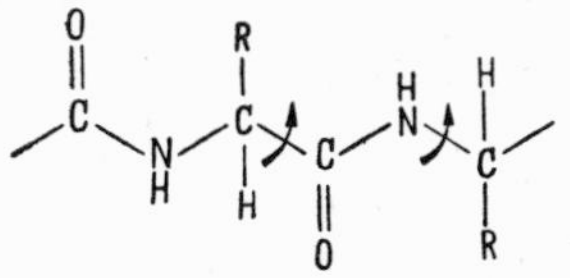

XVII

In approaching the problem of the molecular configuration of protein molecules we may do well to consider these fundamental properties of the polypeptide chain, in the case where the polymer contains non-polar side chains, before examining the proteins themselves. Such properties will be common to all proteins, while the specific character of a given protein will be due to the arrangement and interaction between the twenty-two different amino-acid side chains. In so far as these side-chain interactions are concerned a few synthetic polypeptides with polar side chains have been examined (Hanby, Waley and Watson, 1950; Ambrose, 1950). Polyglutamic acid (XVIII) shows quite marked infra-red dichroism. The main polypeptide chain appears to be folded in the same way as in the polyglutamic esters and other polypeptides with non-polar side chains, the dichroism of the peptide N·H and C:O bonds being very similar. The side chains appear to form chelate rings similar to those which occur in dicarboxylic acids (XIX). These bonds form linkages between chains but do not interfere with the configuration of the main chain. Poly-lysine (XX) also appears to have a folded main chain in which the configuration again is not affected by the polarity of the side chains in the solid film.

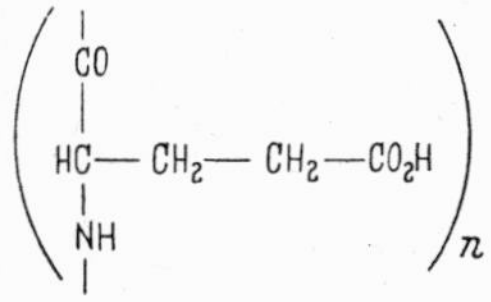

XVIII 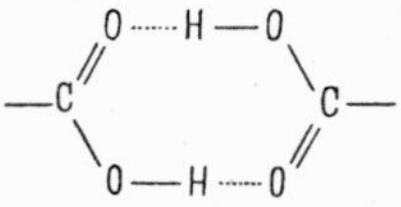   XIX 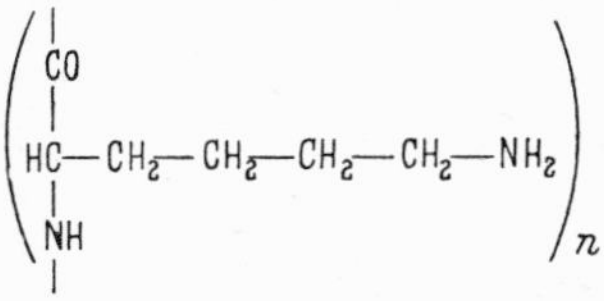   XX

The Structure of Protein Molecules

The classic work of Astbury and Street (1931) and of Astbury and Wood (1933) on wool keratin showed that there were two characteristic x-ray diffraction patterns. In unstretched wool keratin an x-ray reflection corresponding to a periodicity at 5·1 Å along the length of the fibres was observed. In the stretched fibres, reflections rather similar to those of silk fibres could be seen. The results were interpreted to mean that a regular folding of the long-chain molecules had taken

267

place in unstretched wool. This concept has formed the basis for subsequent studies of the behaviour of protein molecules. Astbury (1940) was able to extend these observations to other fibrous proteins such as myosin, the fibrous muscle protein, fibrinogen, the fibre-forming protein of blood, and epidermin, the skin protein. Astbury and Woods (1933) suggested a possible folded structure, which could account for this ' α ' type of diffraction pattern as it was called. Difficulties were experienced (Neurath, 1940) in arranging a molecular packing for this structure and Astbury and Bell (1941) later proposed the alternative form shown in FIGURE 12. The attractive feature of this model lies in the fact that it accounts for the relatively strong x-ray reflection at intervals of 5·1 Å along the fibre axis, as it has a marked periodicity of this kind.

During this time evidence which revealed the importance of hydrogen bonds, in structures containing the amide group, was beginning to accumulate (Buswell, Deitz and Rodebush, 1937). Astbury and Bell suggested that a bond of this kind might hold their castellated rings together at the point marked X–X. It was not possible to satisfy all hydrogen bonds in a fold of this type, however. Huggins (1943) in a theoretical paper proposed that in a stable configuration for a protein chain all available hydrogen bonds should be satisfied. He suggested for the folded or α chain various helical and non-helical ring structures which would satisfy this condition with rings containing seven, eight and ten atoms.

The first experimental evidence to suggest the occurrence of a structure involving only hydrogen bonds formed within the chain, was the work on the synthetic polypeptides already described (Ambrose and Hanby, 1949). An extensive investigation of polypeptides and of fibrous proteins (Ambrose, Elliott and Temple, 1949; Ambrose and Elliott, 1951a, b), indicated that the dichroic effects were quite general and that the α-proteins were similar to the folded polypeptides. The effects were qualitatively less marked in the protein than in the synthetic materials. 'β'-Keratin on the other hand gave dichroic effects similar to those observed in the extended chain form of the synthetic polypeptides (FIGURE 11). It is certainly tempting to conclude that the chain configuration in folded proteins also involves a structure in which the hydrogen bonds are satisfied within the chain by internal ring formation. This interpretation has been the subject of considerable controversy. Let us consider the properties of proteins which make them different from most synthetic polypeptides so far examined. First, we note that most proteins are water-soluble or water-absorbing materials. We might therefore expect some interaction between the water molecule and the amide group.

It does not follow that conditions in a polymer will be similar to those in a compound of low molecular weight. Although the polysaccharides of low molecular weight are rendered highly soluble in water by the presence of the many hydroxyl groups, cellulose is completely insoluble. In solution the hydrogen bonds between polymer chains are being continuously broken and reformed with water molecules in a condition

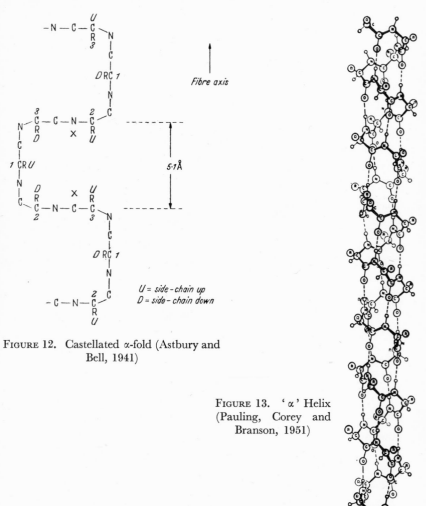

FIGURE 12. Castellated α-fold (Astbury and Bell, 1941)

FIGURE 13. ' α ' Helix (Pauling, Corey and Branson, 1951)

of dynamic equilibrium. As the molecular weight of the polymer is increased, the effects of thermal agitation upon bonds between the polymer chains will become less pronounced, whereas the effect of thermal agitation upon the solvent-polymer bonds will still be marked. Pauling, Corey and Branson (1951) consider that the hydrogen bond between two amide groups is inherently more stable than the bond between an amide group and a water molecule, there being an energy difference between these two states of about 3 kcal. mole^{-1}. We may therefore expect to find that a protein structure in which all the available hydrogen bonds are formed between amide groups will be an energetically stable form in solution. Ambrose and Elliott (1951c) have examined the infra-red spectra of aqueous solutions of proteins in the region of combination bands. In this region it is possible to examine bands which have characteristic frequencies for the folded and for the extended form of chain, without undue interference from water molecules. It is found that the C : O combination frequency of haemoglobin molecules in solution appears to correspond to the folded form of chain observed in the solid state.

The model shown in FIGURE 10 provides the simplest structure for the folded polypeptide and protein in which all available hydrogen bonds are satisfied. Since the publication of the infra-red and x-ray data already described (Ambrose and Hanby, 1949; Ambrose and Elliott, 1951a, b; Bamford, Hanby and Happey, 1951a, b, c) Pauling, Corey and Branson (1951) have proposed an alternative model to account for the experimental data. In this model, the hydrogen bonds form rings within the polypeptide chain, as before, but instead of seven-membered rings, thirteen-membered rings are involved (FIGURE 13).

This model was based on the earlier x-ray diffraction studies of compounds of low molecular weight which contained the amide linkage by Corey (1938) and by Pauling, Corey and Branson (1951). The final structure in its idealized form is an irrational helix, *i.e.* it is a helix which does not repeat itself after an integral number of turns. Although this structure represents an ideal form for the polypeptide chain, with a planar amide group, correct interatomic distances, bond angles and hydrogen-bond lengths, Pauling and Corey (1951a, b) have introduced slight modifications in order to provide some measure of regularity. Such alterations represent only a very slight departure from the configuration corresponding to a minimum of internal energy, while they provide the necessary regularity to account for an x-ray diffraction pattern of the kind observed in synthetic polypeptides and fibrous proteins.

With the helix shown in FIGURE 13, the amide group is planar, as indicated by the previous work on simple molecules containing this group, the hydrogen bonds N—H····O=C are almost linear and the staggered configurations about valency bonds occur. The only difficulty about the structure appears to be a slight overcrowding of the atoms in the centre of the helix. On general grounds we may expect the structure to be very stable. There appear to be few other configurations for a folded polypeptide chain, containing only internal hydrogen bonds, which satisfy all the requirements for an energetically stable form. One other form has been suggested by Pauling, Corey and Branson (1951), which contains larger rings than those shown in FIGURE 13. This structure is also a helix but is much more open than the first form. The empty space which runs down the centre makes it unlikely to be stable, particularly in a solid film, in view of the low density which would be expected. Robinson and Ambrose (1952) have examined many of the possible configurations for the polypeptide chain using the space-filling atomic models described by Hartley and Robinson (1952). They conclude that the only other configuration with internal hydrogen bonds, which is likely to be stable, is the configuration previously proposed by Ambrose and Hanby (1949) as representing the simplest structure which can account for the infra-red dichroism. This model is a modification of that proposed by Huggins (1943) and has also been suggested by Simanouti and Mizushima (1948) on the basis of their studies on hindered rotation in simple molecules.

This model satisfied all the conditions for a stable form, with the exception that the N—H----O=C hydrogen bond deviates from linearity by about $25°$ (VII, $\alpha = 25°$). The hydrogen bond is formed, however, in the direction which meets the lone pair orbital of the oxygen atom. It may therefore be expected to be reasonably stable although not quite so stable as the form which occurs in the helix of Pauling, Corey and Branson.

When we come to consider the known properties of the folded polypeptides in relation to the chain configuration we find that the helix of Pauling, Corey and Branson has many attractive features. This model appears to account in a satisfactory way for many of the reflections in the x-ray diffraction pattern of poly-γ-methyl L-glutamate. The most striking feature is that this model explains the presence of the reflection on or near the meridian corresponding to a spacing of $1·5$ Å (Perutz, 1951); this spacing corresponds to the interval between side chains, measured along the fibre axis as shown in FIGURE 13.

The model also accounts for the very high dichroism shown by this N—H absorption band in poly-γ-benzyl L-glutamate (FIGURE 11). It does not account for the difference between the dichroism of the N—H stretching band (3300 cm^{-1}) and that of the C=O stretching band (1660 cm^{-1}) because in a truly linear hydrogen bond, as it occurs in this model, it would be expected that the N—H and C=O bonds which are parallel should show similar dichroism, as in fact they do show in the β or extended-chain configuration of synthetic polypeptides and Nylon. The type of dichroism observed in FIGURE 11 could be explained in terms of a non-linear hydrogen bond such as occurs in the model of FIGURE 10.

Let us now consider the structures of certain of the naturally occurring fibrous proteins.

271

Silk Fibroin

The structure of silk fibroin was first investigated by Meyer and Mark (1928b) using x-ray diffraction, and it was this work which provided the first real evidence for the existence of long polypeptide chains in proteins. They proposed a structure in which the chains were arranged in an extended form similar to IV with the chains lying parallel to the fibre axis. The importance of hydrogen bonds had not been appreciated at that date. The structure with inter-chain hydrogen bonds shown in FIGURE 14 was proposed by Astbury and Street (1931)

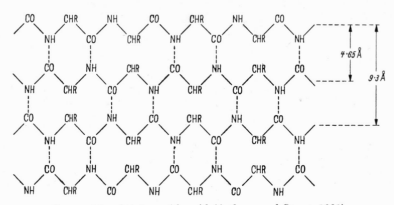

FIGURE 14. *β*-Polypeptide grid (Astbury and Street, 1931)

as a model for the form of keratin obtained on stretching wool in steam. Studies of silk fibroin and feather keratin using polarized infra-red radiation (Ambrose and Elliott, 1951b) have confirmed the existence of this type of structure in both these materials. The repeat of pattern along the fibre axis in the case of the naturally occurring form of *β*-keratin (feather) is 6·2—6·4 Å or a multiple of this interval, whereas in silk the repeat is 7·04 Å. It has been pointed out by Pauling and Corey that the inter-bond distances and other data obtained with single molecules suggest that for an extended polypeptide chain the repeat of pattern would be expected to have a value of 7·24 Å. This value is almost realized in silk and polyglycine.

It seems reasonable to suggest that this shortening of the repeat of pattern which occurs in swan quill may be a consequence of a slight departure from the perfect extended form, *e.g.* free rotation about the bonds joining the peptides to the asymmetric carbon atom (see XVII) could produce this effect. This would represent a departure from the equilibrium position for a staggered form, but the energy of interaction between protein side chains might easily compensate for this change. However, Pauling and Corey (1951, 1953) have suggested alternative configurations for *β*-keratin which they have called the pleated sheet (1951) and rippled sheet (1953) structures. The rippled sheet structure is shown in FIGURE 15. As in the case of the extended chain and grid of Astbury and Street, the polypeptide chains are linked by hydrogen bonds which lie at right angles to the chain axis. This arrangement is in accordance with the experimental data on the infra-red dichroism (Ambrose and Elliott). But the polypeptide chain itself is arranged in a slightly folded configuration, while still satisfying the requirements for a planar amide group.

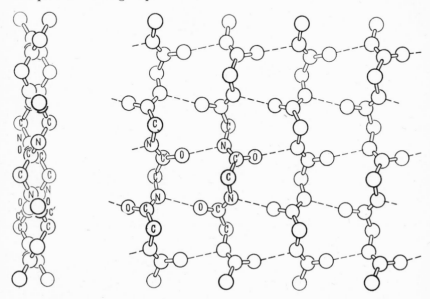

FIGURE 15.   Rippled-sheet structure for β-keratin (Pauling and Corey, 1953)

Pauling and Corey (1953) proposed the rippled sheet structure (repeat 6·5 Å; FIGURE 15) as a model for β-keratin, with the polypeptide chains lying in a parallel arrangement. An alternative form (repeat 7·0 Å), with an antiparallel arrangement, is suggested for silk. It must be pointed out, however, that the x-ray diffraction patterns of synthetic polypeptides such as polyalanine (Bamford, Brown, Elliott, Hanby and Trotter, 1953) show a periodicity along the fibre axis which has a value (6·88 Å) intermediate between that corresponding to the fully extended chain of silk (7·04 Å) and that of the rippled sheet (6·5 Å) of Pauling and Corey (1953).

Keratin and Myosin
It was mentioned previously that the x-ray diffraction pattern due to keratin fibres shows a reflection on or near the meridian due to reflecting planes at intervals of 5·1 Å. This pattern changes to a value corresponding to 6·2—6·6 Å when the fibre is stretched in steam. This change has been called the $\alpha \longrightarrow \beta$ transformation by Astbury. It has

already been pointed out that remarkably similar effects can be obtained in certain synthetic polypeptides and it has also been possible to follow the $\alpha \longrightarrow \beta$ transformation in keratin by studying the infra-red dichroism (Ambrose and Elliott, 1951b; Darmon and Rudall, 1950). As already mentioned, the effects are qualitatively remarkably similar to those observed in the synthetic polypeptides shown in FIGURE 11. The effects are quantitatively much less marked, which is perhaps not surprising when it is remembered that keratin is a complex mixture of proteins secreted by dying cells. Keratin contains a high proportion of amorphous material. The x-ray diffraction pattern is due to the relatively small proportion of crystalline material, whereas both the amorphous and crystalline material give rise to infra-red absorption.

Astbury and Dickinson (1940) were able to show that myosin, the fibrous protein of muscle, will also give an x-ray diffraction pattern when prepared as an orientated film. This pattern is similar in many respects to that obtained with wool keratin, and these authors suggested that the polypeptide chain was folded in a similar way. The infra-red dichroism of such films is also similar to that obtained with folded synthetic polypeptides and ' α '-keratin.

The model for ' α '-keratin proposed by Astbury and Bell (1941) accounted in a satisfactory way for the characteristic meridian reflection corresponding to a periodicity at $5 \cdot 1$ Å along the fibre axis in ' α '-keratin. A reflection due to a periodicity at $1 \cdot 5$ Å is also observed in ' α '-keratin (MacArthur, 1943; Perutz, 1949). At first sight these two periodicities in the molecules appear to be irreconcilable and this has proved one of the chief obstacles for the interpretation in terms of the helix of Pauling, Corey and Branson (1951).

In order to overcome this difficulty Pauling and Corey (1952) have suggested that the primary helix is again coiled in the form of a helix of much longer pitch. Groups of helices are then woven together to produce a structure like a coil of rope. In this way true periodicities corresponding to $5 \cdot 1$ Å and $1 \cdot 5$ Å can be achieved.

With regard to the interpretation in terms of the model shown in FIGURE 10, the true repeat of pattern in this case is $5 \cdot 1$—$5 \cdot 3$ Å. (It would be expected that the maximum reflection would occur at half this distance $2 \cdot 6$ Å although under certain packing conditions this may not be the case.) The reflection at $1 \cdot 5$ Å is however not explained. Ambrose (1951, unpublished observations) pointed out that the fold of FIGURE 10 might explain the presence of the two periodicities in the diffraction pattern if the $5 \cdot 1$ Å reflection were due to a genuine pattern in the protein chain, while the $1 \cdot 5$ Å repeat was due to some packing effect between molecules. According to the model of Pauling and Corey, the $1 \cdot 5$ Å repeat is considered to be due to the pattern in the chain while the $5 \cdot 1$ Å repeat is looked upon as a packing effect.

Both the 5·1 Å and 1·5 Å periodicities have been observed in myosin and in fresh muscle fibres (Huxley, 1953). An interpretation in terms of the model of Pauling, Corey and Branson has presented considerable difficulties. It is generally agreed that the contractile properties of muscle fibres are due to shortening of the polypeptide chains, some-what as rubber chains will contract to a randomly coiled condition, except that in muscle the contraction appears to be due to a more regular folding.

The helix of FIGURE 13 is a comparatively rigid and rod-like structure. It cannot therefore account for the properties of muscle fibres. It has been pointed out that the fold shown in FIGURE 10 is quite flexible in a plane at right angles to the plane of the paper, while still preserving the internal hydrogen bonds. It could therefore account for the mobility of the myosin molecules.

Collagen

The x-ray diffraction pattern due to collagen fibres, such as the tendon of a rat's tail, differs both from the pattern produced by the extended polypeptide chain of silk and from the folded form of α-keratin. The periodicity along the fibre axis is equal to 2·86 Å (Hertzog and Jancke, 1920). Astbury pointed out that this difference was probably due to the presence of a folded form which differed from that of α-keratin. This interpretation has been confirmed by Ambrose and Elliott (1951b) who have shown that collagen fibres possess a characteristic infra-red dichroism which differs from that observed both with the extended chain and with α-keratin. It is generally agreed that this difference is due to the high proportion of proline residues (at least one-fifth). The five-membered ring of proline, which is attached to the main polypeptide chain, is planar (XXI), and when the amide group is also considered to be planar it can be shown with the help of atomic models

$$\text{XXI} \qquad \begin{array}{c} \overset{CH_2}{\diagup \quad \diagdown} \\ CH_2 \qquad CH_2 \\ \diagdown \qquad \diagup \\ -\underset{H}{\overset{|}{C}} - N - \end{array}$$

that it is impossible to pull the polypeptide chain into the fully extended form (Robinson and Ambrose, 1952). A proline residue also affects the hydrogen-bond formation in the chain because the hydrogen atom which normally bonds to the C:O group is absent. The absence of this bond will provide increased flexibility at this point.

An examination of the infra-red dichroism of this material suggests that we are dealing with a structure containing hydrogen bonds between chains, rather similar to the β form of FIGURE 14. But the configuration of the amide group is modified, presumably as a result of the kinking produced by the proline residues. A number of models have been suggested (Astbury, 1940; Huggins, 1943; Ambrose and

Elliott, 1951b; Pauling and Corey, 1951d; Randall, Frazer and North, 1953), but none of them appears to account in a completely satisfactory way for all the physico-chemical, x-ray and spectroscopic data, as for example the infra-red combination spectrum band. We are probably dealing with a compromise structure, as in the rubber molecule described above, in which a nice balance has been produced between hydrogen bonds and the flexibility provided by the proline hinges.

Globular Proteins

It had been fairly generally recognized for a number of years that fibrous proteins consisted of long-chain polypeptides, but this type of structure had not been accepted as fundamental for globular proteins. In fact the compact structure which in many cases gave an almost spherical form to these molecules as determined by ultra-centrifuge and diffusion studies, provided no evidence in favour of such a structure. For this reason Wrinch (1937) proposed a cyclol structure for these materials, in which the peptide group was transformed into a lactam form, which then provided a system of interlocking six-membered rings upon the surface of a polyhedron. The infra-red spectra of proteins, however, indicate the presence of a hydrogen-bonded peptide structure and do not suggest the presence of a lactam (Buswell, Deitz and Rodebush, 1937). Astbury, Dickinson and Bailey (1935) were the first to show that globular proteins could be transformed by a denaturation process into fibrous material, which showed certain diffuse x-ray reflections similar to those observed in stretched (β) keratin, and they were led to suggest that the globular proteins in their native state consisted of coiled-up polypeptide chains. The possibility could not be ruled out, however, that the polypeptide chains were produced by some chemical rearrangement which occurred when the globular protein was denatured, although the infra-red spectra certainly indicated the presence of peptide bonds in the native state (Buswell, Deitz and Rodebush, 1937).

X-ray diffraction studies of crystalline proteins finally provided the evidence that globular proteins do in fact consist of folded long-chain molecules. The early work of Crowfoot (1938) on crystalline insulin had shown that interatomic distances rather similar to those observed in fibrous proteins could also be observed in the Patterson vector synthesis of insulin. There is no space to describe the Patterson synthesis here, but it may be pointed out that it enables interatomic distances to be determined when the phases of the atomic parameters are not known, and it can provide valuable preliminary information about a crystal structure. This method was applied to the case of horse methaemoglobin by Perutz (1949). It indicated that regions of high electron density were running parallel to the a-axis of the crystal and that these regions were separated from each other by a distance of

9·8 Å. Also that they appeared to be packed in an almost hexagonal array. In addition a periodicity could be observed along the length of the rods at intervals of 5·1 Å. This result strongly suggested the presence of parallel polypeptide chains in the molecule in which the individual chains were folded in a manner similar to that which occurs in α-keratin. Supporting evidence for this structure has been obtained by Elliott and Ambrose (1950) who have found that the infra-red dichroism associated with an absorption band due to the N·H bond of the polypeptide chain shows a dichroic effect similar to that observed with α-keratin if the *a*-axis of the crystal is considered to correspond to the fibre axis in keratin.

Carlisle and Scouloudi (1951) have examined crystals of ribonuclease and they also find that rods of vector density which lie parallel, in this case, to the β-axis of the crystal can be observed. Here again a periodicity at 5 Å along the rods can be detected. There are however certain differences in the lateral packing of the rods, as compared with haemoglobin. Polarized infra-red studies of this material have given results which are in reasonable agreement with those observed by the x-ray method (Elliott, 1952).

Perutz (1949) suggested that the chain configuration in the globular proteins might be similar to that of the α-type of fibrous protein. Evidence in favour of the helix has been provided by Pauling and Corey (1951e) and by Riley and Arndt (1952). Bragg, Kendrew and Perutz (1950) have considered the various possible chain configurations which could fit the structures of horse methaemoglobin and met-myoglobin, which also appear to possess a similar structure (Kendrew and Perutz, 1949).

Carlisle, Scouloudi and Spier (1953) considered that the α-helix could not be reconciled with the diffraction pattern of ribonuclease and favoured a structure more of the type shown in FIGURE 10. It has become clear that in addition to the primary or α-fold of the polypeptide chain in globular proteins, a larger scale secondary folding must also take place because the length of the polypeptide chain is greater than the length of the molecule both in haemoglobin and in ribonuclease. We may therefore refer to the primary fold of the polypeptide chain, which is brought about by intra-chain hydrogen bonds, and of the secondary fold which leads to the formation of a globular molecule. The secondary folding appears to be produced by side-chain interactions.

The existence of the secondary folds presents a problem from the point of view of the helix of Pauling, Corey and Branson, since this is a structure consisting of rigid columns which cannot bend to any appreciable extent. If the helix does exist in globular proteins, unfolding with rupture of hydrogen bonds must occur at each ' secondary bend '. It has been suggested that the bending might occur where ' proline hinges ' occur in the chain, but in the case of haemoglobin there do not appear to be sufficient hinges to account for the number of loops required. The structure shown in Figure 10 is flexible in a plane at right angles to the paper, and a satisfactory model can be constructed in which the secondary folds are formed while maintaining a planar amide group, staggered positions about valency bonds and all peptide hydrogen bonds satisfied (Robinson and Ambrose, 1952).

In conclusion it may be said that should the Pauling, Corey and Branson helix prove to be the energetically stable form for the ' α ' fold it is distinctly possible that the fold of Figure 10 may arise where a chain configuration of increased flexibility is required.

General Conclusions Concerning the Structure of Proteins

1. A stable configuration for the polypeptide chain exists, in which the chain is a fully extended planar zigzag. In this structure the hydrogen bonds between the peptide N—H and C=O groups are formed between the chains (inter-chain), and lie at right angles to the chain axis. The repeat of pattern along the fibre axis is $7 \cdot 2$ Å $(2 \times 3 \cdot 6$ Å$)$.

2. When side chains of any appreciable size are attached to the asymmetric carbon atoms (R—C—H) the chain tends to shorten. This occurs for example in β-keratin (repeats $2 \times 3 \cdot 1$ Å). There may be a departure from a genuine staggered form or the chain may assume a pleated sheet structure. The hydrogen bonds are inter-chain as in *1*. The presence of proline rings (XXI) tends to encourage shortening of the chain as in collagen (repeat $n \times 2 \cdot 86$ Å).

3. When the amino-acid side chains are large, the chain passes over into a configuration in which the hydrogen bonds (N—H····O=C) are now formed entirely within a single polypeptide chain (intra-chain) with internal thirteen-membered or seven-membered rings. The structure is probably a helix.

4. The intra-chain bonded form represents a mobile chain which has little attraction for other chains. It is therefore the stable form in solution and appears to occur in globular proteins. In the globular proteins a further stage of folding (secondary folding) of the primarily folded chain takes place, leading to a highly compact structure.

POLYMERS CONTAINING RING STRUCTURES IN THE MAIN CHAIN

The introduction of ring structures, closed by primary valency bonds, will clearly restrict the number of possible configurations for the molecule. In the case of aromatic ring systems the structures are almost invariably planar and variations in the configuration can only arise as a result of rotation about the single-bond linkages which join the rings together. Where saturated ring systems occur, as for example, in the polysaccharides, conformational changes in the ring systems can also take place, like the boat–chair transformation of *cyclo*-hexane (see Chapter 2).

The number of polymers, containing ring systems, which have been thoroughly investigated by physical methods is comparatively small although the chemical constitutions of many of these polymers are known. In this chapter we shall confine ourselves to an examination of a few polysaccharides, such as cellulose, alginic acid and chitin; the structure of these materials has been investigated in part by x-ray and by infra-red methods and the general conclusions will apply to studies of other polymers of this type.

Cellulose

Haworth (1928) showed, by chemical methods, that cellulose consists of 1β:4-linked-glucopyranoside units (XXII). Meyer and Mark

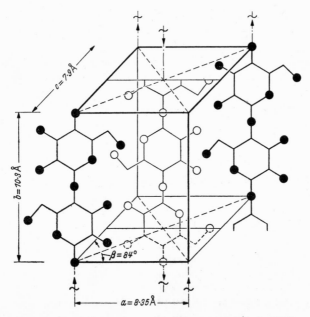

XXII

(1928) examined the x-ray fibre diagram of native cellulose and showed that it belongs to the space group $P\,2_1$; they suggested a monoclinic unit cell for this polymer. This space group, when combined with evidence about the repeat of pattern along the fibre

FIGURE 16. Cellulose structure (Meyer and Misch, 1937): rings shown in outline; circles indicate oxygen atoms

279

axis (10·2 Å), leads to the conclusion that we are dealing with a ribbon-like molecule. Meyer and Mark originally suggested that all the chains should lie parallel to each other, since it might be expected that the fibres would grow in this way. Meyer showed that cellulose II (precipitated with sodium hydroxide) gives the same diffraction pattern as native cellulose. It did not seem likely that all the polymer chains would point in the same direction when precipitated from solution and the structure shown in FIGURE 16 was finally suggested. Certain of the characteristic features of polysaccharides can be distinguished in this structure. Hydrogen bonds are formed between the hydroxyl groups of neighbouring molecules (XXIII), as is shown by the frequency of the hydroxyl absorption bands in the infra-red spectrum. These bonds contribute towards the strength and toughness of cellulose fibres.

The ether linkage (—O—) between the sugar rings is so arranged as to give the maximum possible length for the polymer chain (10·2 Å for two pyranoside rings).

Alginic Acid

This polymer has been identified as polymannuronic acid (XXIV), consisting of 1β:4-linked mannopyranosuronic acid units

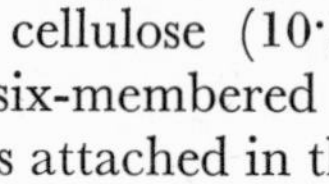

XXIII 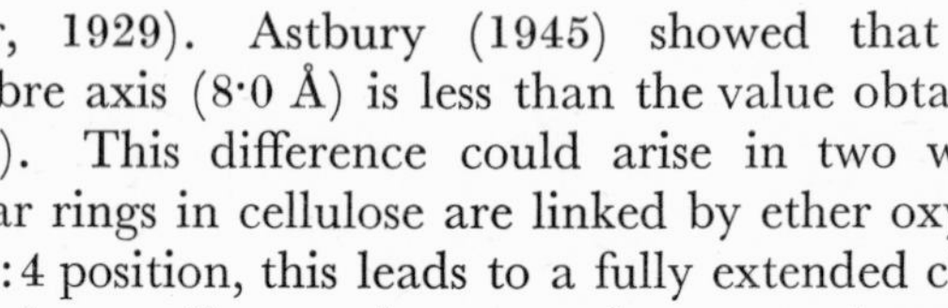   XXIV

(Nelson and Cretcher, 1929). Astbury (1945) showed that the periodicity along the fibre axis (8·0 Å) is less than the value obtained with cellulose (10·3 Å). This difference could arise in two ways. The six-membered sugar rings in cellulose are linked by ether oxygen atoms attached in the 1:4 position, this leads to a fully extended chain structure with the maximum distance between the sugar rings. If linking occurs in a 1:3 or 1:2 position a polymer will be produced with a shorter periodicity. Alternatively, rotation of the sugar rings about the ether linkage could lead to a shortened chain. It is in fact considered that the latter interpretation is correct in the case of alginic acid (Astbury, 1945).

Chitin

Chitin (polyglucosamine; XXV) is of interest because it produces a characteristic x-ray diffraction pattern and the structure has been worked out by Meyer and Pankow (1935). A more recent investigation has been made by Darmon and Rudall (1950) using both x-ray and polarized infra-red methods. Since *N*-acetylhexosamines are prominent constituents of many important polysaccharides such as hyaluronic acid, chondroitin and mucoitin sulphates, specific pneumococcus polysaccharides, blood group A substance and ovomucoid,

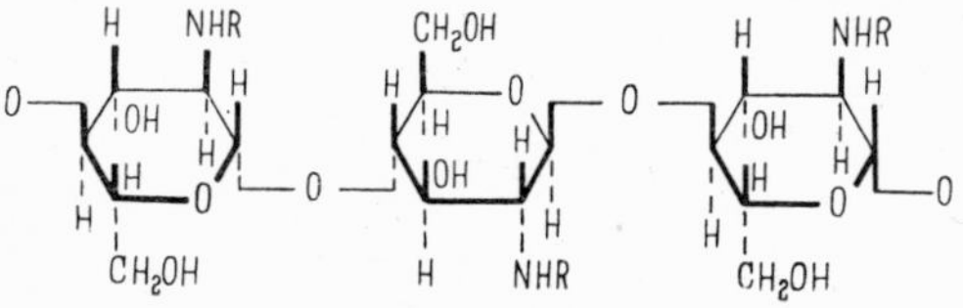

XXV

an understanding of the effects of the —NH—CO— side chains is of considerable importance. The structure proposed by Darmon and Rudall (FIGURE 17) is a modification of that suggested by Meyer and Pankow. In this structure —N—H···O=C hydrogen bonds are formed between the side chains and the infra-red dichroism suggests

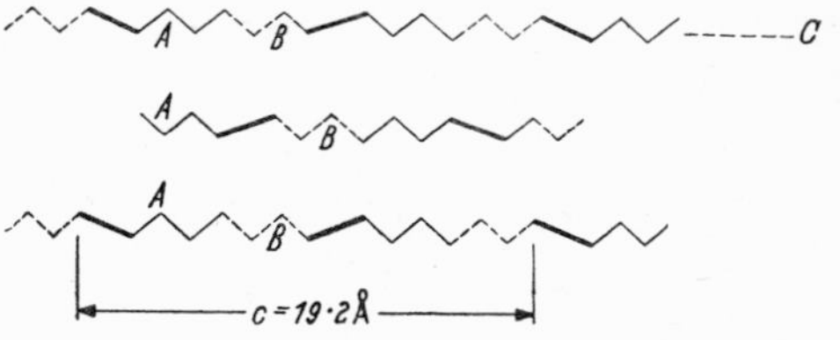

FIGURE 17. Chitin chains (Darmon and Rudall, 1950): (a) side view; (b) end-on view, heavy lines—rings, thin lines—side-chains *A* [in (a)], dashed lines—side-chains *B* [in (a)]

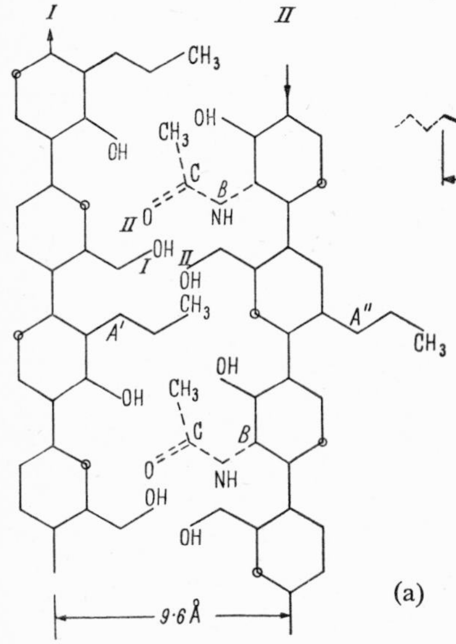

that not only are the hydrogen bonds formed at right angles to the chain axis but that the whole plane of the amide group lies at right angles to the main chain axis. They also concluded that some of the hydrogen bonds occur between the amide carbonyl and the hydroxyl groups of the sugar. The structure appears to arrange itself so that as many of the hydrogen bonds as possible are satisfied, while allowing a reasonably close packing of both the main chains and the side chains; a few of the N—H hydrogen bonds are not satisfied.

Other Polysaccharides

A great variety of sugar rings has been detected in various biological materials. These include chondroitin sulphuric acid (XXVI: Meyer, Odier and Sigrist, 1948), heparin with glucuronic and glucosamine

XXVI

residues bearing the group —NHSO₃H (Charles and Todd, 1940) human tubercle polysaccharides with branched chains containing mannose, arabinose, rhamnose and an aminosugar (Haworth, Kent and Stacey, 1948) *etc.* Where the polymer is called upon to act as a fibrous structural element, a straight chain linked in the 1:4 position on the sugar generally occurs (cellulose, chitin). When a compact storage material is required a branched-chain structure may be present, as in the amylopectin of starch (Meyer, Wertheim and Bernfeld, 1940), while great variations in the polymer configuration appear to occur in the case of the polysaccharides, which are associated with protein and show serological specificity. (For a general review of polysaccharide chemistry, see Whistler and Smart, 1953.)

It is hoped that the account given in this chapter has shown that certain of the governing principles which determine the stereochemistry of compounds of high molecular weight are beginning to become clear. These materials provide the fundamental building units of all biological systems and one is certainly led to adopt an attitude of reverence, when it is seen that such apparently simple principles provide the basis for the building of the beautiful and intricate structures observed in nature.

REFERENCES

Ambrose, E. J. and Elliott, A. (1951 a, b, c) *Proc. roy. Soc. A* **205,** 47; **206,** 206; **208,** 75
— — and Temple, R. B. (1949a) *Nature, Lond.* **163,** 859; (1949b) *Proc. roy. Soc. A* **199,** 183
— and Hanby, W. E. (1949) *Nature, Lond.* **163,** 483
Astbury, W. T. (1940) *J. inter. Soc. Leath. Chem.* **24,** 69; (1945) *Nature, Lond.* **155,** 667
— and Bell, F. O. (1941) *Nature, Lond.* **147,** 696
— Dalgliesh, C. E., Darmon, S. E. and Sutherland, G. B. B. M. (1948) *ibid* **162,** 596
— and Dickinson, S. (1940) *Proc. roy. Soc. B* **129,** 307
— — and Bailey, K. (1935) *Biochem. J.* **29,** 2351
— and Street, A. (1931) *Phil. Trans. A* **230,** 75
— and Woods, H. J. (1933) *ibid A* **232,** 333

Bamford, C. H., Brown, L., Elliott, A., Hanby. W. E. and Trotter, I. F. (1953) *Nature, Lond.* **171,** 1149
— Hanby, W. E. and Happey, F. (1949 a, b) *ibid* **164,** 138, 751; (1951 a, b) *Proc. roy. Soc. A* **205,** 30; **206,** 407
Bartholomé, E. and Karweil, J. (1937) *Naturwissenschaften* **25,** 476
Beach, J. Y. and Turkevich, A. (1939) *J. Amer. chem. Soc.* **61,** 303
Bernal, J. D. and Crowfoot, D. (1933) *Nature, Lond.* **133,** 794
Bragg, L., Kendrew, J. C. and Perutz, M. F. (1950) *Proc. roy. Soc. A* **203,** 321
Bunn, C. W. (1939) *Trans. Faraday Soc.* **35,** 482; (1942a, b) *Proc. roy. Soc. A.* **180,** 40, 67
— and Garner, E. V. (1947) *ibid A* **189,** 39
Buswell, A. M., Deitz, V. and Rodebush, W. H. (1937) *J. chem. Phys.* **5,** 84, 501
Carlisle, C. H., Scouloudi, H. and Spier, S. (1953) *Proc. roy. Soc. B* **141,** 85
— — (1951) *Proc. roy. Soc. A* **207,** 496
Charles, A. F. and Todd, A. R. (1940) *Biochem. J.* **34,** 112
Condon, E. U., Altar, W. and Eyring, H. (1937) *J. chem. Phys.* **5,** 753
Corey, R. B. (1938) *J. Amer. chem. Soc.* **60,** 1598
— and Pauling, L. (1953) *Proc. roy. Soc. B* **141,** 10
Crowfoot, D. (1938) *Proc. roy. Soc. A* **164,** 580
Darmon, S. E. and Rudall, K. M. (1950) *Disc. Faraday Soc.* **9,** 251
Erhardt, F. (1932) *Phys. Z.* **33,** 605
Elliott, A. (1952) *Proc. roy. Soc. A* **211,** 490
— and Ambrose, E. J. (1950) *Disc. Faraday Soc.* **9,** 246
— — and Temple, R. B. (1948) *J. chem. Phys.* **16,** 877
Fuller, C. S., Frosch, C. J. and Pape, N. R. (1940) *J. Amer. chem. Soc.* **62,** 1905
Hanby, W. E., Waley, S. G. and Watson, J. (1950) *J. chem. Soc.* 3239 (Appendix by Ambrose, E. J.)
Hartley, G. S. and Robinson, C. (1952) *Trans. Faraday Soc.* **48,** 847
Haworth, W. N. (1928) *Helv. chim. acta* **11,** 534
— Kent, P. W. and Stacey, M. (1948) *J. chem. Soc.*, 1211, 1220
Hertzog, R. O. and Jancke, W. (1920) *Ber. dtsch. chem. Ges.* **53,** 2162
Huggins, M. L. (1943) *Chem. Rev.* **32,** 195
Huxley, H. E. (1953) *Proc. roy. Soc. B* **141,** 59
Ingold, C. K. (1953) *Structure and Mechanism in Organic Chemistry* pp. 52–54, London, Bell
Katz, J. R. (1925) *Naturwissenschaften,* **13,** 410
Kendrew, J. C. and Perutz, M. F. (1949) in *Haemoglobin* (Symposium, Cambridge, 1948), p. 161, ed. F. J. W. Roughton and J. C. Kendrew, London, Butterworths
Kirkwood, J. G. (1937) *J. chem. Phys.* **5,** 479
Lennard-Jones, J. and Pople, J. A. (1951) *Proc. roy. Soc. A* **205,** 155
Lotmar, W. and Meyer, K. H. (1936) *Mh. Chem.* **69,** 115
Low, B. M. (1953) in *The Proteins,* vol. 1, part *A*, p. 235, ed. Neurath, H. and Bailey, K., New York, Academic Press
Lunde, G., Heen, E. and Oy, E. (1938) *Kolloidzschr.* **83,** 196
MacArthur, I. (1943) *Nature, Lond.* **152,** 38
Mark, H. and von Susich, G. (1928) *Kolloidzschr.* **46,** 11
Meyer, K. H. (1937) *Ber. dtsch. chem. Ges.* **70,** 266
— and Mark, H. (1928a, b) *ibid* **61,** 593, 1932
— and Misch, L. (1937) *Helv. chim. acta* **20,** 232
— Odier, M. E. and Siegrist, A. E. (1948) *ibid* **31,** 1400
— and Pankow, G. W. (1935) *ibid* **18,** 589
— Wertheim, M. and Bernfeld, P. (1940) *ibid* **23,** 865
Mizushima, S. *et al* (1942–44) *Sci Papers Inst. phys. chem. Res. Tokyo.* **39,** 396, 401; **40,** 87, 100, 425; **42,** 1, 5, 27, 51

Müller, A. (1928) *Proc. roy. Soc. A* **120,** 437
Nelson, W. L. and Cretcher, L. H. (1929) *J. Amer. chem. Soc.* **51,** 1914
Neurath, H. (1940) *J. phys. Chem.* **44,** 296
Pauling, L. and Brockway, L. O. (1937) *ibid* **59,** 1223
— and Corey, R. B. (1951a–g) *Proc. nat. Acad. Sci. Wash.* **37,** 235, 241, 251, 256, 261, 272, 282; (1952) *Nature, Lond.* **169,** 494; (1953) *Proc. nat. Acad. Sci. Wash.* **39,** 253
— — and Branson, H. (1951) *ibid* **37,** 205
Perutz, M. F. (1949) *Proc. roy. Soc. A* **195,** 474; (1951) *Nature, Lond.* **167,** 1053
Randall, J. T., Frazer, R. D. B. and North, A. C. T. (1953) *Proc. roy. Soc. B* **141,** 62
Richards, R. E. and Thompson, H. W. (1947) *J. chem. Soc.* 1248
Riley, D. P. and Arndt, U. W. (1952) *Nature, Lond.* **169,** 138
Robinson, C. and Ambrose, E. J. (1951) *Trans. Faraday Soc.* **48,** 854
— and Bott, M. J. (1951) *Nature, Lond.* **168,** 325
Simanouti, T. and Mizushima, S. (1948) *Bull. chem. Soc. Japan* **21,** 1
Whistler, R. L. and Smart, C. L. (1953) *Polysaccharide Chemistry*, New York, Academic Press
Wrinch, D. (1937) *Proc. roy. Soc. A* **161,** 505

8

STEREOSPECIFICITY OF ENZYME REACTIONS

V. P. Whittaker

STEREOCHEMICAL specificity, or stereospecificity, as usually defined, refers to the ability of an enzyme to attack one of a pair of stereoisomers selectively. This phenomenon has been known for almost a century; in addition to its theoretical interest, it has been of great value in establishing the configuration of stereoisomers and in their preparation and resolution.

When biological constituents are capable of existing in more than one stereoisomeric form, these forms usually occur separately and some may not exist as natural products at all. The preservation of one particular stereoisomeric configuration during the multitudinous interconversions which are continually taking place as a result of cellular metabolism is due to this selective action of enzymes. All modern theories of enzyme action start from the assumption that the enzyme forms with the compound upon which it acts—its substrate— an enzyme–substrate complex which subsequently breaks down to give free enzyme and the products of the enzyme reaction. The ability of the enzyme to distinguish between stereoisomers implies a complementary stereoisomerism in the combining points, or active centres, of the enzyme surface. This idea is not difficult to accept when we remember that, chemically, enzymes are proteins, and are thus built up largely of amino-acids having an L-configuration.

Recent studies have shown that stereochemical considerations may enter into enzyme reactions in which the substrate does not itself exhibit stereoisomerism. For example, the cholinesterase of nervous tissue and red cells rapidly hydrolyses 3 : 3-dimethylbutyl acetate (I).

$$CH_3-\underset{\underset{CH_3}{|}}{\overset{\overset{CH_3}{|}}{C}}-CH_2 \cdot CH_2 \cdot O \cdot CO \cdot CH_3 \qquad CH_3-\underset{\underset{CH_3}{|}}{\overset{\overset{CH_3}{|}}{N^+}}-CH_2 \cdot CH_2 \cdot O \cdot CO \cdot CH_3$$

$$I \qquad\qquad\qquad II$$

This compound may be regarded as the carbon analogue of the natural substrate of the enzyme, acetylcholine* (II), since it contains an

* For the sake of simplicity the formulae of quaternary ammonium cations are shown without an accompanying anion.

uncharged quaternary carbon atom in place of the positively charged nitrogen atom of the acetylcholine ion. It has little in common, physically or chemically, with acetylcholine, except the possession of an acetyl group and an almost identical molecular shape. Examples such as this show that the shape of the substrate molecule as a whole is of prime importance in determining whether an enzyme–substrate complex can be formed.

Recent work has further suggested that if the over-all requirements of molecular shape and correct orientation of binding groups are met, considerable latitude may be tolerated in the chemical composition of the link actually severed or even in the nature of the reaction catalysed. Thus proteases attack not only peptide links but also ester links in esters of configuration similar to those of the parent peptides. Certain carboxylic esterases hydrolyse not only carboxylic esters but also structurally analogous phosphate esters; others catalyse the synthesis of hydroxamic acids from carboxylic esters and free hydroxylamine.

Stereospecificity may thus be defined in the widest sense as all those aspects of specificity which have to do with the effect of the shape of the substrate molecule as a determining factor in specificity in contrast to effects attributable to the presence or reactivity of particular atoms or groups.

Although extensive specificity studies have been made with only a few enzymes, the recent literature on this subject is very large. No attempt will therefore be made to give a comprehensive account of modern work ; attention will instead be focused on a few examples which illustrate the broadened concept of stereospecificity just referred to. Whenever possible, reference will be made to review articles which the reader may consult for further information, rather than to the original literature.

EXAMPLES OF STEREOSPECIFICITY

β-D-Glucosidase

Enzymes which have carbohydrates and their derivatives as substrates seem invariably to exhibit stereospecificity, though the degree of specificity varies from enzyme to enzyme. One of these, the β-D-gluco-sidase of almonds, has been very fully investigated in recent years, notably by Helferich, Pigman, Veibel and their co-workers (cf Helferich, 1938 ; Pigman, 1944; Pigman and Goepp, 1948; Veibel, 1950).

β-D-Glucosidase catalyses the hydrolysis of β-D-glucosides to D-glucose and the aglucon. Its specificity may be discussed in terms of structure III, taking first the ring, then group X, and finally the aglucon group R.

286

Ring specificity—The available evidence indicates that β-glucosidase is absolutely specific for the pyranose ring system shown in structure III with free hydroxyls in positions 2, 3 and 4. Thus although crude almond emulsin hydrolyses N-acetyl-β-D-glucosaminides (III, X = CH_2OH, NHAc in place of hydroxyl at C-2) α-D-mannosides and α- and

β-D-*glucoside type*	α-D-*mannoside type*	β-D-*galactoside type*	α-D-*galactoside type*
III	IV	V	VI

Vertical strokes in these Haworth-type formulae indicate hydroxyl groups unless otherwise stated.

β-D-galactosides (IV–VI, X = CH_2OH), the activity towards the glucosaminides and α-galactosides is eliminated by a moderate (10–16 fold) degree of purification, while the α-mannosidase activity is markedly more heat stable. This leaves only inversion at C-4 to be considered. Gottschalk (1950) has summarized the reasons for thinking that this is not a permissible deviation from structure III, in spite of the fact that β-glucosidase and β-galactosidase activities have not so far been separated. These are the very varying ratios of β-galactosidase to β-glucosidase activity in emulsins from related species, differential inhibition of the two activities by D-glucose and D-galactose, the different effects of pH on them, and the widely different extent to which the replacement of the CH_2OH group of the hexoside molecule by H affects the rate of hydrolysis in the two series of glycosides.

The need for free hydroxyls in positions 2, 3 and 4 is shown by the fact that phenyl 3-O-methyl- and phenyl 2 : 4 : 6-tri-O-methyl β-glucosides and the 2-, 3- and 4-toluene-p-sulphonyl derivatives of vanillin β-glucoside are not attacked.

It is interesting that phenyl 2-deoxy-α-D-glucoside, a compound related to both α-mannosides and α-glucosides, is slowly hydrolysed by emulsin. The stability of this activity to heat shows that the α-mannosidase is responsible. Evidently replacement of the C-2 hydroxyl of the mannose ring by H is compatible with enzyme activity. Unfortunately comparable studies with the β-isomer have not been made, so it is not known if β-glucosidase activity is also compatible with this type of modification of the pyranose ring.

Group X—Considerable variations in the group X are compatible with β-glucosidase activity. The most easily hydrolysed compounds appear, indeed, to be those in which X is CH_3 instead of CH_2OH *i.e.* the 6-deoxyglucosides. X may also be H, as there is good evidence that the pentosidase activity of emulsin is not due to specific pentosidases.

An onizable group in this position adversely affects hydrolysis; thus 6-amino-6-deoxyglucosides $(X = CH_2NH_2)$ are only very slowly hydrolysed, whilst β-glucosuronidic acids, commonly called ' glucuro-nides ', in which $X = CO_2H$, are attacked by crude emulsin, but this activity disappears on purification, and must be attributed to a separate β-glucuronidase.

Helferich, Grünler and Gnüchtel (1937) have studied the effect of the size of X on rate of hydrolysis in two series of 6-substituted β-gluco-sides. A good correlation was found between the ' enzyme efficiency ' (for explanation see the legend to FIGURE 1) and the size of the group as measured by Biltz's (1930) molecular volumes, the efficiency falling markedly as the molecular volume increases. A less impressive correlation results if modern values for the van der Waals' radii of the groups are substituted for the Biltz molecular volumes. Nevertheless, it remains true that the enzyme is relatively tolerant of variations in X and these appear to exert mainly a steric effect. Other examples of the effect of size are the very slow rates of hydrolysis of phenyl D-*manno*-β-D-*galacto*heptoside (III, $X = CHOH \cdot CH_2OH$, $R = Ph$) and populin (6-benzoylsalicin; III, $X = CH_2O \cdot CO \cdot C_6H_5$, $R = o\text{-}C_6H_4 \cdot CH_2OH$).

The aglucon group R—The degree of permitted variation in R is even greater than X; it may be an alkyl or aryl group or another sugar. The link between the aglucon and the glucose ring must however be through oxygen, since phenyl β-thioglucoside is not hydrolysed.

As judged by ' enzyme efficiency ' values, aglucons comprising a benzene ring bearing an aldehyde group, like vanillin (4-hydroxy-3-methoxybenzaldehyde) form the most readily hydrolysed glucosides. Aglucons consisting of a second sugar residue are split off more slowly. The lower *n*-alkyl glucosides are also attacked quite slowly, but with increasing chain length, the rate increases till at *n*-heptyl, a rate comparable to that of many substituted phenyl glucosides is attained. Thereafter the rate declines. Chain branching, as in the *tert.*-alkyl glucosides, reduces the rate of hydrolysis, though the glucosides retain a considerable affinity for the enzyme (Veibel, 1950).

Although attempts have been made, notably by Pigman (1944), to generalize about the influence of aglucon structure on the enzymic rate of hydrolysis of β-glucosides, the considerable mass of data does not fall into any simple pattern. This may in part be due to the use of first-order constants for measuring the hydrolysability of a glucoside (the limited value of first-order constants in specificity studies has frequently been pointed out; for a recent discussion see Neurath and Schwert, 1950). A low first-order constant might be due to several factors, a low affinity for the enzyme, a high stability of the enzyme substrate complex, or strong inhibition by the reaction-products. Which of these factors is the main one operating in any given instance can only be discovered by a more complete kinetic study than is provided by the determination of first-order constants alone and, without this information, false generalizations may be made.

The aglucon specificity pattern certainly cannot be accounted for solely in terms of the influence of chemical groupings in the aglucon molecule upon the ease of hydrolysis of the glucosidic link. FIGURE 1 shows that there is no correlation between the acid hydrolysis of a

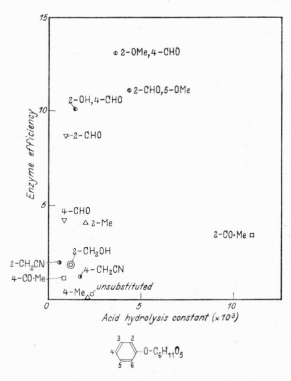

FIGURE 1. Correlation diagram for enzymic and non-enzymic hydrolysis of substituted phenyl-β-glucosides. Drawn from data compiled by Pigman (1944). Enzyme efficiencies are unimolecular rate constants determined under standard conditions.

number of aromatic β-glucosides and their enzymic hydrolysis by β-glucosidase. A similar absence of correlation has been observed for alkyl glucosides, the wide variation in their enzymic rate of hydrolysis being in marked contrast to their nearly uniform rate of acid hydrolysis. Further, the relative rates of enzymic hydrolysis of β-glucosides vary greatly with enzymes from different sources.

This lack of correlation between non-enzymic and enzymic rates of hydrolysis is a rather general finding with hydrolytic enzymes. Mounter and Whittaker (unpublished) found no correlation between the rates of hydrolysis by esterases of a series of p-substituted phenyl acetates and their non-enzymic hydrolysability as predicted from Hammett's (1940) 'sigma values' for the various substituents. A similar absence of correlation is found in Ormerod's (1953) results for the hydrolysis of *m*- and *p*- substituted benzoylcholines by horse serum, though the author's interpretation is somewhat different. (He attributed the hydrolysis of these esters to cholinesterase but did not exclude the possibility that one or both of the two other carboxylic esterases known to be present in horse serum were responsible, at any rate in part, for the hydrolysis.) Widely varying relative rates of hydrolysis of aliphatic esters are observed in the presence of horse serum ali-esterase and cholinesterase, though the specificity pattern of these two enzymes should be identical if the enzymic rates of hydrolysis are determined solely by the non-enzymic hydrolysability of the ester link (Sturge and Whittaker, 1950).

While no doubt substituents do affect enzyme reactions by altering the reactivity of the link under attack, this effect must be subordinate, in many cases, to other effects, notably alterations in the forces binding the substrate to the enzyme. The marked effect, for example, of an aldehyde group in the aglucon of the phenyl glucoside may involve a specific interaction with a group in the enzyme surface. In other cases, less specific binding forces may play a part *e.g.* in the case of the larger alkyl chains and benzene rings. Other substituents may exert a negative effect by affording steric hindrance to the close approach of the substrate to the enzyme surface. Pigman (1944) has suggested that inhibition by liberated aglucon may be a factor lowering the first-order hydrolysis rate in certain cases. Thus the hydrolysis rate of *n*-alkyl β-glucosides may be determined by the relative affinities of the substrate and free *n*-alkyl alcohol for the enzyme. Up to *n*-hexyl the increasing strength of the adsorption forces between the alkyl chain and the enzyme might favour hydrolysis, but after this point the ' progressively decreasing dissociation of the products of hydrolysis . . . would act to inhibit the over-all reaction '.

Synthetic Action of β-Glucosidase

Enzymes are generally considered to be true catalysts, that is, they catalyse the formation of an equilibrium mixture from either side. We should therefore expect glycosidases to catalyse the formation of glycosides from their hydrolysis products, provided these were present in sufficiently high concentration. This has been repeatedly observed, notably by Croft-Hill, Armstrong and Bourquelot and co-workers. In a recent study, Peat, Whelan and Hinson (1952) have shown that almond emulsin, acting on a concentrated glucose solution, synthesized gentiobiose, together with smaller quantities of cellobiose, laminaribiose, sophorose, and $\beta\beta$-trehalose. These sugars represent the five possible ways of linking two glucose molecules together through a β-glucoside link. It is unlikely that disaccharides are synthesized in nature this way; transglycosidases (phosphorylases) provide a more likely mechanism.

Transferase Activity of β-Glucosidase

Takano and Tomoo (1950) have claimed that apricot β-glucosidase possesses glucotransferase action, *i.e.* it can catalyse the transfer of glucose from a donor glucoside to an acceptor substance with the formation of a second glucoside. The system they studied consisted of p-nitrophenyl β-glucoside and methanol or butanol. More p-nitrophenol was liberated than glucose, the balance being accounted for by the simultaneous appearance of either methyl or butyl β-glucoside. It is now realized that 'transferase' activity is a fairly general phenomenon among hydrolytic enzymes. It has been observed with invertases (Bacon, 1952; Fischer, Kohtès and Fellig, 1951; White, 1952), phosphatases (Axelrod, 1948; Appleyard, 1948; Meyerhof and Green, 1950; Morton, 1953) and cholinesterase (Wilson, Bergmann and Nachmansohn, 1950). It seems likely that there is a common mechanism to all these reactions involving a glycosido-enzyme, phosphorylated enzyme or acylated enzyme. This enzyme derivative then reacts with water (hydrolase action) or some other acceptor (transferase action) according to the following scheme:

$$AOR^1 + EH \rightarrow EA + R^1OH$$

$$EA + H_2O \rightarrow EH + AOH \text{ (hydrolase action)}$$

$$EA + R^2OH \rightarrow EH + AOR^2 \text{ (transferase action)}$$

The nature of A, R^1 and R^2 are limited by the specificity of the enzyme.

Transglucosidase (Sucrose Phosphorylase)

Although glycosides can be synthesized *in vitro* by the action of β-glycosidases, the enzymes catalysing the hydrolysis of glycosidic links do not seem to be responsible for the synthesis of glucosides or polysaccharides in nature. Another type of enzyme appears to be involved which utilizes phosphate in place of water. These enzymes are known as phosphorylases.

The two types of reaction are compared in the equations which follow.

$$R-O-R^1 + H-OH \underset{}{\overset{\text{glycosidase}}{\rightleftharpoons}} R-OH + R^1-OH$$

$$R-O-R^1 + H-OPO_3H_2 \underset{}{\overset{\text{phosphorylase}}{\rightleftharpoons}} R-OPO_3H_2 + R^1-OH$$

An interesting phosphorylase has been found in *Pseudomonas saccharophila* and its specificity very thoroughly investigated by Doudoroff,

Hassid and co-workers (Hassid and Doudoroff, 1950; Hassid, Doudoroff and Barker, 1951). This enzyme was first named sucrose phosphorylase, because it catalyses the reaction

Sucrose + phosphate ⇌ glucose 1-phosphate + fructose

Further work showed that the activity of the enzyme is better described by the reaction

R and R^1 may be phosphate, arsenate, any one of several ketofuranoses or the aldopentose, L-arabinose. The reaction essentially involves the transfer of an α-D-glucopyranosyl radical from a ' glucose donor ' to a ' glucose acceptor '. For this reason, the enzyme has been renamed transglucosidase. The known facts about the specificity of this enzyme are presented in TABLE 1. It will be noted that the enzyme is absolutely specific for the α-D-glucose ring. Of great interest is the rapid exchange of radioactivity which occurred between ^{32}P-labelled inorganic phosphate and unlabelled glucose phosphate in the presence of the enzyme, and the similar exchange reaction between sucrose and ^{14}C-labelled fructose in a phosphate-free system. This suggests that an essential step in the transfer reaction is the formation of a glucose derivative of the enzyme, which then reacts with the glucose acceptor according to the scheme

glucose—O—R + enzyme ⇌ glucose-enzyme + ROH

glucose-enzyme + acceptor ⇌ glucose-acceptor + enzyme.

When arsenate is added to glucose donors in the presence of the enzyme, a rapid liberation of free glucose occurs. A highly unstable glucose arsenate is presumed to be an intermediate.

According to Koshland (1952) the reaction is a two-stage nucleophilic displacement reaction with inversion at C-1 at each stage; it follows that the enzyme–glucoside link has the β-configuration. The mechanism of enzyme-catalysed displacement reactions has recently been reviewed (Koshland, 1954).

The enzymic synthesis of sucrose from glucose 1-phosphate and fructose is of exceptional chemical interest since until recently, no-one has succeeded in synthesizing this compound by purely chemical means (a chemical synthesis has just been achieved by Lemieux and Huber, 1953). One reason for this is that the fructose residue is in the unusual furanose form. Apparently the enzyme is specific for D-fructofuranose, and enough of this form exists in equilibrium with D-fructopyranose in solutions of D-fructose to enable the reaction to take place. Gottschalk's work on hexokinase, described below, supports this conclusion. The specificity extends to other ketofuranoses, since three analogues of sucrose have also been synthesized.

TABLE 1. SPECIFICITY OF *Pseudomonas saccharophila* TRANSGLUCOSIDASE
Compiled from Hassid and Doudoroff (1950)

Donor compound	Acceptor compound	Products
The following transfers are catalysed		
α-D-Glucopyranosyl β-D-fructofuranoside (sucrose)	Phosphate	Glucose 1-phosphate
Glucose 1-phosphate	Fructose	Sucrose
Glucose 1-phosphate	Labelled phosphate	Labelled glucose 1-phosphate
Sucrose	Labelled fructose	Labelled sucrose
Glucose 1-phosphate	L-Sorbose	α-D-glucosyl α-L-sorbofuranoside
	D-Xyloketose	α-D-glucosyl β-D-xyloketoside
	L-Araboketose	α-D-glucosyl α-L-araboketoside
	L-Arabinose	3-*O*-α-D-glucosyl-L-arabinose
	Arsenate	Glucose (by spontaneous decomposition of glucose 1-arsenate ?)
Sucrose	Arsenate	Glucose
Sucrose	L-Sorbose	Glucosyl α-L-sorboside
D-Xyloketosyl glucose	Fructose	Sucrose
The following transfers are *not* catalysed		
α-D-Galactose 1-phosphate α-D-Mannose 1-phosphate α-D-Xylose 1-phosphate α-L-Glucose 1-phosphate α-Maltose 1-phosphate	Fructose	
Raffinose	Phosphate	
Glucose 1-phosphate	D-Xylose D-Lyxose D-Arabinose L-Xyloketose D-Araboketose L-Fucose L-Rhamnose D-Glucose D-Mannose D-Galactose L-Fructose	

That the enzyme cannot be regarded as absolutely specific for a furanose ring in the ' acceptor ' group is shown by the synthesis of the reducing disaccharide 3-*O*-α-D-glucosyl-L-arabopyranose. Gottschalk (1950) has pointed out that the configuration of the ring carbon adjacent to the glucoside link is the same in all sugars which are so far known to act as acceptors and suggests that it is this portion only of the ring of the acceptor group for which the enzyme is specific (FIGURE 2). Clearly, more specificity studies will be needed to confirm this suggestion.

| VII | VIII |

FIGURE 2. Configuration of glucosylketofuranoses (VII) and glucosylarabinose (VIII) showing common features of their configuration (to left of broken line) (Gottschalk, 1950).

Hexokinase and Glucowaldenase

The absolute specificity of β-glucosidase and transglucosidase for the β-D-glucose and α-D-glucose configurations respectively is typical of many carbohydrate enzymes. Recent work on hexokinase has revealed an enzyme which is specific for a portion only of the monosaccharide ring. Hexokinase catalyses the reaction

Hexose + adenosine triphosphate $\rightleftharpoons$

hexose 6-phosphate + adenosine diphosphate

Unlike the phosphoroclastic reaction described in the previous section, the equilibrium lies well over on the side of the products.

Hexokinase is of great biological importance, for the utilization of hexoses in energy-yielding reactions appears to depend on their initial phosphorylation by adenosine triphosphate (ATP). The enzyme is widely distributed in cells of all kinds, though one should really speak of 'the hexokinases' rather than 'hexokinase', for there are undoubtedly differences between the hexokinases of animal cells and those of lower forms.

Yeast hexokinase has been the enzyme most studied from the point of view of specificity. It is relatively stable, and has been obtained in a highly purified form as a protein of molecular weight 96,600 (Kunitz and MacDonald, 1946). It appears to be absolutely specific for the phosphate donor, ATP, but will transfer phosphate from this compound to any of the fermentable hexoses, D-glucose, D-mannose and D-fructose. It will be seen (TABLE 2) that fructose is the most rapidly phosphorylated sugar, when the enzyme is saturated, but it has the lowest affinity for the enzyme. Since the sugars are phosphorylated in the 6 position, it is reasonable to suppose that it is the furanose form (X) of fructose, rather than the pyranose form (IX), which is the substrate.

Gottschalk (1950) has confirmed this in the following way. When solid fructose, which exists in the β-D-pyranose form (IX) is added to a yeast suspension at $0°$ (to slow down mutarotation to the β-D-furanose form, X) the rate of fermentation is very slow and almost identical with the rate of mutarotation. With β-D-fructofuranose generated *in situ* by the action of invertase on sucrose, the reaction at $0°$ proceeds rapidly. It is also possible to make the rate of mutarotation the rate-determining reaction at $25°$ by using large amounts of yeast and a low substrate concentration. In the furanose form, the affinity of fructose

TABLE 2. DISSOCIATION CONSTANTS AND RATES OF PHOSPHORYLATION BY
HEXOKINASE
Data compiled by Colowick (1951)

Substrate	Dissociation constant (M)	Maximum rate of phosphory-lation (as % of glucose)
Glucose	$1·5 \times 10^{-4}$	100
Mannose	$1·0 \times 10^{-4}$	50
Fructose	$1·5 \times 10^{-3}$	200
ATP	$1·2 \times 10^{-3}$	—
Mg^{2+}	$2·6 \times 10^{-3}$	—

for the enzyme is twice that of glucose, not one-tenth, as appears when no allowance is made for the fact that fructose is mainly in the pyranose form in solution.

Gottschalk has also succeeded in studying the fermentation of the α (XI, XII, $R^1 = H$, $R^2 = OH$) and β (XI, XII, $R^1 = OH$, $R^2 = H$) anomers of glucose (XI) and mannose (XII) under conditions which

IX   X   XI   XII

reduce the rate of mutarotation to a minimum [low substrate concentration $(0·005 \text{ M})$, pH $4·5$ and $0°$]. His results show that both the α and β forms of the aldohexoses are utilized, the α anomers at a rate about 10 per cent higher than the β-forms. All three naturally occurring substrates of hexokinases have a common configuration at C-3, C-4 and C-5. This suggests that the critical portion of the ring for the combination with the enzyme is that to the left of the broken line in structures X–XII (Gottschalk, 1950). This is supported by the recent findings that D-glucosamine (Brown, 1951; Grant and Long, 1952), D-2-deoxyglucose (Cramer and Woodward, 1952) and D-glucosone are phosphorylated by hexokinase, but that L-glucosone (Johnstone and Mitchell, 1953) is not. All these compounds differ from D-glucose only at C-2. However, derivatives with bulky groups to the right of the broken line are not phosphorylated, *e.g. N*-acetyl-D-glucosamine (Brown, 1951), sucrose, maltose (Kunitz and MacDonald, 1946).

It has been known for many years that some strains of yeast, when grown in the presence of galactose, adapt themselves to the new substrate and become capable of metabolizing it. Galactose can also be utilized by mammals, which convert it to glycogen in the liver. The enzyme which phosphorylates galactose is quite distinct from hexokinase; it has been named galactokinase (Trucco, Caputto, Leloir and Mittelmann, 1948). The phosphorylation product is galactose 1-phosphate, not the 6-phosphate. This is converted by another enzyme into glucose 1-phosphate which then enters the fermentation cycle. The conversion of galactose 1-phosphate to glucose 1-phosphate involves inversion of the asymmetric centre at C-4. How this is accomplished is unknown. Leloir and colleagues (see Leloir, 1953) have shown that the enzyme, which they have named glucowaldenase, requires the coenzyme uridine-diphosphate-glucose. Glucowaldenase is one of several enzymes catalysing inversion and isomerization reactions; these have recently been reviewed by Leloir (1953). Among them are enzymes catalysing the racemization of optically active amino-acids, which are relevant to the problem of the biological role of the D-amino-acids (see Biochemical Society Symposium no. 1, 1948) and mutarotase, described in the following section.

Glucose Oxidase (Notatin)

Glucose oxidase is a flavoprotein produced by *Penicillium notatum* which catalyses the oxidation of glucose to gluconic acid according to the equation

$$C_6H_{12}O_6 + O_2 + H_2O \longrightarrow C_6H_{12}O_7 + H_2O_2$$

The enzyme exerts an antibiotic effect in the presence of glucose and oxygen due to the hydrogen peroxide generated. This action was first observed independently of the enzymic activity; this accounts for the alternative name notatin.

The specificity and the mode of action of the enzyme have been studied by Keilin and Hartree (1948, 1952) and by Bentley and Neuberger (1949). It is a chromoprotein of molecular weight about 149,000 with two molecules of alloxazine adenine dinucleotide per molecule. The initial product of the reaction is δ-gluconolactone. The enzyme behaves like a typical aerobic dehydrogenase. Presumably hydrogen is transferred from the glucopyranose ring to the prosthetic group and thence to oxygen, which is reduced to hydrogen peroxide. Under anaerobic conditions, 2 : 6-dichlorophenolindophenol can act as a hydrogen acceptor.

The enzyme is specific for the β-anomer of glucose; the α form is oxidized at less than 1 per cent of the rate of the β form, which is about the same rate as other sugars (TABLE 3). Discrepancies between the relative rates at which the two forms were oxidized by different samples of notatin, revealed the existence, in certain batches, of a new

TABLE 3. SPECIFICITY OF GLUCOSE OXIDASE
(All compounds D-series)

Substrate	Rate of oxidation (as % of glucose)	Substrate	Rate of oxidation (as % of glucose)
β-Glucose	100	Xylose	0·98
α-Glucose	0·64	Trehalose	0·28
Mannose	0·98	Maltose	0
Allose	0	Melibiose	0·11
Galactose	0·14	Cellobiose	0·09
Altrose	0·16		
Gulose	0	Glucuronic acid	< 0·05
Talose	0	Galacturonic acid	< 0·05
Idose	0	Glucosamine	< 0·05

O-Substituted derivatives of glucose		Other compounds not attacked	
6-Methyl	1·85		
4 : 6-Dimethyl	1·22		
4 : 6-Benzylidene	1·90	Various methylated glucosides and
2-Methyl	0	galactoses, phosphorylated sugars, arab-
3-Methyl	0	inose, fructose, fucose, glucoheptose,
2 : 3-Dimethyl	0	lactose, melizitose, raffinose, rhamnose,
2 : 3 : 6-Trimethyl	0	ribose, sorbose, sucrose, tagatose
2 : 4 : 6-Trimethyl	0		
2 : 3 : 4 : 6-Tetramethyl	0		

enzyme, mutarotase, which catalyses the mutarotation of glucose. The oxidation of glucose thus follows the scheme shown in FIGURE 3.

The specificity of the enzyme is summarized in TABLE 3. It will be seen that it is highly specific for β-D-glucopyranose. Of the other aldohexoses, only mannose, galactose and altrose are significantly attacked. Results with methylated sugars suggest that the hydroxyls in positions 1, 2 and 3 must be free; blocking those at 4 and 6 greatly reduces, but does not entirely abolish, oxidation. So far, no effective competitive inhibitor has been discovered, indicating that the carbohydrates which are not attacked have a very low affinity for the enzyme.

297

Proteolytic Enzymes

The proteolytic enzymes (proteases) are an important class of enzymes which hydrolyse the peptide bonds in proteins and peptides. Formerly they were divided into proteinases, which were supposed to attack only proteins and their derivatives of high molecular weight, and peptidases, which attacked low molecular weight peptides. These latter were further subdivided into aminopeptidases, which attack peptides having a free amino group adjacent to the sensitive link and carboxypeptidases, acting on peptides with a free carboxyl group adjacent to the sensitive link. The pioneer work of Bergmann and his co-workers

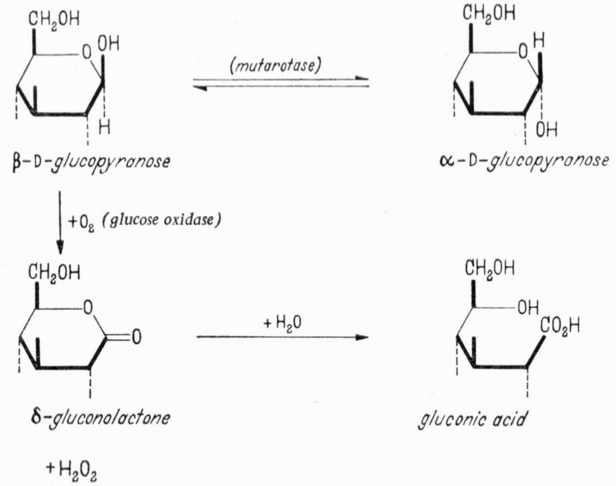

FIGURE 3. Oxidation of glucose by notatin.

(cf Bergmann and Fruton, 1941) established the important fact that typical proteinases could attack simple peptides, provided certain specificity requirements were met, which included the absence of a free amino or carboxyl group on adjacent amino-acid residues. Bergmann renamed these enzymes endopeptidases in contrast to the amino- and carboxy-peptidases which are exopeptidases. An important further addition to our knowledge of these enzymes was the discovery that they could hydrolyse not only peptide and amide links but carboxylic ester, hydroxylamide and hydrazide links in structurally analogous substrates (Schwert, Neurath, Kaufman and Snoke, 1948; Kaufman, Schwert and Neurath, 1948; MacAllister, Harmon and Niemann, 1949). The selective hydrolysis of L-amino-acid esters by pancreatic enzymes has been used for the resolution of amino-acids since 1905, but it was not appreciated till recently that the enzymes involved were peptidases. Some recent work opens up the possibility that dialkylphosphate esters can also be attacked by certain proteases.

Our knowledge of the proteases is conditioned by two main facts: one is the isolation, in the nineteen thirties, of several of the pancreatic proteases in a pure form, and the natural preference of investigators to work with these pure enzymes rather than the less well characterized enzymes of plant and animal tissues; the other is the use of synthetic substrates which, being relatively accessible and of defined constitution, have been used in place of naturally occurring substrates. Relatively little is known about the action of endopeptidases on proteins, but there is evidence that results with simple substrates may not apply without modification. The specificity and properties of the cathepsins and plant proteases have been relatively little explored, but they appear to differ considerably from the better known pancreatic enzymes.

As an example of recent work on the stereospecificity of the proteinases, an endopeptidase, α-chymotrypsin, has been selected. The specificity of the pancreatic proteolytic enzymes and the peptidases have recently been reviewed by Neurath and Schwert (1950) and by Smith (1951) respectively.

α-Chymotrypsin

The chymotrypsins are a group of closely similar enzymes found in the pancreas. All but one are probably derived from a single, enzymically inactive precursor, chymotrypsinogen. This is ' activated ' by a trace of trypsin to give α-chymotrypsin, which has been obtained as a pure crystalline protein of molecular weight about 27,000. During activation three or more peptide bonds are broken. On standing, more bonds open giving β- and γ-chymotrypsin; these compounds are not interconvertible. Experiments at 0° and high trypsin concentrations have led to the discovery of a very unstable enzymically active precursor of α-chymotrypsin, π-chymotrypsin, which is formed from chymotrypsinogen by the opening of only one bond. This is rapidly converted by the opening of a second bond to δ-chymotrypsin and by the opening of two or more bonds to α-chymotrypsin. The interrelationship of the various chymotrypsins is as follows:

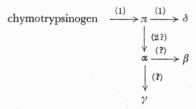

(The figures indicate the numbers of bonds per molecule opened)

There is also evidence for the existence of a second chymotrypsinogen, B-chymotrypsinogen. This is converted to B-chymotrypsin.

The basic requirements for α-chymotrypsin may be summarized by reference to structures XIII and XIV in which the central carbon atoms have the L-configuration. The broken lines show the link severed.

The earliest synthetic substrates (Bergmann and Fruton, 1941; Fruton and Bergmann, 1942) were all of type XIII. R^1CO was derived from an amino-acid (*e.g.* glycine, glutamic acid) or its benzyloxycarbonyl ('carbobenzoxy') derivative. The central amino-acid was L-phenylalanine or L-tyrosine, and the group split off was glycinamide or glycylglycinamide. Later it was recognized that R^3 could be NH_2 and that the group R^1CO could be dispensed with, substrates such as phenylalanine amide and phenylalanyl glycinamide (XIV, $R^1 = NH_2$, $R^3 = NH_2$ or $NHCH_2\cdot CONH_2$) being slowly attacked. Compounds in

$$
\begin{array}{cc}
CO\text{-----}R^3 & CO\text{-----}R^3 \\
| & | \\
R^1\cdot CO\cdot NH\text{---}C\text{---}H & R^1\text{---}C\text{---}H \\
| & | \\
R^2 & R^2 \\
XIII & XIV
\end{array}
$$

which the central amino-acid was glycine, glutamine, arginine, leucine, lysine or alanine, were hydrolysed very slowly or not at all. Subsequent work has established that for the highest rates of hydrolysis, R^2 should contain an aromatic ring system (*e.g.* benzene, as in phenylalanine, tyrosine; indole as in tryptophan) separated by at least one methylene group from the α-carbon atom. If the benzene ring is substituted directly in the α-carbon atom as in phenylglycine derivatives, the compound is unhydrolysable. The only known non-aromatic residue compatible with appreciable hydrolysis in this position is methionine; the order is tryptophan>tyrosine>phenylalanine>methionine. The approximately isosteric norleucine and norvaline derivatives are split much more slowly, so that the role of methionine may be linked in some way to the presence of divalent sulphur in the side chain. In addition to compounds already mentioned, those having serine, threonine or histidine as their central residue and a large number of others not corresponding to structures XIII and XIV are not split.

As far as the secondary peptide group, R^1CO— (formula XIII), is concerned, maximum rates of hydrolysis are obtained when this is benzoyl or nicotinyl. It may also be glycyl, benzyloxycarbonylglycyl, benzyloxycarbonyl or acetyl. However, an acyl group on the α-carbon atom may be dispensed with entirely. Thus the methyl esters of β-phenylpropionic acid and its α-hydroxy and α-chloro derivatives are slowly attacked. These are compounds of type XIV in which $R^1 = H$, OH, or Cl, $R^2 = C_6H_5CH_2$ (as in phenylalanine) and $R^3 = OMe$; R^1 may also be NH_2 as in L-phenylalanine amide. Compounds in which R^1 is CH_3CO—, $C_2H_5O\cdot CO$—, HO_2C—, phthalimido or NH_2CO— are not attacked. Of great interest is the finding that the (+)-forms of methyl α-chloro- and α-hydroxy-β-phenylpropionate are attacked, the former at the same rate as its (−)-enantiomorph, the latter about one-tenth as fast (Snoke and Neurath, 1950). In TABLE 4 the zero-order rate constants (k_3) and the affinities $(1/K_m)$ are given for these substrates relative to benzoyl-L-phenylalanine methyl ester $(XIV, R^1 = C_6H_5CONH—)$, the parent substrate containing a secondary peptide bond. Snoke and Neurath explain their findings in the following way. Since normally only compounds of the L-series are attacked, we must assume that there is three-point attachment

TABLE 4. RELATIVE ZERO-ORDER RATE CONSTANTS AND AFFINITIES FOR METHYL ESTERS OF α-SUBSTITUTED β-PHENYLPROPIONATES AND CHYMOTRYPSIN (Data obtained at pH 7·8 and 25° and recalculated from Snoke and Neurath, 1950)

$$
\begin{array}{cc}
R^1 & CO_2Me \\
\diagdown & \diagup \\
& *CH \\
& | \\
& CH_2Ph
\end{array}
$$

R^1	Configuration at C*†	Relative k_3	Relative affinity
$C_6H_5CONH—$	L_S	100	100
HO—	(−)	2·7	39
Cl—	(±)	1·1	36
HO	(+)	0·26	26
H—		0·05	45

† The (−)-chloro- and (−)-hydroxy- acids both have the same configuration as L_S-phenylalanine (see Chapter 5, p. 195).

between substrate and enzyme. Since modification of groups R^1, R^2 and R^3 all have roughly predictable effects on hydrolysis rates it is reasonable to assume that attachment occurs through (a) the ' secondary peptide ' group, (b) the central side chain, and (c) the susceptible link. The high rate of hydrolysis of compounds containing a secondary peptide link, relative to those which do not, suggests that (a) plays an important role in binding the substrate to the enzyme perhaps through hydrogen bonding with the —CO— and —NH— groups of the link. However, that this role is not essential is evidenced by the hydrolysis of methyl β-phenylpropionate and its (−)-chloro derivative. Under these circumstances, the substrate is effectively attached at only two points; stereochemical specificity would be expected to disappear, as indeed it does. The higher rate of hydrolysis of the chloro compound relative to the unsubstituted compound must be ascribed solely to the inductive effect of the chlorine atom. With —OH, some degree of hydrogen bonding at the ' secondary peptide ' site is possible, and stereospecificity reappears, though it is not absolute. The (−)-hydroxy ester is hydrolysed faster than the purely inductive effect of the —OH group would warrant; while with the (+)-form, the rate falls between that of the (±)-chloro and unsubstituted acids as would be expected from an inductive effect alone.

The fact that a wide variety of bond types can be hydrolysed by chymotrypsin provided other structural conditions are complied with, has already been indicated. The available data suggest that the ease of hydrolysis is in the order ester$>$hydroxylamide$>$glycinamide$>$ amide$>$hydrazide$>$glycylglycinamide. Groups containing a free carboxyl, *e.g.* glycine, are not split off, *i.e.* the enzyme has no carboxypeptidase activity. It is not known if this is also true for groups ionizing as cations. Large groups appear to exert a steric hindrance.

The independent effect which the three structural components exert on the rate of hydrolysis of chymotrypsin substrates is well illustrated by the behaviour of benzoylarginine methyl ester. This is hydrolysed by chymotrypsin, in apparent exception to the rule that only derivatives of tryptophan, tyrosine, phenylalanine and methionine are effective substrates. However, the benzoyl and methyl ester groupings are both optimal, and they are apparently able to render the compound hydrolysable in spite of the presence of an arginine side chain in the central position.

Competitive Inhibitors of α-Chymotrypsin

A large number of competitive inhibitors of chymotrypsin have been discovered by Kaufman and Neurath (1949a, b). They are all structural analogues of chymotrypsin substrates and substantially the same factors which make for high rates of hydrolysis in substrates have been shown to make for effective inhibition also. The specificity requirements are somewhat broader; however, this is understandable when we remember that whereas a substrate must combine with all three points on the enzyme surface to be effectively activated, a substance may need to combine with only one or two points to act as an inhibitor.

The presence of a non-hydrolysable group is the essential prerequisite for inhibition by a structural analogue, otherwise it is likely to be a substrate. A free carboxylic acid group in place of the hydrolysable link (XIII, XIV, $R^3 = OH$) satisfies this requirement, and as we should expect, such compounds as benzoylphenylalanine, the hydrolysis product of the substrates benzoylphenylalanine methyl ester and benzoylphenylalanine amide, are effective inhibitors. Compounds in which $R^3 = CH_3$ are also highly effective.

The structural requirements for the central group R^2 differ somewhat from those of the corresponding substrates. The order of affinity is phenylglycine $>$ phenylalanine $=$ tyrosine $>$ glycine $>$ methionine. Differences also arise with respect to R^1. This may be hydrogen, benzamido or acetamido, but in the acetamido series, only derivatives of amino-acids containing aromatic side chains are effective. Compounds in which $R^1 = NH_2$ or CO_2H are not inhibitors. Surprisingly, phenylpropionic acid (XIV, $R^1 = H$, $R^2 = C_6H_5CH_2$, $R^3 = OH$) is the most inhibitory of all the compounds tested by Kaufman and Neurath. It is probable that a bulky R_3 group reduces inhibitory power. This may account for the fact that N-benzoyl-D-phenylalanine is a more powerful inhibitor than the L-form; in the D-form the benzamido group will be directed away from the enzyme surface.

Inhibition by Organophosphorus Compounds
Among the most toxic organic substances known are a group of phosphorus compounds of the general formula:

XV

where X is a group capable of splitting off as an anion such as F, CN, p-$NO_2 \cdot C_6H_4O$— or $R^1R^2PO_2$ and R^1 and R^2 are alkyl, alkoxy, or dialkylamino. Many of these compounds were studied in Germany in the nineteen thirties as possible substitutes for nicotine in insecticides, and on account of their high toxicity to man were investigated as potential chemical warfare agents by both belligerents in World War II. The so-called ' nerve gases ' belong to this group. Since the war they have found application in medicine and as insecticides.

These compounds are believed to exert their toxic effect by irreversibly inhibiting the enzyme cholinesterase which has the important physiological function of destroying the neuro-effector substance acetylcholine. They are among the most powerful enzyme inhibitors known, producing a detectable effect at concentrations of the order of 10^{-10}M. The physiology of many of these substances is complicated by the fact that they themselves undergo metabolism in the animal body and may be converted to more highly toxic intermediates before being finally destroyed (*cf* Gardiner and Kilby, 1952; Gage, 1953; Casida, Allen and Stahmann, 1953). Confusion has also been created by the unsuspected presence in many samples of traces of biologically much more active impurities (*cf* Aldridge and Davison, 1952).

Cholinesterase is not the only carboxylic esterase sensitive to the organophosphorus compounds; liver esterase, milk lipase (Webb, 1948), citrus fruit acetylesterase (Jansen, Nutting and Balls, 1947), serum B-esterase (Aldridge, 1953b) and human erythrocyte ' aliesterase ' (Mounter and Whittaker, 1953b) are also inhibited. Very many other enzymes including at least one carboxylic esterase (Aldridge, 1953b) are entirely unaffected (Webb, 1948; Jansen, Nutting and Balls, 1948). Although trypsin and chymotrypsin are not typical esterases, both these enzymes are sensitive to di*iso*propyl phosphorofluoridate (fluorophosphate, DFP) (XV, $R^1 = R^2 = Pr^iO$,

X = F), the esterase and proteolytic activities being inhibited *pari passu* (Jansen, Nutting, Jang and Balls, 1949). α-Chymotrypsin is also inhibited by diethyl *p*-nitrophenyl phosphate (XV, $R^1 = R^2 = OEt$, $X = p\text{-}NO_2 \cdot C_6H_4 \cdot O$) (Hartley and Kilby, 1952, 1954) and by a variety of other organophosphorus compounds (Balls and Jansen, 1952).

There is little doubt that the mode of action of all these compounds is the same. They react progressively and irreversibly with the active centres of the enzyme; crystalline inhibited chymotrypsins, containing the phosphorus of the inhibitor and almost identical in physical properties with the original chymotrypsin, have been prepared. Stoicheiometric studies (Hartley and Kilby, 1952; Balls and Jansen, 1952) have shown that one molecule of enzyme EH reacts bimolecularly with one molecule of inhibitor according to the equation:

$$EH + X \cdot POR^1R^2 \longrightarrow E \cdot POR^1R^2 + HX$$

Many enzyme inhibitors are known to act by combining irreversibly with groups in the enzyme which are essential for its action. To give only one example, iodoacetate inhibits many enzymes by combining with essential —SH groups:

$$E{-}SH + I \cdot CH_2CO_2H \longrightarrow E{-}S{-}CH_2CO_2H + HI$$

There is reason to believe, however, that the toxic organophosphorus compounds do not fall into this familiar class of enzyme inhibitors, but comprise a new class of what may be termed ' lethal substrates '. These substrates are not particularly reactive chemically: indeed if the reactivity is increased by making X = Cl in structure XV, the ensuing compound is not particularly effective as an inhibitor because it is so rapidly hydrolysed by the solvent; on the other hand, if X is not anionic enough, *e.g.* —OC_6H_5, the inhibitory power is also weak. It is characteristic of the toxic members of the class that they react more rapidly with the enzyme than with the solvent and this reaction is entirely dependent on the integrity of the active centres, *i.e.* upon the same factors which catalyse the hydrolysis of the substrate. This is not true of substances like iodoacetate or trivalent arsenic which will combine with —SH groups in any protein whether it has enzyme activity or not. The ability of organophosphorus compounds to be ' activated ' by esterases probably depends on a similarity in electronic configuration around the phosphorus and the carboxyl carbon of the substrate. It has been suggested that the action of the esterase on an ester or a phosphorus compound involves the intermediate formation of an acylated or phosphorylated enzyme:

$$EH + R \cdot CO \cdot OR^3 \longrightarrow E \cdot CO \cdot R + R^3OH$$

$$EH + R^1R^2PO \cdot X \longrightarrow E \cdot POR^1R^2 + HX$$

The acylated enzyme is rapidly hydrolysed:

$$E \cdot COR + H_2O \longrightarrow EH + R \cdot CO_2H$$

but the phosphorylated enzyme is stable, perhaps as a result of migration of the phosphoryl group to another group in the enzyme.

Several observations support the phosphorylation hypothesis. An esterase (A-esterase) has been discovered which attacks both phenyl acetates and diethyl p-nitrophenyl phosphate (Aldridge, 1953c; Mounter and Whittaker, 1953b). The latter acts as an inhibitor only in the sense that any substrate will compete for enzyme in the presence of another substrate and lower the total rate of hydrolysis if its rate of hydrolysis happens to be lower than that of the other substrate. Presumably phosphorylated A-esterase is readily hydrolysed, perhaps because of the absence of the second phosphorus-accepting group postulated in the case of susceptible enzymes. Yet another enzyme attacking organophosphorus compounds is the diisopropyl-fluorophosphatase of Mazur (1946). This has recently been purified (Mounter, 1953). It differs in its specificity from A-esterase in that it attacks DFP and TEPP but not diethyl p-nitrophenyl phosphate. It is activated by divalent ions and histidine, and resembles metal activated peptidases in many of its properties. It is possibly significant that carboxypeptidase, claimed to be a metallo-protein by Smith (1951), is DFP-insensitive.

Although the organophosphorus compounds are normally described as irreversible inhibitors, the phosphorylated enzyme (cholinesterase or α-chymotrypsin) can be reactivated by slow hydrolysis or interaction with a second phosphorus acceptor such as hydroxylamine (Hobbiger, 1951; Wilson, 1952; Aldridge, 1953d; Davison, 1953; Cunningham and Neurath, 1953). The reactions are:

$$E \cdot POR^1R^2 + H_2O \longrightarrow EH + HOPOR^1R^2$$

$$E \cdot POR^1R^2 + HOR^3 \longrightarrow EH + R^3O \cdot POR^1R^2$$

When R^1, R^2 are alkoxy, the reaction occurs with sharply decreasing facility in the order $OMe > OEt > OPr^i$, the rate of reactivation being the same for any one dialkylphosphorylenzyme irrespective of the source of the dialkylphosphoryl group (Burgen and Hobbiger, 1951).

If the inactivation of the enzyme involves phosphorylation it should be possible to isolate a phosphorylated amino-acid after gentle proteolysis of the inhibited enzyme. The identification of this amino-acid would incidentally give valuable information about the amino-acid composition of the active centres. Schaffer, May and Summerson (1953) have recently isolated serine phosphoric acid in 30 per cent yield from DFP-inhibited chymotrypsin after peptic and tryptic digestion followed by mild acid hydrolysis. Diisopropyl phosphate did not give this product when digested with chymotrypsin. There are approximately 27 serine residues in the chymotrypsin molecule. One of these might be in a specially reactive state towards DFP, ' presumably because of some as yet unknown configuration of amino-acids in its vicinity ' which constitutes what we know as the active centre of the enzyme. The special character of this one serine residue would also be indicated by the fact that most proteins do not react with DFP regardless of their serine content. Other studies, however, suggest that the primary mode of attack on DFP and substrates may be through histidine or tyrosine rather than serine (see Wagner-Jauregg and Hackley, 1953). These residues have also been suggested as being responsible for hydrolytic activity in cholinesterase (Wilson and Bergmann, 1950b). A phosphorylated histidine residue would be unstable, and the hydroxyl group of serine might be the ultimate phosphorus acceptor. On the other hand it is conceivable that serine phosphate is formed by migration of phosphorus from another amino-acid during acid hydrolysis.

The ability of α-chymotrypsin to ' activate ' the organo-P compounds suggests that the specificity of the enzyme is even wider than indicated by Neurath *et al.* This suspicion is confirmed by the finding of Hartley and Kilby (1952) that p-nitrophenyl acetate and ethyl p-nitro-phenyl carbonate are both split, though at a lower rate than the typical chymotrypsin substrate, L-tyrosine ethyl ester.

The point has been made earlier in this chapter that enzymic activity is dependent on a complementary relationship between the molecular configurations of substrate and enzyme and secondarily, on chemical activation of the susceptible link. As will be seen in a later section, both these factors have been shown to operate in the inter-action of the organophosphorus compounds with the cholinesterases (Aldridge, 1953a, b) and this may well be true of α-chymotrypsin also. The fact that compounds as remote from the ' typical ' substrates as p-nitrophenyl acetate and diethyl p-nitrophenyl phosphate are activated by chymotrypsin may represent an extreme example of chemical activation. It would be interesting to have information about phosphate ester analogues of ' typical ' substrates.

Cholinesterases

It has been known for many years that nervous transmission at certain sites in the animal body is mediated by the release of a substance or substances, identical with or very like acetylcholine. Until recently, the only physiologically active ester of choline known to occur naturally was acetylcholine. However, propionylcholine and another as yet unidentified ester of choline have now been isolated from ox spleen (Banister, Whittaker and Wijesundera, 1953) and urocanylcholine (XVI) has been identified in *Murex trunculus* (Pasini, Vercellone and

Erspamer, 1953). These substances resemble acetylcholine in many of their properties and their presence in animal tissue opens up the possibility that some functions now attributed to acetylcholine may in reality be mediated by other esters.

$$\text{HN} \diagdown \text{N} \quad \text{—CH:CH·CO·O·CH}_2\text{CH}_2\overset{+}{\text{N}}\text{Me}_3$$

XVI

Acetylcholine has an intense physiological action—as little as 0·005 μg produces a detectable contraction in the length of an isolated portion of guinea-pig intestine—but nevertheless, its action is very transient. This was early attributed to its destruction by esterases. The work of Stedman, Stedman and Easson (1932) established that the enzyme which hydrolyses choline esters (choline-esterase, cholinesterase) was distinct from other carboxylic esterases, and later work by Alles and Hawes (1940), Mendel and Rudney (1943) and others showed that cholinesterases from different sources had different specificity patterns. Mendel and Rudney divided cholinesterases into two main types, ' true ' and ' pseudo '. The synonyms ChE-I, e-type, specific and ChE-II, s-type, non-specific are also in use. More recent work has established that there are many different types of cholinesterase. The physiological significance of this fact is not understood at present but may not be unconnected with the existence in nature of more than one physiologically active ester of choline. The nomenclature adopted by Sturge and Whittaker (1950) is used here. The specificity, mode of action and distribution of cholinesterases has been reviewed by Whittaker (1951).

Substrate Specificity of Cholinesterases
Aceto-cholinesterases—The cholinesterases of nervous tissue, erythrocytes, cobra venom (*cf* Whittaker, 1953) and the electric organs of certain fish, form a group of enzymes, closely similar in specificity and other properties. They are ' true ' cholinesterases in the Mendel–Rudney classification. Not all the facts now to be mentioned have been established for all these enzymes, but there is a strong presumption that they apply generally.

This group of enzymes hydrolyses acetylcholine very rapidly; one recent estimate of turnover number (for human erythrocyte cholinesterase) is 295,000 molecules/active centre/min. (Cohen and Warringa, 1953). They have a high affinity for acetylcholine, hydrolysing it most rapidly at very low concentrations ($\sim$ 1mM). At higher concentrations, the rate of hydrolysis is depressed. According to Haldane (1930) and Murray's (1930) theory, this is due to the formation of stable super-complexes between enzyme and substrate.

Aceto-cholinesterases attack a variety of carboxylic esters, including many simple aliphatic esters such as ethyl acetate and triacetin, and aromatic esters such as phenyl acetate. The rate at which these are attacked varies greatly, some being split nearly as fast as acetylcholine; the only ester reported to be split faster than acetylcholine is acetyl-thiocholine (Koelle, 1950). Formate and propionate esters are both split less rapidly than the corresponding acetates; butyrates are split very slowly (6 per cent of acetates) and esters with acyl groups larger than butyrate, very slowly or not at all. The compound $Me_3N^+ \cdot CH_2$ CH_2CO_2Me ('reversed acetylcholine') is also very slowly split (Bass, Schueler, Featherstone and Gross, 1950).

The optimum at acetate, irrespective of the nature of the alcohol or phenol moiety, particularly distinguishes this group of cholinesterases from others and is the basis for the designation ' aceto-cholinesterase '.

The aceto-cholinesterases show a special affinity for the choline configuration. This is shown by the high rate of hydrolysis of choline esters, the effectiveness of choline and choline analogues (including acetylcholine) as competitive inhibitors and, as mentioned in the introduction, the high rate of hydrolysis of the carbon analogue of acetylcholine, 3 : 3-dimethylbutyl acetate (I, p. 285). Other simple aliphatic esters are split less rapidly, at rates which depend on the nearness with which they approach the ' acetylcholine ' configuration. Thus for a series of n-alkyl esters the rate of hydrolysis is maximal with n-butyl esters; further extension of the n-alkyl chain (n-amyl, n-hexyl) leads to a fall in rate, but chain branching at C-3, so as to build up a quaternary carbon atom in this position, leads to an increased rate of hydrolysis. The affinity of these esters for the enzyme (Mounter, 1953) likewise increases as the ' acetylcholine ' configuration is approached*.

These results suggest that the active centres of aceto-cholinesterases possess a configuration which is complementary in shape to that of the acetylcholine molecule. An ester does not have to possess a positive charge to be attacked by the enzyme; it is sufficient if its shape conforms more or less closely to that of acetylcholine. The active centres appear to tolerate a deviation from the optimum shape of about one methyl group (2·0 Å); thus acetyl-α- and β-methylcholines, propionylcholine and the N-ethyl analogues of acetylcholine are all fairly readily split, also such substrates as n-butyl propionate, n-amyl acetate. Compounds which deviate by two such groups (e.g. butyrylcholine, n-hexyl acetate, n-butyl butyrate) are hydrolysed very slowly. Unfortunately the first aliphatic esters tried were butyrates; their failure to be hydrolysed

* Bergmann and Shimoni (1953) have claimed that electric organ cholinesterase does not show the same specificity pattern with n-alkyl acetates as other aceto-cholinesterases. However, their conditions were quite different from those used by the Oxford workers (for references see Whittaker, 1953) and the rates compared were not zero-order with respect to the substrate.

STEREOSPECIFICITY OF ENZYME REACTIONS

gave the false impression that aceto-cholinesterases were specific for choline esters.

The ability of aceto-cholinesterases to attack esters of secondary alcohols must be mentioned, as this is another distinguishing feature of this class of cholinesterases. ' Acetyl-β-methyl choline ' (2-acetoxy-propyltrimethyl ammonium hydroxide) (XVII) and 1 : 3-dimethyl-butyl acetate (XVIII) are split at about one-third the rate of their ' primary ' analogues with no methyl group on the carbon atom adjacent to the ester link.

$$Me_3N^+ \cdot CH_2 \cdot CH(Me) \cdot O \cdot CO \cdot CH_3 \qquad Me_2CH \cdot CH_2CH(Me) \cdot O \cdot CO \cdot CH_3$$
$$XVII \qquad\qquad XVIII$$

Although the degree of approach to the ' choline ester ' configuration is a good guide to the rate at which many cholinesterase substrates are hydrolysed, compounds containing highly polar, or readily polarizable groups may be more rapidly hydrolysed than their molecular shape alone would lead one to expect. Thus chloroacetyl and bromoacetyl esters are much more rapidly hydrolysed than the corresponding propionates with which they are isosteric. Some phenyl acetates are also rapidly hydrolysed (Mounter and Whittaker, 1953b). In the first example, Cl and Br exert a much greater inductive effect than CH_3 on the ester link, making it more readily hydrolysable. If an acylated enzyme is an intermediate as the transacetylase and other properties of the cholinesterases suggest, this effect would also increase the rate of breakdown of the acylated enzyme, and if this step is rate-determining, the enzyme reaction as a whole would be accelerated. The effect is not a simple one, for the enzymic rate of hydrolysis of chloroacetates and bromoacetates relative to the corresponding propionates is markedly dependent on the nature of the alkyl group. The greater polarizability of the halogen atoms and the larger dipole associated with the C—Cl and C—Br links would also be expected to increase the affinity of the haloacetates relative to the corresponding propionates. This has been confirmed (Adams and Whittaker, 1950).

The greater polarizability of the benzene ring might also be expected to increase the affinity and rate of hydrolysis of phenyl acetates. Again the effect is not a simple one, since, as previously mentioned (p. 289) there is no correlation between the enzymic rates of hydrolysis and Hammett's σ values.

Butyro-cholinesterases—The cholinesterases of human and horse serum and dog pancreas have all been highly purified and extensively studied. They differ both in specificity and in their reactions to many inhibitors from the aceto-cholinesterases, and were termed by Mendel and Rudney ' pseudo-cholinesterases '.

One of the earliest differences noted was their ability to hydrolyse aliphatic butyrates. Further studies (*cf* Whittaker, 1951) in extension

309

of earlier results of Glick (1938) and Easson and Stedman (1937) with choline esters showed that butyrate rather than acetate is the optimum acyl group for human and horse serum cholinesterases, irrespective of the nature of the alkyl group. They have accordingly been designated butyro-cholinesterases. A second distinguishing feature is the slowness with which they attack esters of secondary alcohols. Butyryl- and acetyl-β-methylcholine, and 1 : 3-dimethylbutyl butyrate and acetate are all split at less than 10 per cent of the rate of their primary analogues. A reported exception is acetyl-β-methylthiocholine (Koelle, 1950). In other respects the specificity pattern of butyro-cholinesterases is broadly similar to that of the aceto-cholinesterases, particularly in the affinity for the choline configuration as evidenced by the high rate of hydrolysis of 3 : 3-dimethylbutyl esters.

Although butyrate is the optimum acyl group, compounds with bulkier acyl groups are also hydrolysed (*e.g.* benzoylcholine, at about 10 per cent of butyrylcholine rate). The hydrolysis of p-substituted benzoylcholines by horse serum (Ormerod, 1953) has already been referred to (p. 290).

Butyro-cholinesterases are apparently able to hydrolyse carbonate esters. Ravin, Tsou and Seligman (1951) have reported that O-β-naphthoxycarbonylcholine (XIX) is hydrolysed by human serum cholinesterase.

XIX

The serum cholinesterases of dog, cat, duck, squirrel, ferret and pigeon resemble the butyro-cholinesterases of horse and human serum in their choline ester specificity (Myers, 1953).

Propiono-cholinesterases—A number of cholinesterases from different sources are now known which split propionylcholine faster than either acetyl- or butyryl-choline. Some of these, *e.g.* rat tissue (Ord and Thompson, 1951; Davies, Risley and Rutland, 1953; Myers, 1953), hamster serum, and mouse serum (Myers, 1953) propiono-cholinesterases, appear to resemble the butyro-cholinesterases of other species in that they are unable to hydrolyse acetyl-β-methylcholine, do not show auto-inhibition, and are inhibited by the same selective inhibitors. Chick serum contains a propiono-cholinesterase which also resembles butyro-cholinesterases except that it hydrolyses acetyl-β-methylcholine. Chick brain propiono-cholinesterase, on the other hand, more nearly resembles the aceto-cholinesterases of the other species, since it shows auto-inhibition, can hydrolyse acetyl-β-methyl-choline and attacks butyrylcholine at a negligible rate (Myers, 1953).

The propiono-cholinesterase from a *Pseudomonas fluorescens* type organism described by Goldstein and Goldstein (1953) appears to be similar, except that auto-inhibition is not a prominent feature. Nothing is yet known of the non-choline ester specificity of propiono-cholinesterases.

Benzoylcholinesterases—The existence in certain tissues of enzymes hydrolyzing benzoylcholine but not acetylcholine has been suspected for some time (for literature see Koelle, 1953). Recent work by Koelle (1953) on the benzoylcholine hydrolysing enzymes of rabbit serum and intestine suggests that these ' benzoylcholinesterases ' do not differ fundamentally from butyro-cholinesterases except that the order of hydrolysis is butyryl > benzoyl > acetyl instead of butyryl > acetyl > benzoyl. The optimum acyl group and aliphatic ester specificity of these enzymes have not yet been determined.

Other cholinesterases—Cholinesterases of ruminant tissues and certain invertebrates do not fall into any of the known classes of cholinesterases (Banister *et al*, 1953; Davies *et al*, 1953; Augustinsson, 1948).

Inhibitor Specificity of Cholinesterases

Competitive inhibitors—The total number of competitive inhibitors of cholinesterase is very large; relatively few of these, however, are really effective. Some examples are given in TABLE 5. The inhibitors have been roughly classified into three groups on the basis of the concentration required to inhibit activity by 50 per cent (I_{50}). For highest activity, the inhibitor should contain a tertiary or quaternary nitrogen group corresponding to the quaternary nitrogen of choline separated by a distance approximately equal to a two-carbon chain from a second, polar, group corresponding to the carboxylic ester group in the substrate. This is usually a urethane group (XXIV, XXV, XXVIII, XXIX) but may be a dimethyl phosphate (XXVII, R = Me) (Burgen and Hobbiger, 1951) or even a difficultly hydrolysable ester group (XXVI) (Wescoe, Riker and Beach, 1950). This last compound shows that there is no sharp line between substrates and their analogues which are competitive inhibitors. The naturally occurring alkaloid eserine (XXIV), is the archetype of these compounds, for it was the first of the so-called parasympathomimetic drugs (Bergel and Parkes, 1952) shown to be a powerful anti-cholinesterase. Carbamylcholine (XXVIII) is the simplest member of this series.

Several less effective inhibitors have as their polar group, —CN, —CO, —OH, or —Cl (XX–XXIII). One of these is ' nitrogen mustard ' (bis-2-chloroethylmethylamine) (XXIII) the active form of which is probably XXIIIA (Adams and Thompson, 1948). However, weak inhibition is displayed by many compounds not possessing the polar group (organic bases) or having it in an unfavourable position (*e.g.* α-amino-acids; Bergmann, Wilson and Nachmansohn, 1950). The

311

TABLE 5. STRUCTURAL ANALOGUES OF CHOLINE ESTERS WITH ANTI-CHOLINESTERASE ACTIVITY

Weak inhibitors $(I_{50} \geqslant 10^{-2}$ M$)$
Many organic bases, including amino-acids, their esters and amides and quaternary nitrogen compounds ; urethanes ; certain phosphate, arsenate and sulphonate derivatives.

Moderately strong inhibitors $(I_{50}, 10^{-2}$ to 10^{-7} M$)$
Tertiary and quarternary nitrogen bases with appropriately placed polar groups, *e.g.*

$$\text{Me·CO·CH}_2\text{CH}_2\text{.}\overset{+}{\text{N}}\text{HMe}_2 \qquad \text{HO}\!\!-\!\!\bigcirc\!\!-\!\!\overset{+}{\text{N}}\text{Me}_3 \qquad \text{NC·CH}_2\text{·CH}_2\text{·}\overset{+}{\text{N}}\text{HMe}_2$$

XX   XXII

XXI

$$\left(\text{Cl·CH}_2\text{CH}_2\right)_3\text{NMe} \qquad or \qquad \text{Cl·CH}_2\text{CH}_2\overset{\text{CH}_2}{\underset{\underset{\text{CH}_2}{\text{Me}}}{\overset{+}{\text{N}}}}$$

XXIII   XXIIIᴀ

Strong inhibitors $(I_{50} \leqslant 10^{-7}$ M$)$
Tertiary and quarternary nitrogen bases with unhydrolysable or slowly hydrolysable ester groups *e.g.*

XXIV
Eserine

XXV	Me₂N·CO
XXVI	CH₃·CO
XXVII	(RO)₂PO

$$\text{XXV}\ \text{Me}_2\text{N·CO},\ \text{XXVI}\ \text{CH}_3\text{·CO},\ \text{XXVII}\ \text{(RO)}_2\text{PO} \Big\} \text{O}\!\!-\!\!\bigcirc\!\!-\!\!\overset{+}{\text{N}}\text{Me}_3$$

$$\text{H}_2\text{N·CO·O·CH}_2\text{CH}_2\text{·}\overset{+}{\text{N}}\text{Me}_3$$

XXVIII

XXIX

---

latter compounds are interesting in that only the L- series are inhibitory, suggesting that cholinesterases may possess a latent stereospecificity of the classical kind. Further evidence for this is Glick's (1938) finding that only the $(-)$-isomer of acetyl-β-methylcholine is split by cholinesterase. If analogues of the cationic end of the choline ester molecule are weak inhibitors, we should expect analogues of the ester end to be weakly inhibitory also. This may be the basis for the anti-cholinesterase activity of such compounds as lewisite (dichloro-2-chlorovinylarsine), atoxyl (sodium arsanilate, p-NH$_2$·C$_6$H$_4$·AsO$_3$HNa) and sulphanilamide (Mounter and Whittaker, 1953a).

312

Organophosphorus inhibitors—The inhibitors so far described are reversible and competitive, that is, they combine with the active centres of the enzyme in essentially the same way as the substrate and can be displaced from them by the latter. Another, and even more effective, class of anti-cholinesterases are the organophosphorus compounds which were discussed in a previous section. It will be recalled that these compounds are characterized by the fact that they are ' activated ' by the enzyme and react progressively and irreversibly with it. The homologous series of phosphostigmines (XXVII) recently synthesized by Andrews, Atherton, Bergel and Morrison (1952) and studied by Burgen and Hobbiger (1951) are interesting in that they display inhibition of either type according to the nature of R. Dimethyl-phosphostigmine (XXVII, R = Me) behaves like prostigmine (XXV). The diethyl compound (XXVII, R = Et) behaves like tetraethyl pyrophosphate (TEPP, XXX), the inhibited enzyme showing spontaneous reactivation at the same rate as TEPP-inhibited cholinesterase, presumably because the end products are the same diethyl-phosphoryl enzyme. The di*iso*propyl derivative (XXVII, R = Pr^i) behaves like DFP; no reactivation of the highly stable di*iso*propyl-phosphoryl enzyme takes place in either case.

An important distinction between the organophosphorus compounds and eserine and its analogues, is that the former inhibit a wide range of esterases while the latter are, as far as is known, specific for cholinesterases. There are, however, a few cholinesterases which are abnormally insensitive to eserine. One of these is a butyrylcholine hydrolysing enzyme of rat harderian gland (Myers, 1953).

$$(EtO)_2O \cdot P \cdot O \cdot P \cdot O(OEt)_2$$

$$\begin{bmatrix} Pr^i_2 N & O \\ & \diagdown \nearrow \\ & P & O \\ & \diagup \diagdown \\ Pr^i_2 N & \end{bmatrix}_2$$

XXX   XXXI

Effect of cholinesterase type on inhibitor specificity—Cholinesterases differ in their inhibitor specificity just as they do in their substrate specificity. Occasionally these differences are so great as to amount to a selective action on one class of cholinesterase. Thus Nu-683 (XXIX), DFP, and tetra*iso*propylpyrophosphoramide ('*iso*-OMPA'; XXXI) are selective inhibitors for butyro-cholinesterases (Hawkins and Gunter, 1946; Aldridge, 1953a) while ' nitrogen mustard ' (DDM; XXIII) is selective for aceto-cholinesterases (Adams and Thompson, 1948). However, inhibitors with a completely selective action have not been discovered so far, and the degree of selectivity may diminish when optimum substrates are used for the enzymes compared.

According to Aldridge (1953a), the selective action of organo-phosphorus compounds is a function of the size of the phosphoryl group transferred to the enzyme. As the size of this group is increased, it becomes progressively less easily activated by aceto-cholinesterases and more easily activated by butyro-cholinesterases; thus dimethyl p-nitrophenyl phosphate actually inhibits horse blood aceto-cholinesterase nearly twice as effectively as butyro-cholinesterase, while the di*iso*propyl analogue is ten times more effective on the butyro- as on the aceto-cholinesterase. The selective action of competitive inhibitors probably depends on a number of factors of which a negatively charged group present in the active centres of aceto-cholinesterases but not in those of butyro-cholinesterases, may be one. This point is discussed more fully below.

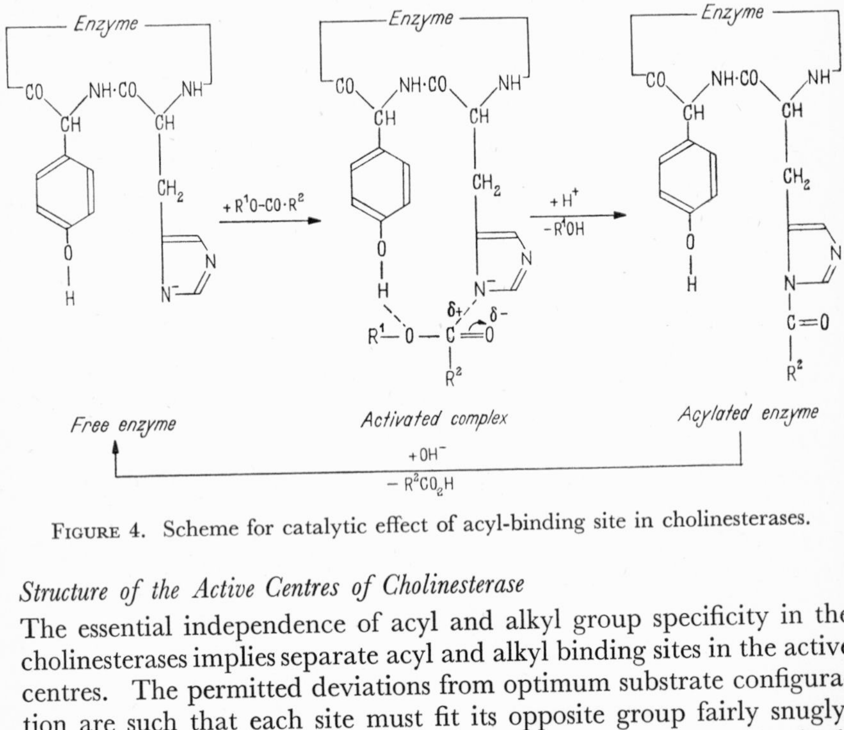

FIGURE 4. Scheme for catalytic effect of acyl-binding site in cholinesterases.

Structure of the Active Centres of Cholinesterase

The essential independence of acyl and alkyl group specificity in the cholinesterases implies separate acyl and alkyl binding sites in the active centres. The permitted deviations from optimum substrate configuration are such that each site must fit its opposite group fairly snugly. Wilson and Bergmann (1950b) have suggested, mainly on the basis of pH effects, that the acyl-binding site contains a nucleophilic group which forms a link with the electrophilic carboxyl carbon of the acyl group, and an electrophilic group which forms a link (possibly a hydrogen bond) with one or other of the ester oxygens. The pK values of these groups suggest that they might be imidazole nitrogen and the hydroxyl or amino-nitrogen of tyrosine respectively. A hypothetical scheme for ester hydrolysis on this basis is presented in FIGURE 4.

The difference between cholinesterases cannot be accounted for solely on the basis of differences in acyl specificity. There is evidence

314

for at least one additional factor which operates at the alkyl end of the molecule. The affinity of acetylcholine is about equal to that of its uncharged carbon analogue for butyro-cholinesterase but is much greater for aceto-cholinesterase. This suggests that the alkyl-binding site in aceto-cholinesterases contains an additional group which interacts with the positive charge on acetylcholine. Calculations based on the greater affinity of choline for aceto-cholinesterase relative to butyro-cholinesterase have shown that a singly ionized group, *e.g.* carboxyl, could account for the increased binding (Adams and Whittaker, 1950). Wilson and Bergmann (1950a) have come to the same conclusion. This ' negative nitrogen-attracting ' group may explain a number of special properties of the aceto-cholinesterases such as inhibition by excess substrate, ability to hydrolyse secondary esters, the effect of positive ions on enzyme activity and selective inhibition by certain organic cations (Whittaker, 1951).

Aconitase

The enzyme aconitase catalyses the formation of an equilibrium mixture of citrate, *iso*citrate and *cis*-aconitate from any one of these substances:

$$
\begin{array}{ccccc}
\text{CH}_2\text{CO}_2\text{H} & & \text{CH}_2\cdot\text{CO}_2\text{H} & & \text{CH}_2\cdot\text{CO}_2\text{H} \\
| & \xrightarrow[+\text{H}_2\text{O}]{-\text{H}_2\text{O}} & | & \xrightarrow[-\text{H}_2\text{O}]{+\text{H}_2\text{O}} & | \\
\text{HO}\cdot\text{C}\cdot\text{CO}_2\text{H} & & \text{C}\cdot\text{CO}_2\text{H} & & \text{CH}\cdot\text{CO}_2\text{H} \\
| & & \| & & | \\
\text{CH}_2\text{CO}_2\text{H} & & \text{CH}\cdot\text{CO}_2\text{H} & & \text{CHOH}\cdot\text{CO}_2\text{H} \\
\text{Citrate} & & \textit{cis}\text{-Aconitate} & & \textit{iso}\text{-Citrate}
\end{array}
$$

It forms an essential link in the tricarboxylic acid cycle which constitutes the terminal pathway of carbohydrate and fat oxidation in the animal organism. Its function is to convert citrate, formed by the condensing enzyme from acetyl-coenzyme A and oxaloacetate, into *iso*citrate which is utilized by the next enzyme in the cycle, *iso*citric dehydrogenase. The product is oxalosuccinate, which is converted via α-ketoglutarate, succinate, fumarate, and malate back to oxaloacetate, which is then available for condensing with a further molecule of acetyl-coenzyme A.

Studies by Wood and his co-workers (see Wood, 1946) showed that carboxyl-labelled pyruvate was converted into α-ketoglutarate labelled on only one carboxyl group. This was held to exclude citrate, a symmetrical molecule, from the cycle. Ogston (1948) pointed out that citrate might be asymmetrically converted to *iso*citrate provided that citrate combined by three-point attachment to an active centre in which the three combining points were not equivalent. Subsequent work (Potter and Heidelberger, 1948) has confirmed that citrate is in fact an intermediary in the cycle. This provides yet another example of the importance of stereochemical factors even with substrates which do not themselves show stereoisomerism.

The essential role of aconitase suggests that specific inhibitors of aconitase would be powerful metabolic poisons. This has been shown to be the basis of the toxic action of fluoroacetate by Peters and co-workers (*cf* Peters, 1952). Apparently fluoroacetyl-coenzyme A can replace acetyl-coenzyme A in the condensation reaction; the product, fluorocitrate, is a powerful competitive inhibitor of aconitase, no doubt because of the close similarity of its shape to citrate, combined with the inertness of the C—F link. *In vivo*, citrate accumulation is a character-istic sign of fluoroacetate intoxication. The conversion of a molecule non-toxic *per se* into a highly toxic substance by essential tissue enzymes has been termed 'lethal synthesis' (Peters, 1952).

STEREOSPECIFICITY AND THE MECHANISM OF ENZYME ACTION
Although Pasteur may be said to have discovered stereospecificity when he found that ammonium D-tartrate but not the L-isomer was fermented by certain moulds, the phenomenon was first systematically studied by Emil Fischer and his pupils, beginning in 1894. This was the logical outcome of Fischer's work on the constitution of sugars and peptides. It was natural to ask whether the many new sugars which he had described, such as talose, gulose, the glucoheptoses and gluco-octoses, shared with the naturally occurring hexoses, D-glucose, D-mannose, D-fructose and D-galactose, the biological property of being fermented by yeast. Fischer and Thierfelder (1894) found that they did not. They attributed this to the existence in the yeast cell of catalytic agents which conformed in their configuration to the fermetable hexoses and not to the other sugars.

Fischer and Thierfelder also noticed that most strains of yeast, in addition to fermenting the monosaccharides just mentioned, could also utilize maltose and other α-D-glucosides, but not lactose. One strain, however, utilized lactose but not maltose or methyl α-D-glucoside. Fischer (1894a, b; 1895a, b) correctly attributed this to the presence in the maltose-fermenting yeasts of an enzyme, maltase, capable of splitting α-glucosides, but without action on β-glucosides, and in the lactose yeast of a specific lactase without action on either α- or β-glucosides. He also recognized that the utilization of sucrose by yeast was dependent on the presence of a third enzyme, invertase, which converts sucrose to glucose and fructose. Fischer also studied almond emulsin; he found that it was distinct from yeast lactase and could hydrolyse a wide range of β-glucosides and β-galactosides, but had no action on α-glycosides. He made extensive use of the specific glyco-sidases for determining the configuration of new glycosides. Fischer summarized his conclusions in the following famous passage (Fischer, 1894a):

316

'Invertin and emulsin, as is well known, bear much resemblance to the proteins and undoubtedly possess, like these, an asymmetrically constructed molecule. Their limited action on the glucosides may thus be explained by the assumption that only by like geometrical structure, may that approach of molecules take place which is requisite for the release of chemical processes. To use a metaphor, I would say that enzyme and glucoside *must fit together like a lock and key**, to be able to exert a chemical action one upon the other.'

Further work showed that enzyme stereospecificity was a widespread phenomenon and extended to compounds showing geometrical isomerism. Thus fumarase catalyses the hydration of fumarate to L-malate and is without action on maleate (Dakin, 1922).

The 'lock-and-key' theory has received much support from the specificity studies of recent years. These have demonstrated, as we have seen, that molecular shape is an important, though not the only, factor in determining which compounds interact with an enzyme, either as substrates or inhibitors. The theory does not, however, explain how specificity is related to other aspects of enzyme action.

Among the many theories which have been advanced to explain the mechanism of enzyme action, three concepts have proved particularly valuable and will now be briefly discussed. These are, the 'polyaffinity theory', the 'strain theory' and the 'intermediate compound' theory. The polyaffinity theory grew out of the observation, of which several examples have been given in this chapter, that modifications of different parts of a substrate molecule frequently exert an approximately independent effect on the rate of enzyme action. Thus the separate specificity requirements of the carbohydrate and aglycon portions of a glycoside suggest that the substrate makes contact at two points on the enzyme surface through the carbohydrate residue and through the aglycon. This was the 'diaffinity' theory of Euler and Josephson (for discussion and references see Haldane, 1930). The 'polyaffinity' theory of Bergmann (*cf* Bergmann, Zervas, Fruton, Schneider and Schleich, 1935) was an extension of this to cover the case of the proteases, where, as we have seen (p. 301), at least three points of contact are required to explain the specificity data. To explain the 'activation' of the substrate, Euler and Josephson suggested that the combining points in the active centres might not correspond exactly with those of the substrate ; when the substrate was adsorbed, 'straining' of the substrate molecule might occur which would make it more reactive. On this theory, structural analogues of the substrate whose unstrained configurations conform to the strained configuration of the substrate, might be expected to be very effective competitive inhibitors. That this idea is not too fanciful is shown by the following

* Reviewer's italics. The translation is as literal as possible in an attempt to preserve the flavour of the original.

example.   The affinity of prostigmine for cholinesterases is about 10^4 greater than that of acetylcholine, with a smaller carbonyl–nitrogen distance.   On the somewhat questionable assumption that the affinity constants (K_1, K_2) represent true equilibrium constants, the difference in the binding energies of the two substances is equal to the difference in the logarithms of the affinity constants multiplied by the gas constant and the absolute temperature $[(\log K_1 - \log K_2)\ RT]$.   The energy difference involved even if only partly accounted for by the stretching of a C—O link in the substrate would correspond to a deformation of several per cent.

Although enzyme reactions are often thought of as involving only one activated intermediate, the ' enzyme–substrate complex ', there is increasing evidence that this is an oversimplification.   We have seen that enzymes catalysing hydrolysis and phosphorolysis reactions also possess transferase activity.   This and other evidence seems to indicate that enzyme reactions may occur in at least two stages, the enzyme–substrate complex being transformed into an unstable intermediate compound between the enzyme and a moiety of the substrate molecule, before finally breaking down to enzyme and products.   Intermediate compound formation has also been invoked to explain oxidative phosphorylation (Velick, 1953).   This mechanism is an extremely likely one, for it is the basis of many examples of organic catalysis (Langenbeck, 1953).

The binding of enzyme and substrate may involve many different types of interaction ranging from normal electrovalent and covalent links through hydrogen bonds to the various types of intermolecular exchange forces such as the van der Waals' dispersion forces.   Pauling has pointed out that van der Waals' forces may make a significant contribution to the total binding energy when the contact area of substrate and enzyme is large.   Stereospecificity may be thought of as arising from the need for accurate spatial correspondence between the combining groups on the enzyme and those in the substrate.   Incorrect orientation may operate against enzyme activity both by failing to bring interacting groups together and also by introducing steric hindrance or ionic repulsion so preventing the close approach of substrate and enzyme.

Enzyme specificity has many analogies with that of antibodies for their antigens.   The study of the antigen-antibody reaction was greatly facilitated by the discovery of Landsteiner that antibody formation can be evoked in response to the injection of antigens consisting of proteins to which synthetic groups have been attached (see Landsteiner, 1945).   The antibody is specific for the attached group which is called the haptenic group (ἅπτειν, to grasp).   Pauling and his associates (cf Pauling, 1948) have studied the specificity of many of these antibodies; they found that the molecular shape of the haptenic group is the main

318

factor in determining the degree of interaction which takes place. In some cases the affinity of the antibody for the haptenic group is in reasonably good agreement with that calculated on the basis of van der Waals' interaction energy. Adams and Whittaker (1950) have applied the method with partial success to cholinesterases. It is hoped to give a fuller account of antibody specificity in a future volume of this series.

The analogy between enzyme and antibody specificity reminds us that enzyme specificity is only one facet of the general phenomenon of biological specificity, which includes the interaction of drugs, hormones and their antagonists with cell receptors and the growth-promoting effect of vitamins and other dietary factors.

REFERENCES

Adams, D. H. and Thompson, R. H. S. (1948) *Biochem. J.* **42,** 170
— and Whittaker, V. P. (1950) *Biochim. biophys. Acta* **4,** 543
Aldridge, W. N. (1953a, b, c) *Biochem. J.* **53,** 62, 110, 117; (1953d) *ibid* **54,** 442
— and Davison, A. N. (1952) *ibid* **52,** 663
Alles, G. A. and Hawes, R. C. (1940) *J. biol. Chem.* **133,** 375
Andrews, K. J. M., Atherton, F. R., Bergel, F. and Morrison, A. L. (1952) *J. chem. Soc.* 780
Appleyard, J. (1948) *Biochem. J.* **42,** 596
Augustinsson, K. B. (1948) *Acta physiol. scand.* **15,** Suppl. 52
Axelrod, B. (1948) *J. biol. Chem.* **172,** 1
Bacon, J. S. D. (1952) *Biochem. J.* **50,** xviii
Balls, A. K. and Jansen, E. F. (1952) *Advanc. Enzymol.* **13,** 321
Banister, J., Whittaker, V. P. and Wijesundera, S. (1953) *J. Physiol.* **121,** 55
Bass, W. B., Schueler, F. W., Featherstone, R. M. and Gross, E. G. (1950) *J. Pharmacol.* **100,** 465
Bentley, R. and Neuberger, A. (1949) *Biochem. J.* **45,** 584
Bergel, F. and Parkes, M. W. (1952) in *Progress in Organic Chemistry*, ed. J. W. Cook, vol. 1 p. 173 London, Butterworths
Bergmann, F. and Shimoni, A. (1953) *Biochem. J.* **55,** 50
— Wilson, I. B. and Nachmansohn, D. (1950) *J. biol. Chem.* **186,** 693
Bergmann, M. and Fruton, J. S. (1941) *Advanc. Enzymol.* **1,** 63
— Zervas, L., Fruton, J. S., Schneider, F. and Schleich, H. (1935) *J. biol. Chem.* **109,** 325
Biochemical Society Symposium no. 1 (1948) *The relation of optical form to biological activity in the amino-acid series* ed. R. T. Williams, Cambridge University Press
Biltz, W. (1930) *Z. phys. Chem.* **151,** 1
Brown, D. H. (1951) *Biochim. biophys. Acta* **7,** 487
Burgen, A. S. V. and Hobbiger, H. (1951) *Brit. J. Pharmacol.* **6,** 593
Casida, J. E., Allen, T. C. and Stahmann, M. A. (1953) *Nature, Lond.* **172,** 243
Cohen, J. A. and Warringa, M. G. P. J. (1953) *Biochim. biophys. Acta* **11,** 52
Colowick, S. P. (1951) in *The Enzymes*, ed. J. B. Sumner and K. Myrbäck, vol. 2, pt. 1, New York, Academic Press
Cramer, F. B. and Woodward, G. E. (1952) *J. Franklin Inst.* **253,** 354
Cunningham, L. W. and Neurath, H. (1953) *Biochim. biophys. Acta* **11,** 310
Dakin, H. D. (1922) *J. biol. Chem.* **52,** 183
Davies, D. R., Risley, J. E. and Rutland, J. P. (1953) *Biochem. J.* **53,** xv
Davison, A. N. (1953) *ibid* **54,** 583

Easson, L. H. and Stedman, E. (1937) *ibid* **31**, 1723
Fischer, E. (1894a, b) *Ber. dtsch. chem. Ges.* **27**, 2985, 3479; (1895a) *ibid* **28**, 1429; (1895b) *Hoppe-Seyl. Z.* **26**, 60
— and Thierfelder, H. (1894) *Ber. dtsch. chem. Ges.* **27**, 2036
Fischer, E. H., Kohtès, L. and Fellig, J. (1951) *Helv. chim. acta* **34**, 1132
Fruton, J. S. and Bergmann, M. (1942) *J. biol. Chem.* **145**, 253
Gage, J. C. (1953) *Biochem. J.* **54**, 426
Gardiner, J. E. and Kilby, B. A. (1952) *ibid* **51**, 78
Glick, D. (1938) *J. biol. Chem.* **125**, 729
Goldstein, D. B. and Goldstein, A. (1953) *J. gen. Microbiol.* **8**, 8
Gottschalk, A. (1950) *Advanc. Carbohyd. Chem.* **5**, 49
Grant, P. T. and Long, C. (1952) *Biochem. J.* **50**, xx
Haldane, J. B. S. (1930) *Enzymes*, London, Longmans
Hammett, L. P. (1940) *Physical Organic Chemistry*, New York, McGraw-Hill
Hartley, B. S. and Kilby, B. A. (1952) *Biochem. J.* **50**, 672; (1954) *ibid* **56**, 288
Hassid, W. Z. and Doudoroff, M. (1950) *Advanc. Carbohyd. Chem.* **5**, 29
— — and Barker, H. A. (1951) in *The Enzymes*, ed. J. B. Sumner and K. Myrbäck, vol. 1, pt. 2, New York, Academic Press
Hawkins, R. D. and Gunter, J. M. (1946) *Biochem. J.* **40**, 192
Helferich, B. (1938) *Ergebn. Enzymforsch.* **7**, 83
— Grünler, S. and Gnüchtel, A. (1937) *Hoppe-Seyl. Z.* **248**, 85
Hobbiger, F. (1951) *Brit. J. Pharmacol.* **6**, 21
Jansen, E. F., Nutting, M. D. F. and Balls, A. K. (1947) *J. biol. Chem.* **170**, 417; (1948) *ibid* **175**, 975
— — Jang, R. and Balls, A. K. (1949) *ibid* **179**, 189
Johnstone, J. H. and Mitchell, I. L. S. (1953) *Biochem. J.* **55**, xvii
Kaufman, S. and Neurath, H. (1949a) *Arch. Biochem.* **21**, 245; (1949b) *J. biol. Chem.* **181**, 623
— Schwert, G. W. and Neurath, H. (1948) *Arch. Biochem.* **17**, 203
Keilin, D. and Hartree, E. F. (1948) *Biochem. J.* **42**, 221; (1952) *ibid* **50**, 331
Koelle, G. B. (1950) *J. Pharmacol.* **100**, 158; (1953) *Biochem. J.* **53**, 217
Koshland, D. E. (1952) *J. Amer. chem. Soc.* **74**, 2286; (1954) in *The Mechanism of Enzyme Action*, ed. W. D. McElroy and B. Glass, The Johns Hopkins Press, Baltimore, Md.
Kunitz, M. and MacDonald, M. R. (1946) *J. gen. Physiol.* **29**, 393
Landsteiner, K. (1945) *The Specificity of Serological Reactions*, 2nd ed. Harvard University Press, Cambridge, Mass.
Langenbeck, W. (1953) *Advanc. Enzymol.* **14**, 163
Leloir, L. F. (1953) *ibid* **14**, 193
Lemieux, R. U. and Huber, G. (1953) *J. Amer. chem. Soc.* **75**, 4118
MacAllister, R. V., Harmon, K. M. and Niemann, C. (1949) *J. biol. Chem.* **177**, 767
Mazur, A. (1946) *ibid* **164**, 271
Mendel, B. and Rudney, H. (1943) *Biochem. J.* **37**, 53
Meyerhof, O. and Green, H. (1950) *J. biol. Chem.* **183**, 377
Morton, R. K. (1953) *Nature, Lond.* **172**, 65
Mounter, L. A. (1953) D. Phil. Thesis, Oxford University, and personal communications
— and Whittaker, V. P. (1953a, b) *Biochem. J.* **53**, 167; **54**, 551
Murray, D. R. P. (1930) *ibid* **24**, 1890
Myers, D. K. (1953) *ibid* **55**, 67
Neurath, H. and Schwert, G. W. (1950) *Chem. Rev.* **46**, 69
Ogston, A. G. (1948) *Nature, Lond.* **162**, 963
Ord, M. G. and Thompson, R. H. S. (1951) *Biochem. J.* **49**, 191
Ormerod, W. E. (1953) *ibid* **54**, 701

Pasini, C., Vercellone, A. and Erspamer, V. (1953) *Liebigs Ann.* **578**, 6
Pauling, L. (1948) *Chem. & Ind.* Suppl. 1 (*Lecture to XI Int. Congr. pure appl. Chem.*)
Peat, S., Whelan, W. J. and Hinson, K. A. (1952) *Nature, Lond.* **170**, 1056
Peters, R. A. (1952) *Proc. roy. Soc. B* **139**, 143
Pigman, W. W. (1944) *Advanc. Enzymol.* **4**, 41
— and Goepp, R. M. (1948) *Chemistry of the Carbohydrates*, New York, Academic Press
Potter, V. R. and Heidelberger, C. (1948) *Nature, Lond.* **164**, 180
Ravin, H. A., Tsou, K. C. and Seligman, A. H. (1951) *J. biol. Chem.* **191**, 843
Schaffer, N. K., May, S. C. and Summerson, W. H. (1953) *ibid* **202**, 67
Schwert, G. W., Neurath, H., Kaufman, S. and Snoke, J. E. (1948) *ibid* **172**, 221
Smith, E. L. (1951) *Advanc. Enzymol.* **12**, 191
Snoke, J. E. and Neurath, H. (1950) *J. biol. Chem.* **182**, 577
Stedman, E., Stedman, E. and Easson, L. H. (1932) *Biochem. J.* **28**, 2056
Sturge, L. M. and Whittaker, V. P. (1950) *ibid* **47**, 518
Takano, K. and Tomoo, M. (1950) *J. Biochem., Tokyo* **37**, 435
Todrick, A., Fellowes, K. P. and Rutland, J. P. (1951) *Biochem. J.* **48**, 360
Trucco, R. E., Caputto, R., Leloir, L. F. and Mittelmann, N. (1948) *Arch. Biochem.* **18**, 137.
Veibel, S. (1950) in *The Enzymes*, ed. J. B. Sumner and K. Myrbäck, vol. 2, pt. 1, New York, Academic Press
Velick, S. F. (1953) *J. biol. Chem.* **203**, 563
Wagner-Jauregg, T. and Hackley, B. E. (1953) *J. Amer. chem. Soc.* **75**, 2125
Webb, E. C. (1948) *Biochem. J.* **42**, 96
Wescoe, W. C., Riker, W. F. and Beach, V. L. (1950) *J. Pharmacol.* **99**, 265
White, J. W. (1952) *Arch. Biochem. Biophys.* **39**, 238
Whittaker, V. P. (1951) *Physiol. Rev.* **31**, 312; (1953) *Biochem. J.* **54**, 660
Wilson, I. B. (1952) *J. biol. Chem.* **199**, 113
— and Bergmann, F. (1950a, b) *ibid* **185**, 479; **186**, 683
— — and Nachmansohn, D. (1950) *ibid* **186**, 781
Wood, H. G. (1946) *Physiol. Rev.* **26**, 198

9

THE STEREOCHEMISTRY OF COMPLEX COMPOUNDS

R. S. Nyholm

THE past twenty years or so have been a period of great advances in coordination chemistry. Following the days of Alfred Werner the subject languished for some years, but more recently there has been a gradual reawakening of interest and the approach has undergone some radical changes. Earlier, there had been a tendency to multiply the number of complex compounds and to deduce their shapes and properties largely from chemical evidence together with a limited number of physical techniques, such as conductivity in water. Recently, however, the fundamental research in inorganic chemistry needed for the atomic energy projects has helped to stimulate interest in coordination chemistry since most compounds of the transition elements, in aqueous solution at least, are complex compounds; furthermore, it has become abundantly clear that this subject offers a wide field for original research, much of which is directly applicable to problems in such varied fields as medical chemistry, analytical chemistry and applied chemistry. The two main causes for the recent developments in this subject, however, predated the atomic energy project and have merely been brought into focus by this work. These two causes are the rise of quantum mechanics and the application of the new physical techniques for studying inorganic complex compounds. These have been developed gradually but they are largely complementary. The workers in quantum mechanics have been able to relate the stereochemistry of inorganic compounds with the more fundamental electronic configuration of the atom, but they are limited, in most cases, to purely qualitative predictions and hence frequently to the indication of what possible shapes may be assumed by a particular molecule. The decision as to which of these is adopted may often be inferred from a knowledge of the physical properties of the molecule, such as its electric dipole moment, magnetic moment, infra-red and Raman spectra, *etc.* The complementary nature of the two factors needs to be emphasized; the magnetic moment of a bivalent nickel complex, for example, requires for its interpretation some acceptable theory relating orbitals used for bond formation with the number of unpaired electrons in the metal atom.

The theoretical basis of stereochemistry of covalent compounds is now well established and it is thought desirable to summarize briefly these principles first. The manner in which modern physical methods may be used to infer stereochemistry will be indicated and recent developments on the theoretical side will then be surveyed. After summarizing the more recent advances in each group of the periodic table, the present position in the rapidly developing field of stereochemical changes which occur during chemical reactions will be outlined. Limitations of space demand that special attention be paid in this article to theoretical developments, but it is hoped that other aspects may be more fully discussed in some later volume.

THEORETICAL BASIS OF STEREOCHEMISTRY

The principles underlying the modern theory of stereochemistry are relatively simple, but in many cases the theory is inclusive rather than exclusive. Usually some physical data are necessary to distinguish between two or more arrangements which are energetically feasible. First, it is necessary to distinguish between the effects on stereochemistry of the two extreme types of binding between atoms—electrovalency and covalency. Electrovalency gives rise to a lattice of charged ions; the arrangement of these ions is determined by their relative numbers, sizes and charges. We are not concerned here with ionic lattices except in so far as they occur by the aggregation of complex ions.

The second kind of binding arises from the sharing of two, or more, electrons between two atoms, forming the so-called ' covalent bond '. If, in a single bond, both electrons come originally from the same atom, the bond is called a coordinate link. Once formed, this is indistinguishable from a covalent bond, except that the two atoms are oppositely charged. Hence, this may be regarded as a covalent bond with considerable polarity. Such polar covalent bonds are generally weaker than ordinary covalent bonds between the same atoms.

A covalent bond may be considered to result from the overlap of two *atomic orbitals* from two originally separate atoms, forming a *molecular orbital* in the resulting molecule. Since the latter bears a relation to the two atomic orbitals from which it is derived, it is reasonable to postulate that the properties of the bond, *e.g.* direction, length, strength, are also related to the properties of the atomic orbitals of the two separate atoms. In polyatomic molecules the formation of a covalent bond may be considered by either the Hund–Mulliken Molecular Orbital Method, or the Pauling–Slater Valence Bond (Localized Pair) Method. Both are approximations because exact quantum mechanical calculations in polyatomic molecules are not yet feasible. For a discussion of stereochemistry the localized pair method has certain advantages and will be adopted here. For a more detailed treatment and references to original work, Coulson's (1952a) recent monograph should be consulted.

323

The basic principles with which we are concerned are as follows:
1. Any covalent bond results from the overlap of two atomic orbitals. When this overlap occurs along the line of centres of two atoms, the link is referred to as a σ bond (*e.g.* as in HCl); when a 'side-ways' overlap occurs the name π bond is used. Thus, the C:C bond in ethylene consists of a σ bond and a π bond.
2. The strength of a bond between two atoms is a function of the amount of overlap of the two atomic orbitals of the two bound atoms*. (This is known as the Principle of Maximum Overlapping; the overlap integral is given by $\int \Psi_A \Psi_B \, d\tau$ where Ψ_A and Ψ_B are the wave functions of the atomic orbitals of the atoms A and B, respectively, and dτ is an element of volume.)
3. The shape of a molecule is decided primarily by the directive properties of the atomic orbitals used in bond formation in order that overlap is a maximum and energy a minimum.

Three types of atomic orbital need concern us, *s*, *p* and *d* orbitals, corresponding to electrons with subsidiary quantum numbers of 0, 1 and 2 respectively. In FIGURE 1 the *number* and *relative energies* of such

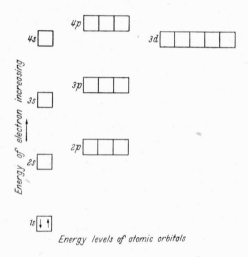

Energy levels of atomic orbitals

FIGURE 1. Sequence of Atomic Orbitals

orbitals at each quantum level in a poly-electronic atom are shown (Coulson, 1952; Pauling, 1945). Each orbital may contain a single unpaired electron (a) or two paired electrons (b) represented :

* Other factors, of course, also affect bond strength, *e.g.* inter-nuclear repulsions. These have been discussed qualitatively by Walsh (1948, 1951) and more quantitatively by Mulliken (1950, 1951) in connection with his proposed 'magic formula' for bond strengths.

The shapes of s, p and one kind of d orbitals are indicated in FIGURE 2.

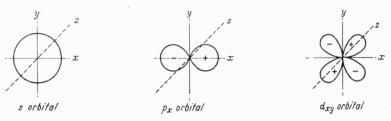

s orbital   *p_x orbital*   *d_{xy} orbital*

FIGURE 2. Shapes of Atomic Orbitals

The significance of the positive and negative sign of the lobes in the case of p and d orbitals has been discussed by Coulson (1952); for our purposes it is unimportant since the probability of finding the electron inside the orbital is given by Ψ^2, which is thus everywhere positive.

In actual molecules the atomic orbitals used for bond formation are rarely pure s, p or d in character. Instead, a process of ' hybridization ' occurs, forming hybrid bond orbitals possessing greater strength and different directional properties from the pure s, p or d orbitals. Thus, mixing of an s and three p orbitals (sp^3 hybridization) gives the familiar arrangement of carbon with four equivalent bonds directed to the corners of a tetrahedron. It is convenient at this juncture to summarize the shapes which arise from the use of the various combinations of orbitals. TABLE 1 gives the results of Kimball (1940), who approached the problem from the point of view of group theory.

The shapes listed in TABLE 1 can be predicted only if one is certain that the orbitals indicated are those actually used for bond formation. Therefore, unless some atomic property can be measured from which we may confidently infer the bonding orbitals, this table is of limited value for predicting stereochemistry. Magnetic data are often useful for this purpose; they sometimes enable one to infer the bonding orbitals used from the number of unpaired electrons. It is usual to assume that the lowest hybrid bond orbitals available above those occupied are used for bond formation. Occasionally this assumption is incorrect for reasons discussed on p. 333.

It is important to keep in mind that in practice the hybrid orbitals are frequently not as simple as shown in TABLE 1 (*cf* Chapter 1, p. 10). Thus, for two bonds to an atom, angles varying from 90° to 180° have been observed, indicating that x in the hybridization $s^x p^{2-x}$ can have almost any value from 0 to 1. Similarly, in molecules of the type AB_3 the hybridization on A may vary from p^3 to sp^2 (see Chapter 1, p. 25). In marked contrast with these observations the four sp^3 bonds in substituted methanes are practically unaffected by varying the groups attached to the carbon atom. Thus, in CHF_3 the F—C—F and H—C—F angles show very little deviation ($\sim 1°$) from the tetrahedral angle, in spite of the high electronegativity of the fluorine atoms (Allen and Sutton, 1950) the bonds to which might be expected to contain more p character than the C—H bonds. The p orbitals project more than an s orbital and hence would enable the bonding electrons to be closer to the fluorine atoms. However, two factors other than the

TABLE 1. STABLE BOND ARRANGEMENTS AND STEREOCHEMISTRY

Coordination No.	Arrangement	Combination of Orbitals
2	Linear	sp, dp
	Angular	p^2, ds, d^2
3	Trigonal plane	sp^2, dp^2, d^2s, d^3
	Unsymmetrical plane	dsp
	Trigonal pyramid	p^3, d^2p
4	Tetrahedral	sp^3, d^3s
	Tetragonal plane	dsp^2, d^2p^2
	Irregular tetrahedron	d^2sp, dp^3, d^3p
	Tetragonal pyramid	d^4
5*	Bipyramid	dsp^3, d^3sp
	Tetragonal pyramid	d^2sp^2, d^4s, d^2p^3, d^4p
	Pentagonal plane	d^3p^2
	Pentagonal pyramid	d^5
6	Octahedron	d^2sp^3
	Trigonal prism	d^4sp, d^5p
	Trigonal antiprism	d^3p^3
	Mixed	d^3sp^3, d^5s, d^4p^2
7†	$[ZrF_7]^{3-}$ structure	d^3sp^3, d^5sp
	$[TaF_7]^{2-}$ structure	d^4sp^2, d^4p^3, d^5p^2
8	Dodecahedron	d^4sp^3
	Antiprism	d^5p^3
	Face-centred prism	d^5sp^2

* In addition to the bipyramid using $(ns)(np)^3(nd)$ orbitals (where n is the principal quantum number), Daudel and Bucher (1945) have shown that if the d orbital is a quantum level one less than that of the s and p, i.e. $(n-1)d$, ns, $(np)^3$ orbitals, a square pyramid is obtained. This conclusion also follows from the group theory approach (Craig, 1953).
† The pentagonal bipyramid (IF$_7$) was not discussed by Kimball. See also Duffey (1950d, 1950e).

stabilization consequent upon the formation of a particular kind of hybridization also affect stereochemistry. These are steric repulsions and the effect of non-bonding lone pairs of electrons. Thus, the NH_3 and H_2O molecules approximate roughly to sp^3 hybridization with one and two electron pairs respectively being involved in the hybridization; on the simple theory one would expect p^3 and p^2 binding respectively with 90° bond angles.

The extent to which bond angles deviate from the 'ideal' values expected for pure p or sp orbital hybridizations has been discussed by several authors; particularly Walsh (1953) (cf Chapter 1); Linnett and Poe (1951); Lennard-Jones and co-workers (1952), and Duncan and Pople (1953). The latter papers emphasize the importance of inter-electronic repulsions in determining valency angles and the part which is played by unshared electron pairs in various stereochemical arrangements. It is interesting to note that some years ago Sidgwick and Powell (1940), in their comprehensive review of stereochemical shapes, noted the relevance of unshared pairs without discussing the atomic orbital which they occupied. Finally, for a discussion of the shapes of certain hybridizations involving higher coordination numbers, the work of Duffey (1949–51) is relevant.

Multiple Bonds

In addition to the overlap of atomic orbitals along the lines of centres giving rise to the σ bond, a ' side-ways ' overlap of atomic orbitals may also occur, giving rise to a π bond. This additional π binding results in three important effects: (i) an increase in total bond strength as compared with the single σ bond; (ii) decreased internuclear distance as compared with a single σ bond; and (iii) (usually) limitations on twisting or rotation of the bond owing to the steric requirements for the side-ways overlap of the π bond. This may affect stereochemistry. In general, the additional increment of bond strength resulting from a π bond is not as much as that of a σ bond owing to the smaller overlap integral, but this need not necessarily be true; Mulliken (1952) has put forward the view that in the N_2 molecule, in which there are one σ bond and two π bonds, the σ bond actually makes a *negative* contribution to the bond strength owing to the close proximity of the two nitrogen atoms. He proposes that the whole of the binding arises from the π overlap. Two kinds of π bonds are possible, corresponding to the ' covalent ' and ' coordinate ' bonds. In the first type each of the two bound atoms supplies one electron each to the π electron pair. Such a π bond occurs, for example, in ethylene. In the second type of π bond both electrons come originally from the same atom. This second type of π bond requires (a) that one atom has an electron pair available for donation and (b) that the second atom has a suitable vacant p or d orbital which can overlap with and hence make use of the electron pair. Such ' dative π bonds ' (Dewar, 1946; Walsh, 1947; Chatt, 1950–52) are considered by Pauling (1945) to occur in many complex cyanides, metal cyanides and nitro-compounds of the transition metals. They are probably much more common than has hitherto been supposed. In TABLE 2 a summary is given of the various types of π bonds together with some examples.

Finally, it should be pointed out that in many, if not most, cases the structures of metal complexes, such as those in TABLE 2, cannot be represented satisfactorily by any one single structure and that resonance among single and double bond structures may occur. A major factor in the contribution of each is probably the tendency for the atoms to acquire a charge relative to one another in some measure related to their electronegativities, as well as the tendency for this charge to be as small as possible. Pauling (1948) has proposed that the charge on an atom always lies between $+1$ and -1 units and is usually close to zero; he suggests that this inherent tendency influences the contributions to the resonance hybrid.

TABLE 2. TYPES OF π BONDS

Ordinary π Bond	Dative π Bond
One electron initially from each atom.	Both electrons from same atom. In the examples quoted, except the first, the metal atom supplies both electrons in the bond.
$p\pi$—$p\pi$ e.g. in $H_2C\!\!=\!\!CH_2$	$p\pi$—$p\pi$ as in H_3C $\diagdown$ $B\!\!\stackrel{\leftarrow}{=}\!\!N$ $\diagup$ CH_3* H_3C $\diagup$ $\diagdown$ CH_3
$p\pi$—$d\pi$ O $O\ O$ O $\diagdown\diagup$ $\diagdown\diagup$ e.g. in SO_3, S , S , $\downarrow$ $\parallel$ O O etc; $R_3P\!\!=\!\!O$; $R_2S\!\!=\!\!O$	$d\pi$—$p\pi$ e.g. as in $Fe\!\!=\!\!C\!\!=\!\!N$ in cyanides; O $-$ $Fe\!\!=\!\!N$ $\nearrow$ in nitrites; $\searrow$ O $Ni\!\!=\!\!C\!\!=\!\!O$ in carbonyls.
	$d\pi$—$d\pi$ e.g. as in $Ni\!\!=\!\!AsR_3$ in tertiary arsine complexes; $Pt\!\!=\!\!PR_3$ in tertiary phosphine complexes; $Pd\!\!=\!\!SR_2$ in sulphine complexes.

* See Raman spectra studies by Becher and Goubeau (1952) and electric dipole measurements by Becher (1952).

PHYSICAL METHODS OF INVESTIGATION

It is not intended to discuss here in detail the various modern physical methods for the determination of stereochemistry of coordination compounds, but the reliability of such methods and the newer applications of certain of these techniques will be considered.

Classical Techniques

The classical techniques for studying stereochemistry include chemical methods, optical resolution, molecular weight determinations, conductivity and potentiometric studies. Of these, the oldest method is probably that involving chemical methods of replacement; this was widely used in inorganic complexes until fairly recently but is now generally regarded as most unreliable except in certain special cases. In general, the arrangement of groups around a central metal atom was inferred from various chemical reactions involving replacement, it being assumed that the incoming group necessarily took the place originally occupied by the outgoing group. This method was applied particularly for ' proving ' that two acid radicals, *e.g.* two —NO_2 groups, were in *cis* rather than *trans* positions, because they could be replaced by a chelate group such as the oxalate group which for steric reasons must necessarily occupy two *cis* positions in the molecule. On this basis it was erroneously concluded that Erdmann's salt, $NH_4^+[Co(NH_3)_2(NO_2)_4]^-$, was a *cis*-diammine complex of octahedral cobalt rather than a *trans* compound. Treatment of the complex with the oxalate group yielded two compounds, one of which was resolvable. Since to be optically active the latter must be a *cis*-diammino-*cis*-dinitro-oxalato compound, it was assumed that the two NH_3 groups in the original Erdmann's salt were also in *cis* positions. Such an argument makes the (unjustified) assumption that no migration of groups, other than those being replaced, occurs during chemical reactions. That such an assumption was unjustified had been demonstrated by the early work of Werner and more recent studies amply verify this. Finally, it has been shown by Wells (1936) by x-ray crystallography that the silver salt derivative of Erdmann's salt, chosen for convenience, is actually the *trans* isomer. This subject is discussed in greater detail on p. 350.

Optical resolution is the second long-established method for studying stereochemistry. With four-covalent metals the preparation of stable ions of the type $[M.ABCD]^{n+}$ is not practicable and to establish the tetrahedral arrangement of groups around a metal one must use a suitable unsymmetrical chelate group. For example, the tetrahedral arrangement of the valencies around the zinc atom in zinc[II] bis-8-hydroxyquinoline-5-sulphonic acid has been confirmed by re-solution of this ion in pyridine solution (Liu and Bailar, 1951). With octahedral coordination the use of an unsymmetrical chelate group is no longer necessary and the following types of complex ions have been resolved: $[M(chelate)_3]^{n\pm}$; $[M(chelate)_2X_2]^{n\pm}$ (provided that the two X groups are in *cis* positions); and more complex types such as $[M(chelate)X_2Y_2]^{n\pm}$, provided that the X and Y groups are in suitable *cis* positions. The resolution of an eight-covalent ion, $[U(C_2O_4)_4]^{2-}$ has been reported (Marchi and McReynolds, 1943; *cf* Marchi, 1943), but in this instance the result does not indicate unambiguously the stereochemistry of the ion as it does with a six-covalent metal atom (see p. 347).

In structural investigations, the method of x-ray crystallography must always be regarded as the final arbiter but it is important to emphasize that in the absence of a complete determination some uncertainty as to the structure often remains. Some of the earlier investigations would repay further investigation on this account. Owing to the time taken to carry out a complete structural analysis, the total number of determinations being carried out in relationship to the number needed is small. There is a need for the study by x-rays of more of the key compounds, the elucidation of the structure of which will enable many other problems to be solved. The method of electron diffraction, whilst less widely applicable than the x-ray method, owing to the necessity for using compounds in the gas phase, is nevertheless specially valuable in certain cases because it is possible to effect a structure determination on a compound without the possible constraining effects of crystal lattice forces.

The foregoing methods are more direct than the more recent techniques, *e.g.* the use of electric dipole moments, magnetic susceptibility and spectroscopic measurements. The results of the last-named method must be used in conjunction with other physical measurements and require certain theoretical assumptions before the shape of a molecule may be inferred.

Electric Dipole Moments

The value of electric dipole moments is well known but their limitations are now more widely recognized. Since the elegant use of this technique by Jensen (1936a) in his study of the isomerism of bivalent platinum compounds of the type PtX_2Y_2 (X=halogen; Y=AsR_3, PR_3, SR_2, *etc*), its application has been extended to the complexes of other transition metals. By this means it has been shown that $CoCl_2$, $2Et_3P$ is either *cis* planar or tetrahedral (Jensen, 1936c), and that whereas $NiCl_2$, $2Et_3P$ is *trans* planar, the compound $Ni(NO_3)_2$, $2Et_3P$ is either *cis* planar or tetrahedral (Jensen, 1936b). The technique is most safely employed in complex chemistry for distinguishing between two possible structures for which a large difference in dipole moment is expected. Thus, Jensen found that of the two isomers having the formula $PtCl_2$, $2Et_3P$, one had a dipole moment of approximately 0 Debye units (D) whereas the other had a moment of about 12D. These values are consistent with the hypothesis that the former is a *trans* planar isomer and the latter a *cis* planar one. However, the second conclusion is conditional only, as the high dipole moment is also consistent with a tetrahedral arrangement of the bonds. The greatest care must be taken in deducing the stereochemistry of an inorganic molecule from its dipole moment when there is only a relatively small difference between the moments of the possible stereochemical arrangements. For inorganic compounds two main limitations arise from uncertainty as to the contribution from (a) atom polarization, and (b) the contribution to the total dipole moment of unshared electron pairs on the metal atom, if any, particularly when the central atom is two- or three-covalent.

With regard to the first of these, it is common practice in calculating the electric dipole moments of organic compounds to allow 5 per cent of the electronic polarization for atom polarization. With inorganic complexes, however, we are dealing with atoms of much higher atomic weights and the atomic polarizations are probably correspondingly

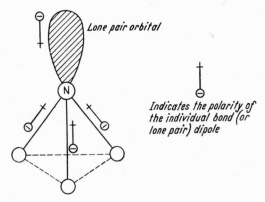

FIGURE 3. Diagram of NF_3 molecule

higher. Thus, in metallic tris-acetylacetones it has been shown that atom polarization is as high as 50 per cent of the total polarization (Coop and Sutton, 1938). The problem becomes serious for molecules with a small dipole moment like $NiBr_3$, $2Et_3P$, the structure of which has been inferred largely from the electric dipole moment (Jensen and Nygaard, 1949). In this molecule a large correction for atom polarization must be assumed. There is a need for further work on this subject to set up a more reliable method for estimating atomic polarizations of heavy atoms, perhaps by compiling tables of constitutive corrections.

The position regarding the contribution of unshared pairs to the moment is rather confusing. Until recently it was customary to regard the dipole moment of a molecule as the vector sum of all the bond dipoles. However, it has been shown that in molecules like H_2O and NH_3 the lone-pair moments are comparable in size with those calculated for the bond dipoles themselves (Coulson, 1952; Duncan and Pople, 1953). Here, then, the measured dipole moment of the whole molecule cannot be regarded as the vector sum of two O—H or three N—H moments as the case may be. The problem is thrown in sharp relief by quoting the figures for nitrogen trifluoride, NF_3. In 1936, Watson, Kane and Ramaswamy (1936) showed that the electric dipole moment of this substance is only about $0 \cdot 2D$. By comparing this value with that of NH_3, for which the electric dipole moment is $1 \cdot 46D$, it was concluded that the NF_3 molecule is flat or nearly so. However, more recently Schomaker and Chia-Si Lu (1950) have found by electron diffraction that the molecule is actually pyramidal with an F—N—F angle of $102 \cdot 5°$ comparable with that of the H—N—H angles in NH_3 ($106°$ $47'$). The small electric dipole is observed because in the pyramidal NF_3 molecule the vector sum of the three N—F bond moments (with negative end on the F atoms) is nearly equal to but opposite in sign and direction from the moment of the lone-pair on the nitrogen atom (FIGURE 3). This difficulty does not arise as a rule when we are dealing with four- or six-covalent atoms because lone-pairs are usually not present.

Magnetic Susceptibility Measurements

The use of magnetic measurements as a stereochemical tool has been extended considerably since the enunciation of Pauling's theories relating bonding orbitals and stereochemistry. Like electric dipole moments, magnetic moment measurements fall into the category of 'indirect' stereochemical methods. They are of value for those elements for which different stereochemical arrangements are associated with different numbers of unpaired electrons, *i.e.* the first transition series of metals from Ti to Cu; also, they apply, but to a lesser extent, to compounds of metals in the other two transition series. Clearly, the number of unpaired electrons is also dependent upon the valency and this must be known before attempting to use the magnetic moment to deduce the stereochemistry. The basic principles of the Pauling theory relating stereochemistry in the first transition series with magnetic moments are:

1. For most purposes the number of unpaired electrons in an atom may be computed from the ' spin only ' formula*, *i.e.* magnetic moment $\mu = \sqrt{\{n(n+2)\}}$ Bohr magnetons (B.M.) where n = number of unpaired electrons.

2. When the magnetic moment of a complex is essentially the same as that of the free ion† (*i.e.* no spin coupling occurs) the bonds do not involve $3d$ orbitals. In the Pauling terminology the binding is ' ionic '.

3. Spin coupling with a reduction of either two or four in the number of unpaired electrons indicates that $3d$ orbitals are being used for (' covalent ') bond formation. This necessitates the transfer of un-paired electron(s) originally occupying the $3d$ orbital(s) now used for bond formation. Usually these displaced electron(s) pair off with other unpaired non-bonding $3d$ electrons.

* The size of the orbital contribution rarely gives rise to any doubt as to the *number* of unpaired electrons.
† Provided that the free ion contains *more* than three $3d$ electrons; this proviso is necessary because magnetic moments do not distinguish between $4s4p^34d^2$ and $3d^24s4p^3$ octahedral binding when three $3d$ electrons or less are present, *e.g.* Cr^{III}.

4. If no vacant $3d$ orbital(s) are available to accommodate the displaced electron(s) referred to in *3* then electron(s) may be promoted to vacant orbital(s) above those used for bond formation.

5. The orbitals used for σ bond formation are usually those immediately above those occupied by non-bonding electrons provided that these are a permissible combination for bond formation. This assumption is unreliable in certain cases where no electron pairing occurs (*cf* square Cu^{II} discussed below).

These principles are illustrated in FIGURE 4 by showing the electronic configuration of various complexes of bivalent cobalt. In (*iii*) no electron pairing occurs; in (*iv*) spin pairing occurs owing to covalent bond formation using *one* $3d$ orbital. In (*v*) two $3d$ orbitals are used for covalent bond formation, one electron being promoted.

Complex	Electronic Arrangement			Unpaired electrons	μ(B.M.) observed
	$3d$	$4s$	$4p$		
(*i*) Co (Metal)	[↓↑│↓↑│↓│↑]	[↓↑]	[│ │]	–	–
(*ii*) Co²⁺ (Free ion)	[↓↑│↓↑│↓│↑]	[ ]	[│ │]	3	4·8–5·2
(*iii*) Co^II Four tetrahedral $4s4p^3$ bonds	[↓↑│↓↑│↓│↑]	[↓↑]	[↓↑│↓↑│↓↑]	3	4·3–4·8
(*iv*) Co^II Four square planar $3d4s4p^2$ bonds	[↓↑│↓↑│↓↑│↓│↓↑]	[↓↑]	[↓↑│↓↑│]	1	2·1–2·9
(*v*) Co^II Six octahedral $3d^24s4p^3$ bonds	[↓↑│↓↑│↓↑│↓↑│↓↑]	[↓↑]	[↓↑│↓↑│↓↑]	$5s$ [↓]	1	1·7–1·9

FIGURE 4. Electronic Arrangement, Magnetic Moments and Stereochemistry of Cobaltous Complexes

For a more complete survey of this subject, and of the use of magnetism in inorganic chemistry generally, a recent review is available (Nyholm, 1953a).

The Effect of Stereochemistry on the Orbital Contribution

The simple Pauling theory relating stereochemistry, bond type and magnetic moment makes use of the magnetic moment solely for the purpose of determining the number of unpaired electrons in the complex. However, it is well known that the 'spin only' formula for the first transition series is only approximately true, and in some instances the magnetic moment exceeds the 'spin only' value by a considerable amount. In those Co^{II} complexes, for example, where no electron pairing occurs, the moment varies from 4·4 to 5·2 B.M.; the calculated 'spin only' value is only 3·88 B.M. This 'orbital increment' arises from the fact that the orbital contribution to the magnetic moment is often only incompletely 'quenched' by the electrical field of the surrounding atoms. Van Vleck (1932) showed that the quenching effect of the electrical field varied according to the symmetry of the field and also with the type of Stark splitting which occurred. (The Stark effect is analogous to the Zeeman effect and arises from the fact that the degenerate levels of an atom are separated in an electrical field of sufficient intensity.)

For those ions which are in S states (*i.e.* have zero orbital angular momentum), no variation in the magnetic moment with the symmetry of the surrounding field is observed and the moment agrees closely with the spin only value; examples of this include the Mn^{2+} and Fe^{3+} ions in solution, or in the solid state. For ions in D or F spectroscopic states, however, the moment is often affected seriously by the arrangement of the surrounding atoms. Thus, for an ion in an F state (*e.g.* Co^{2+} or Ni^{2+}) an essentially cubic field splits the sevenfold degenerate level into a singlet and two triplet levels. The arrangement of these levels is called a Stark pattern. If the singlet is the lowest lying energy level the atom behaves very much as though it were in an S state with negligible orbital contribution and the spin only formula holds well. Under suitable conditions, however, the pattern of energy levels can be 'inverted'; when this occurs the lower lying triplet gives rise to a large orbital contribution. Whether the Stark pattern is 'upright' or 'inverted' depends upon the stereochemistry of the surrounding groups—hence in suitable cases the size of the orbital contribution becomes diagnostic of stereochemistry. Although the use has been restricted mainly to complexes which involve 'ionic' bonds, the size of the orbital contribution can be used to infer stereochemistry in certain cases where the binding is 'covalent'.

Several simple examples of the first type are known. Thus, the effect of a tetrahedral and of an octahedral arrangement of the ligands around a bivalent cobalt atom has been investigated by Bose (1948), Penney and Schlapp (1932) and Gorter (1932, 1947) (see also Van Vleck, 1932). These results show that in the tetrahedral case there should be a much greater quenching effect than when the surrounding atoms are octahedral; this is owing to the fact that for a tetrahedral arrangement of the ligands the singlet is the lowest lying level. Experimental results agree with these conclusions. The magnetic moments of a large number of octahedral complexes such as $[Co(NH_3)_6]^{2+}[ClO_4]^-_2$, $[Co(En)_3]^{2+}Cl^-_2$, $[Co(H_2O)_6]^{2+}Cl^-_2$ vary between 4·9 and 5·2 B.M. ($En = H_2N:CH_2·CH_2·NH_2$); however, the moments of the tetrahedral complexes are invariably less than this. The moments of the $[CoCl_4]^{2-}$, $[CoBr_4]^{2-}$, $[CoI_4]^{2-}$ and $[Co(CNS)_4]^{2-}$ ions for example vary from 4·3 to 4·7 B.M. (Kanekar, 1953). The opposite, however, should hold for bivalent nickel; here a tetrahedral arrangement should give rise to less quenching than with an octahedral arrangement owing to the fact that the Stark pattern is inverted. The experimental values for octahedral complexes of the type $[Ni(NH_3)_6]^{2+}$ $[ClO_4]^-_2$ are of the order of 3·1 B.M., whereas the moments of (presumably) tetrahedral complexes, e.g. bis-acetylacetone-nickel (II), are generally higher. The case of Ni^{II}, however, is not so clear cut as with Co^{II}. More experimental data are needed before the orbital contribution can be used to infer the stereochemistry of other elements, such as Fe^{II} and Cu^{II}.

Little work has been done on the orbital contribution of complexes in which ' covalent ' binding occurs. Interesting data are available for Co^{II} however. Two types of covalent Co^{II} complexes are known, in each of which there is only one unpaired electron. In the first type the Co^{II} atom is four-covalent and square planar using $3d4s4p^2$ bond orbitals, the unpaired electron occupying a 3d orbital (FIGURE 4, iv). In the second case the atom is octahedral and since two 3d orbitals are required for bond formation it is assumed that the unpaired electron is promoted to the 5s orbital (FIGURE 4, v); support for this hypothesis is afforded by the fact that this electron may be removed fairly easily by oxidation. The magnetic moments of such octahedral complexes, e.g. $[Co(NO_2)_6]^{4-}$, $[Co(diarsine)_3]^{2+}$ are about 1·9 B.M. (Figgis and Nyholm, 1954), i.e. not much in excess of the spin-only value of 1·73 B.M., which value is predicted for a 5s electron since orbital angular momentum should be zero. On the other hand, the moments of the square complexes vary from 2·1 to 2·9 B.M. Although a theoretical study of the effect of crystalline fields on the single d electron has not been carried out, it appears that square Co^{II} complexes can be distinguished from octahedral ones by making use of the empirical rule that the former have moments 2·1 to 2·9 B.M. and the latter 1·7 to 1·9 B.M.

It is likely that this criterion of stereochemistry can be extended to check other cases where the promotion of a single electron to a higher s orbital is predicted. This was suggested by Burstall and Nyholm for the octahedral Ni^{III} complexes of o-phenylene-bis-(dimethylarsine) in which the Ni^{III} atom is isoelectronic with Co^{II}. It is significant that the magnetic moment is again of the order of only 1·9 B.M.

Spectroscopic Measurements

The use of infra-red, Raman and microwave spectra in inorganic chemistry is confined more to the study of simple rather than of complex molecules (see Chapter 1). Nevertheless, the use of infra-red and

Raman spectra in confirming the tetrahedral shape of the $Ni(CO)_4$ molecule (Crawford and Horowitz, 1948) and for deducing the shape of other metallic carbonyls is noteworthy. The use of infra-red and Raman spectra in complex chemistry is bound to be extended further. They may prove as valuable in the study of strengths of bonds as for the purpose of stereochemistry.

RECENT THEORETICAL DEVELOPMENTS

The Use of d Orbitals in Complexes

Within the limited compass of this survey some selection must be made from the many developments of the past few years. Therefore, in view of their special relevance to coordination chemistry, particular attention is paid here to the part played by d orbitals in complex formation. Earlier, it was mentioned that in four- or six-covalent complexes the use of hybrid bond orbitals involving d orbitals with the *same* number as the s and p, or with *one less*, could be envisaged. This arises from the fact that the energy differences between the $(n-1)d$ level and the ns-np levels on the one hand and the ns-np levels and the nd levels on the other, are not very great. Pauling (1945) discussed particularly the importance of the $(n-1)dnsnp$ combinations but suggested that, in the transition metal complexes at least, the use of $nsnpnd$ hybrids was energetically unlikely. Thus, although the bonding orbitals in cobalt (III) ammines, *e.g.* $[Co(NH_3)_6]^{3+}Cl^-_3$ or in six-covalent complex cyanides, *e.g.* $K_3Fe(CN)_6$, were regarded as $3d^2 4s 4p^3$, the bonds in the Co^{II} ammine $[Co(NH_3)_6]^{2+}Cl^-_2$, which is less stable than its cobaltic analogue, or in potassium ferrioxalate $K_3Fe(C_2O_4)_3$, were described as 'ionic'. In some ways the term is unfortunate since it tends to over-emphasize the relationship with the electrostatic type of bond as in sodium chloride. By ionic was meant a bond in which the attraction was essentially ion-dipole in nature, the central metal atom retaining its charge and the exchange integral being negligible; above all, in such complexes the number of unpaired electrons in the complex is the same as in the free ion.

Huggins (1937) appears to have been the first to propose that $4d$ orbitals might be involved in the binding of some transition metal complexes. Other workers have suggested that the term ionic was inappropriate; thus, Sugden (1943) drew attention to the similarity of ferric and cobaltic tris-acetylacetone in their physical properties other than magnetism. He proposed that some kind of 'covalent' bonds were involved in *both* cases. Pauling (1948) recognized the problem and suggested that for many octahedral complexes ionic bonds might be regarded as involving four $4sp^3$ bonds resonating among six positions.

If the use of $4d$ orbitals for octahedral binding be accepted, it is no longer necessary to propose the improbable 'promotion' of electrons in many complexes, the properties of which are inconsistent with the supposed presence of highly energetic electrons. Such a promotion was postulated in the $[Ni(dipyridyl)_3]^{2+}$ ion (Palmer, 1944). This ion is stable enough for resolution and where resolution could be effected it has been inferred (Johnson, 1935) that 'lower' ($3d$) orbitals were being used for bond formation. If two electrons were promoted, however, one might expect that the $[Ni(dipyridyl)_3]^{2+}$ could be oxidized to Ni^{IV} by the removal of these. This oxidation, however, has not been observed. Furthermore, Burstall and Nyholm (1952) have pointed out that if this promotion did occur the two electrons might be expected to go into a $5s$ orbital in which they are paired, resulting in diamagnetism. This behaviour is, in fact, observed with the complex ion $[Ni(diarsine)_3]^{2+}$ which is diamagnetic and which can be oxidized.

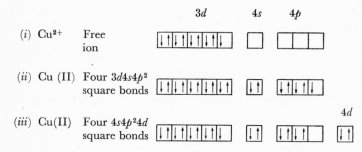

FIGURE 5. Electronic configuration of copper complexes

Another case where the postulated promotion is improbable is in square Cu^{II} complexes. Pauling (1945) suggested that in these compounds $3d4s4p^2$ bonds were used, one unpaired electron being promoted to a $4p$ orbital (FIGURE 5, ii). Again, however, facile oxidation to Cu^{III} is not observed. Ray and Sen (1948) suggested, therefore, that in some square complexes at least the binding involves $4s4p^24d$ orbitals rather than $3d4s4p^2$.

Once it is suggested that 'upper' ($4d$) orbitals might be used in hybridization, many of the complexes previously considered to possess 'ionic' bonds may then be regarded as involving 'upper covalent bonds' instead (Burstall and Nyholm, 1953). Taube (1952b), for example, has suggested that, in the two kinds of complexes of the first transition series, the distinction is between 'inner' ($3d$) and 'outer' ($4d$) orbital binding rather than 'covalent' and 'ionic' bonds respectively.

A thorough investigation of the feasibility of using both upper and lower d orbitals for both σ and π bond formation has been carried out recently by Craig, Maccoll, Nyholm, Orgel and Sutton (1954). Using modified Slater wave functions the overlap integrals were calculated for various possible combinations. The more relevant qualitative results obtained are summarized as follows:

σ *Bond Formation*

1. When two types of octahedral bond orbitals are feasible, one using higher (*e.g.* $4s4p^34d^2$) and the other lower (*e.g.* $3d^24s4p^3$) *d* orbitals, then the more electronegative groups will favour the use of the higher *d* orbitals.

2. When more than one *d* orbital is used in d^2sp^3 octahedral binding both *d* orbitals must be in the same shell (*e.g.* $3d4s4p^34d$ is not an energetically allowable combination for octahedral bonds).

3. In comparing sp^3 with d^2sp^3 bonds it is found that:

(*a*) At all chemically interesting lengths, octahedral d^2sp^3 bonds, no matter whether the *d* orbitals are in the lower or higher quantum shell, are stronger than sp^3 bonds at the same bond length.

(*b*) As a rule, good overlap will be obtained at greater lengths with the octahedral hybridization of type $nsnp^3nd^2$ than with $(n-1)d^2nsnp^3$ orbitals. In other words the higher *d* orbitals lead to longer bonds.

4. Owing to less shielding of the bonding electrons by the non-bonding *d* electrons, σ bonds will be stronger the higher the valency state of the metal atom.

π *Bond Formation*

1. In general this type of binding is much less sensitive to differences in electronegativity.

2. With square complexes two strong π type bonds may be formed at right angles to one another. With octahedral complexes three strong π type bonds may be formed, these being at right angles.

3. When using a single *d* electron in bond formation it seems reasonable to expect a bond about half as strong as that resulting from the use of an electron pair.

4. Some degree of π binding is possible even in complexes in which upper (4*d*) σ bonds are used.

Certain other conclusions emerged from the investigation but the above are of major importance in connection with stereochemistry. The conclusions concerning the use of *d* orbitals in σ bond formations offer a general explanation for a number of experimental facts. It is noteworthy that the 4*d* orbitals project much more than 3*d*. This can involve an overlap in covalent bond closer to the ligand than when the lower (3*d*) orbitals are used. This is important when forming complexes with the more electronegative ligands. Instead of talking of ' ionic-covalent ' resonance we may look on the link as an unsymmetrical covalent bond. The relevance of this in other molecules is discussed by Coulson (1952b) who emphasizes the reduced emphasis placed today on the concept of 'ionic-covalent' resonance. Thus, in the first transition series (Ti→Cu) it is known certain elements (*e.g.* Ni^{II} and Co^{II}) give rise to four-covalent complexes for which both a *square* and a *tetrahedral* arrangement of the bonds are observed. The factors which decide which of the two stereochemical arrangements will be adopted in a four-covalent nickel(II) or cobalt(II) complex have occupied the attention of many chemists [reviewed by Mellor, 1943, and Nyholm, 1953b]. In the case of nickel one type is usually blue or green in colour and has a magnetic moment of approximately 3·2 to 3·4 Bohr magnetons, indicating the presence of two unpaired electrons. Two good examples of this class are bis-acetylacetone-nickel(II) and bis-triethyl-phosphine nickel(II) nitrate; the molecular weight of at least the latter compound has been measured in benzene solution and it is monomeric, establishing that the nickel atom is four-covalent. If the two unpaired electrons in these compounds occupy $3d$ orbitals, no $3d$ orbitals are available for bond formation. Since the next four orbitals available are $4s4p^3$, it was generally assumed that a tetrahedral arrangement would obtain in these compounds. Surprisingly, experimental evidence in support of this assumption has only recently been forthcoming. The magnetic evidence does not exclude square planar arrangement if the bond orbitals are $4s4p^24d$. The present position may be summarized as follows:

(*a*) Curtis, Lyle and Lingafelter (1952) have shown by x-rays that bis-salicylaldehyde-nickel(II) is isomorphous with the corresponding zinc complex but is not isomorphous with the cupric complex. Since all four-covalent cupric complexes which have been investigated are square and all known four-covalent zinc complexes are tetrahedral, this must be taken as good evidence for the tetrahedral arrangement in the nickel compound.

(*b*) Bullen and Lonsdale (1953) have established that bis-acetylace-tone-nickel(II) is not isomorphous with the corresponding square cupric complex.

(*c*) The electric dipole moment of Ni(NO$_3$)$_2$, 2Et$_3$P is 8·85D (Jensen, 1936b), and unless one postulates a less likely *cis*-planar arrangement of the two NO$_3$ groups in a *square* complex, this result is most satisfactorily explained by a tetrahedral arrangement of the four bonds.

(*d*) The relatively high orbital contribution to the magnetic moment in four-covalent Ni^{II} complexes can be explained on the basis of a tetrahedral arrangement of the four attached groups (for summary see Nyholm, 1953a).

(*e*) Studies of the fine structure of the K-x-ray absorption edges suggest that four-covalent Ni^{II} complexes which are paramagnetic are tetrahedral (Beeman and Mitchell, 1952).

The second class of four-covalent Ni^{II} complexes are diamagnetic. It is of interest to note that the para- and dia-magnetic nickel complexes may usually be distinguished by colour, the former being as a rule some shade of blue or green, whilst the latter are generally red, brown or yellow. However, this criterion is not a reliable guide to stereochemistry, since there are many octahedral complexes of bivalent nickel which are also red in colour (e.g. the $[Ni(dipyridyl)_3]^{2+}$ or $[Ni(diarsine)_3]^{2+}$ ions). It is safer to say that those complexes of Ni^{II} which have a sharp absorption band at or near 4000 Å are usually diamagnetic; however, since the four-covalent diamagnetic complexes are planar and as nearly all diamagnetic nickel complexes are four-covalent, it is easily seen that the red colour usually indicates a square arrangement of bonds. The experimental evidence in support of the square arrangement is very strong and includes convincing x-ray and electric dipole measurements; the subject has been reviewed by Mellor (1943) and Nyholm (1953b). The square arrangement in diamagnetic four-covalent Ni^{II} complexes was predicted from quantum mechanics by Pauling (1931, 1932). However, the factors which decide whether the binding will be $3d4s4p^2$ square or $4s4p^3$ tetrahedral have been the subject of much speculation and work. From a survey of experimental material, including a magnetic study of a large number of complexes which they prepared, Mellor and Craig (1940) noted that the more electronegative elements, e.g. four oxygen atoms, gave the tetrahedral arrangement, whereas the less electronegative, e.g. sulphur, often gave the square planar arrangement. They showed, however, that generalizations based solely on the electronegativity of the attached groups were unreliable since four atoms of low electronegativity could give a tetrahedral arrangement if steric factors prevented the formation of four square bonds. These observations may be interpreted in the light of the above theoretical summary; the use of a $3d$ orbital in a $3d4s4p^2$ combination requires the use of atoms of fairly low electronegativity. The more electronegative groups, however, will use the higher orbitals, i.e. $4s4p^3$. It is also of interest to note that the paramagnetic four-covalent Ni^{II} complexes have a very marked tendency to pass to the six-covalent state—thus, bis-acetylacetone nickel(II) readily forms a bis-aquo compound— and here the use of $4s4p^34d^2$ bonds would give rise to stronger binding than with $4s4p^3$ alone. Furthermore, there is no need to promote any electrons, which would be necessary if the binding were $3d^24s4p^3$.

The above work also enables one to understand why some groups, e.g. the —CN group, can effect electron pairing whereas others, like F⁻, rarely do so. An examination of the experimental data reveals that groups of high electronegativity do not cause pairing whereas those of low electronegativity usually do. For example, in octahedral Co^{II} complexes NH_3, H_2O and pyridine do not cause electron pairing

340

whereas $—NO_2$, $—CN$ and $—AsR_3$ do. The groups of high electronegativity favour overlap at greater distances from the metal atom than
do those of low electronegativity and, hence, the former favour the use
of higher $4d$ orbitals without electron pairing.

The significance of the work on π bonds is also noteworthy. Firstly,
they undoubtedly increase the strength of binding of the groups of low
electronegativity. It is generally accepted that the bond strength of
A–B is a function of the electronegativities of both A and B (Gordy,
1946; Walsh, 1948). In comparison with groups like F or O, the
σ bond to an As atom is expected to be relatively weak; however, its
ability to form π bonds must largely compensate for this.

The directional properties of π bonds in metal complexes give rise to
important stereochemical effects. For a ligand like Et_2Te or Et_3Sb,
in which the donor is of very low electronegativity, a weak σ bond is
expected and the π bond might well make a major contribution to the
bond strength. Under these circumstances, the fact that π bonds tend
to be at right angles should favour a *cis* arrangement of these groups
in complexes like $PtCl_2$, $2Et_2Te$ or $PdCl_2$, $2 Et_3Sb$. It is significant
that Jensen (1937) reported that Pt^{II} complexes of ligands such as
Et_2Te could be isolated as their *cis* forms only. Chatt and his colleagues (1951, 1952) have studied *cis-trans* equilibria for Pt^{II} and Pd^{II}
complexes in benzene (thereby eliminating possible lattice constraining
forces) and confirm that, as we pass down any vertical group of
ligands, the percentage of *cis* form in the equilibrium mixture steadily
increases.

The possible use of $3d$ orbitals, in combination with $2s$ and $2p$ for
compounds of first row elements has been discussed by Gillespie
(1953). It is shown that the use of $2s2p^33d$ hybridization for the
transition state in bimolecular substitution at a saturated carbon atom
does not involve an improbably large energy of promotion. (See,
however, Jaffé, 1953.)

STEREOCHEMISTRY IN THE PERIODIC TABLE
In this section some of the recent developments in the periodic table
are summarized under the appropriate coordination numbers from
two to eight.

Coordination Number Two
The bonds in a two-covalent atom may be collinear or angular. Since
the former arrangement commonly arises from sp hybridization it is
expected to occur and is observed in the following cases:

(*a*) The group I*B* metals (Cu, Ag, Au) when univalent.

(*b*) The group II*B* metals (Zn, Cd and Hg) in their bivalent compounds.

(*c*) The group III*B* (In and Tl) in salts of the type $[Alkyl_2Tl]^+X^-$.

In group IB the tendency to form two-covalent complexes increases in the sequence $Cu^I < Ag^I < Au^I$; in fact, the coordination number of Au^I appears to exceed two only if chelate groups are attached. Because of their shape, chelate groups force the metal atom to use two p orbitals for binding. The simple phosphine or arsine complexes, *e.g.* $[Au(Hal),R_3P]^0$ are all monomeric (Mann and Purdie, 1940), and, like other cases where the crystal structure of a two-covalent gold complex has been determined, the two bonds are collinear (Sidgwick, 1950). However, the cuprous iodide complexes of the same empirical formula are tetramers in the solid state and in solution (Mann, Purdie and Wells, 1936); and in these tetramers the Cu^I atom is four-covalent (tetrahedral). Recently, it has been shown that the chloride as well as the bromide and iodide allow this polymerization to form tetramers (Nyholm, 1952).

Polyhalide ions such as $[ICl_2]^-$, I_3^- are also linear (Mooney, 1939). However, complex ions in which two V-shaped bonds are formed by a metal atom are apparently rare. A large number of simple bent molecules are known, *e.g.* H_2O, but this arrangement of bonds is expected in complexes such as $L \rightarrow Tl$—Hal or $L \rightarrow In$—Hal if they are monomeric (where L is a ligand). Such a complex has not yet been isolated.

Coordination Number Three

The two common shapes, the trigonal plane (usually sp^2 hybridization) and the trigonal pyramid (varying from p^3 to sp^3 hybridization) are found in simple molecules and, less frequently, in complex compounds. Where polymerization does not take place the trigonal plane arrangement is found for the Group III halides (*e.g.* BCl_3). The trigonal pyramid is found in complex ions like $[R_3S]^+$ in Group VI. No special developments during the past few years call for comment.

An unusual shape is shown by ClF_3. Two of the C—F bonds are approximately collinear and the other is perpendicular to them (Burbank and Bensey, 1953). This suggests the use of p^2d bonds; this shape has not been reported in a complex compound. This T-shaped molecule appears to be the first of its kind reported.

Coordination Number Four

The two most common shapes are the square plane (dsp^2 bonds) and regular tetrahedral (d^3s or sp^3 bonds) arrangements. Certain elements (*e.g.* Co^{II}, Ni^{II}) show both of these structures depending upon the attached groups (see p. 339).

The complexes of univalent gold pose an interesting problem. It has been reported (Dothie *et al*, 1939) that $K^+[Au(CN)_2X]^-$, where X is dipyridyl or *o*-phenanthroline, contains square coordinated Au^I. This is in contrast with the usual stereochemistry of four-covalent

Ag^I and Cu^I, which are tetrahedral. Au^I complexes of the type $[Au(diarsine)_2]^+X^-$ (where X is a univalent radical and diarsine, a chelate ditertiary arsine), which are doubtless four-covalent, have been described (Nyholm, 1950). Like the corresponding Cu^I complexes these are diamagnetic, suggesting a tetrahedral arrangement. Attempts to resolve such compounds using an unsymmetrical chelate are in progress.

Stephenson (1954) has found that 9 cm x-ray powder photographs of the two substances $[Cu \ (diarsine)_2]^+I^-$ and $[Au \ (diarsine)_2]^+I^-$ show an almost identical distribution of lines and intensities. This supports the view that the compounds are isomorphous, and since all four-covalent cuprous complexes which have been examined are tetrahedral, this provides the first evidence of tetrahedrally coordinated univalent gold.

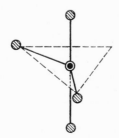

FIGURE 6. $TeCl_4$ Structure

The irregular tetrahedron is probably more common than is generally realized. Thus, the $TeCl_4$ molecule, for which p^3d binding is expected, has the shape of an irregular tetrahedron (Stevenson and Schomaker, 1940) predicted by Kimball (1940). A similar structure is expected for four-covalent complexes of the pentavalent halogens; it has been shown by Helmholtz and Rogers (1940) that such an arrangement does indeed occur in $K^+[IO_2F_2]^-$. The shape may be conveniently regarded as that of a trigonal bipyramid with a lone pair of electrons replacing one of the equatorial atoms (see FIGURE 6). This p^3d irregular tetra-hedron is expected for the following four-covalent complexes: Group VIIA (if pentavalent), Group VIA (if quadrivalent), Group VA (if tervalent), Group IVA (if bivalent) and Group IIIA (if univalent). Complex ions like $[AsCl_4]^-$ (unless polymeric) illustrate the third of these, but their structures do not appear to have been studied. This ion should be distinguished from the $[XY_4]^+$ ions of Group V elements, e.g. $[PCl_4]^+$ or $[PBr_4]^+$, for which the hybridization is sp^3 leading to a regular tetrahedron (Clark, Powell and Wells, 1942; Powell and Clark, 1940). Other examples of the irregular tetrahedron with p^3d bonds include Ph_2SeCl_2, Ph_2SeBr_2 and $(p\text{-tolyl})_2SeBr_2$ (McCullough and Hamburger, 1941, 1942). For the structure of the $SeCl_4$ molecule, however, which is a regular tetrahedron, see Lister and Sutton (1941). An excellent survey by Sharpe (1952) of the stereochemistry of the interhalogen compounds and their complexes is available.

Coordination Number Five

As might be expected from symmetry considerations, five-covalent complexes are usually bipyramidal but the square pyramid is probably more common than formerly supposed. The bipyramid usually arises from the use of $(ns)(np^3)(nd)$ bond orbitals; this is true for the pentahalides of the Group V elements in the gas phase. The square pyramid can

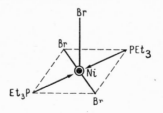

FIGURE 7. Structure Proposed for $NiBr_3, 2Et_3P$

arise from several different kinds of orbital hybridization (see TABLE 1, p. 326). The simplest molecule having this shape is IF_5 (Braune and Pinnow, 1937); the bonding orbitals expected here are $6p^36d^2$ (*cf* Sharpe, 1952; Lord, Lynch, Schumb and Slowinski, 1950). Jensen and Nygaard (1949) have suggested that the electric dipole moment of the compound $NiBr_3, 2Et_3P$, in which the nickel atom is five-covalent, is most readily explained by the square pyramidal structure shown in FIGURE 7. Magnetic data show that this compound contains one unpaired electron which, if in a $3d$ orbital, means that the bond orbitals

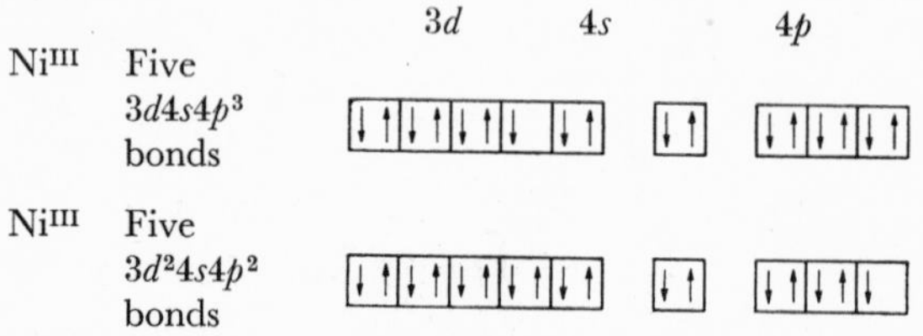

		$3d$	$4s$	$4p$
Ni^{III}	Five $3d4s4p^3$ bonds	⇅⇅⇅⇅↿↓	⇅	⇅⇅⇅
Ni^{III}	Five $3d^24s4p^2$ bonds	⇅⇅⇅⇅⇅	⇅	⇅⇅

FIGURE 8. Electronic arrangement of Ni^{III} complexes

are probably $3d4s4p^3$. This combination of a lower d orbital with the $4s4p^3$ bonds should give a square pyramid (see p. 326). If the unpaired electron is promoted, enabling the use of $3d^24s4p^2$ bonds, a square pyramid is still to be expected (see FIGURE 8).

A good deal of work involving the oxidation of square complexes is taking place at present with a view to the isolation of other square pyramidal structures.

Barclay and Nyholm (1953) have studied the complexes formed by the tri-tertiary arsine tri-dentate group

$$CH_2CH_2CH_2As(CH_3)_2$$
$$CH_3As$$
$$CH_2CH_2CH_2As(CH_3)_2$$

(TRIAS) with various transition metals. Complexes of Ni^{II} and Co^{II} having the formulae $NiBr_2,TRIAS$ and $CoI_2,TRIAS$ have been prepared which are non-electrolytes and monomeric in nitrobenzene solution. Their stability in air, and the fact that they may be oxidized to Ni^{III} and Co^{III} complexes respectively indicates that all three arsenic atoms are coordinated. It is suggested, therefore, that the Ni^{II} and Co^{II} atoms are five-covalent in these complexes, the molecules being square pyramidal in shape.

The assignment of a bipyramidal structure to $Fe(CO)_5$ on the basis of electron diffraction measurements (Ewens and Lister, 1939) has been questioned by Jensen and Nygaard (1949). These workers point out that the diamagnetism is more consistent with the use of $3d4s4p^3$ bonds and, hence, with a square pyramidal shape. However, the ease with which spin coupling occurs in carbonyls is well known; furthermore, the bipyramid structure is supported by infra-red studies (Sheline and Pitzer, 1950).

Coordination Number Six
This is the most usual coordination number found in complex compounds and in nearly every case the bonds are arranged octahedrally around the metal atom. This arrangement indicates d^2sp^3 binding irrespective of whether a lower or higher d orbital is involved.

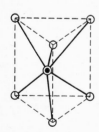 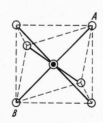 

| Trigonal Prism | Trigonal Antiprism* | Octahedron |

FIGURE 9

* Note that the trigonal antiprism may be regarded as an octahedron with one axis (*AB*) drawn out or made shorter than the other two.

It should be mentioned, however, that arrangements other than the octahedron have been observed (FIGURE 9). Thus, in the giant molecule of MoS_2 polymerization occurs giving an arrangement in which the Mo atom is surrounded by six groups occupying the corners of a trigonal prism (Dickinson and Pauling, 1923). By way of contrast, nickel arsenide, which contains six-covalent nickel atoms, has a structure in which both the trigonal prism and the trigonal antiprism are observed (summarized by Wells, 1945).

It is of interest to note the peculiar arrangement in six-covalent cupric complexes. These are more common than is usually supposed, e.g. $[Cu(NH_3)_6]^{2+}X^-_2$ (Peyronel, 1941). The crystal structure work on Cu^{II} complexes has revealed that this atom has a marked tendency to form four coplanar bonds of normal length, but the other two bonds required to complete the octahedral arrangement are longer (Wells, 1949). Orgel (1953) has offered an explanation for this in terms of the crystalline field theory.

Coordination Number Seven

For a long time chemists were somewhat reluctant to accept a coordination number of seven in chemical compounds, chiefly owing to the feeling that the lack of symmetry in such a structure would mitigate against its occurrence. However, several well-defined cases have been established.

The best known is the K_3ZrF_7 structure elucidated by Hampson and Pauling (1938). The structure consists of an octahedron with an extra fluorine atom added at the *middle* of one face (see FIGURE 10A). Magnetic data do not differentiate between d^3sp^3 or d^5sp binding since the compound is diamagnetic; the principle that one uses the lowest energy levels available appears to favour d^5sp, but, on the other hand, it is tempting to suggest that the shape arises simply from an octahedral d^2sp^3 arrangement by using one more d orbital.

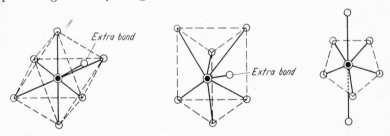

A. $[ZrF_7]^{3-}$ Structure   *B.* $[TaF_7]^{2-}$ Structure   *C.* IF$_7$ Structure

FIGURE 10

A different structure is found in the iso-electronic $[TaF_7]^{2-}$ ion (Hoard, 1939). In this case the arrangement of bonds is most readily visualized by adding one more atom to the centre of one of the rectangular faces of a trigonal prism (see FIGURE 10B). A similar arrangement of seven groups around the Zr atom occurs in zirconium oxysulphide (McCullough, Brewer and Bromley, 1948).

The $[NbF_7]^{2-}$ ion has a similar structure. Again magnetic data are not diagnostic of the orbitals used, but it seems likely that the orbitals are d^4sp^2 arising from the addition of one p bond to the arrangement used in a trigonal prism, namely d^4sp. More recently, the structure of IF_7 has been determined; in this case the orbitals one would expect to be used are $6s6p^36d^3$. This agrees with the shape deduced from infra-red and Raman spectra studies (Lord, Lynch, Schumb and Slowinski, 1950; Scott, 1950; *cf* Duffey, 1950d), *viz* a pentagonal bipyramid (see FIGURE 10C).

For a pentagonal plane the combination is d^3p^2 and the addition of one s and one p orbital gives a combination with two bonds perpendicular to the plane.

Coordination Number Eight

Although many compounds have been known for some time in which the central metal atom almost certainly has a coordination number of eight, the stereochemistry of compounds of this type received scant attention before the last decade or so. As pointed out by Marchi, Fernelius and McReynolds (1943), only three of the many possible arrangements of eight bonds had been definitely established. At first sight one might expect that an arrangement of the eight surrounding atoms at the corners of a cube (as in CsCl) would be the most probable arrangement. However, this is not so and its improbability can be demonstrated on theoretical grounds. Kimball (1940) has pointed out that the cube requires the use of f orbitals and even then it arises only from the use of d^3fsp^3 or d^3f^4s hybrid bond orbitals. The shapes shown in TABLE 1 result from more stable bond arrangements. The structure of $K_4Mo(CN)_8$ was reported by Hoard and Nordsieck (1939), this being the first structure determination on an eight-covalent complex. The arrangement is that shown in FIGURE 11A, namely a dodecahedron, which has eight vertices, with triangular faces (see FIGURE 11A). This indicates the use of d^4sp^3 bond orbitals. Later (Hoard, 1943), the structure of the second type of eight-covalent complex was reported. Hoard showed that the $[TaF_8]^{3-}$ ion involved the square antiprism, most simply visualized as the shape obtained when two squares are placed one above the other, as in a cube, followed by the rotation of one square through 45° in a plane parallel to the plane of the other square (see FIGURE 11B). This shape should also obtain with OsF_8 but the structure of this has not yet been determined. Uranium is another element which shows a coordination number of eight, this being illustrated by the oxalato complex of U^{IV}, *viz* $K^+_4[U(C_2O_4)_4]^{4-}$. The fact that this ion may be resolved (Marchi and McReynolds, 1943) necessarily excludes the possibility that the shape is either that of the cube or the trigonal prism with two extra bonds along the unique axis; if either of these two shapes occurred in the complex it would not be capable of being resolved owing to internal symmetry. However, the data do not allow one to distinguish between the square Archimedes antiprism and the dodecahedron which are the most likely arrangements; both could involve the use of the hybrid bond orbitals d^4sp^3. The magnetic moment of this complex has been measured (Sacconi, 1949) and suggests the presence of two $5f$ electrons. Sacconi took this to mean that covalent binding occurs but it is not possible to deduce with any confidence what orbitals are used for bond formation. A theoretical discussion of the most probable orbitals used in eight-coordination has been given by Duffey (1950c); cf Racah (1943).

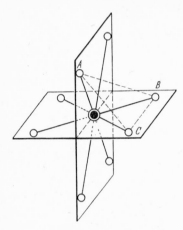

FIGURE 11A. Arrangement of groups in a dodecahedron on two intersecting planes. One triangular face (ABC) is shown

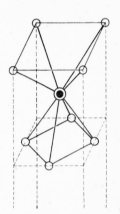

FIGURE 11B. [TaF_8]$^{3-}$ Structure

Coordination Numbers Exceeding Eight

Although no structural or, indeed, reliable analytical data are available, the existence of osmium complexes with a coordination number of nine or ten has been envisaged by Sidgwick (1950). It is pointed out that, since OsF_8 combines with NaF, complexes such as $NaOsF_9$ and Na_2OsF_{10} are feasible.

STERIC CHANGES DURING CHEMICAL REACTIONS

During the past few years, considerable attention has been paid to the study of the mechanism of substitution in complex compounds. An excellent review by Taube (1952) is available summarizing the qualitative observations concerning ease of substitution in complex ions in solution; the relationship between lability and the electronic configuration of the metal atom has been examined in particular. The behaviour of six-covalent complexes has received most attention but some studies on tetrahedral and square planar four-covalent complexes have also been carried out.

Changes at Four-covalent Atoms

For substitution at a tetrahedral four-covalent metal atom, some relationship with the behaviour of a four-covalent carbon atom might be expected. As discussed by de la Mare in Chapter 3, substitution at a saturated carbon atom may take place by two mechanisms. In the first of these the kinetics are first order with respect to the carbon compound and independent of the concentration of the attacking agent. It is generally accepted (Hughes, 1951) that the rate-determining step is an ionization, with the formation of a three-covalent carbonium ion as the intermediate (S_N1 mechanism). In the second type, the reaction rate depends on the concentration both of the carbon compound and of the attacking reagent. The bimolecular reaction is assumed to proceed via a bipyramidal intermediate state (S_N2 mechanism). For the other elements of Group IV, however, substitution seems to occur by a different kind of mechanism. Thus, whereas CCl_4 is unreactive to water, compounds like $SiCl_4$ and the other Group IV halides are attacked and hydrolysed with extreme ease. This difference is generally attributed to the fact that, unlike carbon and other first row elements, silicon and later elements have vacant upper d orbitals in the same quantum shell as the sp^3 bonding orbitals; these are available for the formation of stable complexes with coordination numbers higher than four. Thus, SiF_4 forms the $[SiF_6]^{2-}$ ion readily but no corresponding carbon compound is known. Swain, Esteve and Jones (1949) have made use of this idea to explain the rate of hydrolysis of Ph_3SiF. They postulate that a five-covalent intermediate complex Ph_3SiF,H_2O is formed with a water molecule, and that the rate-determining step in hydroloysis is the rate at which this intermediate breaks down to form $Ph_3Si(H_2O)^+$ and F^- ions. This theory is clearly capable of being extended to the later elements in the group. However, little work has been carried out either on the rate of substitution in complexes of tetrahedrally coordinated metals or on the mechanism whereby their optically active compounds racemize. With metals it is not easy to obtain stable compounds containing two or more different groups attached (like $CR^1R^2R^3R^4$), and to effect resolution it is necessary to make use of unsymmetrical chelate groups. With the more ionic halides like $ThCl_4$, which are largely ionized in the solid state, solvolysis probably involves direct coordination with the metal ion to form complex ions of the type $[Th(EtOH)_n]^{4+}$ (Hughes, 1951). The mechanism of hydrolysis of Zr^{IV} complexes has also been discussed by Bradley, Halim and Wardlaw (1950, 1951).

The mechanism of substitution in square complexes has been discussed but the data are meagre and mostly qualitative. Adamson, Welker and Wright (1951) have found that whereas CN^- exchange with complex ions containing no vacant $3d$ or $4p$ orbitals, e.g. $[Co(CN)_6]^{3-}$, is very slow, exchange with the $[Ni(CN)_4]^{2-}$ and

$[Pd(CN)_4]^{2-}$ ions is very rapid. The rate was too fast for measurement and it was pointed out that either an ionization mechanism or a bimolecular reaction, with H_2O or CN^- as the attacking agent, might occur. Martell and Calvin (1952) suggested that a five-covalent $[Ni(CN)_5]^{3-}$ intermediate ion is formed during the exchange, the incoming CN^- ion making use of the vacant $4p$ orbital of the nickel atom. However, although the existence of the $[Ni(CN)_5]^{3-}$ ion in solutions containing excess cyanide ion has been established by spectrophotometric studies (Morris, 1953), it should not be assumed that this is necessarily the intermediate. If it could be shown that the exchange involves second order kinetics and that the rate depends on both the $[Ni(CN)_4]^{2-}$ and CN^- ion concentrations, this would be presumptive evidence for such an intermediate.

It is interesting to note the different chemical reactivity of *cis* and *trans* forms of certain square complexes. Thus, whereas the *cis* form of $PtCl_2,2Et_3P$, or the corresponding Et_3As compound, reacts almost instantaneously with silver nitrate in alcoholic solution, the *trans* form does not react for some hours. By way of contrast, *trans* $PtCl_2,2NH_3$ reacts instantly with silver nitrate whereas the *cis* form is much less reactive. Syrkin (1948) suggested that there is some connection between the reactivity of the Cl atoms and the percentage of p character in the Pt—Cl bonds; the p orbitals project more than the ds hybrids and this is considered to lead to a more polar bond. However, before any theories of substitution can be seriously considered rate studies are essential.

Changes in Octahedral Complexes

The mechanism of substitution in, and the racemization of, octahedral complexes has received much more attention; an excellent review by Basolo (1953) is available. Earlier the results were largely qualitative, or involved the study of what reaction products were formed in various substitutions, but during the last ten years in particular a body of kinetic data has been accumulated. The history of the subject is important since it shows how reluctant most chemists have been to accept the idea that migration of groups occurs in octahedral complexes during substitution. In the first instance it will be convenient to discuss substitution and racemization separately, although, as will be seen, there is not necessarily any difference in mechanism. In the first case a different chemical compound may be formed but in the second the reactant has undergone, at the end of the reaction, no change in chemical composition but only a change in stereochemistry. Nevertheless chemical reactions may have taken place during the racemization.

Werner (1893–1912) made a detailed study of the effect of various kinds of substituting reagents on cobaltic complex ions and noted that in the replacement of one group X by an attacking ion Y four kinds of stereochemical change were observed. A series of bis-ethylenediamino cobalt (III) complex ions of the general formula $[CoEn_2(NH_3)X]^{2+}$ (where X is a univalent negative group) were attacked by another group Y which displaced either X or the NH_3 group; each of the following types of steric behaviour were observed:

(a) *cis→cis* e.g. *cis*-$[CoEn_2(NH_3)Br]^{2+}+NH_3→cis$-$[CoEn_2(NH_3)_2]^{3+}$

(b) *cis→trans* e.g. *cis*-$[CoEn_2(NH_3)Cl]^{2+}+SCN^-$
$$→trans\text{-}[CoEn_2(SCN)Cl]^+$$

(c) *trans→trans* e.g. *trans*-$[CoEn_2(NH_3)Cl]^{2+}+NO_2^-$
$$→trans\text{-}[CoEn_2(NO_2)Cl]^+$$

(d) *trans→cis* e.g. *trans*-$[CoEn_2(NH_3)Cl]^{2+}+OH^-$
$$→cis\text{-}[CoEn_2(NH_3)(OH)]^{2+}$$

More recently, Bailar and his collaborators (1936–1940) studied substitution in some optically active cobaltammines and obtained important results. On treating $(-)$-*cis*-$[CoEn_2Cl_2]^+$ ions in aqueous solution with excess solid silver carbonate, they obtained the $(-)$-$[CoEn_2(CO_3)]^+$ ion, necessarily *cis* because of the steric requirements of the CO_3^{2-} group. By way of contrast, when they used potassium carbonate instead of silver carbonate, the $(+)$-$[CoEn_2(CO_3)]^+$ ion was obtained. It was found, however, that when the aqueous solution of the $(-)$-$[CoEn_2Cl_2]^+$ ion was allowed to stand for some hours before treatment with silver carbonate, the $(+)$-$[CoEn_2(CO_3)]^+$ ion was obtained. This different result may be attributed to the fact that on standing another stage of substitution occurs, namely the formation of the $[CoEn_2Cl(H_2O)]^{2+}$ ion, as shown by the work of Mathieu (1936). Later, Bailar, Haslam and Jones (1936) showed that the $(-)$-*cis*-$[CoEn_2Cl_2]^+$ ion was converted into the *cis*-$[CoEn_2(NH_3)_2]^{3-}$ ion with either the $(+)$ or $(-)$ form in excess (*i.e.* the resulting material is optically active) by treating the dichloro compound with liquid ammonia. The authors considered that their result in the CO_3^{2-} substitution was the first demonstration of a Walden inversion in inorganic chemistry. As will be seen presently, a radical rearrangement of *all* the bonds to the Co^{III} atom, such as takes place at a carbon atom, need not necessarily be assumed to occur; in which case the term ' Walden inversion in inorganic chemistry ' is a descriptive rather than a stereochemical analogy.

First Order Kinetics

As might be expected, because of the lack of other suitable solvents, substitution in octahedral complexes has been studied mainly in water as the solvent. Under these circumstances, aquation is generally the main reaction owing to the strong coordination ability of H_2O in water.

However, attack by the strongly nucleophilic OH^- ion is certainly bimolecular (Puente, 1945; Bronsted and Livingston, 1927) in aqueous solution, *e.g.* $[Co(NH_3)_5X]^{2+}+OH^-\rightarrow[Co(NH_3)_5OH]^{2+}+X^-$. The replacement of the Cl, Br and NO_3 groups by water from complex ions of the general formula $[Co(NH_3)_5X]^{2+}$ has been studied by several investigators. Lamb and Fairhall (1923) have studied the replacement of Cl, Br, I, NO_3 and SO_4 groups by water in $[Ir(NH_3)_5X]^{2+}$ ions and Freundlich and Bartels (1922) have investigated the replacement by H_2O of Cl, Br and I groups from the $[Cr(NH_3)_5X]^{2+}$ ion.

All of these substitutions are shown to be kinetically first order but this does not disclose the mechanism ; this could be either bimolecular with solvolytic attack, or unimolecular with an ionization as the rate-determining step in the substitution. Some support for the view that the reaction proceeds by the former mechanism is provided by the fact that the ratio of the rates of displacement by water of the Cl, Br and NO_2 groups is nearly the same as for the replacement of these groups by OH^-, a reaction which is definitely bimolecular*. Basolo, Bergmann and Pearson (1952) have shown that second-order kinetics are obtained when an acetato or substituted acetato group is replaced by H_2O or OH^- from ions of the type $[Co(NH_3)_5OAc]^{2+}$. As pointed out by Taube (1952a) [see also Brown, Ingold and Nyholm (1953)] however, the evidence is not unambiguous in the absence of proof that it is the Co—O and not the O—Ac bond which is broken during substitution. Rutenberg and Taube (1952) have shown that the rate of exchange of H_2O with hexahydrated tervalent metal ions and with $[Co(NH_3)_5(H_2O)]^{3+}$ is mainly first order with respect to the complex ion. They favour the view that the reaction is S_N1 but emphasize that, in the absence of more experimental data, the results do not enable one to conclude with any certainty that this is true.

In an attempt to overcome the difficulty resulting from the attack by H_2O when water is used as solvent, Brown, Ingold and Nyholm (1953) have studied the kinetics of substitution in complex ions of the type $[CoEn_2X_2]^+$ using methanol as solvent. It has been shown that when a chlorine atom of the complex $(+)$-*cis*-$[CoEn_2Cl_2]^+$ is displaced by reagents of the series NO_3^-, SCN^-, Cl^-, Br^-, NO_2^-, N_3^-, MeO^-, OH^- the kinetic order begins to change from first to second after SCN^- in the above sequence. The specific rate also increases from NO_2^- to MeO^- in the above sequence. The complex ion $(+)$-*cis*-$[CoEn_2Cl_2]^+$ undergoes two steric rearrangements in dry methanol, one a racemization, the other a *cis–trans* change. Both of these changes are rate controlled by the heterolysis of a Co—Cl bond, the rate of loss of optical activity being the same as the rate of exchange of isotopically

---

* For a discussion of bimolecular reactions which may proceed via the conjugate base, see Bronsted (1926); Brown, Ingold and Nyholm (1953).

labelled chlorine. Once free from the complex the chlorine ion re-enters from at least two different directions, 82 per cent of these re-entries leading to the *trans*-dichloro isomers. These results can be interpreted to mean that the racemization and substitution both take place as a result of a unimolecular mechanism involving the formation of a five-covalent* intermediate ion as the transition state. The possibility of re-entry of the chloride ion in two different ways accounts for the formation of both *cis*- and *trans*-isomers. The five-covalent intermediate ion is considered to be either a bipyramid or a square pyramid. The former makes it easy to interpret the formation of both *cis*- and *trans*-isomers on re-entry of the chlorine, but the bond orbitals likely to be involved favour the latter. As yet, however, it has not been possible to choose between these two models with real confidence.

The above demonstration that the rate of radio-active Cl^- ion exchange with the complex $(+)$-*cis*-$[CoEn_2Cl_2]^+$ is the same (within experimental error) as the rate of racemization indicates that in this case the racemization clearly does not involve an *intra*-molecular mechanism.

Second Order Kinetics

Before attempting to interpret the second-order kinetics obtained by Brown and Ingold (1953) for substitution in the $[CoEn_2Cl_2]^+$ ion (*e.g.* with N_3^-), it is desirable to consider more generally the likely transition state in bimolecular reactions at octahedral atoms. When a bimolecular mechanism is indicated for substitution at a six-covalent metal atom, the formation of a seven-covalent intermediate ion as the transition state is frequently postulated. The nature of this transition state has been the subject of speculation although the supporting experimental data are still meagre.

Three kinds of octahedral complex should be considered; (*a*) those using upper ($4d$) orbitals with $4s4p^34d^2$ bonds *e.g.* the $[FeF_6]^{3-}$ ion; (*b*) those using lower ($3d$) orbitals, $3d^24s4p^3$ bonds, but in which there is a vacant $3d$ orbital (*e.g.* the $[V(CN)_6]^{3-}$ ion) or in which a $3d$ orbital can be made available by pairing of two $3d$ electrons (*e.g.* the $[Mn(CN)_6]^{3-}$ ion); (*c*) those using lower ($3d$) orbitals for bond formation, $3d^24s4p^3$ bonds, but in which no $3d$ orbital can be made available except by promotion of electron(s), *e.g.* the $[Fe(CN)_6]^{3-}$ or $[Co(CN)_6]^{3-}$ ions which would require the promotion of one or two $3d$ electrons respectively to make available a $3d$ orbital for the incoming group. If a d orbital is used in the seven-covalent intermediate the problem of substitution in (*a*) is straightforward as the transition state could be $4s4p^34d^3$. Similarly, in (*b*) a transition state involving

---

* The possibility that a CH_3OH molecule is coordinated in the sixth position cannot be ignored, however.

353

$3d^34s4p^3$ bonds could be formed without very much difficulty. In the case of (c) however, the possibility of a seven-covalent transition state is much more difficult to visualize. It would be necessary to postulate the (improbable) promotion of two $3d$ electrons or to suggest that a $4d$ or a $4f$ orbital can hybridize with $3d^24s4p^3$ bonds. The latter possibility is energetically most unlikely.

Two stereochemical arrangements have been suggested for the shape of a seven-covalent transition state: the pentagonal bipyramid (IF_7 structure, FIGURE 10C) or the $[ZrF_7]^{3-}$ structure (FIGURE 10A). Basolo, Stone and Pearson (1953) prefer the former whereas Adamson (1951) has suggested that the latter is most feasible since it arises from a more likely combination of bond orbitals. This latter arrangement is the structure which from simple geometry one might expect. It could be visualized as arising from the entry of the attacking group at the centre of one of the triangular faces. To obtain the pentagonal bipyramid transition state the incoming group is assumed to enter midway between two of the attached groups. However as the number of octahedral substitutions which have been definitely established as bimolecular is very few in number, the reactions for which a seven-covalent intermediate need even be postulated are also few.

Support for the above hypothesis of bimolecular substitution in the case of substitution of radio cyanide ion in certain complex cyanides has been claimed by Adamson and co-workers (1951). It has been shown that the order of increasing rate of attack by CN^- is $[Co(CN)_6]^{3-}$, $[Fe(CN)_6]^{3-} < [Cr(CN)_6]^{3-} \ll [Mn(CN)_6]^{3-}$. In the first two complex ions a $3d$ orbital can be made available only by promoting electron(s) whereas in the case of $[Mn(CN)_6]^{3-}$ this can be achieved by electron pairing. The kinetics of exchange for the $[Mn(CN)_6]^{3-}$ ion are independent of the concentration of CN^-; this reaction is considered to involve attack by a water molecule as the rate-determining step. Since the rate is independent of ionic strength it is concluded that only one charged reactant is involved in the rate determining reaction.

Taube (1952a) considers that the availability of 'inner' d orbitals in a six-covalent complex is important in the interpretation of the reactivity of complex ions. Where such a d orbital is available he suggests that substitution via an intermediate seven-covalent complex can be expected. On this basis he is able to correlate fairly satisfactorily the electronic configuration of a metal atom in various complexes with their relative labilities. It is noteworthy that octahedral complexes of the earlier members of the first transition series are more labile than the later ones, $e.g.$ Co^{III}. However, unless bimolecular kinetics are demonstrated, the assumption of a seven-covalent intermediate is only speculative.

We now return to bimolecular reactions of the type cis-$[CoEn_2Cl_2]^+$ $+X^-$. As yet we have not referred to the possible ways in which the intermediate ion in substitution decomposes. In substitutions like $[Cr(CN)_6]^{3-}+CN^-$ the end product is always the same since one finishes up again with a hexa-cyano complex ion. However, with a *heterogeneous* octahedral complex ion *e.g.* $[CoEn_2Cl_2]^+$ the possibility of intra-molecular rearrangement during decomposition can lead to important changes in stereochemistry of the parent octahedral ion. Brown, Ingold and Nyholm (1953) have re-examined some of Werner's ideas with this possibility in mind and have pointed out that $(+)\rightarrow(-)$ changes and $cis\rightarrow trans$ changes in cis $[CoEn_2X_2]^-$ complexes are not as different as they appear at first sight. Both types of change could arise from a mechanism involving an edge-displacement. This is shown diagrammatically in FIGURE 12, the reaction here involving replacement of X by Y. It is postulated that Y^- attacks the Co atom at the centre of one of the triangular faces, coming in at π_1, π_2, π_3, or π_4 (almost certainly at π_1 or π_2 since of the faces adjacent to R these are the farthest away from the outgoing group X).

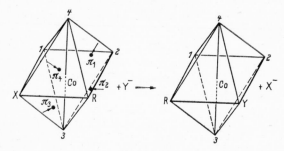

FIGURE 12

This is followed by the (simultaneous) loss of X^-, a movement of R to the position formerly occupied by X and a movement of Y to the position formerly occupied by R. A careful examination reveals that both $cis\rightarrow trans$ and $(+)\rightarrow(-)$ changes fall within the scope of this hypothesis, because the description of the process as $(+)\rightarrow(-)$ or $cis\rightarrow trans$ depends upon the location of some unaffected reference atom A. If A is at position *1*, the reaction shown in FIGURE 12 is a $cis\rightarrow trans$ change, *i.e.* cis-AX$\rightarrow trans$-AY; if A is at *2* a $trans\rightarrow cis$ change occurs, *i.e.* $trans$-AX$\rightarrow cis$-AY. On the other hand, if A is at positions *3* or *4* we get either a $(+)\rightarrow(-)$ or a $(-)\rightarrow(+)$ change. It is of interest to note that if substitution occurs in a *trans* compound, *e.g.* $[CoEn_2X_2]^+$+ $Y^-\rightarrow[CoEn_2XY]^+$+$X^-$ *every* act of bimolecular substitution should result in the formation of a cis-XY derivative. In FIGURE 12 the second X group would be at position *2* and since R takes up a position *trans* to *2*, Y^- must occupy a cis position. This corollary is being examined.

An investigation of the attack of an OH^- ion in water on the *trans*-$[CoEn_2Cl(SCN)]^+$ ion (Ingold and Tobe, 1953) indicates that this expectation is not realized to the extent of 100 per cent, some *trans*-$[CoEn_2(OH)(SCN)]^+$ being formed. An explanation in terms of the actual position of entry on a triangular face will be discussed in a forthcoming paper.

The analogy with the case of bimolecular substitution at a saturated carbon atom is obvious. This hypothesis offers promise as a unifying theory of bimolecular octahedral substitution since it does offer a satisfactory explanation for both kinds of observed change.

Intra-molecular Mechanisms

So far no reference has been made to the possibility of intra-molecular rearrangement without substitution taking place. Such a mechanism has been proposed in order to explain the first-order racemization rates

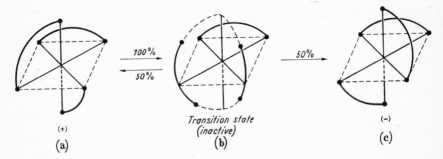

(+)
(a)

Transition state
(inactive)
(b)

(-)
(c)

FIGURE 13

of certain octahedral complexes containing three chelate groups, *e.g.* $[Co(oxalato)_3]^{3-}$ (Johnson and Mead, 1933). Other examples of first-order racemization of this kind include the ions $[Fe(dipyridyl)_3]^{2+}$ (Davies and Dwyer, 1952, 1953); $[Ni(o\text{-phenanthroline})_3]^{2+}$ (Basolo, 1953, p. 508); $[Co(biguanidinium)_3]^{3+}$ (Ray and Dutt, 1941, 1943). The first-order kinetics have been observed in water and other solvents. Earlier, Werner (1912–1923) suggested that the racemization of these substances involved an intra-molecular mechanism in which there is a momentary rupture of the metal-ligand bond at one end of the chelate group which is followed by reorganization of the chelate groups around the metal atom. Thomas (1921) suggested an ionization mechanism to explain the racemization of the $[M^{III}(oxalato)_3]^{3-}$ ions, the intermediate being a planar four-covalent bis-oxalato ion which is necessarily optically inactive. Beese and Johnson (1935) criticized the ionization hypothesis because oxalate ions had no effect upon the first-order racemization rate. As pointed out by Brown (1952), however, the oxalate ions affect the *back* reaction, by which time racemization has already taken place. Long (1941) examined the reaction of radioactive oxalate ion with Cr^{III} and Co^{III} tris-oxalate complexes but observed virtually no exchange. Nevertheless, under the same conditions racemization took place fairly rapidly. Ray and Dutt (1943) propose that first-order racemization in complex ions of this type involves intra-molecular rearrangement. They suggest that in the transition stage the ion assumes a configuration *intermediate* between the $(+)$ and $(-)$ forms; from this intermediate state it is considered to slip back with equal probability into $(+)$ and $(-)$ forms. This would explain the racemization. The $(+)$ and $(-)$ forms and the intermediate are shown in FIGURE 13. The intermediate state is clearly optically inactive. It is considered to arise from the ' slipping ' of two chelate groups through 45° in planes passing through the metal atom and the two bonds to the chelate groups.

A mechanism which involves some kind of intramolecular rearrangement seems probable in certain cases for which the rate of racemization is demonstrably much faster than the rate of dissociation of the complex. Thus, the rate at which one chelate group is lost by the complex ions $[Fe(phenanthroline)_3]^{2+}$ is only about one tenth as fast as the rate of racemization (Lee, Kolthoff and Leussing, 1948 ; Ruben, Kamen, Allen, and Nahinsky, 1942). However in analogous Ni^{II} complexes the rate of racemization is approximately the same as the rate of dissociation (Davies and Dwyer, 1952). It is significant that the bond orbitals in the nickel complex are probably $4s4p^34d^2$ rather than $3d^24s4p^3$ as is the case with the Fe^{II} and Fe^{III} complexes. The former type of hybridization allows of attack by solvent molecules using one of the empty $4d$ orbitals with ease whereas in the latter the transition state is less energetically favourable. Here at least the racemization may take place by a dissociation mechanism.

In those cases where the rate of dissociation is comparable with the rate of racemization it is feasible that the rate-determining step in both metal exchange and racemization is the heterolysis of one metal–ligand bond; alternatively, the first stage could be mono-solvation, the subsequent stages (both of breakdown and synthesis) being more rapid. If this hypothesis is correct it is necessary to postulate that for some complexes a change in bond type occurs at some stage during aquation. Thus, whereas the $[Fe(CN)_6]^{3-}$ ion is diamagnetic using $3d^24s4p^3$ bonds, the hexa-aquo ion, $[Fe(H_2O)_6]^{2+}$, is paramagnetic with ' ionic ' or higher level covalent bonds. As there can be no resonance between these there must be some point in aquation at which there is a discontinuous change in bond type. It is probably significant that the rate of exchange of H_2O with Co^{III} complexes is always much slower; in this case even the $[Co(H_2O)_6]^{3+}$ ion contains ' covalent ' $3d^24s4p^3$ bonds, there being no change in bond type at any stage in the process (Hunt, Rutenberg and Taube, 1952; Rutenberg and Taube, 1952; Friedman, Hunt, Plane and Taube, 1951).

REFERENCES

Adamson, A. W., Welker, J. P. and Wright, W. B. (1951) *J. Amer. chem. Soc.* **73,** 4786

Allen, P. W. and Sutton, L. E. (1950) *Acta cryst. Camb.* **3,** 46

Bailar, J. C. and Auten, W. J. (1934) *J. Amer. chem. Soc.* **56,** 774

— Haslam, J. H. and Jones, E. M. (1936) *ibid* **58,** 2226

— Jonelis, F. G. and Huffman, H. E. (1936) *ibid* **58,** 2224

— and Peppard, D. E. (1940a, b) *ibid* **62,** 105, 820

Barclay, G. A. and Nyholm, R. S. (1953) *Chem. & Ind.* 378

Basolo, F. (1953) *Chem. Rev.* **52,** 459

— Bergmann, F. G. and Pearson, R. G. (1952) *J. phys. Chem.* **56,** 22

— Stone, B. D. and Pearson, R. G. (1953) *J. Amer. Chem. Soc.* **75,** 819

Becher, H. J. (1952) *Z. anorg. Chem.* **270,** 273

— and Goubeau, J. (1952) *ibid* **268,** 133

Beeman, W. W. and Mitchell, G. (1952) *J. chem. Phys.* **20,** 1298

Beese, N. W. and Johnson, C. H. (1935) *Trans. Faraday Soc.* **31,** 1632

Bose, A. (1948) *Indian J. Phys.* **22,** 25

Bradley, D. C., Abd-el Halim, F. M. and Wardlaw, W. (1950) *J. chem. Soc.* 3450; (1951) *ibid* 280

Braune, H. and Pinnow, P. (1937) *Z. phys. Chem.* **35B,** 239

Bronsted, J. N. (1926) *ibid* **122,** 383

— and Livingstone, R. (1927) *J. Amer. chem. Soc.* **49,** 435

Brown, D. D. (1952) Thesis, University of London

— and Ingold, C. K. (1953) *J. chem. Soc.* 2680

— — and Nyholm, R. S. (1953) *ibid* 2674

— and Nyholm, R. S. (1953) *ibid* 2696

Bullen, G. J. and Lonsdale, K. (1953) Personal communication

Bunton, C. A. and Llewellyn, D. R. (1953) *J. chem. Soc.* 1092

Burbank, R. D. and Bensey, F. N. (1953) *J. chem. Phys.* **21,** 602

Burstall, F. H. and Nyholm, R. S. (1952) *J. chem. Soc.* 3570

Calvin, M. and Martell, A. E. (1952) *Chemistry of the Metal Chelate Compounds,* New York, Prentice-Hall, p. 324

Chatt, J. (1950a) *J. chem. Soc.* 2301; (1950b, c) *Nature Lond.* **165,** 637, 859

— and Wilkins, R. G. (1952a, b) *J. chem. Soc.* 273, 4300; (1953) *ibid* 70

— and Williams, A. (1951) *ibid* 3061

Clark, D., Powell, H. M. and Wells, A. F. (1942) *ibid* 642

Coop, I. E. and Sutton, L. E. (1938) *ibid* 1269

Coulson, C. A. (1952a) *Valence* Oxford, University Press; (1952b) *Annu. Rev. phys. Chem.* 5

Craig, D. P. (1953) Personal communication

— Maccoll, A., Nyholm, R. S., Orgel, L. E. and Sutton, L. E. (1954) *J. chem. Soc.* 332; see also Orgel, L. E. (1951) *Nature, Lond.* **167,** 434

Crawford, B. L. and Horowitz, W. (1948) *J. chem. Phys.* **16,** 147

Curtis, D. H., Lyle, F. K. C. and Lingafelter, E. C. (1952) *Acta cryst. Camb.* **5,** 388

Daudel, M. R. and Bucher, A. (1945) *J. Chim. phys.* **42,** 6

Davies, N. R. and Dwyer, E. P. (1952) *Trans. Faraday Soc.* **48,** 244; (1953) *ibid* **49,** 180

Dewar, M. J. S. (1946a, b) *J. chem. Soc.* 406, 777

Dickinson, R. G. and Pauling, L. (1923) *J. Amer. chem. Soc.* **45,** 1466

Dothie, H. J., Llewellyn, F. J., Wardlaw, W. and Welch, A. J. E. (1939) *J. chem. Soc.* 426

Duffey, G. S. (1949a, b) *J. chem. Phys.* **17,** 196, 1328; (1950, a–e); *ibid* **18,** 128, 510, 746, 943, 1444; (1951 a–c) *ibid* **19,** 92, 553, 963

Duncan, A. B. F. and Pople, J. A. (1953) *Trans. Faraday Soc.* **49,** 217

Ewens, R. W. G. and Lister, M. W. (1939) *ibid* **35,** 681

Figgis, B. N. and Nyholm, R. S. (1954) *J. chem. Soc.* 12

Freundlich, H. and Bartels, R. (1922) *Z. phys. Chem.* **101,** 177

Friedman, H. L., Hunt, F. P., Plane, R. A. and Taube, H. (1951) *J. Amer. chem. Soc.* **73,** 4028

Gillespie, R. J. (1952) *J. chem. Soc.* 1002

Gordy, W. (1946) *J. chem. Phys.* **14,** 305

Gorter, C. J. (1932) *Phys. Rev.* **42,** 437; (1947) *Paramagnetic Relaxation* Amsterdam, Elsevier

Hampson, G. C. and Pauling, L. (1938) *J. Amer. chem. Soc.* **60,** 2702

Helmholtz, L. and Rogers, M. T. (1940) *ibid* **62,** 1537

Hoard, J. L. (1939) *ibid* **61,** 1252

— (1943) (Referred to in footnote by Marchi, Fernelius and McReynolds, 1943 *cf* Calvin and Martell, 1952)

— and Nordsieck, H. H. (1939) *J. Amer. chem. Soc.* **61,** 2853

Huggins, M. L. (1937) *J. chem. Phys.* **5,** 527

Hughes, E. D. (1951) *Quart. Rev. chem. Soc., Lond.* **5,** 245

Hunt, J. P., Rutenberg, A. C. and Taube, H. (1952) *J. Amer. chem. Soc.* **74,** 268

Jaffé, H. H. (1953) *J. chem. Phys.* **21,** 1893

Jensen, K. A. (1936a, b, c) *Z. anorg. Chem.* **229,** 225, 265, 282; (1937) *ibid* **231,** 365

— and Nygaard, B. (1949) *Acta chem. scand.* **3,** 474

Johnson, C. H. (1935) *Trans. Faraday Soc.* **31,** 1612

— and Mead, A. (1933) *ibid* **29,** 626

Kanekar, C. R. (1953) Thesis, University of London

Kimball, G. E. (1940) *J. chem. Phys.* **8,** 188

Lamb, A. B. and Fairhall, L. T. (1923) *J. Amer. chem. Soc.* **45,** 378

Lee, T. S., Kolthoff, I. M. and Leussing, D. L. (1948) *ibid* **70,** 3596

Lennard-Jones, J. and Pople, J. A. (1952) *Proc. roy. Soc.* **210A,** 190 (and earlier references therein)

Linnett, J. W. and Poë, A. J. (1951) *Trans. Faraday Soc.* **47,** 1033

Lister, M. W. and Sutton, L. E. (1941) *ibid* **37,** 393

Liu, J. C. I. and Bailar, J. C. (1951) *J. Amer. chem. Soc.* **73,** 5432

Long, F. A. (1941) *J. Amer. chem. Soc.* **63,** 1353; *cf* (1939) *ibid* S70

Lord, R. C., Lynch, M. A., Schumb, W. C. and Slowinski, E. J. (1950) *ibid* **72,** 522

McCullough, J. D., Brewer, L. and Bromley, L. A. (1948) *Acta cryst. Camb.* **1,** 287

— and Hamburger, G. (1941) *J. Amer. chem. Soc.* **63,** 803; (1942) *ibid* **64,** 508

Mann, F. G. and Purdie, D. (1940) *J. chem. Soc.* 1235

— — and Wells, A. F. (1936) *ibid* 1503

Marchi, L. E. (1943) *J. Amer. chem. Soc.* **65,** 2257

— Fernelius, W. C. and McReynolds, J. P. (1943) *ibid* **65,** 329

— and McReynolds, J. P. (1943) *ibid* **65,** 333

Mathieu, J. P. (1936a, b) *Bull. Soc. chim. Fr.* **3,** 2121, 2151

Mellor, D. P. (1943) *Chem. Rev.* **33,** 137

— and Craig, D. P. (1940) *J. roy. Soc. N.S.W.* **74,** 495

Mooney, R. C. L. (1939) *Z. Kristallogr.* **100,** 519

Morris, B. S. (1953) Unpublished experiments

Mulliken, R. S. (1950) *J. Amer. chem. Soc.* **72,** 4493; (1951a) *J. chem. Phys.* **19,** 900; (1951b) *Quantum Mechanical Methods in Valence Theory,* Office of Naval Research, U.S.A.

— (1952) *J. phys. Chem.* **56,** 295

Nyholm, R. S. (1950) *Nature, Lond.* **168,** 705; (1952) *J. chem. Soc.* 1257; (1953a) *Quart. Rev. chem. Soc. Lond.* **7,** 377; (1953b) *Chem. Rev.* **53,** 263

Orgel, L. E. (1953) *J. chem. Soc.* 4756

Palmer, W. G. (1944) *Valency,* Cambridge University Press

Pauling, L. (1931) *J. Amer. chem. Soc.* **53**, 1367; (1932) *ibid* **54**, 988; (1945) *The Nature of the Chemical Bond* Cornell University Press; Ithaca, N.Y.; (1948a) *Victor Henri Memorial Volume*, Liége, p. 1; (1948b) *J. chem. Soc.* 1461
Penney, W. and Schlapp, R. (1932a, b) *Phys. Rev.* **41**, 194; **42**, 666
Peyronel, G. (1941) *Gazz. chim. ital.* **71**, 363
Powell, H. M. and Clark, D. (1940) *Nature, Lond.* **145**, 971
Puente, H. A. and Lelong, A. L. M. (1943) *An. Asoc. quim. argent.* **31**, 5
Racah, G. (1943) *J. chem. Phys.* **11**, 214
Ray, P. and Dutt, N. K. (1941) *J. Indian chem. Soc.* **18**, 289; (1943) *ibid* **20**, 81
— and Sen, D. N. (1948) *ibid* **25**, 473
Ruben, S., Kamen, M. D., Allen, M. B. and Nahinsky, P. (1942) *J. Amer. chem. Soc.* **64**, 2297
Rutenberg, A. C. and Taube, H. (1952) *J. chem. Phys.* **20**, 825
Sacconi, L. (1949) *R. C. Atti Accad. Lincei* **6**, 639
Schomaker, V. and Chia-Si, Lu (1950) *J. Amer. chem. Soc.* **72**, 1182
Scott, R. L. (1950) *J. chem. Phys.* **18**, 1420
Sharpe, A. G. (1950) *Quart. Rev. chem. Soc. Lond.* **4**, 115
Sheline, R. K. and Pitzer, K. S. (1950) *J. Amer. chem. Soc.* **72**, 1107
Sidgwick, N. V. (1950) *The Chemical Elements and Their Compounds* Oxford University Press
— and Powell, H. M. (1940) *Proc. roy. Soc. A* **176**, 153
Stephenson, N. C. (1954) Personal communication
Stevenson, D. P. and Schomaker, V. (1940) *J. Amer. chem. Soc.* **62**, 1267
Sugden, S. (1943) *J. chem. Soc.* 328
Swain, C. G., Esteve, R. M. and Jones, R. H. (1949) *J. Amer. chem. Soc.* **71**, 965
Syrkin, Y. (1948) *Bull. Acad. Sci. U.R.S.S. (Classe Sci. chim.)* 69
Taube, H. (1952a) *J. phys. Chem.* **56**, 25; (1952b) *Chem. Rev.* **50**, 69
Thomas, W. (1921) *J. chem. Soc.* **119**, 1140; (1922) *ibid* **121**, 196
— and Fraser, R. (1923) *ibid* **123**, 2973
Van Vleck, J. H. (1932) *Electric and Magnetic Susceptibilities* Oxford University Press
Walsh, A. D. (1947a) *J. chem. Soc.* 89; (1947b) *Nature, Lond.* **159**, 165; (1948) *J. chem. Soc.* 398; (1951) *Proc. roy. Soc. A* **207**, 13; (1953) *J. chem. Soc.* 2260, etc.
Watson, H. E., Kane, G. P. and Ramaswamy, K. L. (1936) *Proc. roy. Soc. A* **156**, 137
Wells, F. A. (1936) *Z. Kristallogr.* **95**, 74; (1945) *Structural Inorganic Chemistry* Oxford University Press; (1949) *Acta. cryst. Camb.* **2**, 175
Werner, A. (1912) *Ber. dtsch. chem. Ges.* **45**, 3061; (1893–1912) For detailed references see the review by Basolo (1953)

APPENDIX

BOND LENGTHS AND VALENCY ANGLES

Allan Maccoll

IT is often important to be able to estimate the size and shape of fairly complex organic molecules, the structures of which have not been precisely determined. The purpose of this appendix is to show how this may be done. It is not intended that a high degree of precision should be obtained; rather that a rough estimate may be made in a simple fashion, to help in problems of structural and mechanistic chemistry. Precise data for small molecules have been given by Walsh (Chapter 1).

As a first approximation, two simple assumptions may be made:

1. The length of a bond of a given type formed between two atoms A and B depends only upon the nature of A and B, and not upon any other atoms with which they may be bonded.

2. The angle between two bonds of a given type formed by an atom is independent of the environment of the central atom. ' Type ' here is used in a sense which distinguishes

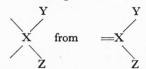

Both of these assumptions need to be modified if precise estimates of molecular geometry are required.

BOND LENGTHS

The first of these assumptions is equivalent to that of the additivity of atomic radii, which has been used, for example, by Pauling (1940). The breakdown of this assumption has led to modifications such as that suggested by Schomaker and Stevenson (1941). Since only a limited number of bonds will be discussed here, it was felt to be more convenient to tabulate interatomic distances rather than atomic radii. These interatomic distances are shown in TABLE 1, together with the reference molecule from which the distance was taken. Explicit references to the original literature are not given; fully documented tables have been given by Wheland (1944), Allen and Sutton (1950), and Huggins (1953). These are, of course, in addition to the Tables of Atomic Radii of Pauling and of Schomaker and Stevenson, mentioned above.

TABLE 1. BOND LENGTHS

Bond	Length (Å)	Reference Molecule
	Single Bonds	
H—H	0·75	H_2
H—C	1·09	CH_4
H—N	1·01	NH_3
H—O	0·94	CH_3OH
H—F	0·93	HF
H—P	1·42	PH_3
H—S	1·34	CH_3SH
H—Cl	1·28	HCl
H—Br	1·42	HBr
H—I	1·62	HI
C—C	1·54	C_nH_{2n+2}
C—N	1·47	CH_3NH_2, $(CH_3)_2 NH$, $(CH_3N)_2$
C—O	1·44	CH_3OH
C—F	1·39	CH_3F
C—P	1·87	$(CH_3)_3P$
C—S	1·82	CH_3SH, $(CH_3)_2S$
C—Cl	1·78	CH_3Cl
C—Br	1·94	CH_3Br
C—I	2·13	CH_3I
N—N	1·47	N_2H_4
N—O	1·37	CH_3ONO, NH_2OCH_3
N—Cl	1·76	$NHCl_2$
O—O	1·48	H_2O_2
O—P	1·65	P_4O_6
O—S	1·70	Estimated[a]
O—Cl	1·69	Cl_2O
	Double Bonds	
C=C	1·35	C_2H_4
C=N	1·27	Estimated[a]
C=O	1·24	CH_3CO_2H
C=S	1·55	CS_2
N=N	1·24	$(CH_3N)_2$
N=O	1·22	CH_3NO_2, CH_3ONO_2
O=P	1·54	$PO_4{}^{2-}$ [b]
O=S	1·49	Estimated[a, c]
	Triple Bonds	
C≡C	1·20	C_2H_2
C≡N	1·16	CH_3CN
N≡N	1·10	N_2

a These values are estimated with the use of Pauling's table of covalent radii (Pauling, 1940).

b It is difficult to estimate the effect of the negative charges.

c The bond length in the SO molecules is 1·49 Å.

When the values given in TABLE 1 are used to calculate the size of a molecule, the maximum error per bond is generally about $\pm 0\cdot05$ Å. In most cases, however, the reliability of the final estimate will be much better than this. Some structural factors affecting bond distances will now be discussed.

Multiple Bonding and Conjugation
There is a tendency to general bond shortening when one of the atoms of a bond is multiply-bonded to another atom. Thus in ethane ($H_3C \cdot CH_3$), ethylene ($H_2C : CH_2$) and acetylene (HC $\vdots$ CH) the C—H distances are respectively 1·094, 1·071 and 1·057 Å. (This shortening can be understood in terms of the change in hybridization of the carbon atom from tetrahedral (sp^3) to trigonal (sp^2) to digonal (sp).) A much more marked effect is however produced by conjugation. Thus in vinyl chloride ($CH_2:CHCl$) the C—Cl distance is reduced to 1·69 Å, to be compared with 1·78 Å in methyl chloride (CH_3Cl). An identical shortening is observed in *p*-dichlorobenzene. The same effect is observed with C—C bonds in hydrocarbons, such as buta-1 : 3-diene, di-acetylene (buta-1 : 3-diyne) and diphenyl (I, II, III: all distances in formulae are in Å).

I   II   III

In the carboxylate ion the two C—O distances become identical at 1·27 Å; this lies between the values to be expected for C—O (1·44 Å) and C:O (1·2 Å). Similarly for the nitro group; found, N—O, 1·22 Å; expected N—O, 1·37Å; estimated N:O, 1·15 Å.

Aromatic and Heterocyclic Systems
The case of aromatic and heterocyclic systems is of special importance. Thus in benzene, the carbon–carbon distance is 1·39 Å (*cf* 1·54 Å in ethane and 1·35 Å in ethylene) and the carbon–hydrogen distance 1·08 Å. These values will probably be sufficiently accurate to use in aromatic systems for most purposes; to give an idea of the observed variations, the dimensions of 1:2:5:6-dibenzanthracene determined by x-ray diffraction (Robertson and White, 1947) are shown in IV.

IV

For the carbon–nitrogen distance in six-membered aromatic (*e.g.* pyridine) rings, the value 1·36 Å may be used. As pyrrole (V), furan (VI) and thiophen (VII) are special cases, their structures are shown in detail (Schomaker and Pauling, 1939). The values in parentheses were assumed in determining the structures.

V   VI   VII

It will thus be seen that particular care has to be taken in deciding the distances to use in molecules which cannot be represented by a single structural formula.

TABLE 2. BOND ANGLES

Most angles are probably accurate to within $\pm 5°$. Examples of some useful groups are shown in VIII – XI.

VIII	IX	X	XI
Ester	Nitro	Carbonyl	Sulphoxide (pyramidal)

Structure	Angle	Reference Molecule
X—C—Y	109°	Substituted methanes
C—O—H	106°	CH_3OH
C—N—H	107°	Estimated
C—S—H	95°	Estimated
C—N—C	109°	$(CH_3)_2NH$
C—O—C	111°	$(CH_3)_2O$
C—P—C	100°	$(CH_3)_3P$
C—S—C	100°	Estimated
C=C—H	120°	C_2H_4
C=C—C	124°	$iso\text{-}C_4H_8$
C=C=C	180°	C_3H_4 (allene)
C—C=O	121°	$(CH_3)_2CO$
O=C—O	124°	$CH_3.CO_2CH_3$
O—N—O	127°	CH_3NO_2
O—N—O	180°	CH_3ONO

BOND ANGLES

Some general rules may be laid down regarding bond angles. In the first place, for a singly bonded carbon atom the bond angles lie very close to the tetrahedral value (109°). Secondly, for structures of the type X=Y—Z, the X—Y—Z angle lies between 120 and 125°. Thirdly, the structures XY≡Z and X=Y=Z are linear. Where an atom possesses unshared pairs of electrons, e.g. oxygen in water or nitrogen in ammonia, the bond angles lie between 90° and 109°, tending rather more closely to the latter value. Some of the more common bond angles are given in TABLE 2.

VAN DER WAALS' RADII

In treating the problem of steric hindrance, it is often important to be able to estimate whether or not two atoms or groups will interfere with each other. This may be done in terms of the van der Waals' radii of the atoms concerned, which have been derived from a consideration of the distances of closest approach of non-bonded atoms. Values due to Pauling (1940) are shown in TABLE 3. Examples showing the use of similar radii in diphenyl derivatives are given by Braude and Waight (Chapter 4, p. 146).

TABLE 3. VAN DER WAALS' RADII OF ATOMS

Atom	Radius (Å)	Atom	Radius (Å)
H	1·2	P	1·9
N	1·5	S	1·85
O	1·4	Cl	1·80
F	1·35	Br	1·95

CH₂ radius 2·0 Å. Half thickness of aromatic molecule, 1·85 Å.

Hydrogen Bonding

The stereochemistry of the hydrogen bond has been discussed by Hunter (Chapter 6). A possible consequence of hydrogen bonding (X — H ····· Y) is to bring the two atoms joined (X and Y) closer than the sum of their van der Waals' radii. Thus in the formic acid dimer the oxygen–oxygen distance (O — H ···· O) is 2·67 Å, to be compared with the radius sum of 2·80 Å. However, this is not always so, and in many cases no very great error will arise if this shortening be neglected.

REFERENCES

Allen, P. W. and Sutton, L. E. (1950) *Acta cryst., Camb.* **3,** 46
Huggins, M. L. (1953) *J. Amer. chem. Soc.* **75,** 4123
Pauling, L. (1940) *The Nature of the Chemical Bond* Cornell University Press
Robertson, J. M. and White, J. G. (1947) *J. chem. Soc.* 1001
Schomaker, V. and Pauling, L. (1939) *J. Amer. chem. Soc.* **61,** 1769
— and Stevenson, D. P. (1941) *ibid* **63,** 37
Wheland, G. W. (1944) *The Theory of Resonance* New York, Wiley

ADDITIONAL REFERENCES

CHAPTER 2

PAGE

Review with special reference to monocyclic compounds : Orloff, H. D. (1954) *Chem. Rev.* **54,** 347

41, 60, 66   Decalols, decalylamines and decahydronaphthoic acids : Dauben, W. G., Tweit, R. C. and Mannerskantz, C. (1954) *J. Amer. chem. Soc.* **76,** 4420

45   Hydrogen bond in cyclic diols ; infra-red evidence : Kuhn, L. P. (1954) *J. Amer. chem. Soc.* **76,** 4323

49   Perhydrophenanthrene ketones : Robins, P. A. and Walker, J. (1954) *J. chem. Soc.* in the press

53   Future refinements of conformational analysis in bicyclic and polycyclic systems will include the consideration of other special non-bonded interactions, *e.g.* 1 : 8 in *trans*- and *cis*-decalins, 1 : 7 (or 2 : 8) in *cis*-decalins (W.K.)

58, 82   Triterpenoid, euphol ; boat-chair transformation and methyl group migrations. Barton, D. H. R., McGhie, J. F., Pradhan, M. K. and Knight, S. A. (1954) *Chem. & Ind.* in the press

60   Carboxylic acids : Shoppee, C. W. and Stephenson, R. J. (1954) *J. chem. Soc.* 2230 ; 2705 (with Roberts, G.)

60   Yohimbine alkaloids : Chatterjee, A., Bose, A. K. and Pakrashi, S. (1954) *Chem. & Ind.* 491

61   Cocaine : Findlay, S. P. (1954) *J. Amer. chem. Soc.* **76,** 2855 ; Kovaćs, O., Fodor, G. and Weisz, I. (1954) *Helv. chim. acta* **37,** 892

71, 73   Ring contraction of steroid 11α : 12β-diols : Wendler, N. L., Hirschmann, R. F., Slates, H. L. and Walker, R. W. (1954) *Chem. & Ind.* 901

71   Steroid $C : D$ ring rearrangement ; further references : Hirschmann, R., Snoddy, C. S., Hiskey, C. F., and Wendler, N. L. (1954) *J. Amer. chem. Soc.* **76,** 4013 ; Elks, J., Phillips, G. H., Taylor, D. A. H. and Wyman, L. J. (1954) *J. chem. Soc.* 1739

81   Tropine and granatoline (as CXXXIV with [CH$_2$]$_3$ in place of [CH$_2$]$_2$ bridge) Archer, S. and Lewis, T. R. (1954) *Chem. & Ind.* 853

82   9-Hydroxy derivatives of dehydroabietic acid (α-tetralol types) : Subluskey, L. A., Sanderson, T. F. and Hays, J. T. (1954) *Abstr. Pap. Amer. chem. Soc.* 126th Meeting, p. 52O

83   Conformation of acyclic compounds : Mizushima, S. (1954) *Internal Rotation* New York, Academic Press (in the press)

Fused six- and five-membered rings : Hexahydroindanes : Dreiding, A. S. (1954) *Chem. & Ind.* 992 ; Eliel, E. L. and Pillar, C. (1954) *Abstr. Pap. Amer. chem. Soc.* 126th Meeting, p. 52O : 5-Substituted *cis*-hexahydroindanes : Dauben, W. G. and Jiu, J. (1954) *J. Amer. chem. Soc.* **76,** 4426

PAGE

Steroid sapogenins : Conformation of ring *F* : Taylor, D. A. H. (1954) *Chem. & Ind.* 1066 ; Wall, M. E., Eddy, C. R. and Serota, S. (1954) *J. Amer. chem. Soc.* **76,** 2849, 2850 ; Ziegler, J. B., Rosen, W. E. and Shabica, A. C. *ibid* 3865 ; Callow, R. K. and James, V. H. T. (1954) *Chem. & Ind.* 691 ; Dickson, D. H. W., Elks, J., Evans, R. M., Long, A. G., Oughton, J. F. and Page, J. E. (1954) *ibid* 692

Chapter 4

Additional references (p. 175, B) on more complex wave-mechanical treatments of unsaturation electrons.

Albrecht, A. C. and Simpson, W. T. (1953) *J. chem. Phys.* **21,** 940

Baldcock, G. R. (1950) *Proc. phys. Soc.* **63A,** 585

Blumenfeld, L. A. (1947) *J. phys. Chem., Moscow* **21,** 529 ; (1948) *Bull. Acad. Sci. U.R.S.S.* **12,** 595

Brown, D. A. and Dewar, M. J. S. (1954) *J. chem. Soc.* 2134

Coulson, C. A. (1948) *Proc. phys. Soc.* **60,** 257

— and Jacobs, J. (1951) *Proc. roy. Soc. A* **206,** 287

— Craig, D. P. and Jacobs, J. (1951) *ibid* 297

Craig, D. P. (1949) *J. chem. Phys.* **17,** 1358 ; (1950) *Proc. roy. Soc. A* **200,** 390, 401

Dewar, M. J. S. (1950) *J. chem. Soc.* 2329

Griffith, J. S. (1953) *Trans. Faraday Soc.* **49,** 345

Jaffé, H. H. (1953) *J. chem. Phys.* **21,** 1287

Kuhn, H. (1948) *Helv. chim. acta* **31,** 1441 ; (1949) *ibid* **32,** 2247

Longuet-Higgins, H. C. (1948) *Proc. phys. Soc.* **60,** 270

— Rector, C. W. and Platt, J. R. (1950) *J. chem. Phys.* **18,** 1174

Matsen, F. A. (1950) *J. Amer. chem. Soc.* **72,** 5243

Nikitine, S. (1952) *Gazz. chim. ital.* **82,** 476

Pariser, R. and Parr, R. G. (1953) *J. chem. Phys.* **21,** 466, 767

Platt, J. R. (1950) *ibid* **18,** 1168

Pullman, A. and Berthier, G. (1953) *C. R. Acad. Sci., Paris* **236,** 1494

Roothaan, C. C. J. and Mulliken, R. S. (1948) *J. chem. Phys.* **16,** 118

Rudenberg, K. and Parr, R. G. (1951) *ibid* **19,** 1268

— and Scherr, C. W. (1953) *ibid* **21,** 1565

Scherr, C. W. (1953) *ibid* **21,** 1582

Simpson, W. T. (1949) *ibid* **17,** 1218

Chapter 5

Review : Freudenberg, K. (1954) *Mh. Chem.* **85,** 537

183, 205, α-Hydroxyacids : Horn, D. H. S. and Pretorius, Y. Y. (1954) *J. chem.* 219 *Soc.* 1460

186 Desylamine (Ph·CO·CHNH$_2$·Ph) and related compounds : Watson M. B. and Youngson, G. W. (1954) *Chem. & Ind.* 658

PAGE

189   Camphor: Freudenberg, K. and Lwowski, W. (1954) *Liebigs Ann.* **589,** 213

190, 211   Zingiberene (sesquiterpene): Arigoni, D. and Jeger, O. (1954) *Helv. chim. acta,* **37,** 881

190, 212   Lanostenol, direct correlation with steroids : Barton, D. H. R., Ives, D. A. J., Kelly, R. B., Woodward, R. B. and Patchett, A. A. (1954) *Chem. & Ind.* 605 ; *J. Amer. chem. Soc.* **76,** 2852. Euphol, *see* reference under Chapter 2

191, 219   2-Phosphoglyceric acid : Ballou, C. E. and Fischer, H. O. L. (1954) *J. Amer. chem. Soc.* **76,** 3188

198   Asymmetric synthesis : Prelog, V., Wilhelm, M. and Bright, D. B. (1954) *Helv. chim. acta* **37,** 221

200   Configuration of C-20 in steroids by conformational analysis : Arigoni, D., Riniker, B. and Jeger, O. (1954) *Helv. chim. acta* **37,** 878

200   Steric control in *ortho*-Claisen rearrangement : Hart, H. (1954) *J. Amer. chem. Soc.* **76,** 4033

208, 212   Extension of Hudson's lactone rule to polycyclic compounds, Klyne, W. (1954) *Chem. & Ind.* 1198

215   Lignans (correlations within group, *not* with glyceraldehyde) : Hartwell, J. L., Schrecker, A. W., Leiter, J. and Shilling, W. L. (1954) *Abstr. Pap. Amer. chem. Soc.* 125th Meeting, 11M, *cf* (1953) *J. Amer. chem. Soc.* **75,** 5916, 5924 ; (1954) **76,** 752 ; but see also Press, J. and Brun, R. (1954) *Helv. chim. acta* **37,** 190

215   Biotin sulphoxide (asymmetric sulphur atom) : Wright, L. D. and Cresson, E. L. (1954) *J. Amer. chem. Soc.* **76,** 4156

219   Methadone (Et·CO·CPh₂·CH₂·CH(NMe₂)·Me): Beckett, A. H. and Casy, A. F. (1954) *Nature, Lond.* **173,** 1231, *cf* morphine (reference on p. 222)

220   *iso*-Citric acid and α-aminotricarballylic acid (correlation at α-carbon atom) : Greenstein, J. P., Izumiya, N., Winitz, M. and Birnbaum, S. M. (1954) *Abstr. Pap. Amer. chem. Soc.* 126th Meeting, 3C

220   Sphingosine : Kiss, J., Fodor, G. and Banfi, D. (1954) *Helv. chim. acta* **37,** 1471

221   Streptomycin, configuration of glycoside links : Wolfrom, M. L., Cron, M. J., DeWalt, C. W. and Husband, R. M. (1954) *J. Amer. chem. Soc.* **76,** 3675

Chapter 7

Faraday Society, Informal Discussion on Structure of Synthetic Poly-peptides and Silk Proteins, Maidenhead, 1954 (to be published). See especially Rudall, K. M. ' New x-ray pattern for an α-protein showing a layer structure '.

257   Fluorocarbon chain [CF₂]ₙ; x-ray studies : Bunn C. W. and Howells, E. R. (1954) *Nature, Lond.* **174,** 549

275   Collagen, new structure. Huggins, M. L. (1954) *J. Amer. chem. Soc.* **76,** 4045

276   New Fourier synthesis for haemoglobin using heavy atom to determine phase of reflections : Perutz, M. F. (1954) *International Crystallography Conference* Paris ; reviewed in *Nature, Lond.* **174,** 379

ADDITIONAL REFERENCES

CHAPTER 8

PAGE

288   More specificity data for β-glucosidase : Nath, R. L. and Rydon, H. N. (1954) *Biochem. J.* **57,** 1

296   *cis-trans*-Isomerase : Knox, W. E. and Edwards, S. W. (1954) *Fed. Proc.* **13,** 242

300   Hydrolysis of carbonyl-activated carbon–carbon bonds by α-chymo-trypsin ; the new substrates conform to XIV with $R^1 = H$, $R^2 = C_6H_5CH_2$ or p-HO·$C_6H_4CH_2$ and $R_3 = CH_2$·CO_2Et : Doherty, D. G. and Thomas, L. (1954) *ibid* 200

316   Evidence that the synthesis of fluorocitrate from fluoroacetate *in vivo* does not proceed by way of the condensing enzyme : Dominguez, A. M., Shideman, F. E., Mahler, H. R. and Hift, H. (1954) *ibid* 349

CHAPTER 9

326   A criticism of the reliability of Kimball's Table in regard to eight-covalent complexes : Higman, B. (1953) *J. chem. Phys.* **21,** 2224

336   A discussion of multiple bonds involving d orbitals in tetrahedral, planar and octahedral complexes : Jaffé, H. H. (1954) *J. phys. Chem.* **58,** 185

339   Ni^{II}-bis-salicylaldoxime also has been shown by x-rays to contain a square planar coordinated Ni^{II} atom : Merritt, L. L. (1953) *Analyt. Chem.* **25,** 718

341   A criticism of the premises upon which Gillespie's arguments are based : Dewar, M. J. S. (1953) *J. chem. Soc.* 2885

342   X-ray examination shows that the polyhalide PCl_6I contains linear $[ICl_2]^-$ ions as well as tetrahedral $[PCl_4]^+$ ions : Zelezny, W. F. and Baenziger, N. C. (1952) *J. Amer. chem. Soc.* **74,** 6151
An interesting example of a linear two-covalent oxygen atom occurs in the binuclear complex $K_4[Cl_5Ru\!-\!O\!-\!RuCl_5]H_2O$: Mathieson, A. M., Mellor, D. P. and Stephenson, N. C. (1952) *Acta cryst., Camb.* **5,** 185

343   Aurous iodide has also been shown to involve tetrahedrally coordinated Au^I ; the structure is similar to that of CuI but some distortion occurs : Harris, C. M., Nyholm, R. S. and Stephenson, N. C. (1954, unpublished)

SUBJECT INDEX

Absolute configuration, 178
Acceleration,
  steric, 93–4, 108–9
  synartetic, 101
Acetals of polyhydric alcohols, 61
Acetocholinesterases, 307–9
Acetone derivatives of cyclic glycols, 55–6
Acetophenones, ultra-violet spectra, 144–8
Acetoxysteroids, infra-red spectra, 167–9
Acetylcholine, 285–6, 306–9, 315
Acid salts, hydrogen bonds in, 246–8
Acids,
  branched chain, configuration, 188–90, 192–3, 197, 202–3, 205, 214
  hydroxy, configuration, 182–3, 186–7, 219, 220
  strength of, and hydrogen bonding, 241–2
Aconitase, 315–6
Activation
  energies,
    alkyl bromides, 92
    cycloalkyl bromides, 104
    racemization in diphenyl compounds, 122
  of inhibitors by enzyme, 304, 313
Active centres of enzymes, possible structures of, 314–5
Acyclic compounds, conformations, 48, 250–2
Addition reactions, 114–20
Adenosine triphosphate, in hexokinase reaction, 294–5
Adipic acid, β-methyl-, 188
Adrenaline, configuration, 213–4
Alcohols, allylic, configuration, 211
  cyclic, reactions of, 57–60, 62–5, 67, 69–73, 75–7, 79–80
  hindered, and hydrogen bonding, 233–5
  polyhydric, acetals of, 61
  secondary, configuration, 182–3, 194–5, 199–200, 205–6, 211–2
Alginic acid, 280
Alicyclic diols, hydrogen bonds in, 239
Alicyclic rings, conformation and infra-red spectra, 164–71
Alkaloids, configuration, 212, 222
Allylic alcohols, configuration, 211
Aluminium alkoxide reductions of cyclic ketones, 74, 200
Amide group in polymers, see also Polypeptides, 261–3, 281
Amides, 240–1, 244
Amines, cyclic, reactions of, 62–3, 66
  secondary, configuration, 185–8, 194–5
Amino-acids, configuration, 180, 184–8, 194–5, 206–7, 213, 214, 219, 221
Amino-alcohols, configuration, 185, 188, 213–4, 220
  cyclic, rearrangements of, 69, 71–3

p-Aminophenol, 243
Angles, valency, 3, 10–19 (tables), 24–34, 364–5
Anhydro compounds, sugars, 76–7, 80
Anomeric configuration of glycosides, 184, 193–4, 208, 214
ante-iso-Acids, configuration, 189, 205
Anthracenes, perhydro-, conformations, 49–50
Antigen–antibody reaction, stereospecificity in, 318–9
Arndt–Eistert method, 196
Aromatic compounds, asymmetric, configuration, 186–8, 220–1
  bond lengths in, 363–4
  spectra, 139–48, 153–5, 175
Arsenic, complex compounds of, 343, 345
Association, molecular and hydrogen bonds, 228–30, 235–6, 240–1, 244
Asymmetric synthesis, 198–201
Asymmetry, optical, of diphenyls, 120–2, 143–4
Atomic orbitals, 29–34, 323–5
  polarization, 331
Atoxyl as cholinesterase inhibitor, 312
Axial bonds, 37–8, 82
Azido-acids, configuration, 96, 194–5, 207
Aziridines, configuration, 221
Azobenzene derivatives, 163–4
Azomethines, 163–4
Azo-compounds, o-hydroxy, hydrogen bonds in, 237–9

Beckmann rearrangement, 103, 196
Benzene, bond lengths in, 363
Benzene hexachloride, 43, 113–4
Benzenoid hydrocarbons, ultra-violet spectra, 139–48, 153–5, 175
Benzoic acids, substituted, strengths of, 241–2
Benzoylcholinesterases, 290, 311
Benzylisoquinoline alkaloids, configuration, 222
'Bifurcated' hydrogen bonds, 228
Bimolecular elimination, 64–5, 112–4
Bimolecular nucleophilic substitution, 66–8, 90–6, 194–5
Biological activity and conformation, 77–8
Bipyramid structures, in complexes, 344, 345
Boat conformation of cyclohexane rings, 36, 40, 42–5, 78–81
Boiling points and hydrogen bonding, 233–5
Bond
  angles, 10–19, 24–34, 364–5
  arrangements, stable, 326
  lengths, 2–4, 7, 10–19 (tables), 361–4
Bonds, π and σ, 327–8, 337–8
Borneol derivatives, rearrangements of, 80, 106–9

Boron, stereochemistry of complex compounds, 342
Branched chain compounds, configuration, 188–90, 192–3, 197, 202–3, 214, 220
Bridged ring structures,
  boat forms, 79–80
  unreactivity of halides, 96
Bromoketones,
  cyclic, conformations, 54–5
  infra-red and ultra-violet spectra, 169–170
Butane, conformations of, 48
Butanediols, configuration, 220
Butan-2-ol, configuration, 182–3, 205
Butanol, 2-methyl, configuration, 188, 192–3
cycloButyl compounds, rearrangements of, 104–6
Butyric acid,
  α-methyl-, configuration, 188, 197
  β-hydroxy-, configuration, 183
Butyro-cholinesterases, 309–10

CADMIUM, complex compounds of, 341
Camphane derivatives,
  conformation, 79–80
  rearrangement, 108–9
Camphor, configuration, 189
Carbanion reduction process, 75
Carbinols, configuration, 182–4, 194–5, 198–200, 205, 211–2
Carbohydrates,
  configuration, 180, 182–4, 193–4, 208, 214
  conformation of, see Pyranosides
  enzymic reactions of, 286–98, 316–7
  high molecular weight, 279–82
Carbonates, acid, hydrogen bonds in, 247–8
Carbonium ions in
  addition reactions, 116–8
  rearrangement, 102–3, 106–10
  substitution, 96–7
Carbonyl compounds, asymmetric synthesis with, 200–1
Carboxyl groups in cyclic compounds, conformation of, 60–1, 63
Carboxylic esters, hydrolysis of, 111
Carotenes, 132–6
Cellulose, 279–80
Cevine alkaloids, 50
Chair conformations of
  cyclohexane rings, 37 et seq
  pyranosides, 37, 50–2, 75–7
Chelate rings, 229–34, 237–9, 241–2
Chitin, 280–1
Chloramphenicol, configuration, 221
Chloro-acids, configuration, 187, 195, 220
Cholesterol,
  addition of halogens, 118–20
  configuration of side-chain, 190, 212
  derivatives, rearrangement of, 109–10
Cholinesterases, 285–6, 306–15
Chondroitin sulphuric acid, 282
Chromophores, partial, 131–6, 149–53
Chymotrypsin, 299–306

Cinchona alkaloids, configuration, 222
cis-trans change in octahedral complexes, 351–3, 355
cis-trans-isomerism, see Geometrical isomerism
  in polymers, 253, 259–60
Citrate in tricarboxylic acid cycle, 315–6
isoCitric acid, configuration, 220
Citronellal, configuration, 189, 190
Cobalt, complexes of, 329, 333–6, 345, 349, 351–7
Coenzyme A and tricarboxylic acid cycle, 315–6
Collagen, 275–6
Combustion, heats of, and conformations, 46–8
Competitive inhibition of enzymes, 302–3, 311–2
Complex compounds, 322–60
Complexing of
  cyclic glycols, 52, 75–7
  pyranosides, 52, 75–7
Configurational relations, kinetic evidence for, 96, 194–5
Conformations of
  acyclic compounds, 48, 250–2
  alicyclic rings and infra-red spectra, 164–71
  conjugated systems about a single bond, 136–54
  of six-membered rings, 36–89
Coniine, configuration, 221
Conjugated systems, light absorption and stereochemistry, 128–64
Conjugation,
  π–p and π–σ, 154–5
  effect on bond lengths, 363
Constellation, see also conformation, 37
Coordination compounds, 322 et seq
Coplanarity
  and resonance, 130–1, 136–7
  of chelate rings with benzene nucleus, 231–2
Copper, complex compounds of, 337, 341–3, 346
Copper complexes of amino-acids, 207
Correlation of configurations, 177–222 (summary, 180)
Corynanthine, stereochemistry of, 61, 65
Crystal structure, hydrogen bonds and, 242–8
Crystallography, x-ray
  and configuration, 214–5
  of complex compounds, 330
Cuprammonium derivatives of glycols and pyranosides, 52, 75–6
Curtius rearrangement, stereochemistry of, 103, 196
Cyanine dyes, conjugation in, 155
Cyclic compounds,
  addition to, 118–9
  asymmetric synthesis with, 199–200
  correlation with glyceraldehyde, 189–90, 192–3, 199–200
  elimination from, 64–5, 112–4
  substitution in, 66–8, 98–9, 104–10

Cyclic intermediates in
  addition reactions, 115, 117–20
  rearrangements, 101–2
  substitution reactions, 98–9
Cyclitols, conformation, 45, 77–8

DATIVE π-bonds, 327
Decalins, 40–1, 47–50
Decalols, configurations of, 168–9
Denaturation of proteins, 276
Diaminobutanes, configuration, 220
Diaryls, steric hindrance and coplanarity
  in, 139–44
Diazocyanides, infra-red spectra of, 163–4
1 : 2-Dichloroethane, conformation, 251
Dichroism, infra-red, see Infra-red spectra of
  polymers
Dienes, conformation about a single bond,
  136–9
Dienones, ultra-violet spectra, 149–53
Diethyl p-nitrophenyl phosphate, 304
Diffraction of
  electrons, 2–3
  x-rays, 1–2
Diketopiperazine, 240
Dimensions, atomic, 145–6, 361–4
Dimethylbutyl acetates, action of cholines-
  terase, 285, 308
Diphenyl derivatives, racemization of, 120–2
Diphenyls, 139–44
Dipole moments,
  and conformations, 44–5
  and interplanar angles, 148
  of complex compounds, 330–2
Diisopropyl phosphorofluoridate (DFP), 303
Dispersion, rotatory, 207
Displacement reactions involving asym-
  metric centres, 194–8
Displacement rule (optical rotations), 206–12
Dissociation constants of acids, and hy-
  drogen bonds, 241–2
Distance rule (optical rotations), 204–6
Distances, interatomic, 4, 10–19, 361–4
  in cyclohexane derivatives, 40
Diterpenoids, configuration, 190, 211
Dodecahedron, in complex compounds,
  347–8
Double bonds, geometrical isomerism and
  infra-red spectra, 156–64

ECGONINE, stereochemistry of, 60–1
Eclipsed conformation of butane, 48
Electron density maps, bonded hydrogen
  in, 227–8
Electron diffraction, 2–3, 330
  and conformation, 42–3
Electronic spectra, 7–9, 128–55
  molecular orbital theory of, 130–1
Electrons,
  lone-pair, and molecular shape, 26
  number of, and molecular shape, 10–19,
    26–8, 32–3
  repulsion between, and molecular shape,
    33–4
Electrostatic forces, effect on conformations,
  54–5

Elimination
  in cyclohexane derivatives, 58–9, 64–5
  mechanisms, 112–4
Endopeptidases, 298–306
Energies, activation, see Activation energies
Energy
  barriers between comformations, 47
  differences between conformations, 46–50
  interaction, of non-bonded atoms, 146
Enolization of cyclic ketones, 55, 83
Enols, hydrogen bonding of, 229–30
Enzyme(s)
  active centres, possible structures of, 314
  action and configurations, 213–4
  efficiency, 288, 289
  reactions, stereospecificity of, 285–321
Ephedrine, configuration, 221
Epoxide rings, opening, of in cyclic com-
  pounds, 74
Epoxycyclohexane, conformation, 82
Equatorial bonds, 37–8, 82
Equilibration, cyclic alcohols, 57–60, 79–80
Eserine as cholinesterase inhibitor, 311–2
Esterases, 286, see also Cholinesterases
Esterification
  mechanism, 111
  of cyclic alcohols, 58–9, 61–2, 79–80
Esters,
  cyclic, conformation and hydrolysis of,
    58–9, 61–2
  hydrolysis of, 111
Ethers, configuration, 194–5
Ethylene
  ketones, ultra-violet spectra, 149–53
  oxides, configuration, 221
Ethyleneimines, configuration, 221
Ethylenes, halogeno- elimination from, 114
Ethylenic compounds, infra-red spectra,
  156–63, 176
Eudesmol, configuration, 190, 221
Excited states, molecular shape of, 7–9, 28–9

FENCHONE, configuration, 189
Fibre repeat, 254
Fibrinogen, 268
Fibroin, 272
Fibrous proteins, 267–76
Fischer convention for glyceraldehyde,
  177–8
Fluoroacetates, toxic action of, 316
Fluorides, acid, hydrogen bond in, 247
Formic acid, 243
Furan, bond lengths in, 364

GALACTOKINASE, 296
Galactose, phosphorylation of, 296
Gauche conformation of butane, 48
Geometrical isomerism and
  enzyme specificity, 317
  hydrogen bonds, 236–41
  infra-red spectra, 156–64
  ultra-violet spectra, 128–36
Globular proteins, 276–8
Glucosamine,
  configuration, 208, 213
  polymers, 280–1
Glucose oxidase, 296–7

β-D-Glucosidase, 286–91
Glucowaldenase, 296
Glyceraldehyde as reference substance for configurations, 177–8
Glycerides, asymmetric, configuration, 191
Glycerol, asymmetric derivatives of, configuration, 190–1, 219–20
Glycerophosphoric acids, configuration, 191, 219–20
Glycols, cyclic,
  complexing, 52, 75–7
  rearrangements, 73
Glycosides,
  anomeric, configuration, 184, 193–4, 208, 214
  enzymic reactions, 286–94
Gold, complex compounds, 341–3
Grid structures of polypeptides, 262, 264
Grignard reaction
  in asymmetric synthesis, 198, 200, 201
  of cyclic halogen compounds, 75
Gutta-percha, 259

HAEMOGLOBIN, 276–7
Halides, secondary, configuration, 194–5, 205
α-Halocyclanones, conformations, 54–5, 169–70
Halogenoethylenes, elimination from, 114
Halogens,
  addition to olefins, 114–20
  complex compounds of, 342–4, 347
Halogen-substituted acids, configuration, 96, 187, 194–5
Haptenic group, stereospecificity, 318–9
Heats of combustion and conformations, 46–7
Helix in polypeptide chains, 268–71, 274
Heparin, 282
Heptacovalent structures, 346–7
Heterocyclic compounds,
  bond lengths in, 364
  conformations, 37, 41–2, 44, 45, 50–2, 60, 61, 75–7, 80–1
Heterolytic reactions, stereochemical factors in, 90–120
cycloHexane derivatives,
  comparison with cyclopentane, 67–8
  configuration, 189–90, 192–3, 199–200, 221
  conformation, 36–89
  infra-red spectra, 164–71
Hexatomic molecules, shapes of, 18–19
Hexokinase, 294–6
Hexosamines, N-acetyl, in polymers, 280–2
Hexosans, stereochemistry of, 76–7, 80
cycloHexyl compounds, asymmetric, configuration, 186
High molecular weight, compounds of, 250–84
Hindrance, steric, 61–3, 91–3, 104
  in derivatives of diphenyl, 120–2
  spectral effects, 132–5, 138–55
Hofmann degradation of amides, 103, 196
D-Homosteroids, 69, 71

Hudson's Rules (carbohydrates), 208
Hybridization of orbitals, 31–4, 325
Hydantoins, 207
Hydrides, metal, reduction of cyclic ketones by, 74
Hydrocarbons,
  asymmetric, configuration, 189–90, 192–3, 198, 205, 220, 221
  long-chain polymers, 251, 257–60
Hydrogen bond, 223–49
  and infra-red absorption, 164–71, 233, 235, 237, 239
  and melting points, 237, 238, 243
  in polymers, 252–3, 262–5, 268–73, 278, 280, 281
  lengths of, 365
Hydrogen chloride, addition reactions, 118
Hydrogen cyanide, 243
Hydrogen in electron density maps, 227–8
Hydrogenation, catalytic, of cyclic ketones, 74
Hydrolysis, enzymic and nonenzymic, comparison, 288–90
Hydrolysis of esters, 111
  cyclic, 58–9, 61–3
Hydrolytic enzymes, 286–96, 298–315
Hydroxy-acids, configuration, 182–3, 186–8, 194–5, 199, 206–7, 213, 219
Hydroxyl groups, hydrogen bonding and infra-red spectra, 166, 171
Hydroxylysines, configuration, 220
Hydroxyproline, configuration, 214, 221
Hydroxysteroids, infra-red spectra, 167–8
Hypochlorous acid, addition to olefins, 118

IMINO-COMPOUNDS, ortho-substituted, hydrogen bonds in, 231–3
Inactivation of enzymes by phosphorylation, 304–6
Indium, complex compounds, 341, 342
Inertia, moments of, 4–7
Infra-red spectra, 5–7
  and conformations, 45–6, 54–5, 83, 164–71
  and geometrical isomerism, 156–64
  and Raman spectra, 164, 166
  of polymers, 252–5, 258–9, 262–7, 271, 275–7, 281
Inhibition of enzymes, 302–6, 311–4
Inhibitors of cholinesterase, 311–4
Inositol, configuration, 193
Instability factors and conformations, 50–2
Interatomic distances, 10–19, 361–4
  in cyclohexane derivatives, 40
Intermediate compound theory of enzyme action, 317–8
Intermediates,
  cyclic, see Cyclic intermediates,
  in reactions of octahedral complexes, 353, 355–7
  transient, conformation of, 77
Internal S_N2 reactions, 106–9
Interplanar angles in substituted acetophenones, 146–8
Intramolecular nucleophilic rearrangement, S_{Ni}, 66, 110

Intramolecular rearrangements of complex compounds, 355–7
Inversion, Walden, 94–6, 194–5, 197–8
Iodine, complex compounds, 342, 347, 354
Ionone derivatives, ultra-violet spectra, 150–3
Iridium, complex compounds, 352
Iron, complex compounds, 345, 353, 354, 356, 357
Irreversible inhibition of enzymes, 313
Isatin, 240
Isomerism. geometrical, about double bonds, 156–64
Isorotation, rules of, 208
Isotopic compounds,
bond lengths, 4
infra-red spectra, 156, 165
moments of inertia, 6–7

KEPHALINS, configuration, 191
Keratin, 264, 267–8, 273–4
α-Ketoesters, in asymmetric synthesis, 198–200
Ketones,
cyclic,
brominated, conformation of, 54–5
reduction of, 58–9, 74
ethylenic, 149–53
Kinetics
of enzyme reactions, 288–9
of reactions of octahedral complexes, 351–6
reaction, 90–125

LACTIC acid, configuration, 182–4, 187, 194
Lanosterol, configuration, 190, 215
Layer structure in polymers, 261–2
Lecithin, configuration, 191
Lethal substrates, 304
Lethal synthesis, 316
isoLeucine, configuration, 214, 220
Lewisite as cholinesterase inhibitor, 312
Limonene, configuration, 189
Linearity of hydrogen bond, 224–8
Localized Pair Method, 323
Lock-and-key analogy, for enzyme action, 317
Lone-pair electrons and molecular shape, 26
Longifolene, configuration, 212
Lossen reaction, 103, 196
Lumistanol, configuration of, 167–8
Lupene derivatives, stereochemistry of, 70
Lupinine, configuration, 222

MACROMOLECULES and hydrogen bonds, 244, 252 et seq
Magnetic susceptibility, 332–5
Malic acid, configuration, 182, 202–3
β-Malolactonic acid, hydrolysis of, 111
Mandelic acid, configuration, 186–7
Manganese, complex compounds, 353, 354
Mechanisms, reaction, stereochemical factors in, 90–125
Medium-sized rings, conjugation in, 153

Melting point
and hydrogen bonds, 234, 237, 238
curves, 202
Menthol, configuration, 189
Menthyl derivatives, eliminations from, 112–3
Mercury, complex compounds, 341
Methyl group migrations, 69–73
Methylcyclohexanes, conformation of, 46, 47, 51
Methyl-substituted compounds, see generally under parent compound
Microwave spectra, 3–5
Migrations, alkyl groups, 68–73, 100–1, 103, 106–9
Molecular orbitals, 323–8
and shape, 29–34
application to electronic spectra, 130–1
Molecular rotation differences, 209–12
Molybdenum, complex compounds, 345, 347
Moments of inertia of molecules, 4–7
Monocarboxylic acids and hydrogen bonds, 224–5, 243
Monoterpenes, configuration, 188–9, 190, 205, 211–2
Morphine, configuration, 222
Multiple bonds, 327–8
lengths, 362–4
Myosin, 268, 273–4

NATURAL occurrence and conformation, 77–8
Neighbouring group effects, 67, 97–100, 106–10
Neoergosterols, conformation of, 83
Nickel, complex compounds, 330, 336, 337, 339–40, 344, 345, 349–50, 356
Niobium, complex compounds, 347
p-Nitroaniline, 243
'Nitrogen mustard' as cholinesterase inhibitor, 313
Nitrogen pentoxide, structure, 1–2
Nomenclature of optically active compounds, 179, 181
Noradrenaline, configuration, 213–4
Norcamphane series, conformation of, 79–80
C-Nor-D-homosteroids, 71
Notatin (glucose oxidase), 296–7
Nucleophilic substitution, 90–110, 194–5
Nucleosides, configuration, 193–4
'Nu-683' as cholinesterase inhibitor, 312, 313
Nylon, 261–3

OCTAHEDRAL, complexes, 345
reactions in, 350–7
Octahydropyridocoline, conformation, 41–2
Octahydropyrrocoline, configuration, 222
cycloOctatetraene, 153
Olefins, addition reactions of, 114–20
Oligosaccharides, linking of units, 208, 214
enzymic synthesis of, 290–4
'iso-OMPA' as cholinesterase inhibitor, 313

Optical
asymmetry of diphenyls, 120–2, 143–4
resolution of complex compounds, 329
rotations
and correlation of configurations, 204–12
of polymers, 256, 266–7
superposition, rule of, 204
Orbital contribution to magnetic moments, 333–5
Orbitals, 29–34, 323–8, 336–41
d, in complexes, 336–41
Organophosphorus compounds, inhibition of enzymes by, 303–6, 311–3
Osmium, complex compounds, 347–8
Oxalic acid, 224–5
Oxazolines, configuration, 222
Oximes, 225–6, 237
Oxirans (ethylene oxides), configuration, 221
Oxocompounds, effect of bromine on spectra, 54–5, 169–70
Oxy-acids, hydrogen bonds in, 245–8

π-BONDS, 117, 327–8, 338
Pantoic acid, configuration, 219
Partial chromophores, 131–6, 149–53
Penicillin, configuration, 214, 215
*cyclo*Pentane derivatives, comparison with *cyclo*hexane, 67–8
Pentatomic molecules, shapes of, 15–18
*neo*Pentyl halides, reactions of, 92, 100, 103
Peptide bonds, enzymic hydrolysis of, 298–306
Peracid cleavage of ketones, 196–7
Perhydrophenanthrenes,
conformation, 42, 49–50
' 4 : 5 effect,' 53, 54
Periodic table, stereochemistry in, 341–8
Phenanthrenes, perhydro-, conformation, 42, 49–50
Phenols,
hindered, 235–6
hydrogen bonding in, 230–1, 235–9, 243, 245
Phenylalanine, configuration, 195, 221
Phenylsubstituted compounds, configuration, 186–8, 195, 220–1
Phosphates, acid, hydrogen bonds in, 246–7
Phosphatidic acids, configuration, 191
Phosphorus
complex compounds, 343, 344
compounds, organic, inhibition of enzymes by, 303–6, 311–3
derivatives of glycerol, *etc*, 191, 219–20
Phosphorylases, 291–4
Phosphorylation
and inactivation of enzymes, 304–6
of hexoses, 291–6
Phosphostigmines, as cholinesterase inhibitors, 312–3
Pinacolyl alcohol, configuration, 201, 206
α-Pinene, configuration, 189
Pinocampheols, conformation, 81
Pipecolinic acid, configuration, 221
α-Piperidone, 240

Plant growth regulators (α-aryloxypropionic acids), configuration, 221
Pleated sheet structure of proteins, 272–3
Polar bonds, *see* Axial bonds
Polar groups in polymers, 261–3
Polarization, atomic, 331
Polarized radiation, infra-red spectroscopy using, 254, 255, 257–9, 262–7, 271, 275, 281
Polyaffinity theory of enzyme action, 317
Polyalanine, 273
Polyamides, 261–3
Poly*iso*butane, 263
Polyenes, spectra, 132–6
Polyglutamic acid (and esters), 265–7, 281
Polyglycine, 264
Polyleucine, 264
Polylysine, 267
Polymers,
hydrogen bond in, *see* Hydrogen bond
stereochemistry of, 250–84
Polypeptides, 264–8, 271, 273
Poly-phenylalanine, 264
Polysaccharides, 279–82
linking of units, 208, 214
Polythene, 257–8
Projection diagrams, valencies, 39–40
Proline
configuration, 221
in polypeptides, 275, 277
*cyclo*Propane derivatives, configuration, 221
Propiono-cholinesterases, 310–1
Propionylcholine, isolation of, 306
*cyclo*Propyl compounds, reactions of, 105–6
Propylene glycol, configuration, 220
*iso*Propylidene derivatives of cyclic glycols, 55–6
Prostigmines, as cholinesterase inhibitors, 312–3
Proteins,
enzymic hydrolysis of, 298–306
fibrous, 272–6, 278
globular, 276–8
structure of, 263–78
Proteolytic enzymes, 298–306
Purine nucleosides, configuration, 193–4
Pyramid, square, in complexes, 344–5
Pyranose anomers, stability of, 52, 60
Pyranosides,
complexing behaviour, 75–7
conformation of, 37, 50–2, 75–77, 80
instability factors, 50–2
Pyridine, bond lengths in, 364
Pyrolytic reactions, stereochemistry of, 65
Pyrrole, bond lengths in, 364
Pyrrolidines, configuration, 221

QUASI-RACEMIC compounds, 201–4
Quinic acid, configuration, 221
Quinol, 243

RACEMIZATION,
in substitution, 96–7
intramolecular, of complexes, 356–7
of diphenyl derivatives, 120–2
Radii, van der Waals', 145–6, 365

Raman spectra, 5
  and conformation, 45
  and infra-red spectra, 156–7, 160–1, 164, 166
Reaction mechanisms, stereochemical factors in, 90–125
Reaction, steric changes during, 348–57
Rearrangements accompanying unimolecular substitution, 100–3, 105–6
Reduction processes involving carbanions, 75
Resolution, optical, of complex compounds, 329
Resorcinol, 245
Retention of configuration in substitutions, 97–100
Ribonuclease, 277
Ring
  closures, in correlations, 192–4
  opening and conformation, 73–4
  structures in polymers, 275, 278–82
  systems, rearrangement of, 58–9, 70–3, 80, 105–9
Rippled sheet structure of proteins, 272–3
Rotation spectra, 3–5
Rotations, optical, and correlations, 204–12
Rubber, 259–60
Rule of shift (rotations), 206

i-steroid rearrangement, 109–10
I-strain, 67
SACCHARIDES, linking of units, 208, 214
Salicylic acid, 227–8, 241
Salts, acid, hydrogen bonds in, 246–8
Saytzeff Rule, 112, 113
Schmidt reaction, 196
Sector method for electron diffraction, 3
Selenium, complex compounds, 343–4
Sequence rule for nomenclature of asymmetric compounds, 181
Serine phosphate, from inhibited chymotrypsin, 305
Sesquiterpenoids, configuration, 190, 211–2
Shapes of molecules, 1–35, 326
Sheet structure of polypeptides, 272–3
1 : 2 Shifts, 68–73, 103
Shikimic acid, configuration, 192, 221
Side chains, effect on polymer configuration, 263
Silicon, tetracovalent, reaction at, 349
Silk fibroin, 272
Silver, complex compounds, 341–2
Single bonds, conformation about, ultra-violet spectra and steric hindrance, 136–55
Skew conformation of butane, 48
Spectra,
  infra-red
    and conformation of alicyclic rings, 45–6, 54, 83, 164–71
    and geometrical isomerism 156–64
  of complex compounds, 335–6
  of simple molecules, 3–9
  ultra-violet, and conformation about single bonds, 136–55
  visible and ultra-violet, and geometrical isomerism about double bonds, 128–36

Spectroscopy and stereochemistry, 126–76
Sphingosine, configuration, 220
Square antiprism, in complexes, 348
Square planar complexes, 333, 335, 337, 339, 349–50
  reaction at four-covalent atoms in, 349–50
Staggered conformation of butane, 48
Steric acceleration, 93–4, 108–9
Steric hindrance
  and conformation about single bonds, 136–55
  in bimolecular substitution, 91–3, 104
  in cyclohexane derivatives, 58–9, 61–3
Stereospecificity of enzyme reactions, 285–321
Steroid glycosides, configuration, 208
Steroids,
  configuration, 190, 199–200, 204, 209–12, 214–5
  conformation and reactions of, 56, 58–61, 67, 69, 70, 71, 73–5, 77, 79, 83
  infra-red spectra, 166–70
  natural occurrence and conformation, 77
Strain theory of enzyme action, 317–8
Strength of acids and hydrogen bonding, 241–2
Streptose, configuration, 221
Styrylcarbinols, ultra-violet absorption of, 154–5
Substitution
  in octahedral complexes, 350–7
  of halogen for hydrogen atoms, effect on molecular shape, 24, 25, 33
  nucleophilic, 90–110, 194–5
  in cyclohexane derivatives, 66–8
Succinic acids, alkyl, configuration, 188, 202–3, 220
Sucrose, enzymic synthesis of, 292
Sugars,
  configuration, 181–4, 221
  conformation, see Pyranosides
Sulphanilamide as cholinesterase inhibitor, 312
Sulphites, cyclic, reactions of, 73
Sulphonic esters, hydrolysis of, 111
Sulphur, complex compounds, 342
Superposition, rule of optical, 204
Susceptibility, magnetic, 332–5
Synartetic acceleration, 101
Synthesis, enzymic, of oligosaccharides, 290–4

TANTALUM, complex compounds, 346–8
Tartaric acids, configuration, 182–3, 220
Tellurium, complex compounds, 343
Terpenes, configuration, 188–90, 193, 199–200, 205, 209–12, 215
Tetracycline derivatives, 50
Tetraethylpyrophosphate (TEPP) as cholinesterase inhibitor, 313
Tetrahedral atoms, reaction mechanisms, 349
Tetrahedron,
  in complexes, 340, 342–3, 349
  irregular, 343
Tetralin, conformation, 82

Tetratomic molecules, 12–15, 24–9
Thallium, complex compounds, 341, 342
Theoretical basis of stereochemistry, 323–8
Thermal decompositions of cyclic esters, 65, 114
Thermodynamics, conformations and, 46
Thiolsuccinic acid, configuration, 202–3
Thiophene, bond lengths in, 364
Thorium, complex compounds, 349
Three-point attachment of substrate of enzyme, 301, 315
Threonine and related compounds, configuration, 214, 220
Transferase activity of hydrolytic enzymes, 291
Transglucosidase, 291–4
Triatomic molecules, 10–12, 24–34
Tricarboxylic acid cycle, 315–6
Trienes, conjugated, isomerism and infra-red spectra, 163
Trienones, ultra-violet spectra, 151–2
Trigonal
    antiprism in complexes, 345, 346
    bipyramid in complexes, 343
    prism in complexes, 345, 346
    pyramid, in complexes, 342
Triphenylmethane dyes, conjugation in, 155
Triterpenes,
    configuration, 190, 199–200, 209–12, 215
    conformation and reactions, 54, 57–9, 70
    natural occurrence and conformation, 77
Tropine, configuration, 61, 80–1, 170–1

ULTRA-VIOLET spectra, 128–55
    bromoketones, 55
Unimolecular elimination, 64, 112–3
Unimolecular nucleophilic substitution, 66–7, 96–7, 100–3
Unpaired electrons, 332–3
Unsaturated
    groups in polymers, 253

Unsaturated—contd.
    hydrocarbons, polymeric, 259–60
    six-membered rings, 81–3
    systems, as neighbouring groups. 109–10
Unshared electron pairs, 26, 75, 326, 331
Uranium, complex compounds, 329, 347
Urea, hydrogen bonds in, 226
Urethanes, as cholinesterase inhibitors, 311–2
Uridine diphosphate glucose, 296
Urocanylcholine, 306–7

VALENCE bond method, 323–7
Valency
    angles, see Angles
    bonds and infra-red dichroism, 255
    diagrams, projection, 40
isoValine, configuration, 213
Vanadium, complex compounds, 353
van der Waals' radii, 145–6, 365
Vibration-rotation spectra, 5–7, 156–71
Vicinal action in optical rotations, 204, 209

WAGNER rearrangement, 100–3
Walden inversion, 94–6, 194–5, 197–8
Water, hydrogen bonds in, 224
Wolff rearrangement, 103
Wool keratin, 264, 267–8, 273–4

XANTHATES, decomposition of, 65
X-rays, diffraction of, 1–2
    and configurations, 178, 214–5
    and conformation, 43–4
    by complex compounds, 330
    by polymers, 253 et seq

YOHIMBINE alkaloids, 60–1, 65, 212

ZIGZAG chain, in polymers, 251, 257–8
Zinc, complex compounds, 341
Zirconium, complex compounds, 346, 349, 354